Laboratory Manual for General Chemistry

Chemistry 1500

Author

Beran

ISBN 9781119012078

Printed in the United States of America SKY10035541_073122

List of Titles

Laboratory Manual for Principles of General Chemistry, 10th edition
by J. A. Beran
 ISBN: 978-1-118-62151-6

Table of Contents

Laboratory Manual for Principles of General Chemistry

10th Edition

J. A. Beran
Regents Professor, Texas A&M University System
Texas A & M University—Kingsville

WILEY

The author of this manual has outlined extensive safety precautions in each experiment. Ultimately, it is your responsibility to practice safe laboratory guidelines. The author and publisher disclaim any liability for any loss or damage claimed to have resulted from, or been related to, the experiments.

VP & PUBLISHER Petra Recter
ACQUISITIONS EDITOR Nick Ferrari
PROJECT EDITOR Jennifer Yee
MARKETING MANAGER Kristine Ruff
ASSOCIATE PRODUCTION MANAGER Joyce Poh
SENIOR PHOTO EDITOR Lisa Gee
COVER PHOTO ©Ocean/Corbis

This book was set in Times LT Std by MPS Limited, and printed and bound by Quad Graphics.
The cover was printed by Quad Graphics.

This book is printed on acid free paper. ♾

Founded in 1807, John Wiley & Sons, Inc. has been a valued source of knowledge and understanding for more than 200 years, helping people around the world meet their needs and fulfill their aspirations. Our company is built on a foundation of principles that include responsibility to the communities we serve and where we live and work. In 2008, we launched a Corporate Citizenship Initiative, a global effort to address the environmental, social, economic, and ethical challenges we face in our business. Among the issues we are addressing are carbon impact, paper specifications and procurement, ethical conduct within our business and among our vendors, and community and charitable support. For more information, please visit our website: www.wiley.com/go/citizenship.

Library of Congress Cataloging-in-Publication Data

Beran, J. A. (Jo Allan), author.
Laboratory manual for principles of general chemistry / Jo Allan Beran, Regents Professor, Texas A&M University System, Texas A & M University—Kingsville.—Tenth edition.
pages cm
ISBN 978-1-118-62151-6 (pbk.)
1. Chemistry—Laboratory manuals. I. Title.
QD45.B475 2014
542—dc23

2013034275

Printed in the United States of America

10 9 8 7 6 5 4 3 2 1

skynescher/iStockphoto

Preface

Chemistry laboratories have changed with advances in technology and safety issues.

Which came first in chemistry? Was it the experiments that led to well-documented principles or was it the principles that led to developing experiments? The answer is obvious … historically, observations of chemical phenomena were made from which explanations were developed. Experiments were undertaken from which explanations were made and written in textbooks. Serendipity in chemistry has played a major role in break through discoveries; an unexpected observation was made, analyzed, and interpreted and new science was born. Good scientists believe in their data. Therefore, the sequence for science development is that

experiments write textbooks, textbooks don't write experiments.

The **Laboratory Manual for Principles of General Chemistry** has focused on the laboratory experience through each of its nine previous editions. Realizing that all experimental conclusions are not the same, each conclusion is dependent upon identifying an appropriate experimental procedure, selecting the proper apparatus, employing the proper techniques while systematically analyzing and interpreting the data, and minimizing the inherent variables associated with the student scientist. As a result of "good" data, a scientific and analytical conclusion is made which may or may not "be right," but consistent with the data. This approach has been prevalent throughout the previous nine editions of this manual.

The Front Cover. The front cover of the 10th edition was selected to illustrate how a student's scientific knowledge steadily grows and matures when various experiences and observations associated with the scientific experience are encountered.

Growing a plant in a flower bed or glazed pottery requires time, patience, practice and experience. The weather, the soil, the moisture, the fertilizer all factor into the growth of a plant. Nutrients and environmental factors affect the development and the maturation process of the young, vulnerable test tube plant. Experimentation provides the avenue by which the plant matures with desirable characteristic and properties.

Students of general chemistry and the general chemistry laboratory in particular, grow through this same process. Chemicals are mixed in test tubes under varying conditions of temperature, pressure, and concentrations resulting in observations from which interpretations and hypotheses result. Further experimentation provides additional "cause & affect" observations leading to an even better understanding and appreciation of the experiment. The process continues. Consequently, the scientific maturation process of the student continues much like the challenges of the "plant."

The general chemistry laboratory is a beginning for observing chemical phenomena from which chemical principles develop for a better understanding, not only for chemistry majors but also for all students who desire to have a career in a science-based discipline.

With this focus, reviewers have supported the challenges and format offered in previous editions—the experiments are interesting, informative, challenging, and have good pedagogy regarding laboratory techniques, safety, and experimental procedures. The reporting and analyzing of the data and the questions (pre- and post-lab) seek to focus on the intuitiveness of the experiment. In the 10th edition, an emphasis for handling data has been moved to the front of the manual and entitled **Data Analysis**; points of analysis are placed as margin notes as appropriate in the experiments.

While all comments of users and reviewers from the previous editions have been heavily weighed, the task of presenting the "perfect" manual, like chemistry and science in general, is impossible. The manual, in itself, is an ongoing experiment and will continue to be.

Breadth (and Level) of the 10th Edition

This manual covers two semesters (or three quarters) of a general chemistry laboratory program. A student may expect to spend three hours per experiment in the laboratory; limited, advanced preparation and/or extensive analysis of the data may lengthen this time. The experiments were chosen and written so that they may accompany any general chemistry text.

Features of the 10th Edition

Safety and Disposal. "Safety first" is again emphasized throughout the manual, with recent advisories and guidelines being added. **Laboratory Safety and Guidelines** outlines personal and laboratory safety rules and issues. Icons in the Experimental Procedures cite **Cautions** for handling various chemicals, the proper **Disposal** of chemicals, and the proper **Cleanup** of laboratory equipment. ***Prelaboratory Assignment*** questions often ask students to review the safety issues for the experiment.

Laboratory Techniques. Numbered icons cited at the beginning of each experiment and within the Experimental Procedure are referenced to basic laboratory techniques that enable the student to complete the experiment more safely and efficiently. The **Laboratory Techniques** section provides a full explanation of 17 basic general chemistry laboratory techniques (along with the corresponding icons) that are used throughout the manual.

Handling small test tubes are encountered throughout the manual – those techniques have been moved from Dry Lab 4, to the **Laboratory Techniques** section. The technique for mixing solutions in a test tube has been added to Laboratory Technique 7, Handling Small Volumes; the technique for heating solutions in test tubes, flasks, or beakers has been added to Laboratory Technique 13, Heating Liquids and Solutions.

Data Analysis. A new section toward the front of the manual incorporates a greater emphasis on presenting and analyzing experimental data. The seven parts (A–G) of the **Data Analysis** section includes emphasis on the use and significance of significant figures and of data averages, standard deviations, and relative standard deviations. Additionally, graphing guidelines are included for the construction of graphical data and the interpretations that can be gathered from graphs. These analytical techniques are emphasized throughout the manual as margin notes where appropriate.

Organization. The experiments are categorized according to subject matter. This format was widely accepted by users and reviewers and retained in the 10th edition. For example, all redox experiments are grouped in Part J such that the sequential numbering of the experiments within Part J indicates a greater degree of complexity. *Experiment 27*, Oxidation–Reduction Reactions, is the simplest of the experiments involving oxidation–reduction reactions, and *Experiment 33*, Electrolytic Cells: Avogadro's Number, is perhaps the most difficult of the oxidation–reduction experiemnts.

Report Sheets. Report Sheets are more user-friendly! Data entries on the Report Sheet are distinguished from calculated entries—the calculated entries are shaded on the Report Sheet. Students also are encouraged to engage appropriate software for analyzing and plotting data.

Additionally, at the discretion of the instructor, the web site www.wiley.com/college/chem/brean provides downloadable Excel Report Sheet templates for each experiment where a numerical analysis is required.

New to the 10th Edition

Prelaboratory Assignment and Laboratory Questions. New to the Prelaboratory Assignment is a problem that analyzes representative experimental data solved in a format paralleling that of the Report Sheet for analyzing data from the Experimental Procedure. Only the experiments that require an analytical analysis have this type of question in the Prelaboratory Assignments. The design of the question is to better prepare the handling and the reporting of experimental data.

Additionally, many of the questions are new or revised in the ***Prelaboratory Assignment*** and ***Laboratory Questions*** in the 10th edition and all of the questions have been reviewed for clarity.

Revised Experiments. All of experiments from the ninth edition have been retained but have been addressed for clarity in the Experimental Procedures for obtaining good data while using proper chemical techniques and on the Report Sheet for recording and analyzing data. These refinements have become increasingly important for today's students who continue to develop, in general, a multitude of state-of-the-art electronic skills.

The Next Step. The Next Step is a feature added to the eighth edition and has been met with anticipated inclusion into open-ended laboratory programs. Based on the tools and techniques gained with completion of the experiment, The Next Step takes students from its completion to ideas for an independent, self-designed experience or experiment.

Laboratory Equipment. Simple laboratory glassware and equipment, shown in the early sections of the manual, are necessary for completing most experiments. Where appropriate, the apparatus or technique is shown in the experiment with a line drawing or photograph. Analytical balances, spectrophotometers (*Experiments 34* and *35*), pH meters (*Experiment 18*), and multimeters (*Experiments 32* and *33*) are suggested; however, if this instrumentation is unavailable, these experiments can be modified without penalizing students.

Contents of the Tenth Edition

The manual has five major sections:

- **Laboratory Safety and Guidelines.** Information on self-protection, what to do in case of an accident, general laboratory rules, and work ethics in the laboratory are presented.
- **Laboratory Documentation.** Guidelines for recording and reporting data are described. Suggestions for setting up a laboratory notebook are presented.
- **Data Analysis.** Seven topics focus on presenting reliable and interpretive data that are collected and analyzed.
- **Laboratory Techniques.** Seventeen basic laboratory techniques present the proper procedures for handling chemicals and apparatus. Techniques unique to qualitative analysis (*Experiments 37–39*) are presented in *Dry Lab 4*.
- **Experiments and Dry Labs.** Thirty-nine experiments and four "dry labs" are subdivided into 12 basic chemical principles.
- **Appendices.** Five appendices include conversion factors, names of common chemicals, vapor pressure of water, concentrations of acids and bases, and water solubility of inorganic salts.

Contents of Each Experiment

Each experiment has six sections:

- *Objectives.* One or more statements establish the purposes and goals of the experiment. The "flavor" of the experiment is introduced with an opening photograph.
- *Techniques.* Icons identify various laboratory techniques that are used in the Experimental Procedure. The icons refer students to the **Laboratory Techniques** section where the techniques are described and illustrated.
- *Introduction.* The chemical principles, including appropriate equations and calculations that are applicable to the experiment, and general interest information are presented in the opening paragraphs. New and revised illustrations have been added to this section to further enhance the understanding of the chemical principles that are used in the experiment.
- *Experimental Procedure.* The Procedure Overview, a short introductory paragraph, provides a perspective of the Experimental Procedure. Detailed, stepwise directions are presented in the Experimental Procedure. Occasionally, calculations for amounts of chemicals to be used in the experiment must precede any experimentation.
- *Prelaboratory Assignment.* Questions and problems about the experiment prepare students for the laboratory experience. The questions and problems can be answered easily after studying the Introduction and Experimental Procedure. The new Prelaboratory Assignment question, formatted to that of the Report Sheet, is designed to subsequently facilitate the analysis of data in the experiment. This question-type appears in those experiments requiring quantitative results.
- *Report Sheet.* The Report Sheet organizes the observations and the collection and analysis of data. Data entries on the Report Sheet are distinguished from calculated (shaded) entries. *Laboratory Questions*, for which students must have a thorough understanding of the experiment, appears at the end of the Report Sheet.

Instructor's Resource Manual

The *Instructor's Resource Manual* (available to instructors from Wiley) continues to be most explicit in presenting the details of each experiment. Sections for each experiment include:

- Overview of the experiment
- Instructor's Lecture Outline
- Teaching Hints
- Representative or expected data and results
- Chemicals Required
- Special Equipment
- Suggested Unknowns
- Answers to the Prelaboratory Assignment and Laboratory Questions
- Laboratory Quiz

Offered as a supplement to the *Instructor's Resource Manual* is a Report Sheet template for those experiments requiring the numerical analysis of data. The format of the templates is based on Microsoft Excel software and is available from Wiley on adoption.

The Appendices of the *Instructor's Resource Manual* detail the preparation of all of the solutions, including indicators, a list of the pure substances, and a list of the special equipment used in the manual *and* the corresponding experiment number for each listing. Users of the laboratory manual have made mention of the value of the *Instructor's Resource Manual* to the laboratory package.

Reviewers

The valuable suggestions provided by the following reviewers for this ninth edition are greatly appreciated:

Sylvia Diaz
University of Texas – Pan American

Dimitrios Giarikos
Nova Southeastern University

Stepen Z. Goldberg
Adelphi University

Sarah Hansen
Columbia University

Al Hazari
University of Tennessee, Knoxville

Randa Roland
University of California – Santa Cruz

Acknowledgments

The author thanks Dr. John R. Amend, Montana State University, for permission to use his basic idea in using emission spectra (without the aid of a spectroscope) to study atomic structure (*Dry Lab 3*); Dr. Gordon Eggleton, Southeastern Oklahoma State University, for encouraging the inclusion of the paper chromatography experiment (*Experiment 4*); the general chemistry faculty at Penn State University, York Campus for the idea behind the thermodynamics experiment (*Experiment 26*); and to Dr. Stephen Goldberg, Adelphi University, for his insightful chemical and editorial suggestions and opinions throughout the writing of the 10th edition.

What a staff at Wiley! Thanks to Jennifer Yee, Senior Project Editor, for her keen insight, helpful suggestions, and unending commitment to see the manual through its birth; Joyce Poh, Associate Production Manager, for coordinating the production of the manual; Lisa Gee, Senior Photo Editor, for assistance in obtaining the photographs for this edition; Kenji Ngieng, Designer; Kristine Ruff, Senior Marketing Manager; and Ashley Gayle, former Editorial Assistant for Chemistry at Wiley.

A special note of appreciation is for Judi, who has unselfishly permitted me to follow my professional dreams and ambitions since long before the first edition of this manual in 1978. She has been the "rock" in my life. And also to Kyle and Greg, who by now have each launched their own families and careers—a Dad could not be more proud of them and their personal and professional accomplishments. My father and mother gave their children the drive, initiative, work ethic, and their blessings to challenge the world beyond that of our small Kansas farm. I shall be forever grateful to them for giving us those tools for success.

James E. Brady, St. Johns University, Jamaica, NY, who was a coauthor of the manual in the early editions, remains the motivator to review and update the manual and to stay at the forefront of general chemistry education. Gary Carlson, my *first* chemistry editor at Wiley, gave me the opportunity to kick off my career in a way I never thought possible or even anticipated. Thanks Jim and Gary.

The author invites corrections and suggestions from colleagues and students.

J. A. Beran
Regents Professor, Texas A&M University System
Department of Chemistry
Texas A&M University—Kingsville
Kingsville, TX 78363

Courtesy of Thermo Fisher Scientific

Laboratory Safety and Guidelines

Wearing proper laboratory attire protects against chemical burns and irritations.

The chemistry laboratory is one of the safest environments in an academic or industrial facility. Every chemist, trained to be aware of the potential dangers of chemicals, is additionally careful in handling, storing, and disposing of chemicals. Laboratory safety should be a constant concern and practice for everyone in the laboratory.

Be sure that you and your partners practice laboratory safety and follow basic laboratory rules. It is your responsibility, *not* the instructor's, to *play it safe*. A little extra effort on your part will assure others that the chemistry laboratory continues to be safe. Accidents do and will occur, but most often they are caused by carelessness, thoughtlessness, or neglect.

The inside front cover of this manual has space to list the location of important safety equipment and other valuable reference information that are useful in the laboratory. You will be asked to complete this at your earliest laboratory meeting.

This section of the manual has guidelines for making laboratory work a safe and meaningful venture. Depending on the specific laboratory setting or experiment, other guidelines for a safe laboratory may be enforced. Study the following guidelines carefully before answering the questions on the ***Report Sheet*** of *Dry Lab 1*.

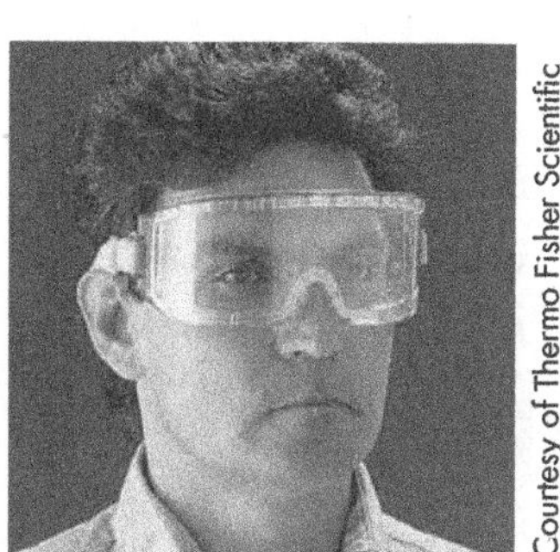

Courtesy of Thermo Fisher Scientific

Goggles for eye protection.

A. Self-Protection

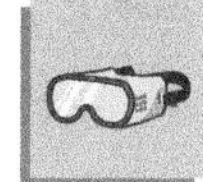

1. Approved safety goggles or eye shields *must be worn* at all times to guard against the laboratory accidents of others as well as your own. Contact lenses should be replaced with prescription glasses. Where contact lenses must be worn, eye protection (safety goggles) is *absolutely necessary*. A person wearing prescription glasses must also wear safety goggles or an eye shield. Discuss any interpretations of this with your laboratory instructor.
2. Shoes *must* be worn. Wear only shoes that shed liquids. High-heeled shoes; open-toed shoes; sandals; shoe tops of canvas, leather, or fabric straps or other woven material are *not* permitted.
3. Clothing should be only nonsynthetic (cotton). Shirts and blouses should not be torn, frilled, frayed, or flared. Sleeves should be close-fit. Clothing should cover the skin from "neck to below the knee (preferable to the ankle) and *at least* to the wrist." Long pants that cover the tops of the shoes are preferred.

   Discuss any interpretations of this with your laboratory instructor.
4. Laboratory aprons or coats (nonflammable, nonporous, and with snap fasteners) are highly recommended to protect outer clothing.
5. Gloves are to be worn to protect the hand when transferring corrosive liquids. If you are known to be allergic to latex gloves, consult with your instructor.
6. Jewelry should be removed. Chemicals can cause a severe irritation if concentrated, under a ring, wristwatch, or bracelet; chemicals on

Adam Gault/Getty Images

Laboratory gloves protect the skin from chemicals.

fingers or gloves can cause irritation around earrings, necklaces, and so on. It is just a good practice of laboratory safety to remove jewelry.

7. Secure long hair and remove (or secure) neckties and scarves.
8. Cosmetics, antibiotics, or moisturizers are *not* to be applied in the laboratory.
9. *Never* taste, smell, or touch a chemical or solution (see B.4 below). Individual allergic or sensitivity responses to chemicals cannot be anticipated. Poisonous substances are not always labeled.

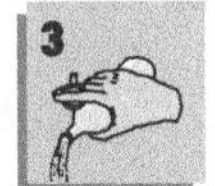

10. *Technique 3*, page 20, provides an extensive overview of the proper handling of chemicals, from the dispensing of chemicals to the safety advisories for chemicals (NFPA standards). Additionally, online access to the MSDS collection of chemicals[1] provides further specifics for all chemicals that are used in this manual.

    All other techniques in the **Laboratory Techniques** section describe procedures for safely conducting an experiment. Be sure to read each technique carefully before the laboratory session for completing a safe and successful experiment.
11. Wash your hands often during the laboratory, but *always* wash your hands with soap and water before leaving the laboratory! Thereafter, wash your hands and face in the washroom. Toxic or otherwise dangerous chemicals may be inadvertently transferred to the skin and from the skin to the mouth.

B. Laboratory Accidents

Doug Martin/Science Source

An eye wash can quickly remove chemicals from the eyes; a safety shower can quickly remove chemicals from the body.

1. Locate the laboratory safety equipment such as eyewash fountains, safety showers, fire extinguishers, and fume hoods. Identify their locations on the inside front cover of this manual.
2. **Report all accidents** or injuries, even if considered minor, *immediately* to your instructor. A written report of any and all accidents that occur in the laboratory may be required. Consult with your laboratory instructor.
3. If an **accident occurs,** *do not panic*! The most important first action after an accident is the care of the individual. ***Alert your laboratory instructor immediately!*** If a person is injured, provide or seek aid *immediately.* Clothing and books can be replaced and experiments can be performed again later. Second, take the appropriate action regarding the accident: clean up the chemical (see B.8, page 3), use the fire extinguisher (see B.6 below), and so on.
4. Whenever your skin (hands, arms, face, etc.) comes into contact with chemicals, quickly flush the affected area for several minutes with tap water followed by thorough washing with soap and water. Use the eyewash fountain to flush chemicals from the eyes and face. *Get help immediately.* Do *not* rub the affected area, especially the face or eyes, with your hands before washing (see A.11 above).
5. Chemical spills over a large part of the body require immediate action. Using the safety shower, flood the affected area for at least 5 minutes. Remove all contaminated clothing if necessary. Use a mild detergent and water only (no salves, creams, lotions, etc.). Get medical attention as directed by your instructor.
6. In case of fire, discharge a fire extinguisher at the base of the flames and move it from one side to the other. Small flames can be smothered with a watchglass (do *not* use a towel because it may catch on fire). Do *not* discharge a fire extinguisher when a person's clothing is on fire—use the safety shower. Once the fire appears to be out of control, *immediately* evacuate the laboratory.
7. For abrasions or cuts, flush the affected area with water. Any further treatment should be given only after consulting with the laboratory instructor.

[1] See http://ilpi.com/msds

For burns, the affected area should be rubbed with ice, submerged in an ice-water bath, or placed under running water for several minutes to withdraw heat from the burned area. More serious burns require immediate medical attention. Consult with your laboratory instructor.

8. Treat chemical spills in the laboratory as follows:
   - Alert your neighbors and the laboratory instructor
   - Clean up the spill as directed by the laboratory instructor
   - If the substance is volatile, flammable, or toxic, warn everyone of the accident
9. *Technique 4*, page 21, provides information for the proper disposal of chemicals after being used in the experiment. Improper disposal can result in serious laboratory accidents. Read that section carefully—it may prevent an "undesirable" laboratory accident. If you are uncertain of the proper procedure for the disposing of a chemical, ***ask!***

C. Laboratory Rules

In addition to the guidelines for self-protection (Part A), the following rules must be followed.

1. *Smoking, drinking, eating, and chewing* (including gum and tobacco) are not permitted at any time because chemicals may inadvertently enter the mouth or lungs. Your hands may be contaminated with an "unsafe" chemical. Do not place any objects, including pens or pencils, in your mouth during or after the laboratory period. These objects may have picked up a contaminant from the laboratory bench.
2. Do *not* work in the laboratory alone. The laboratory instructor must be present.
3. Assemble your laboratory apparatus away from the edge of the lab bench ($\geq$ 8 inches or $\geq$ 20 cm) to avoid accidents.
4. Do *not* leave your experiment unattended during the laboratory period: This is often a time when accidents occur.
5. Inquisitiveness and creativeness in the laboratory are encouraged. However, variations or alterations of the Experimental Procedure are forbidden without prior approval of the laboratory instructor. If your chemical intuition suggests further experimentation, first consult with your laboratory instructor.
6. Maintain an orderly, clean laboratory desk and drawer. Immediately clean up all chemical spills, paper scraps, and glassware. Discard wastes as directed by your laboratory instructor.
7. Keep drawers or cabinets closed and the aisles free of any obstructions. Do *not* place book bags, athletic equipment, or other items on the floor near any lab bench.

Laboratory facilities must be designed for safety.

8. At the end of the laboratory period, completely clear the lab bench of equipment, clean it with a damp sponge or paper towel (and properly discard), and clean the sinks of all debris. Also clean all glassware used in the experiment (see *Technique 2*, page 19).
9. Be aware of your neighbors' activities: You may be a victim of their mistakes. Advise them of improper techniques or unsafe practices. If necessary, tell the instructor.
10. For all other rules, **listen to your instructor!** Additional laboratory rules and guidelines can be added to this list at the bottom of this page.

D. Working in the Laboratory

1. Maintain a wholesome, professional attitude. Horseplay and other careless acts are prohibited.
2. The operation of cell phones and other electronic "entertainment" equipment is strictly forbidden.
3. Do *not* entertain guests in the laboratory. Your total concentration on the experiment is required for a safe, meaningful laboratory experience. You may socialize with others in the lab, but do not have a party! You are expected to maintain a learning, scientific environment.
4. Scientists learn much by discussion with one another. Likewise, you may profit by discussion with your laboratory instructor or classmates—but *not* by copying from them.
5. *Prepare for each experiment.* Review the Objectives and Introduction to determine the "chemistry" of the experiment, the chemical system, the stoichiometry of the reactions, the color changes to anticipate, and the calculations that will be required. A thorough knowledge of the experiment will make the laboratory experience more time efficient and scientifically more meaningful (and result in a better grade!). Complete the ***Prelaboratory Assignment.***
6. Review the Experimental Procedure.
   - Try to understand the purpose of each step.
   - Determine if any extra equipment is needed and be ready to obtain it all at once from the stockroom.
   - Determine what data are to be collected and how they are to be analyzed (calculations, graphs, etc.). Review the **Data Analysis** section.
   - Review the **Laboratory Techniques** and the **Cautions,** because they are important for conducting a safe and rewarding experiment.
7. Review the ***Report Sheet.*** Complete any calculations required before data collection can begin during the laboratory period. Determine the data to be collected, the number of suggested trials, and the data analysis required (e.g., calculations, graphs).
8. Review the Laboratory Questions at the conclusion of the ***Report Sheet*** before *and* as you perform the experiment. These questions are intended to enhance your understanding of the chemical principles on which the experiment is based.
9. Above all, *enjoy* the laboratory experience. Be prepared, observe, think, and anticipate during the course of the experiment. Ultimately, you will be rewarded.

Notes on Laboratory Safety and Guidelines

Masterfile

Data Documentation

Laboratory data should be carefully recorded.

The lifeblood of a good scientist depends on the collection of reliable and reproducible data from experimental observations and on the analysis of that data. The data must be presented in a logical and credible format; that is, the data must appear such that other scientists will believe in and rely on the data that you have collected.

Believe in your data, and others will have confidence in it also. A scientist's most priceless possession is integrity. Be a scientist. Scientists are conscientious in their efforts to observe, collect, record, and interpret the experimental data as best possible. Only honest scientific work is acceptable.

You may be asked to present your data on the ***Report Sheet*** that appears at the end of each experiment, or you may be asked to keep a laboratory notebook (see Part C for guidelines). For either method, a customary procedure for collecting, recording, and presenting data is to be followed. A thorough preview of the experiment will assist in your collection and presentation of data.

A. Recording Data

1. Record all data entries *as they are being collected* on the ***Report Sheet*** or in your laboratory notebook. Be sure to include appropriate units after numerical entries. Data on scraps of paper (such as mass measurements in the balance room) may be confiscated.
2. Record the data *in permanent ink* as you perform the experiment.
3. If a mistake is made in recording data, cross out the incorrect data entry with a *single* line (do *not* erase, white out, overwrite, or obliterate) and clearly enter the corrected data nearby (see Figure A.1). If a large section of data is deemed incorrect, then write a short notation as to why the data are in error, place a single diagonal line across the data, and note where the correct data are recorded.
4. For clarity, record data entries of values <1 with a zero in the "one" position of the number; for example, record a mass measurement as 0.218 g rather than .218 g (see Figure A.1).
5. Data collected from an instrument or computer printout should be securely attached to the ***Report Sheet***.

	Trial 1
Mass of $CaCO_3$ sample, initial	0.218 g
Mass of $CaCO_3$, after heating	~~0.184 g~~ 0.164
Mass of CO_2 in sample	0.054 g

Figure A.1 Procedures for recording and correcting data.

B. Accessing Supplementary Data

You may profit by frequent references to your textbook or, for tabular data on the properties of chemicals, the *CRC Handbook of Chemistry and Physics,* published by the Chemical Rubber Publishing Company of Cleveland, Ohio, or the *Merck Index,* published by Merck & Co., Inc., of Rahway, New Jersey. Books are generally more reliable and more complete sources of technical information than are classmates.

The Internet has a wealth of information available at your fingertips. Search the Web for additional insights into each experiment. In your search, keep in mind that many Web sites are not peer-reviewed and therefore must be judged for accuracy and truth before being used.

There are several search engines that can lead you to most any information regarding your experiment; equipment, safety of chemicals, procedures, representative data, etc.

Masterfile

Scientific data can be obtained from the Internet or analyzed with appropriate software.

C. Laboratory Notebook

The laboratory notebook is a personal, permanent record—that is, a journal, of the activities associated with the experiment or laboratory activity. The first 3–4 pages of the notebook should be reserved for a table of contents. The laboratory notebook should have a sewn binding, and the pages must be numbered in sequence.

Each new experiment in the laboratory notebook should begin on the right-hand side of a new page in the laboratory notebook, and it should include the following sections with clear, distinct headings:

Courtesy of Thermo Fisher Scientific

Laboratory notebook

- The title of the experiment
- Beginning date of the experiment
- Bibliographic source of the experiment
- Coworkers for the experiment
- The purpose and/or objective(s) of the experiment
- A brief, but clearly written Experimental Procedure that includes the appropriate balanced equations for the chemical reactions and/or any modifications of the procedure
- A list of cautions and safety concerns
- A brief description or sketch of the apparatus
- A section for the data that is recorded (see **Data Documentation**, Part A and **Data Analysis**, Part A) as the experiment is in progress, (i.e., the ***Report Sheet***). This data section must be planned and organized carefully. The quantitative data is to be organized, neat, and recorded with the appropriate significant figures and units: Any observed, qualitative data must be written legibly, briefly, and with proper grammar. All data must be recorded in *permanent ink.* Allow plenty of room to record observations, comments, notes, and so on.

Data Analysis

- A section for data analysis that includes representative calculations, an error analysis, instrument and computer printouts, graphical analyses (see **Data Analysis** in the next section), and organized tables. Where calculations using data are involved, be orderly with the first set of data. Do *not* clutter the data analysis section with arithmetic details. All computer printouts must be securely attached.
- A section for results and discussion

At the completion of each day's laboratory activities, the laboratory activity should be dated and signed by the chemist, any coworker, *and* the laboratory instructor at the bottom of of each page.

The laboratory instructor will outline any specific instructions that are unique to your laboratory program.

Common Laboratory Desk Equipment Checklist

				First Term		Second Term		Third Term	
No.	Quantity	Size	Item	In	Out	In	Out	In	Out
1	1	10-mL	graduated cylinder						
2	1	50-mL	graduated cylinder						
3	5	—	beakers						
4	2	—	stirring rods						
5	1	500-mL	wash bottle						
6	1	75-mm, 60°	funnel						
7	1	125-mL	Erlenmeyer flask						
8	1	250-mL	Erlenmeyer flask						
9	2	25 × 200-mm	test tubes						
10	6	18 × 150-mm	test tubes						
11	8	10 × 75-mm	test tubes						
12	1	large	test tube rack						
13	1	small	test tube rack						
14	1	—	glass plate						
15	1	—	wire gauze						
16	1	—	crucible tongs						
17	1	—	spatula						
18	2	—	litmus, red and blue						
19	2	90-mm	watch glasses						
20	1	75-mm	evaporating dish						
21	4	—	dropping pipets						
22	1	—	test tube holder						
23	1	large	test tube brush						
24	1	small	test tube brush						
	1	—	marking pen						

Yoav Levy/Phototake

Special Laboratory Equipment

Number	Item	Number	Item
1	reagent bottles	16	porcelain crucible and cover
2	condenser	17	mortar and pestle
3	500-mL Erlenmeyer flask	18	glass bottle
4	1000-mL beaker	19	pipets
5	Petri dish	20	ring and buret stands
6	Büchner funnel	21	clamp
7	Büchner (filter) flask	22	double buret clamp
8	volumetric flasks	23	Bunsen burner
9	500-mL Florence flask	24	buret brush
10	–10°C–110°C thermometer	25	clay pipe-stem triangle
11	100-mL graduated cylinder	26	rubber stoppers
12	50-mL buret	27	wire loop for flame test
13	glass tubing	28	pneumatic trough
14	U-tube	29	rubber pipet bulb
15	porous ceramic cup	30	iron support ring

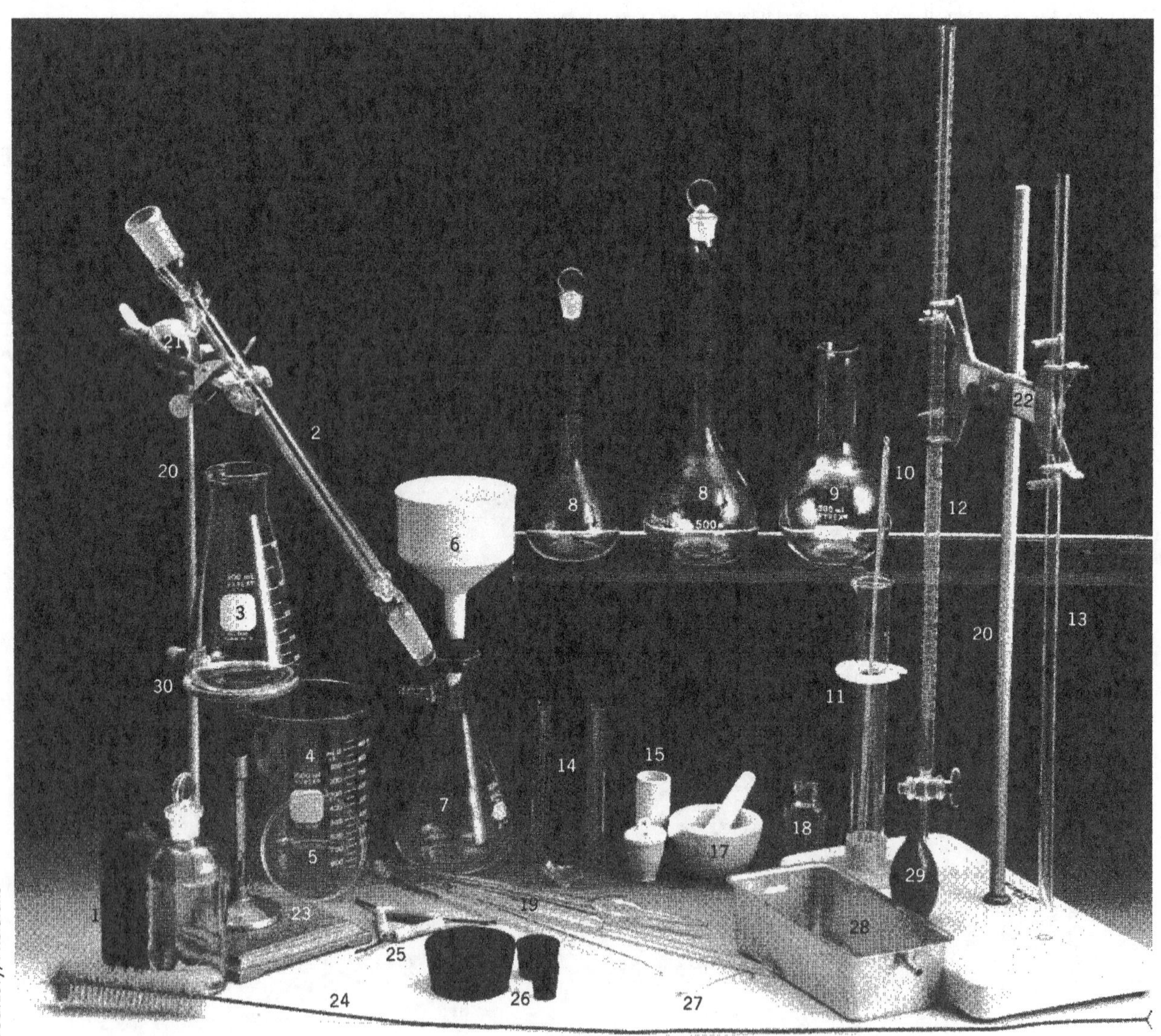

YoavLevy/Phototake

Data Analysis

Calculators with graphing capabilities are an asset for analyzing scientific data

DonNichols/iStockphoto

Confidence in a scientific theory depends on the reliability of the experimental data on which the theory is based. For this reason, a scientist must be concerned about the quality of the data he or she collects. Of prime importance are the **accuracy** of the data—how closely the measured values lie to the true values and the **precision**—how reproducible are the collected data.

To obtain accurate data, we must use instruments that are carefully calibrated for a properly designed experimental procedure. Miscalibrated equipment, such as a balance or buret, may result in reproducible but erred data. Flawed instruments or experimental procedures result in **systematic errors**—errors that can be detected and corrected. As a result of systematic errors, the data may have good **precision** but not necessarily have good **accuracy**. To have good accuracy of data, the systematic errors must be minimized.

Systematic errors: Determinate errors that arise from flawed equipment or experimental design

Precision: Data with small deviations from an average value have high precision

Accuracy: Data with small deviations from an accepted or accurate value have good accuracy

Random errors: Indeterminate errors that arise from the bias of a chemist in observing and recording measurements

Because scientists collect data, **random errors** may also occur in measurements. Random errors are a result of reading or interpreting the value from the measuring instrument. For example, reading the volume of a liquid in a graduated cylinder to the nearest milliliter depends on the best view of the bottom of the meniscus, the judgment of the bottom of the meniscus relative to the volume scale, and even the temperature of the liquid. A volume reading of 10.2 mL may be read as 10.1 or 10.3, depending on the chemist and the laboratory conditions. When the random errors are small, all measurements are close to one another, and we say the data are of *high precision*. When the random errors are large, the values cover a much broader range and the data are of *low precision*. Generally, data of high precision are also of high accuracy, especially if the measuring device is properly calibrated.

A. Significant Figures

Quantitative data, both collected and calculated, must reflect the reliability and precision of the measurements obtained from laboratory instruments and equipment. The significance of significant figures lies in an indication of the precision of those measurements and the calculated results. Keep in mind that recording and calculating data with the correct number of significant figures does not improve the accuracy of the final result, only the precision.

Thus, significant figures indicate clearly the precision of the instrument for each measurement.

In this laboratory, many measurements are made with a variety of instruments. Pay heed to the precision of each instrument that is used in your analysis. For examples,

- A balance: read and record a mass to the nearest centigram (±0.01 g) or to the nearest milligram (±0.001 g), depending upon the balance.
- A buret: read and record a volume to the nearest hundredths of a milliliter (±0.01 mL).

The number of significant figures in a measurement equals the number of figures that are certain in the measurement *plus* one additional figure that expresses uncertainty. The first uncertain figure in a measurement is the last significant figure of the measurement. The mass measurement (0.218 g) has three significant figures. The first uncertain figure is the 8, which means that the confidence of the measurement is between 0.219 g and 0.217 g, or 0.218 ± 0.001 g.

Rules for Significant Figures.

- Significant figures are used to express measurements that indicate the precision of the measuring instrument.
- All definitions (e.g., 12 inches = 1 foot) have an infinite number of significant figures.
- For the addition and subtraction of data with significant figures, the answer is rounded off to the number of decimal places equal to the *fewest* number of decimal places in any one of the *measurements*.
- For the multiplication and division of data with significant figures, the answer is expressed with the number of significant figures equal to the *fewest* number of significant figures for any one of the *measurements*.

Scientific Notation. Expressing measurements in scientific notation often simplifies the recording of measurements with the correct number of significant figures. For example, the mass measurement of 0.218 g, expressed as 2.18×10^{-1} g, clearly indicates three significant figures in the measurement. Zeros at the front end of a measurement are not significant.

Zeros at the end of a measurement of data may or may not be significant. However, again that dilemma is clarified when the measurement is expressed in scientific notation. For example, the volume of a sample written as 200 mL may have one, two, or three significant figures. Expressing the measurement as 2×10^2 mL, 2.0×10^2 mL, or 2.00×10^2 mL clarifies the precision of the measurement as having one, two, or three significant figures, respectively. Zeros at the end of a number *and* to the right of a decimal point are always significant: 0.0240 g has 3 significant figures.

In reporting data for your observations in this laboratory manual, follow closely these guidelines for using significant figures to correctly express the precision of your measurements and the reliability of your calculations.

Rounding Calculations. Most confusion with significant figures occurs when expressing the final results of an experiment. A first rule for performing a calculation of data is to maintain all digits during the mix of calculations and then round off the final result to that of the measurement having the least number of significant figures in your Experimental Procedure.

Rules For Rounding.

- If the first nonsignificant figures are greater than 5, round up—round 1.37581 to 1.38.
- If the first nonsignificant figure is 5 only, round up—round 2.485 to 2.49. Also, there is an alternative rule that says to round to the even number—round 2.485 to 2.48. The author prefers the former, but check with your instructor before submitting your final results.

B. Average (or Mean) Value, $\bar{x}$

Methods of analyzing experimental data, based on statistics, provide information on the degree of precision of the measured values. Applying the methods is simple, as you will see, but to understand their significance, examine briefly the **standard error curve** (Figure B.1a).

If we make a large number of measurements of a quantity, the values would fluctuate about the average value (also called the *mean value*). The **average, or mean, value** is obtained by dividing the sum of all the measured values by the total number of values. If x_1, x_2, x_3, and so on are measured values, and there are n of them, then the average value, $\bar{x}$, is computed as

$$\text{average (or mean) value, } \bar{x} = \frac{x_1 + x_2 + x_3 + \cdots + x_n}{n} \qquad \text{(B.1)}$$

Most values lie close to the average, but some lie farther away. If we plot the frequency with which a measured value occurs versus the value of the measurement, we obtain the curve in Figure B.1a. When the random errors are small (high-precision data, Figure B.1b), the curve is very narrow, and the peak is sharp. When the random errors are large (low-precision data, Figure B.1c, page 12), the data are more spread out, and the error curve is broader and less sharp.

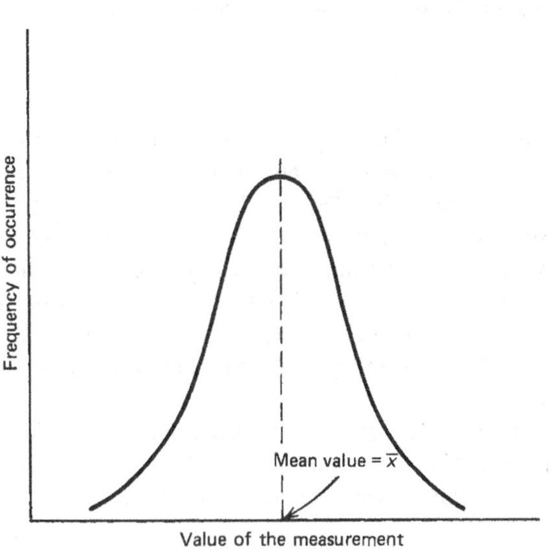

Figure B.1a The standard error curve

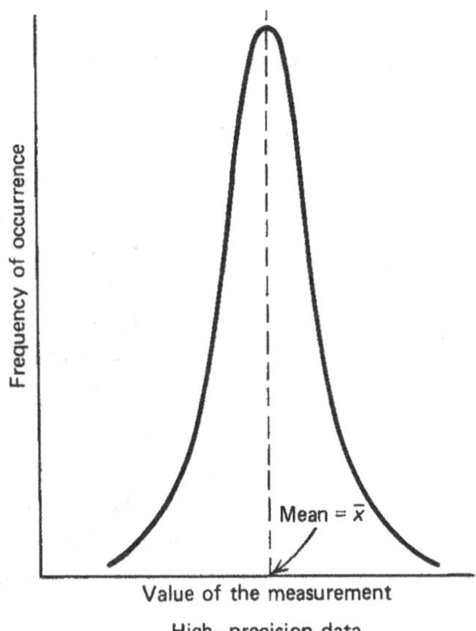

Figure B.1b Error curve for high-precision data

C. Standard Deviation, s

Statistics gives us methods for computing quantities that tell us about the width of the error curve for our data and, therefore, about the precision of the data, even when the amount of data is relatively small. One of the most important statistical measures of precision is the **standard deviation,** s. To calculate the standard deviation, we first compute the average value, $\bar{x}$. The next step is to compute the *deviation*, d, from the average value for *each* measurement—the difference between the average and each measured value:

$$\text{deviation, } d_i = \bar{x} - x_i \qquad \text{(C.1)}$$

d_i is the deviation for the measured value, x_i. The standard deviation is obtained by squaring the deviations of all measurements, adding the squared values together, dividing this sum by $n - 1$ (where n is the number of measurements), and then taking the square root:

$$\text{standard deviation, } s = \sqrt{\frac{d_1^2 + d_2^2 + \cdots + d_n^2}{(n-1)}} \qquad \text{(C.2)}$$

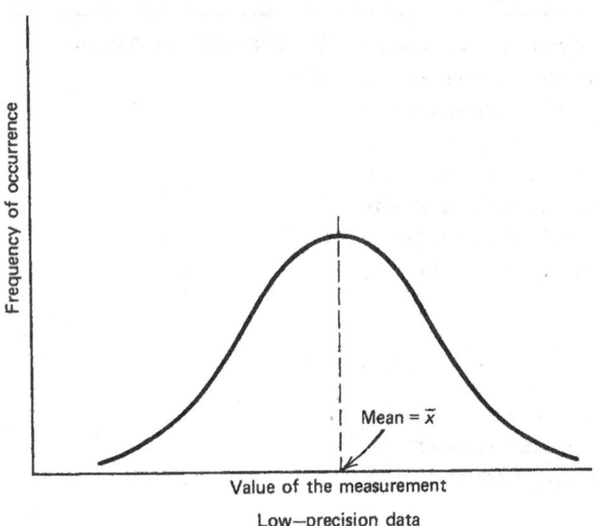

Figure B.1c Error curve for low-precision data

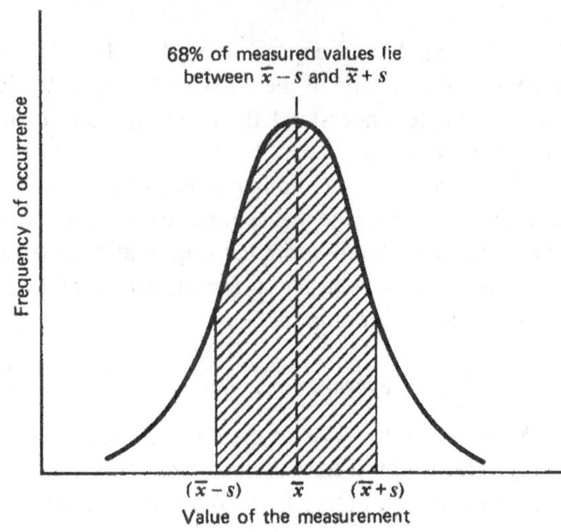

Figure C.2a Relationship of the standard deviation to the error curve

The standard deviation means that if we make yet another measurement, the probability that its value will lie within $\pm s$ of the average value is 0.68. In other words, 68 percent of the measurements lie within $\pm s$ of the average value (i.e., within the range $\bar{x} - s$ to $\bar{x} + s$). On the error curve in Figure C.2a, this represents the measurements falling within the shaded area. If we obtain a large calculated s from a set of measured values, it means that the error curve for our data is broad and that the precision of the data is low (Figure C.2b); a small value of s for a set of data means that the error curve is narrow, and the precision of the data is high (see Figure C.2c). Thus, s is a statistical measure of the precision of the data.

For most scientific data, three results is the *absolute minimum* number for determining the standard deviation of the data. Chemists tend to require four or more results for a meaningful interpretation of the standard deviation value of the data.

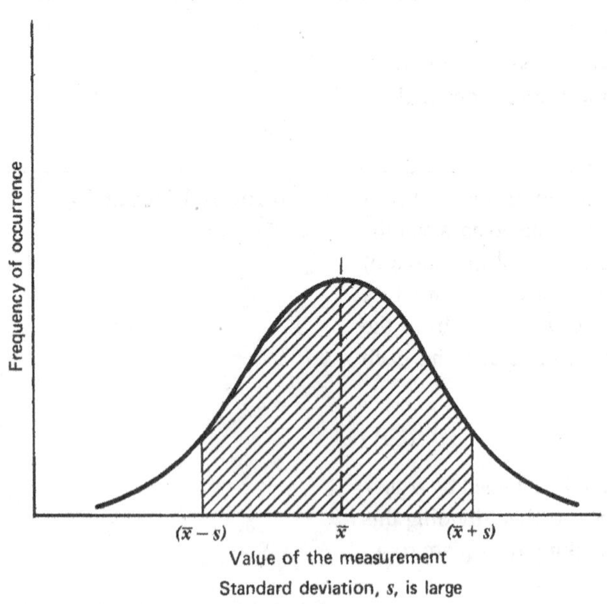

Figure C.2b Data set with a large standard deviation

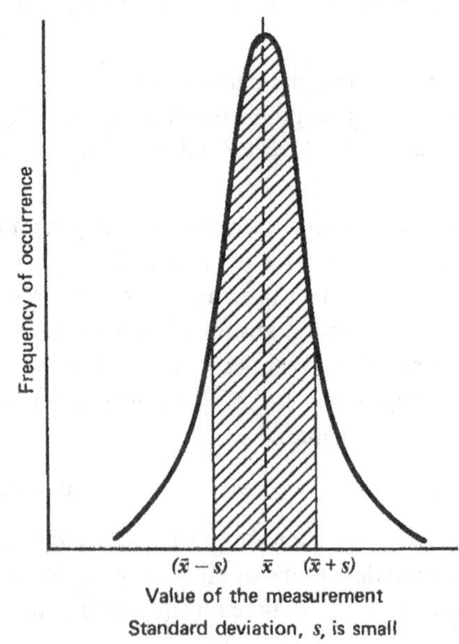

Figure C.2c Data set with a small standard deviation

D. Relative Standard Deviation

The ratio of the standard deviation to the average value of the data often gives a better appreciation for the precision of the data. The ratio, called the relative standard deviation (RSD), is either expressed in parts per thousand (ppt) or parts per hundred (pph or percent). When expressed as a percentage, the RSD is referred to as %RSD or as the coefficient of variation (CV) of the data.

$$\text{RSD} = \frac{s}{\bar{x}} \times 1{,}000 \text{ ppt} \quad \text{(D.1)}$$

$$\%\text{RSD (or CV)} = \frac{s}{\bar{x}} \times 100\% \quad \text{(D.2)}$$

The RSD or CV expresses precision of the data—the smaller the RSD or CV, the greater the precision for the average value of the data.

As an example that illustrates how these statistical methods are applied, suppose that four analyses of an iron ore sample give the following data with four significant figures:

Trial	Mass of Iron per kg Ore Sample
1	39.74 g/kg
2	40.06 g/kg
3	39.06 g/kg
4	40.92 g/kg

$$\text{average (or mean) value, } \bar{x} = \frac{39.74 + 40.06 + 39.06 + 40.92}{4} = 39.94 \text{ g/kg}$$

To calculate the standard deviation and percent relative standard deviation (or coefficient of variation), compute the deviations and their squares. Let's set up a table.

Trial	Measured Values	$d_i = \bar{x} - x_i$	d_i^2
1	39.74 g	0.20	0.040
2	40.06 g	–0.12	0.014
3	39.06 g	0.88	0.77
4	40.92 g	–0.98	0.96
	$\bar{x}$ = 39.94 g		Sum = 1.78

$$\text{standard deviation, } s = \sqrt{\frac{1.78}{4-1}} = 0.77$$

$$\%\text{RSD (or CV)} = \frac{0.77}{39.94} \times 100 = 1.93\%$$

The precision of our analysis is expressed in terms of a standard deviation; the amount of iron in the sample is reported as 39.94 ± 0.77 g Fe/kg of sample, meaning that 68 percent of subsequent analyses should be in the range of 39.94 ± 0.77 g Fe/kg of sample. The percent relative standard deviation, %RSD (or coefficient of variation, CV), of the precision of the data is 1.93 percent.

E. Relative Error

Scientists check the *accuracy* of their measurements by comparing their results with values that are well established and considered accepted values. Many reference books, such as the Chemical Rubber Company's (CRC) *Handbook of Chemistry and Physics*, are used to check a result against an accepted value. To report the relative error in *your* result, take the absolute value of the difference between your measured value and the accepted value and divide this difference by the accepted value. Taking x to be your measured value and y to be the accepted value,

$$\text{relative error} = \frac{|x - y|}{y} \quad \text{(E.1)}$$

Relative error may be expressed as percent or parts per thousand, multiplying the relative error by 100 or 1,000.

F. Graphing Data

A well-designed graph of experimental data is a very effective organization of the data for observing trends, discovering relationships, or predicting information. It is therefore worthwhile to learn how to effectively construct and present a graph and how to extract information from it.

In general, a graph is constructed on a set of perpendicular axes; the vertical axis (the *y* axis) is the **ordinate**, and the horizontal axis (the *x* axis) is the **abscissa**.

Constructing a graph involves the following five steps whether the graph is constructed manually or with the appropriate software such as Excel.

1. **Select the axes.** First choose which variable corresponds to the ordinate and which one corresponds to the abscissa. Usually, the dependent variable is plotted along the ordinate and values of the independent variable along the abscissa. For example, if we observe how the pressure of a gas responds to a change in volume, pressure is the dependent variable. We therefore assign pressure to the vertical *y*-axis (ordinate) and volume to the horizontal *x*-axis (abscissa); we say we are plotting pressure versus volume. Be sure to label each axis by indicating the units that correspond to the variables being plotted (Figure F.1).
2. **Set the scales for the axes.** Construct the graph so that the data fill as much of the space of the graph as possible. Therefore, choose scales for the *x*- and *y*-axes that cover the range of the experimental data. For example, if the measured pressure range is 150 to 740 torr, choose a pressure scale that ranges from 100 to 800 torr. This covers the entire data range and allows us to mark the major divisions at intervals of 100 torr (Figure F.1). When choosing the scale, always choose values for the major divisions that make the smaller subdivisions easy to interpret. With major divisions at every 100 torr, minor divisions occur at every 50 torr. This makes plotting values such as 525 torr very simple.

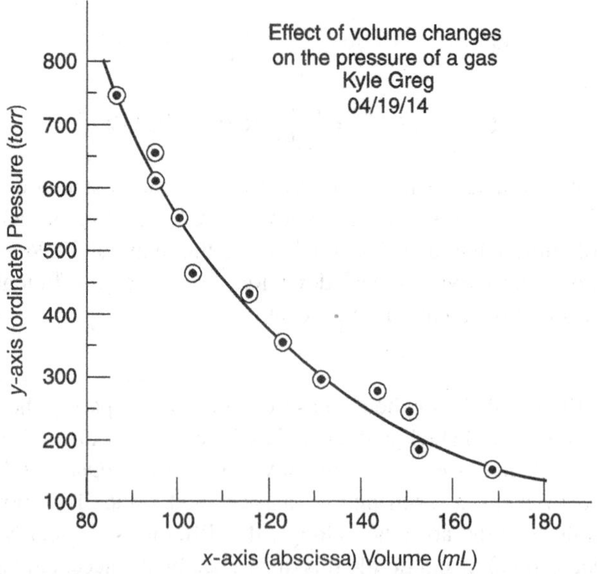

Figure F.1 An example of a properly drawn and labeled graph showing how the pressure of a gas depends on the volume of that gas

Construct the scale for the x-axis in the same manner. In Figure F.1, the volumes range from 170 mL at a pressure of 150 torr to 85 mL at a pressure of 750 torr. The scale on the x-axis ranges from 80 to 180 mL and is marked off in 20-mL intervals. Label each axis with the appropriate units.

There are a few additional points to note about marking the scales of a graph:

- The values plotted along the axes do not have to begin at zero at the origin; in fact, they seldom do.
- The size of the minor subdivisions should permit estimation of all the significant figures used in obtaining the data (if pressure measurements are made to the nearest torr, then the pressure scale should be interpreted to read to the nearest torr).
- If the graph is used for extrapolation, be sure that the range of scales covers the range of the extrapolation.

3. **Plot the data.** Place a dot for each data point at the appropriate place on the graph. Draw a small circle around the dot. *Ideally*, the size of the circle should approximate the estimated error in the measurement. For most software graphing programs, error bars can be added to the data points to better represent the precision of the data. If you plot two or more different data sets on the same graph, use different-shaped symbols (triangle, square, diamond, etc.) around the data points to distinguish one set of data from another.
4. **Draw a curve for the best fit.** Draw a *smooth* curve that best fits your data. This line does not have to pass through the centers of all the data points, or even through any of them, but it should pass as closely as possible to all of them. Most software has the option of adding a trendline to the plotted data. Generally, several options as to the type of trendline are offered—select the one that best fits your data.

   Note that the line in Figure F.1 is not drawn through the circles. It stops at the edge of the circle, passes undrawn through it, and then emerges from the other side.
5. **Title your graph.** Place a descriptive title in the upper portion of the graph, well away from the data points and the smooth curve. Include your name and date under the title.

G. Straight-Line Graphs

Often, the graphical relationship between measured quantities produces a straight line. This is the case, for example, when we plot pressure versus temperature for a fixed volume of gas. Such linear relationships are useful because the line corresponding to the best fit of the data points can be drawn with a straight edge and because quantitative (extrapolated) information about the relationship is easily obtained directly from the graph.

Algebraically, a straight line is described by the equation

$$y = mx + b \tag{G.1}$$

m is the slope of the straight line and b is the point of intersection of the line with the y-axis when $x = 0$ (Figure G.1). The slope of the line, which is usually of greatest interest, is determined from the relationship

$$m = \frac{y_2 - y_1}{x_2 - x_1} = \frac{\Delta y}{\Delta x} \tag{G.2}$$

Figure G.2 illustrates the determination of the slope for a typical plot of pressure versus temperature. First, plot the data and then draw the *best straight line.* Next, choose points *on the drawn line* corresponding to the easily readable values along the x-axis. Read corresponding y values along the y-axis (see dotted lines), and then compute the slope.

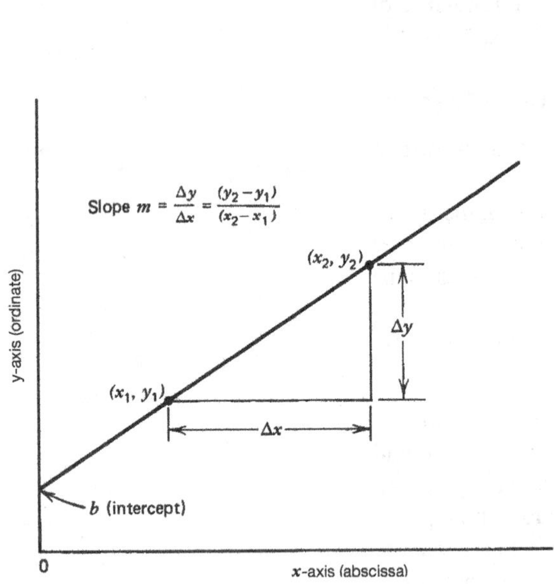

Figure G.1 The slope and intercept for a straight line, $y = mx + b$

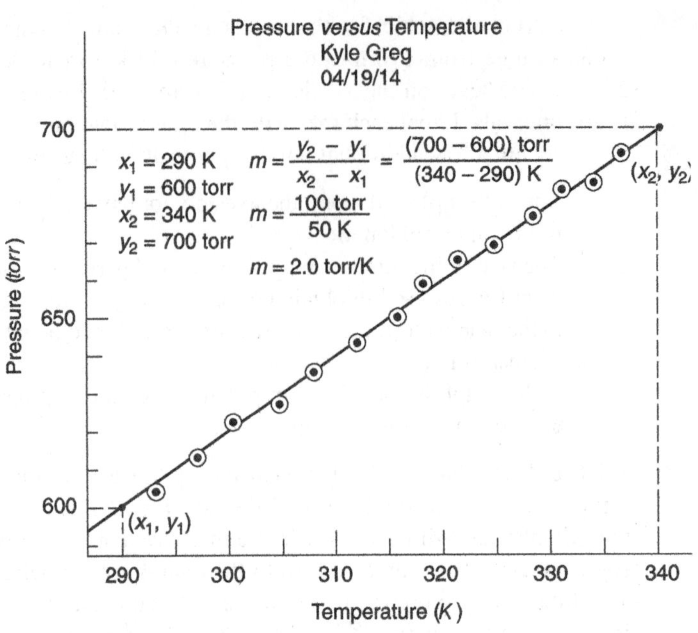

Figure G.2 Determination of the slope of a straight line drawn for a plot of pressure versus temperature for a gas

Using appropriate software, if a straight line is the selected trendline, the equation for the straight line is generally given, from which the slope and y-intercept can be obtained. See Figure G.3.

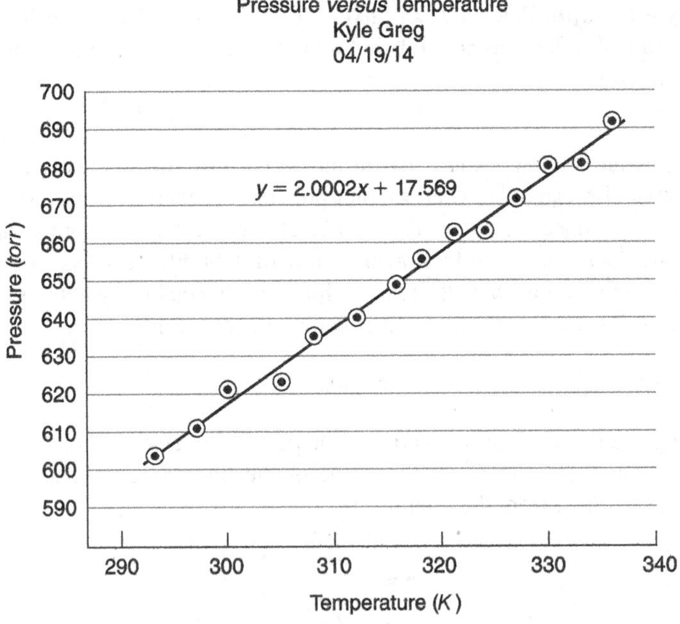

Figure G.3 Using Microsoft Excel, the equation for the trendline provides the slope and y-intercept for the pressure versus temperature data.

Caracterdesign/iStockphoto

Laboratory Techniques

The application of proper laboratory techniques improves the precision of data.

Scientific data that are used to analyze the characteristics of a chemical or physical change must be collected with care and patience. The data must be precise; that is, they must be reproducible to within an "acceptable" margin of error. Reproducible data implies that the data collected from an observed chemical or physical change can be again collected at a later date by the same scientist or another scientist in another laboratory.

A scientist who has good laboratory skills and techniques generally collects good, reproducible data (called **quantitative data**). For that reason, careful attention as to the method (or methods) and procedures by which the data are collected is extremely important. This section of the laboratory manual describes a number of techniques that you will need to develop for collecting quantitative data in a safe manner. You do not need to know the details for all of the techniques at this time (that will come with each successive experiment that you encounter), but you should be aware of their importance, features, and location in the laboratory manual. Become *very* familiar with this section of the laboratory manual! Consult with your laboratory instructor about the completion of the ***Laboratory Assignment*** at the end of this section.

In the Experimental Procedure of each experiment, icons are placed in the margin at a position where the corresponding laboratory technique is to be applied for the collection of "better" data. The following index of icons identifies the laboratory techniques and page numbers on which they appear:

Technique 1. Inserting Glass Tubing through a Rubber Stopper ***p. 19***

Technique 2. Cleaning Glassware ***p. 19***

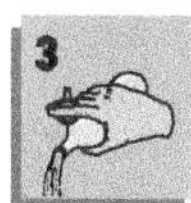

Technique 3. Handling Chemicals ***p. 20***

Technique 4. Disposing of Chemicals ***p. 21***

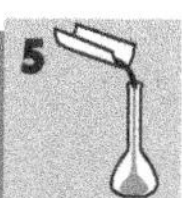

Technique 5. Preparing Solutions ***p. 21***

Technique 6. Measuring Mass ***p. 22***

Technique 7. Handling Small Volumes ***p. 23***

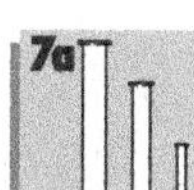
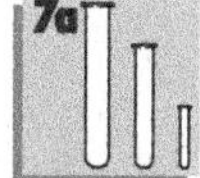

A. Test Tubes for Small Volumes ***p. 23***

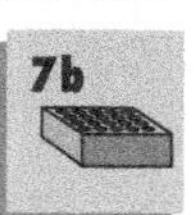

B. Well Plates for Small Volumes ***p. 23***

TECHNIQUE 1. INSERTING GLASS TUBING THROUGH A RUBBER STOPPER

Caution: *Perhaps more accidents occur in the general chemistry laboratory as a result of neglect in this simple operation than all other accidents combined. Please review and practice this technique correctly when working with glass tubing. Serious injury can occur to the hand if this technique is performed incorrectly.*

Moisten the glass tubing and the hole in the rubber stopper with glycerol or water (**Note:** glycerol works best). Place your hand on the tubing 2–3 cm (1 in.) from the stopper. Protect your hand with a cloth towel (Figure T.1). Simultaneously *twist* and *push* the tubing slowly and carefully through the hole. Wash off any excess glycerol on the glass or stopper with water and dry.

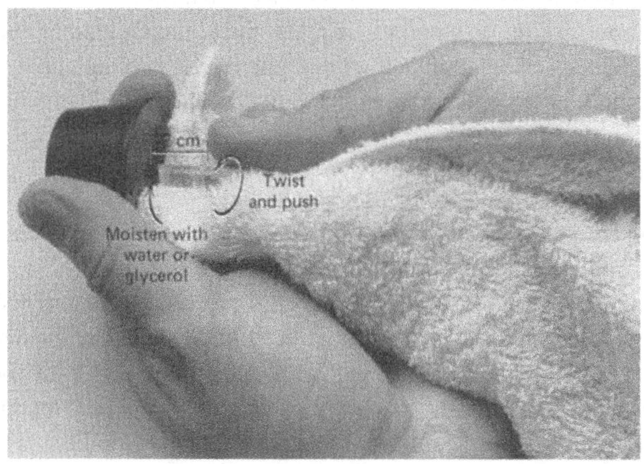

Jo A. Beran

Figure T.1 Inserting glass tubing through a rubber stopper

TECHNIQUE 2. CLEANING GLASSWARE

A chemist is very concerned about contaminants causing errors in experimental data. Cleanliness is extremely important in minimizing errors in the precision and accuracy of data. *Glassware should be clean before you begin an experiment and should be cleaned again immediately after completing the experiment.*

Clean all glassware with a soap or detergent solution using *tap water*. Use a laboratory sponge or a test tube, pipet, or buret brush as appropriate. Once the glassware is thoroughly cleaned, first rinse several times with tap water and then once or twice with *small amounts* of deionized water. Roll each rinse around the entire inner surface of the glass wall for a complete rinse. Discard each rinse through the delivery point of the vessel (i.e., buret tip, pipet tip, beaker spout). For conservation purposes, deionized water should never be used for washing glassware, only for final rinsing.

Invert the clean glassware on a paper towel or rubber mat to dry (Figure T.2a). Do *not* wipe or blow-dry because of possible contamination. Do *not* dry heavy glassware (graduated cylinders, volumetric flasks, or bottles), or for that matter any glassware, over a direct flame.

The glassware is clean if, following the final rinse with deionized water, no water droplets adhere to the clean part of the glassware (Figure T.2b).

Courtesy of Thermo Fisher Scientific

A laboratory detergent

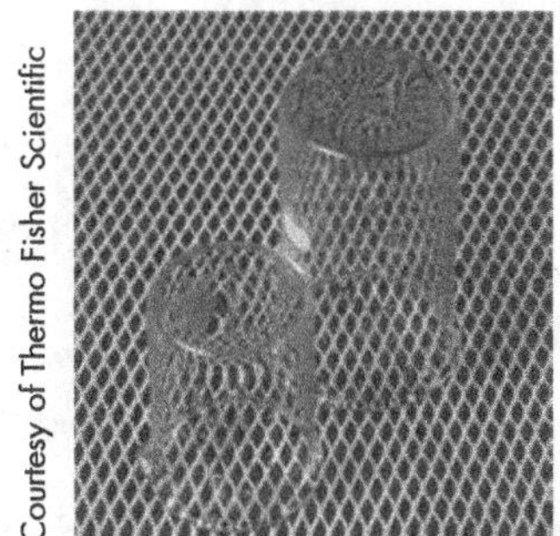

Courtesy of Thermo Fisher Scientific

Figure T.2a Invert clean glassware on a paper towel or rubber mat to air-dry.

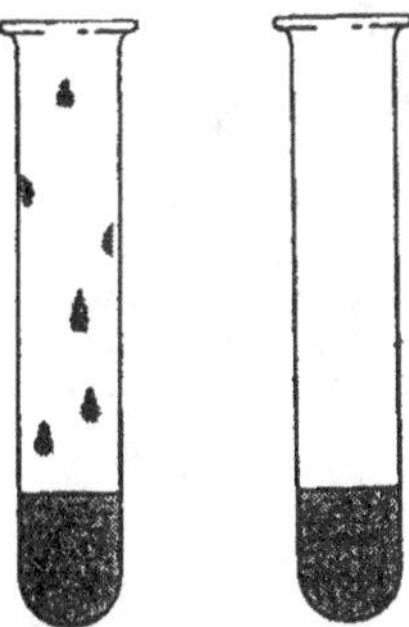

Figure T.2b Water droplets (left) do *not* adhere to the wall of clean glassware (right).

Technique 3. Handling Chemicals

Laboratory Safety and Guidelines also include the handling of chemicals. Chemicals are safe to handle when only a few precautionary guidelines are followed.

- *Read the label* on a reagent bottle at least *twice* before removing any chemicals (Figure T.3a). The wrong chemical may lead to serious accidents or "unexplainable" results in your experiments (see *Dry Lab 2* for an understanding of the rules of chemical nomenclature). *Techniques 9 and 10* illustrate the correct procedures for transferring solids and liquid reagents.
- Avoid using excessive amounts of reagents. *Never* dispense more than the experiment calls for. *Do not return excess chemicals to the reagent bottle!*
- *Never* touch, taste, or smell chemicals. Skin, nasal, and/or eye irritations may result. If inadvertent contact with a chemical does occur, wash the affected area immediately with copious amounts of water and inform your laboratory instructor (see **Laboratory Safety**, B.4, 5).
- Properly dispose of chemicals. See *Technique 4*.

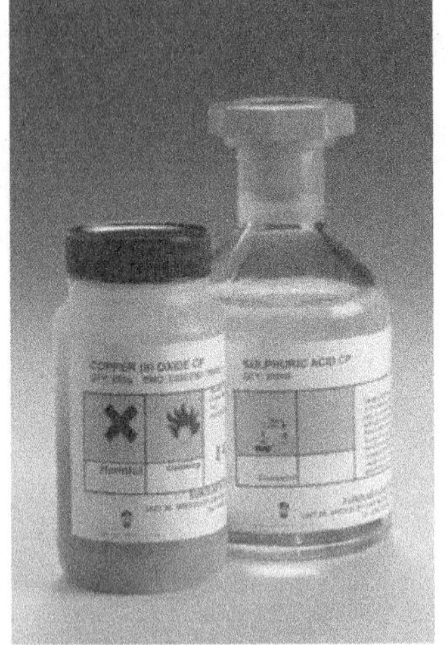

Martyn F. Chillmaid/Science Source

Figure T.3a Chemicals are labeled with systematic names (see *Dry Lab 2*).

Chemicals are often labeled according to National Fire Protection Association (NFPA) standards that describe the four possible hazards of a chemical and a numerical rating from 0 to 4. The four hazards are health hazard (blue), fire hazard (red), reactivity (yellow), and specific hazard (white). A label is shown in Figure T.3b.

If you wish to know more about the properties and hazards of the chemicals you will be working with in the laboratory, safety information about the chemicals is available in a bound collection of Material Safety Data Sheets (MSDS). The MSDS collection is also accessible on various Web sites (see **Data Documentation**, Part B), (e.g., at www.ilpi.com/msds).

In this manual, the international caution sign (shown at left) is used to identify a potential danger in the handling of a solid chemical or reagent solution or hazardous equipment.

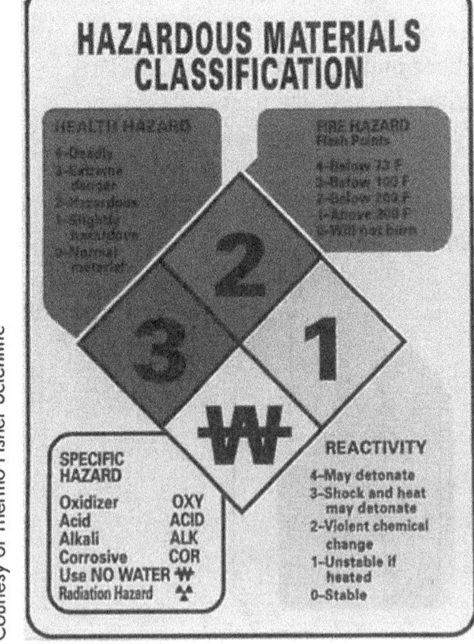

Courtesy of Thermo Fisher Scientific

Figure T.3b Hazardous materials classification system

Courtesy of Thermo Fisher Scientific

Figure T.4 Waste disposal containers are available in the laboratory.

TECHNIQUE 4. DISPOSING OF CHEMICALS

Most all chemicals used in the experiments of this manual are considered "safe" but must be properly disposed after use for safety and environmental concerns.

- Assume *nothing* (besides soap and water) is to be discarded in the sink.
- Discard waste chemicals as directed in the Experimental Procedure or by the laboratory instructor. *Read the label* on the waste container *at least twice* (Figure T.4) before discarding the chemical. Carelessness that may result in improper mixing of waste chemicals can cause serious laboratory accidents. ***"When in doubt, ask your instructor; it's the safe thing to do!"***
- Note the location of each disposal icon in the Experimental Procedure as the point at which disposal is to occur.

The final disposal of chemicals is the responsibility of the stockroom personnel. Information for the proper disposal of chemicals is also available from the MSDS collection or at various Web sites.

TECHNIQUE 5. PREPARING SOLUTIONS

The preparation of an aqueous solution is often required for an Experimental Procedure. The preparation begins with either a solid reagent or a solution more concentrated than the one needed for the experiment. At either starting point, the number of *moles* of compound required for the experiment is calculated: (1) From a solid, the mass and the molar mass of the compound are needed to calculate the number of moles of compound required for the preparation of the solution, (2) from a more concentrated solution, the concentration and volume (or mass) of the diluted solution must be known in order to calculate the number of moles of compound needed for the preparation of the aqueous solution. In both cases, the calculated (and then also measured) moles of compound are diluted to final volume. Knowledge of moles and mole calculations is absolutely necessary.

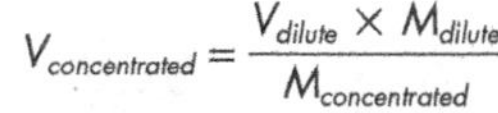

$$\text{moles solute} = \frac{\text{grams solute}}{\text{molar mass solute}}$$

$$V_{concentrated} = \frac{V_{dilute} \times M_{dilute}}{M_{concentrated}}$$

In the laboratory preparation, *never* insert a pipet, spatula, or dropping pipet into the reagent used for the solution preparation. Always transfer the calculated amount from the reagent bottle as described in *Techniques 9 and 10.*

Solutions are commonly prepared in volumetric flasks (Figure T.5) according to the following procedure:

- Place deionized water (or less concentrated solution) into the volumetric flask until it is one-third to one-half full.
- Add the solid (or add the more concentrated reagent) *slowly, while swirling,* to the volumetric flask. (**Caution:** *Never dump it in!*)
- Once the solid compound has dissolved or the more concentrated solution has been diluted, add deionized water (dropwise if necessary) until the calibrated "mark" etched on the volumetric flask is reached (see *Technique 16A* for reading the meniscus). While securely holding the stopper, invert the flask slowly 10–15 times to ensure that the solution is homogeneous.

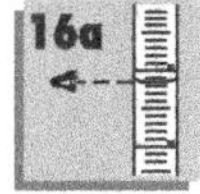

(a)

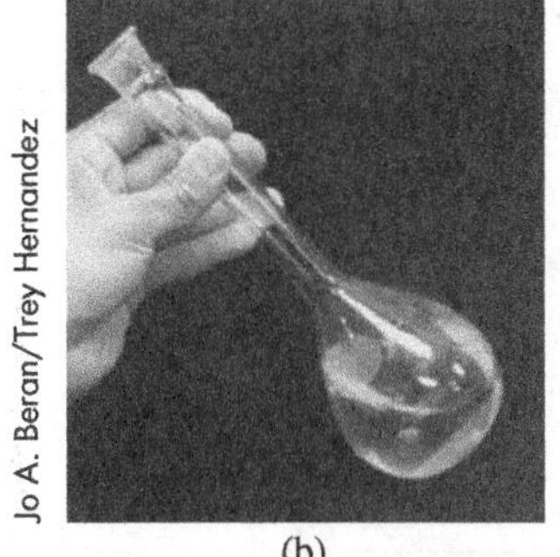

(b)

(c)

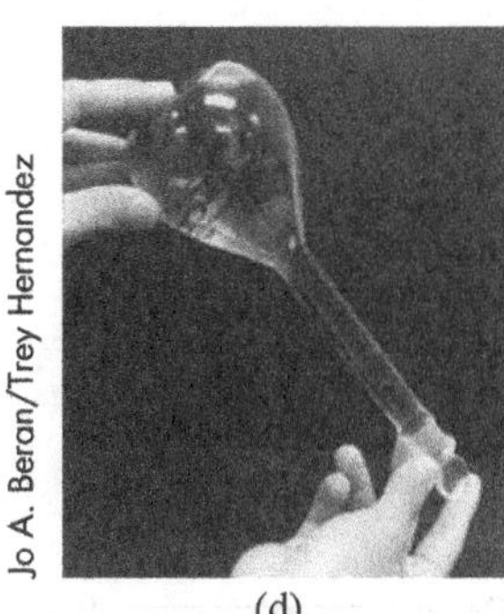

(d)

Figure T.5 Place water (or the less concentrated solution) into the flask before slowly adding the solid or more concentrated solution. Dilute the solution to the "mark" with water; stopper and invert the flask 10–15 times.

Technique 6. Measuring Mass

The laboratory balance is perhaps the most used *and abused* piece of equipment in the chemistry laboratory. Therefore, because of its extensive use, you and others must follow several guidelines to maintain the longevity and accuracy of the balance:

- Handle with care; balances are expensive.
- If the balance is not leveled, see your laboratory instructor.
- Use weighing paper, a watchglass, a beaker, or some other container to measure the mass of chemicals; do *not* place chemicals directly on the balance pan.
- Do *not* drop anything on the balance pan.
- If the balance is not operating correctly, see your laboratory instructor. Do *not* attempt to fix it yourself.
- After completing a mass measurement, return the mass settings to the zero position.
- *Clean the balance and balance area of any spilled chemicals.*

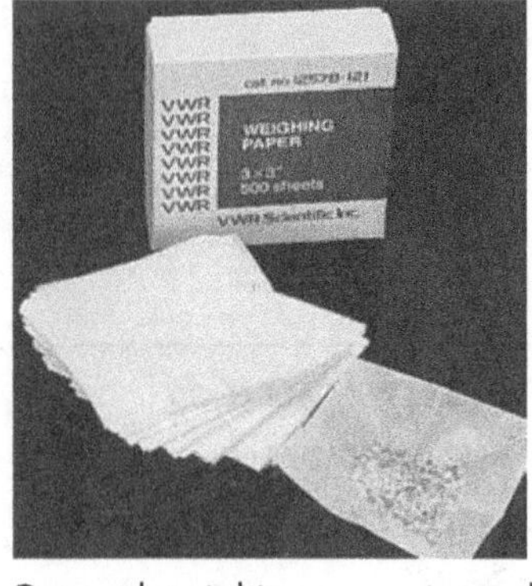

Courtesy of VWR International, LLC

Creased weighing paper is used for measuring the mass of solids.

Tared mass: mass of sample without regard to its container

The mass measurement of a sample can be completed in two ways. In the traditional method, the mass of weighing paper or a clean, dry container (such as a beaker, watchglass, or weighing boat) is first measured and recorded. The sample is then placed on the weighing paper or in the container and this combined mass is measured. The mass of the weighing paper or container is then subtracted from the combined mass to record the mass of the sample.

On modern electronic balances, the mass of the weighing paper or container can be tared out—that is, the balance can be zeroed *after* placing the weighing paper or container on the balance, in effect subtracting its mass immediately (and automatically). The sample is then placed on the weighing paper or in the container, and the balance reading *is* the mass of the sample.

For either method, the resultant mass of the sample is the same and is called the **tared mass** of the sample.

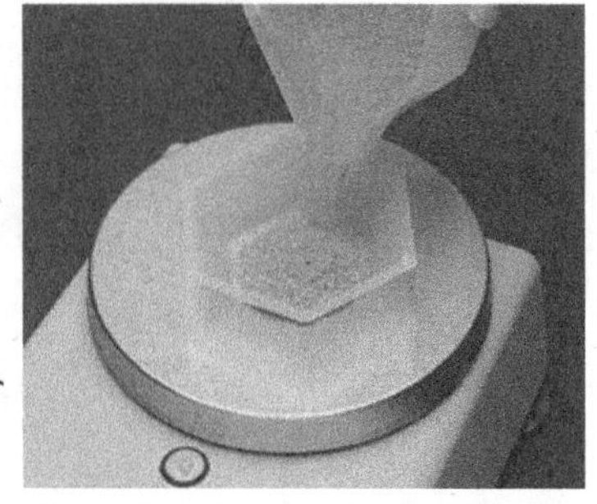

Courtesy of Thermo Fisher Scientific

Plastic (or aluminum) weighing dishes are used for measuring the masses of solids.

Different electronic balances, having varying degrees of sensitivity, are available for use in the laboratory. It is important to know (by reading the Experimental Procedure) the precision required to make a mass measurement and then to select the appropriate balance. It may save you time during the data analysis. Record mass measurements that reflect the precision of the balance—that is, the correct number of significant figures (see **Data Analysis**, Part A). These balances are shown in Figures T.6a through T.6c.

Balance	Sensitivity (g)
Top-loading (Figure T.6a)	±0.01 or ±0.001
Top-loading (Figure T.6b)	±0.0001
Analytical (Figure T.6c)	±0.00001

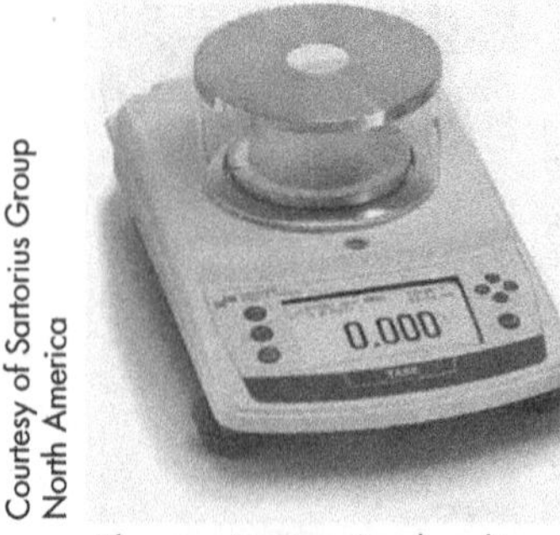

Courtesy of Sartorius Group North America

Figure T.6a Top-loading balance, sensitivity of ±0.01 g and/or ±0.001 g.

Courtesy of VWR International, LLC

Figure T.6b Analytical balance, sensitivity of ±0.0001 g.

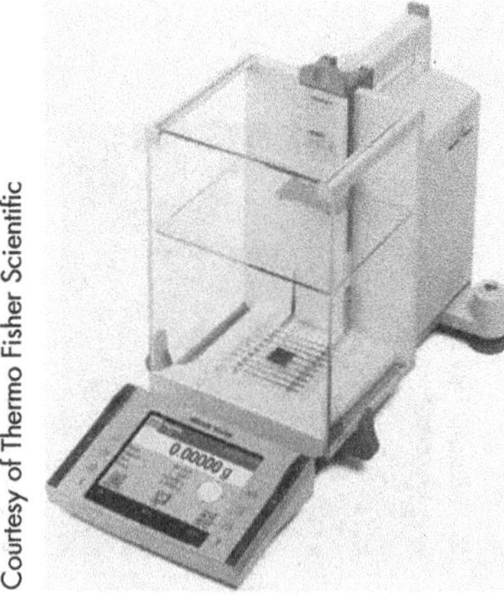

Courtesy of Thermo Fisher Scientific

Figure T.6c Analytical balance, sensitivity of ±0.00001 g.

Technique 7. Handling Small Volumes

The use of smaller quantities of chemicals for synthesis and testing in the laboratory offers many safety advantages and presents fewer chemical disposal problems. Many of the Experimental Procedures in this manual were designed with this in mind. Handling small volumes requires special apparatus and technique.

A. Test Tubes for Small Volumes

7a

Small test tubes are the chemist's choice for handling small volumes. Common laboratory test tubes are generally of three sizes: the 75-mm (or 3-inch) test tube, the 150-mm (or 6-inch) test tube, and the 200-mm (or 8-inch) test tube (Figure T.7a). The approximate volumes of the three test tubes are:

75-mm (3-inch) test tube	~3 mL
150-mm (6-inch) test tube	~25 mL
200-mm (8-inch) test tube	~75 mL

The 75-mm test tube is often recommended for "small volume" experiments.

When mixing solutions in a test tube, either (1) stir the solution with a stirring rod, (2) agitate the solution by tapping the side of the test tube, or (3) stopper the test tube and invert, but *never* use your thumb (Figure T.7b)!

B. Well Plates for Small Volumes

Alternatively, a "well plate" can be used for several or for a series of reaction vessels (Figure T.7c). The well plate is especially suited for experiments that require observations from repeated or comparative reactions. The well plate most often recommended is the 24-well plate in which each well has an approximate volume of 3.5 mL (compared to a 3 mL for a small test tube).

For either technique, the Beral pipet, (a plastic, disposable pipet), or a dropping pipet (usually made of glass) is often used to transfer small volumes of solutions to and from the test tubes or well plate. The Beral pipet has a capacity of about 2 mL, and some have volume graduation marks on the stem.

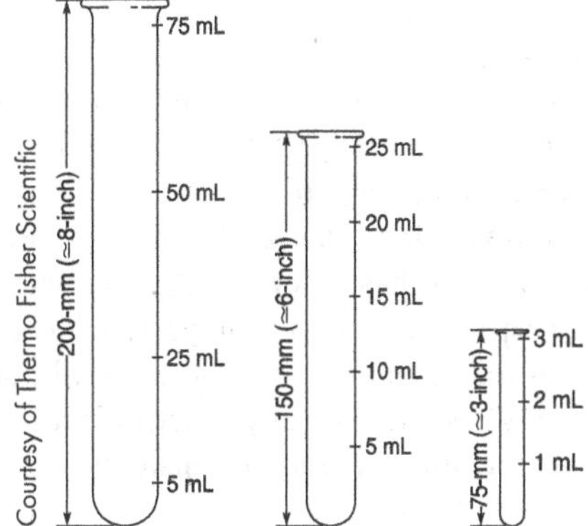

Figure T.7a The three common-size test tubes for containing reagent solutions

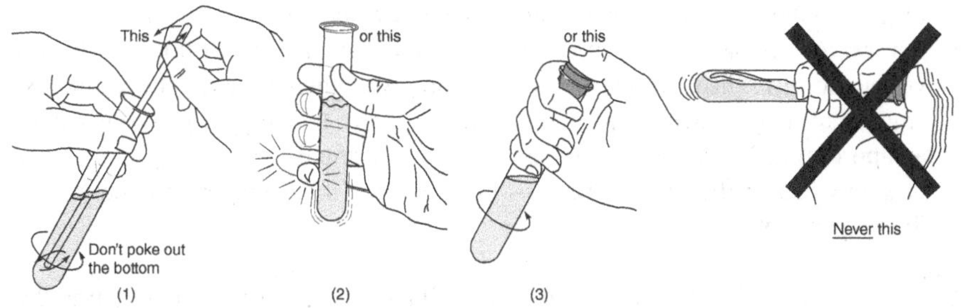

Figure T.7b Technique for mixing solutions in a test tube.

Courtesy of Corning Incorporated

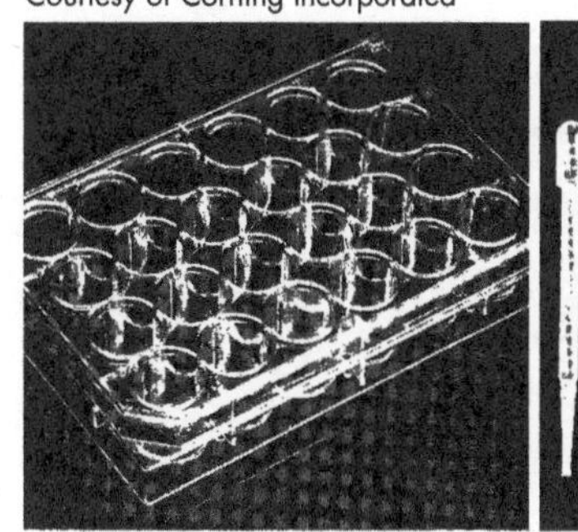

Figure T.7c A 24-well plate and Beral pipet are used for containing and transferring small quantities of reagent solutions.

Technique 8. Collecting Water-Insoluble Gases

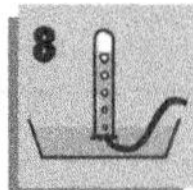

Gases that are relatively insoluble in water are collected by water displacement. The gas pushes the water down and out of the water-filled gas-collecting vessel (Figure T.8a). The gas-collecting vessel (generally a flask or test tube) is first filled with water, covered with a glass plate or plastic wrap (no air bubbles must enter the vessel, Figure T.8b), and then inverted into a deep pan or tray half-filled with water. The glass plate or plastic wrap is removed, and the tubing from the gas generator is inserted into the mouth of the gas-collecting vessel.

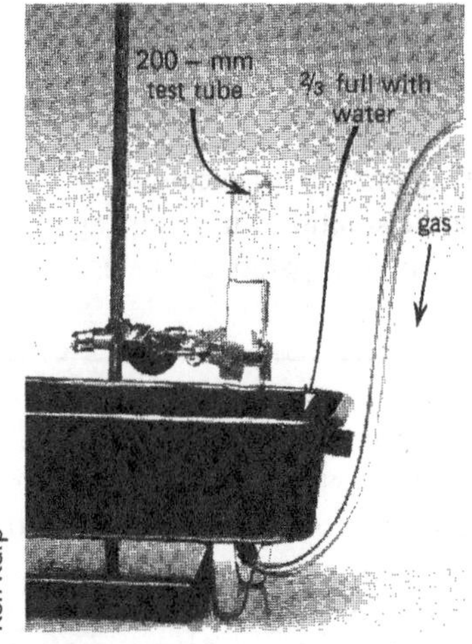

Figure T.8a Collection of water-insoluble gas by the displacement of water

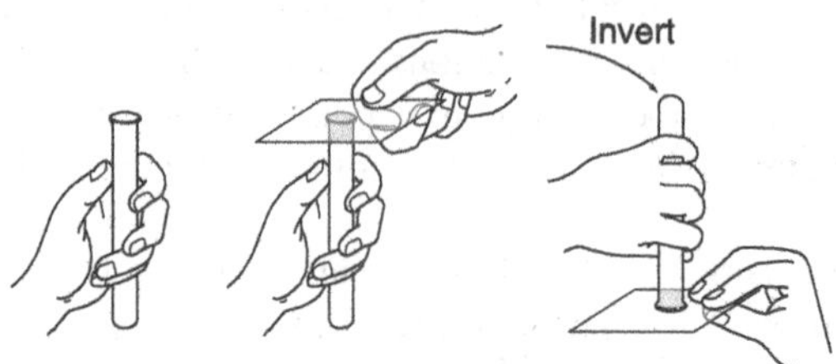

Figure T.8b Inverting a water-filled test tube

Technique 9. Transferring Solids

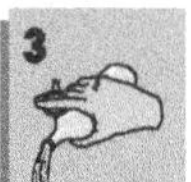

Read the label on the bottle *twice* to be sure it is the correct chemical. For example, is the chemical for the experiment iron(II) acetate or iron(III) acetate? Is it the anhydrous, trihydrate, or pentahydrate form of copper(II) sulfate?

Safety, again, is of primary importance. Always be aware of the importance of *Technique 3*. If the reagent bottle has a hollow glass stopper or if it has a screw cap, then place the stopper (or cap) top side down on the bench (Figure T.9a). To dispense a solid from the bottle, hold the label against your hand, tilt, and roll the solid reagent back and forth. Avoid using a spatula or any other object to break up or transfer the reagent to the appropriate container unless your instructor *specifically* instructs you to do so.

- For *larger quantities* of solid reagent, dispense the solid into a beaker (Figure T.9b) until the estimated amount has been transferred. Try not to dispense any more reagent than is necessary for the experiment. Do not return any excess reagent to the reagent bottle—share the excess with another chemist.
- For *smaller quantities* of solid reagent, first dispense the solid into the inverted hollow glass stopper or screw cap. And then transfer the estimated amount of reagent needed for the experiment from the stopper or screw cap to an appropriate vessel. Return the excess reagent remaining in the glass stopper or screw cap to the reagent bottle—in effect, the solid reagent has never left the reagent bottle.

When you have finished dispensing the solid chemical, *recap* and return the reagent bottle to the reagent shelf.

Figure T.9a Transferring a solid chemical from a glass ground reagent bottle. Place the glass stopper top side down.

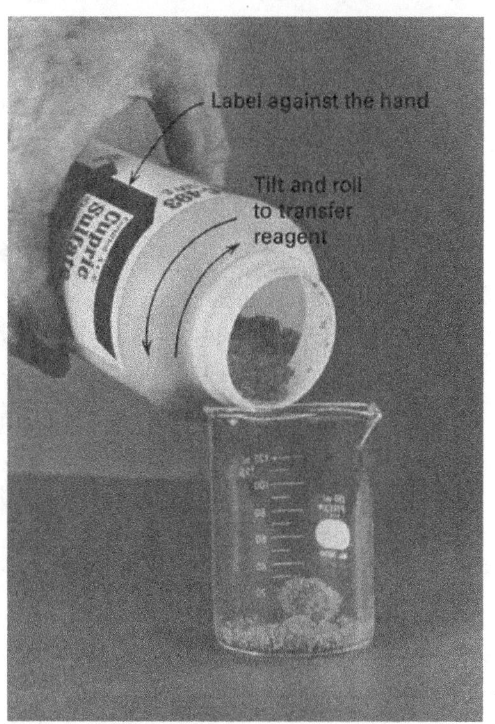

Figure T.9b Tilt and roll the reagent bottle back and forth until the desired amount of solid chemical has been dispensed.

Technique 10. Transferring Liquids and Solutions

Read the label. When a liquid or solution is to be transferred from a reagent bottle, remove the glass stopper and hold it between the fingers of the hand used to grasp the reagent bottle (Figures T.10a, b, pages 25–26). Never lay the glass stopper on the laboratory bench; impurities may be picked up and thus contaminate the liquid when the stopper is returned. If the reagent has a screw cap, place the top side down on the lab bench.

To transfer a liquid from one vessel to another, hold a stirring rod against the lip of the vessel containing the liquid and pour the liquid down the stirring rod, which, in turn, should touch the inner wall of the receiving vessel (Figures T.10b, c, page 26). Return the glass stopper or screw cap to the reagent bottle.

Do *not* transfer more liquid than is needed for the experiment. Do *not* return any excess or unused liquid to the original reagent bottle.

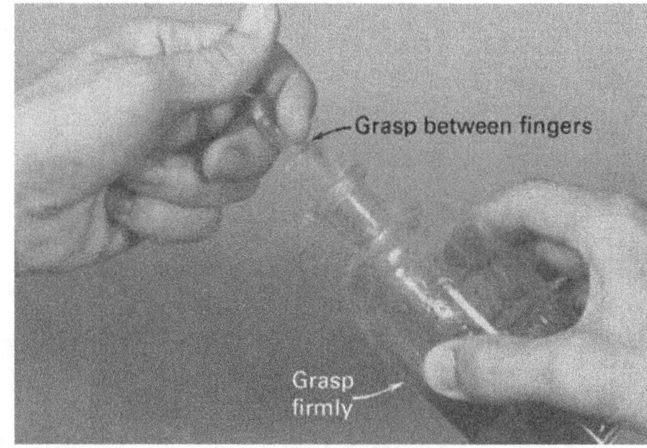

Figure T.10a Remove the glass stopper and hold it between the fingers of the hand that grasps the reagent bottle.

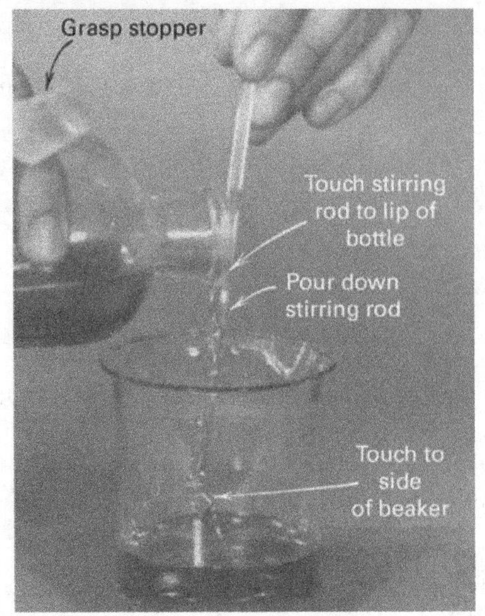

Figure T.10b Transfer the liquid from the reagent bottle with the aid of the stirring rod.

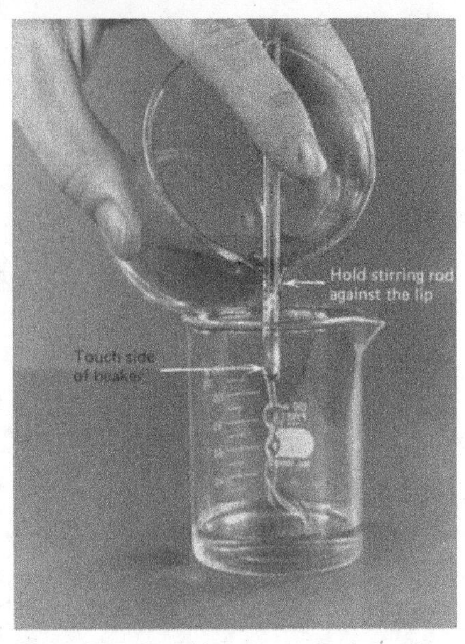

Figure T.10c The stirring rod should touch the lip of the transfer vessel and the inner wall of the receiving vessel.

Technique 11. Separating a Liquid or Solution from a Solid

A. Decanting a Liquid or Solution from a Solid

A liquid can be decanted (poured off the top) from a solid if the solid clearly separates from the liquid in a reasonably short period of time. Allow the solid to settle to the bottom of the beaker (Figure T.11a) or test tube. Transfer the liquid (called the **supernatant or decantate**) with the aid of a clean stirring rod (Figure T.11b). Do this slowly so as not to disturb the solid. Review *Technique 10* for the transfer of a liquid from one vessel to another.

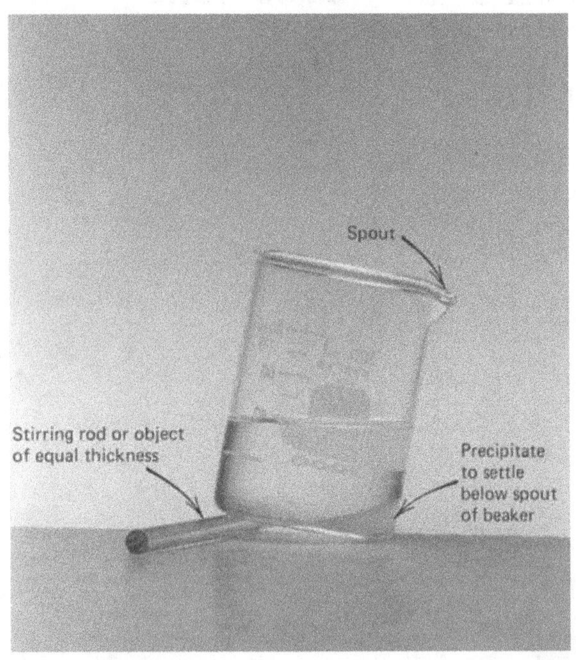

Figure T.11a Tilt the beaker to allow the precipitate to settle at the side. Use a stirring rod or a similar object to tilt the beaker.

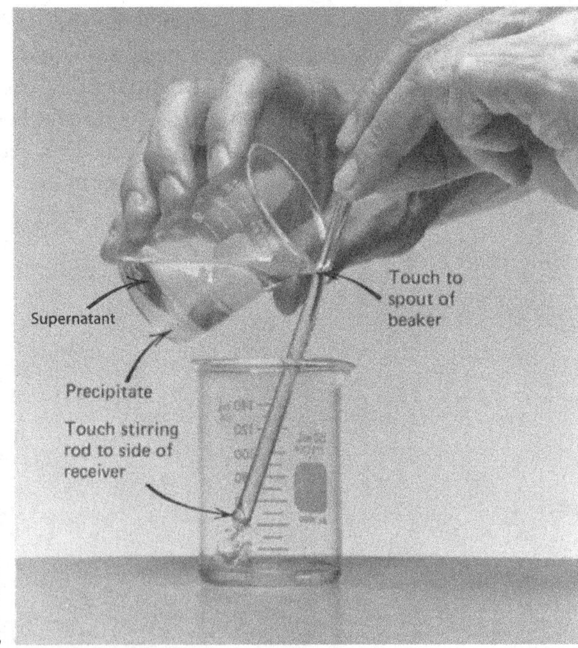

Figure T.11b Transfer the supernatant to a receiving vessel with the aid of a stirring rod.

B. Preparing Filter Paper for a Filter Funnel

If a solid is to be separated from the liquid using a filtering process, then the filter paper must be properly prepared. For a **gravity filtration** procedure, first fold the filter paper in half (Figure T.11c), again fold the filter paper to within about 10° of a 90° fold, tear off the corner (a *small* tear) of the outer fold unequally, and open. The tear enables a close seal to be made across the paper's folded portion when placed in a funnel.

Place the folded filter paper snugly into the funnel. Moisten the filter paper with the solvent of the liquid–solid mixture being filtered (most likely this will be deionized water) and press the filter paper against the top wall of the funnel to form a seal. Support the funnel with a clamp or in a funnel rack.

C. Gravity Filtration

Filtrate: the solution that passes through the filter in a filtration procedure

Transfer the liquid as described in *Technique 10* (Figure T.11d). The tip of the funnel should touch the wall of the receiving beaker to reduce any splashing of the **filtrate.** Fill the bowl of the funnel until it is *less than* two-thirds full with the mixture. Always keep the funnel stem full with the filtrate; the weight of the filtrate in the funnel stem creates a slight suction on the filter in the funnel, and this hastens the filtration process.

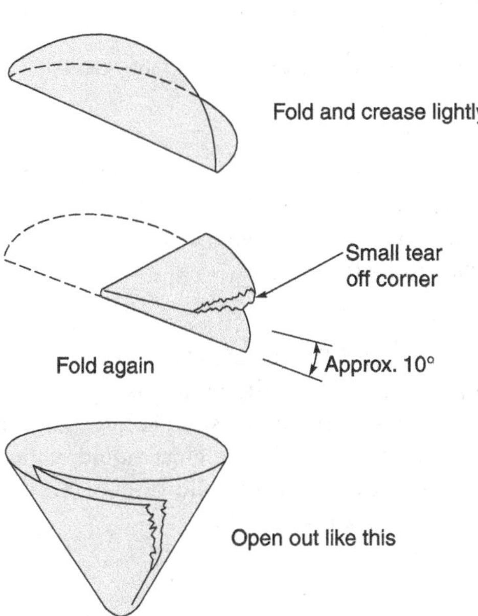

Figure T.11c The sequence of folding filter paper for a filter funnel in a gravity filtration procedure

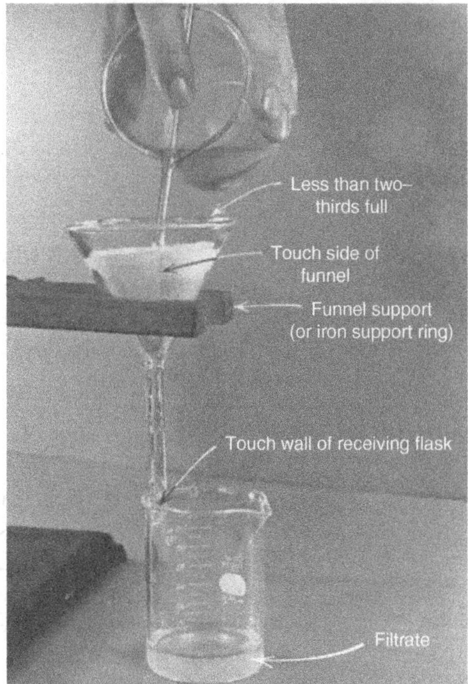

Figure T.11d The tip of the funnel should touch the wall of the receiving flask, and the bowl of the funnel should be one-half to two-thirds full.

D. Flushing a Precipitate from the Beaker

Flush the precipitate from a beaker using a wash bottle containing the mixture's solvent (usually deionized water). Hold the beaker over the funnel or receiving vessel (Figure T.11e, page 28) at an angle such that the solvent will flow out and down the stirring rod into the funnel.

E. Vacuum Filtration

Set up the vacuum filtration apparatus as shown in Figure T.11f, page 28. A Büchner funnel (a disk of filter paper fits over the flat, perforated bottom of the funnel) set into a filter flask connected to a water aspirator is the apparatus normally used for vacuum filtration. Seal the disk of filter paper onto the bottom of the funnel by applying a light suction to the filter paper while adding a small amount of solvent.

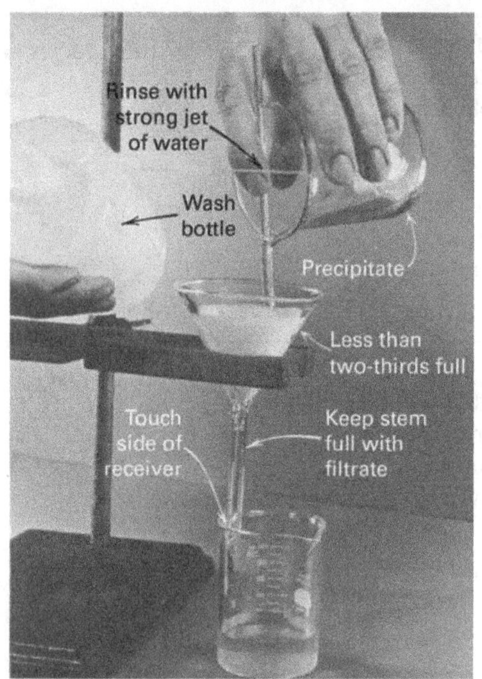

Figure T.11e Flushing the precipitate from a beaker with the aid of a "wash" bottle

Figure T.11f The aspirator should be fully open during the vacuum-filtering operation.

Once the filter paper is sealed, turn the water faucet attached to the aspirator *completely* open to create a full suction. Transfer the mixture to the filter (*Technique 10*) and wash the precipitate with an appropriate liquid. To remove the suction, *first* disconnect the hose from the filter flask and then turn off the water.

F. Centrifugation

Supernatant: the clear liquid covering a precipitate

A centrifuge (Figure T.11g) spins at velocities of 5,000 to 25,000 revolutions per minute! A liquid–solid mixture in a small test tube or centrifuge tube is placed into a sleeve of the rotor of the centrifuge. By centrifugal force, the solid is forced to the bottom of the test tube or centrifuge tube and compacted. The clear liquid, called the **supernatant,** is then easily decanted without any loss of solid (Figure T.11h). This quick separation of liquid from solid requires 20–40 seconds.

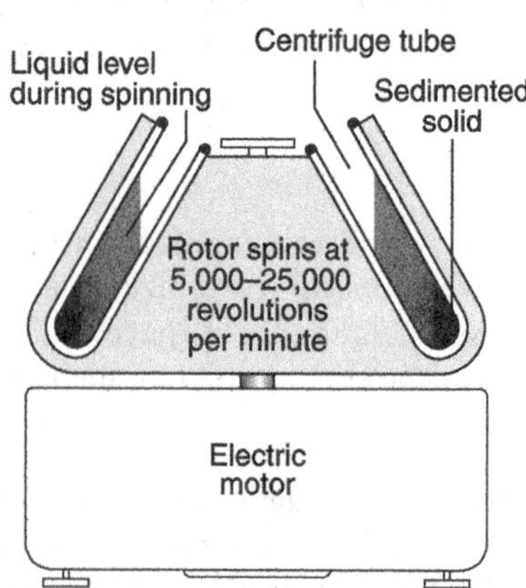

Figure T.11g A laboratory centrifuge forces the precipitate to the bottom of the centrifuge tube.

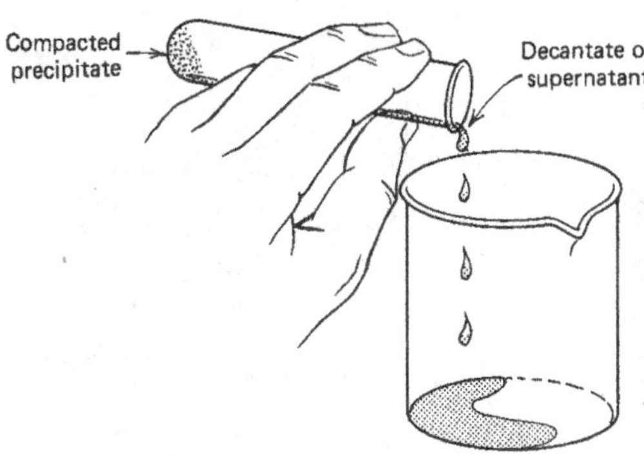

Figure T.11h Decant the supernatant from the compacted precipitate.

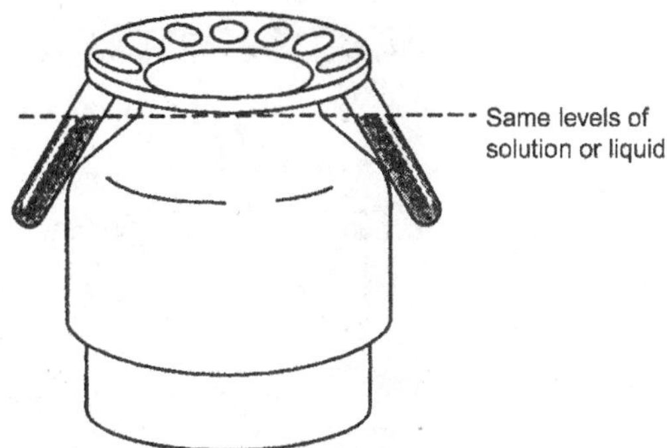

Figure T.11i Balance the centrifuge by placing tubes with equal volumes of liquid opposite each other inside the metal sleeves of the rotor.

Observe the following precautions in operating a centrifuge:

- Never fill the centrifuge tubes to a height more than 1 cm from the top.
- Label the centrifuge tubes to avoid confusion of samples.
- *Always* operate the centrifuge with an *even* number of centrifuge tubes containing equal volumes of liquid placed opposite one another in the centrifuge. This *balances* the centrifuge and eliminates excessive vibration and wear. If only one tube needs to be centrifuged, then balance the centrifuge with a tube containing the same volume of solvent (Figure T.11i).
- *Never* attempt to manually stop a centrifuge. When the centrifuge is turned off, let the rotor come to rest on its own.

Technique 12. Venting Gases

Fume hoods (Figure T.12a, page 30) are used for removing "undesirable" gases from a reagent such as concentrated hydrochloric acid or from a chemical reaction. These gases may be toxic, corrosive, irritating, or flammable. If there is a question about the use of a fume hood, hedge on the side of safety and/or consult with your instructor.

When using a fume hood:

- Turn on the hood air flow before beginning the experiment
- Never place your face inside of the fume hood
- Set the equipment and chemicals at least 6 inches back from the hood door
- Do not crowd experimental apparatus when sharing the use of a fume hood

On occasion, the space in the fume hoods is not adequate for an entire class to perform the experiment in a timely manner. With the *approval of your laboratory instructor,* an improvised hood (Figure T.12b, page 30) can be assembled. For the operation of an improvised hood, a water aspirator draws the gaseous product from above the reaction vessel; the gas dissolves in the water. To operate the "hood," completely open the faucet that is connected to the aspirator in order to provide the best suction for the removal of the gases. As a reminder, *never* substitute an improvised hood for a fume hood if space is available in the fume hood.

Technique 13. Heating Liquids and Solutions

Many procedures call for a solution to be heated. Heating a mixture either accelerates the rate of a chemical reaction or causes the formation of larger crystals of precipitate, allowing its separation to be more complete.

Hot liquids and solutions can be cooled by placing the glass vessel either under flowing tap water or in an ice bath.

Caution: *Flammable liquids should* ***never*** *be heated (directly or indirectly) with a flame. Always use a hot plate—refer to Techniques 13A and 13B where hot plates are used.*

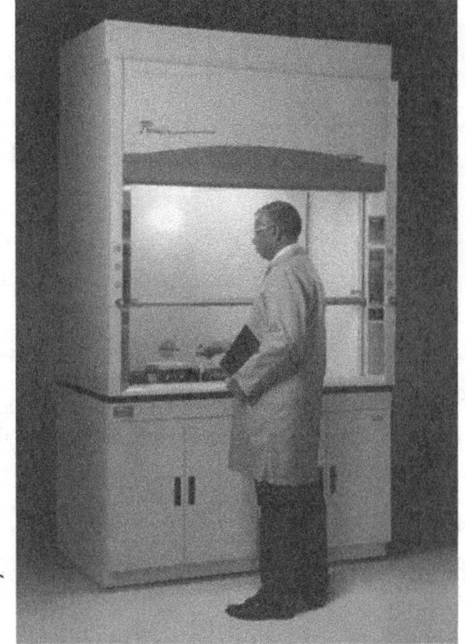
Courtesy of Thermo Fisher Scientific

Figure T.12a A modern laboratory fume hood.

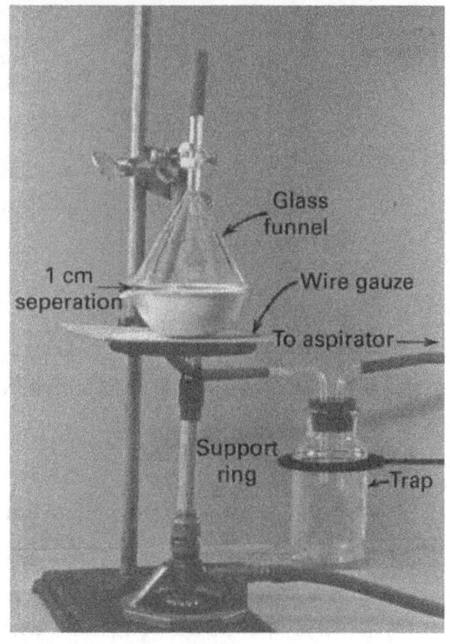

Jo A. Beran

Figure T.12b Position a funnel, connected to a water aspirator, over the escaping gases. A hot plate is often substituted for the Bunsen flame.

A. Beaker or flask

Nonflammable liquids in beakers or flasks that are more than one-fourth full can be *slowly* heated directly with a hot plate (Figure T.13a). (**Caution:** *Hot plates are hot*! *Do not touch*!) Caution must be taken *not* to heat the liquid too rapidly as "bumping" (the sudden formation of bubbles from the superheated liquid) may occur. To avoid or to minimize bumping, place a stirring rod followed by constant stirring or **boiling chips** into the liquid. If a stirring hot plate is used, place the stir bar into the liquid and turn on the stirrer (Figure T.13b).

Boiling chips (also called boiling stones): small, porous ceramic pieces—when heated, the air contained within the porous structure is released, gently agitating the liquid and minimizing boiling. Boiling chips also provide nucleation sites on which bubbles can form.

Courtesy of Thermo Fisher Scientific

Boiling chips

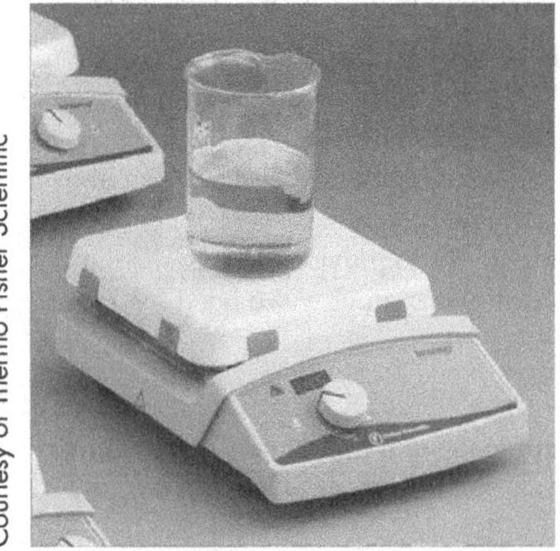
Courtesy of Thermo Fisher Scientific

Figure T.13a A hot plate may be used to maintain solutions in a beaker or flask at a constant, elevated temperature for an extended time period.

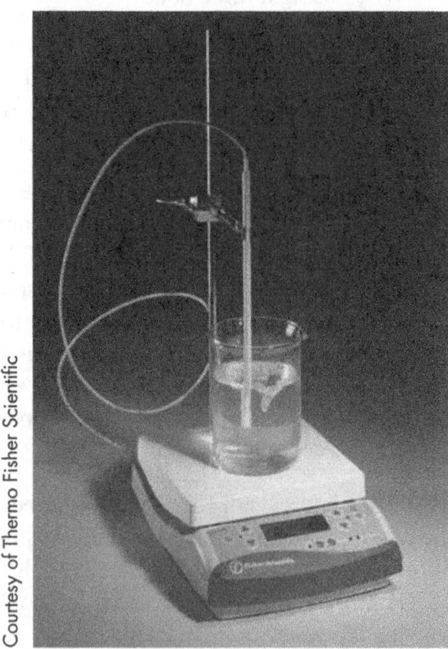
Courtesy of Thermo Fisher Scientific

Figure T.13b A stirring hot plate may be used to heat a liquid and minimize "bumping."

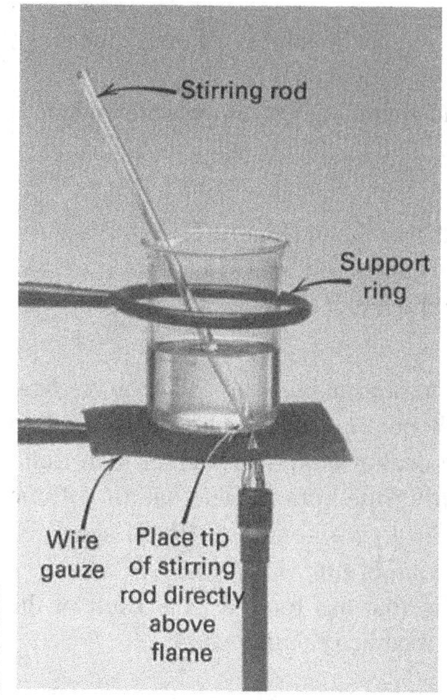

Figure T.13c Place the flame directly beneath the tip of the stirring rod in the beaker. Boiling chips may also be placed in the beaker to avoid "bumping."

Figure T.13d A hot water bath may be used to maintain solution in test tubes at a constant, elevated temperature for an extended time period.

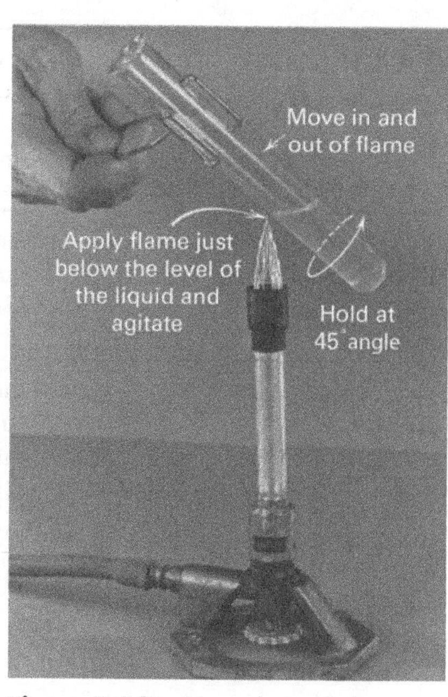

Figure T.13e Move the test tube circularly in and out of the *cool* flame, heating the liquid or solution from top to bottom.

A direct flame may also be used to heat the liquid in a beaker or flask. Support the beaker or flask on a wire gauze that is centered over an iron ring; use a second iron ring placed around the top of the beaker or flask to prevent it from being knocked off. Position the flame directly beneath the tip of the stirring rod (Figure T.13c) or add boiling chips to avoid or to minimize bumping.

B. Test Tubes

Small quantities of liquids in test tubes that need to be maintained at a constant, elevated temperature over a period of time can be placed in a hot water bath (Figure T.13d). The heat source may be a hot plate or direct flame, depending on the chemicals being used. The setup is the same as that for heating a liquid in a beaker (see *Technique 13A*).

To heat one or several solutions in test tubes in a hot water bath, a 150-mL beaker containing ~100 mL of deionized water in satisfactory. The test tubes can be placed directly into the bath, supported by the wall of the beaker. Maintain a warm-water bath with a hot plate or **cool flame**.

Cool flame: a nonluminous flame supplied with a reduced supply of fuel.

C. Test Tube over a "Cool" Flame

Safety first should be followed when using this technique for directly heating liquids in test tubes.

A **cool flame** is a nonluminous flame supplied with a reduced supply of fuel. In practice, the rule of thumb for creating a cool flame for heating a liquid in a test tube is as follows: *If you can feel the heat of the flame with the hand that is holding the test tube clamp,* ***the flame is too hot!***

For direct heating of a liquid in a test tube, the test tube should be less than one-third full of liquid. Hold the test tube with a test tube holder at an angle of about 45° with the flame. Move the test tube circularly and continuously in and out of the cool flame, heating from top to bottom, mostly near the top of the liquid (Figure T.13e). **Caution:** *Never fix the position of the flame at the base of the test tube, and never point the test tube at anyone; the contents may be ejected violently if the test tube is not heated properly.*

See *Technique 13B* for heating a solution in a test tube to a specified elevated temperature; the hot water bath in *Technique 13B* is a safer, but slower, procedure.

TECHNIQUE 14. EVAPORATING LIQUIDS

To remove a liquid from a vessel by evaporation, the flammability of the liquid must be considered. This is a safety precaution.

Use a fume hood or an improvised hood (*Technique 12*) as recommended to remove irritating or toxic vapors.

A. Use of Direct Heat

A nonflammable liquid can be evaporated with a direct flame (Figure T.14a). Place the liquid in an evaporating dish centered on a wire gauze and iron ring. Use a gentle, "cool" flame (*Technique 13c*) to slowly evaporate the liquid.

B. Use of Indirect Heat

Flammable *or* nonflammable liquids can be evaporated using a hot plate as the heat source. Place the liquid in an evaporating dish on top of a beaker according to Figure T.14b. Gentle boiling of the water in the beaker is more efficient than rapid boiling for evaporating the liquid. Avoid breathing the vapors. The use of a fume hood (*Technique 12*) is strongly recommended if large amounts of liquid are to be evaporated into the laboratory. Consult with your laboratory instructor.

For removing the final dampness from a solid that has formed as a result of the evaporation, consider using a drying oven as described in *Technique 15A*.

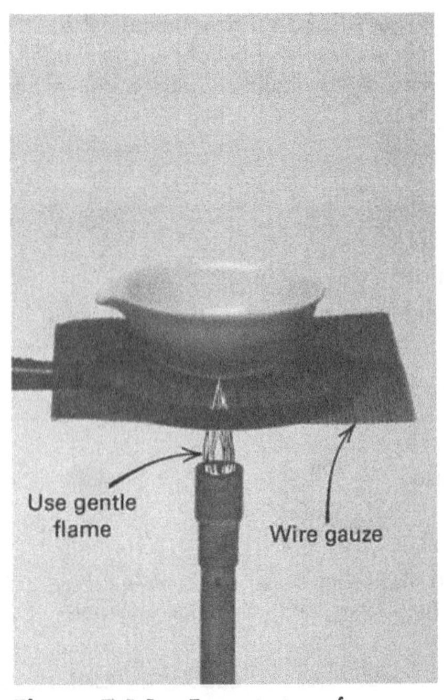

Jo A. Beran

Figure T.14a Evaporation of a nonflammable liquid over a low, direct flame. A hot plate may be substituted for the flame.

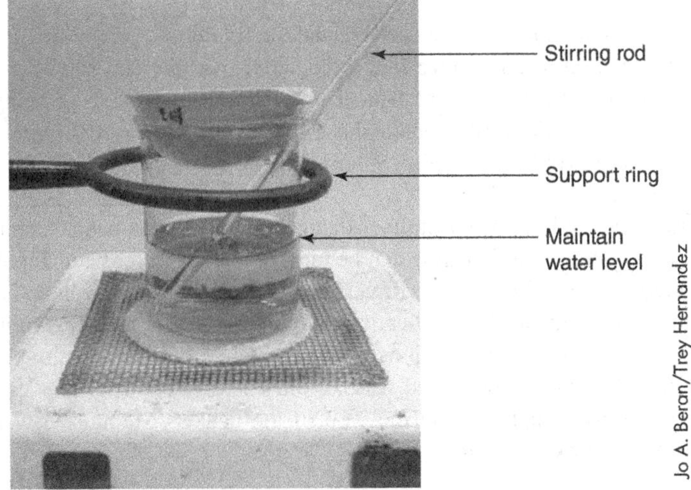

Jo A. Beran/Trey Hernandez

Figure T.14b Evaporation of a flammable liquid over a steam bath using a hot plate for the heat source

TECHNIQUE 15. HEATING SOLIDS

Solids are heated to dry them or to test their thermal stability. A drying oven is often used for low temperature heating, and porcelain crucibles are used for high temperature heating. Beakers and test tubes can be used for moderately high temperature heating.

A. Heating in a Drying Oven

When solid chemicals are left exposed to the atmosphere, they often absorb moisture. If an exact mass of a solid chemical is required for a solution preparation or for a reaction, the absorbed water must be removed before the mass measurement is made on the balance. The chemical is often placed in an open container (usually a Petri dish or beaker) in a drying oven (Figure T.15a) set at a temperature well above room

Courtesy of Thermo Fisher Scientific

Figure T.15a A modern laboratory drying oven

Courtesy of Thermo Fisher Scientific

Courtesy of Thermo Fisher Scientific

Figure T.15b A simple laboratory desicooler (left) or a glass desiccator (right) contains a desiccant (usually anhydrous $CaCl_2$) to provide a dry atmosphere.

temperature (most often at ~110°C) for several hours to remove the adsorbed water. The container is then removed from the drying oven and placed in a desiccator (*Technique 15B*) for cooling to room temperature. **Caution:** *Hot glass and cold glass look the same—the container from the drying oven is hot and should be handled accordingly.* See your laboratory instructor.

B. Cooling in a Desiccator

When a Petri dish or beaker containing a solid chemical is cooled in the laboratory, moisture tends to condense on the outer surface, adding to the total mass. To minimize this mass error, and for quantitative work, substances and mixtures that may tend to be hygroscopic are placed into a desiccator (Figure T.15b) until they have reached ambient temperature.

A desiccator is a laboratory apparatus that provides a dry atmosphere. A desiccant, typically anhydrous calcium chloride, $CaCl_2$, absorbs the water vapor from within the enclosure of the desiccator. The anhydrous calcium chloride forms $CaCl_2{\bullet}2H_2O$; the hydrated water molecules can be easily removed with heat (modified *Technique 14A*), and the calcium chloride can then be recycled for subsequent use in the desiccator.

C. Using a Crucible

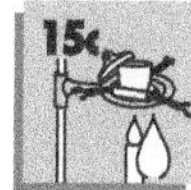

For high temperature combustion or decomposition of a chemical, porcelain crucibles are commonly used. To avoid contamination of the solid sample, thoroughly clean the crucible (so it is void of volatile impurities) prior to use. Often-used crucibles tend to form stress fractures or fissures. Check the crucible for flaws; if any are found, return the crucible to the stockroom and check out and examine a second crucible.

1. **Drying or firing the crucible.** Support the crucible and lid on a clay triangle (Figure T.15c, page 34) and heat in a hot flame until the bottom of the crucible glows a dull red. Rotate the crucible with crucible tongs to ensure complete "firing" of the crucible—that is, the combustion and volatilization of any impurities in the crucible. Allow the crucible and lid to cool to room temperature while on the clay triangle or *after* several minutes in a desiccator (*Technique 15B*).[1]

[1] If the crucible still contains detectable impurities, add 1–2 mL of 6 *M* HNO_3 (**Caution:** *Avoid skin contact, flush immediately with water*), and evaporate *slowly* to dryness in the fume hood. Consult with your instructor before beginning this procedure.

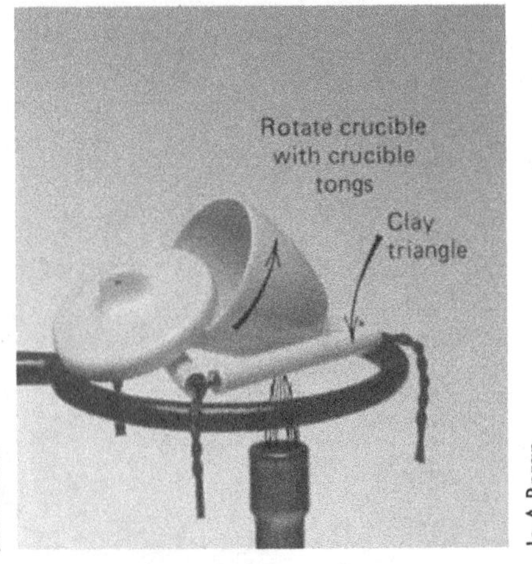

Figure T.15c Drying or firing a crucible and cover

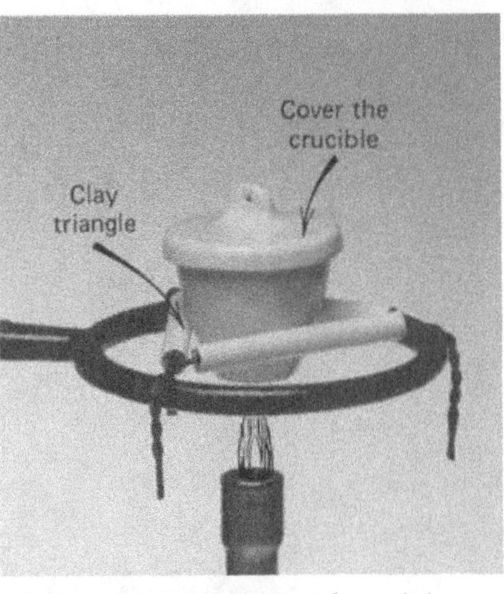

Figure T.15d Ignition of a solid sample in the absence of air

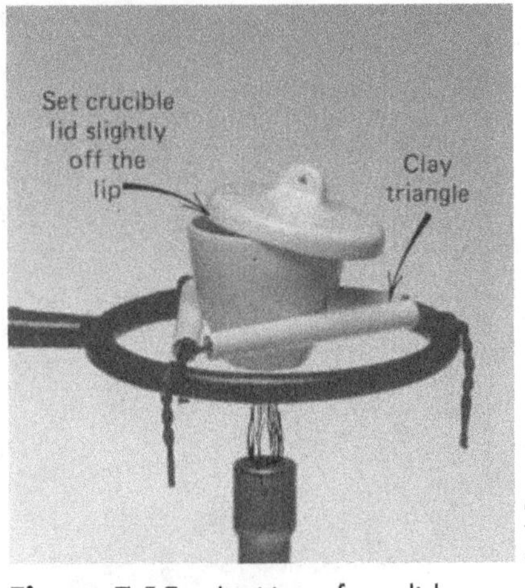

Figure T.15e Ignition of a solid sample in the presence of air for complete combustion

2. **Igniting contents in the absence of air.** To heat a solid sample to a high temperature but *not* allow it to react with the oxygen of the air, set the crucible upright in the clay triangle with the lid covering the crucible (Figure T.15d). Use the crucible tongs to adjust the lid.
3. **Igniting contents for combustion.** To heat a solid sample to a high temperature and allow it to react with the oxygen of the air, slightly tilt the crucible on the clay triangle and adjust the lid so that about two-thirds of the crucible remains covered (Figure T.15e). Use the crucible tongs to adjust the lid.

Technique 16. Measuring Volume

The careful measurement and recording of volumes of liquids are necessary to obtain quantitative data for a large number of chemical reactions that occur in solutions. Volumes must be read and recorded as accurately as possible (to the correct number of significant figures) to minimize errors in the data.

A. Reading and Recording

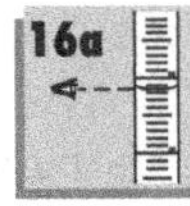

1. **Reading a meniscus.** For measurements of liquids in graduated cylinders, pipets, burets, and volumetric flasks, the volume of a liquid is read at the *bottom of its meniscus.* Position the eye horizontally at the bottom of the meniscus (Figure T.16a) to read the level of the liquid. A clear or transparent liquid is read more easily, especially in a buret, by positioning a black mark (made on a white card) behind or just below the level portion of the liquid. The black background reflects off the bottom of the meniscus and better defines the level of the liquid (Figure T.16b). Substituting a finger for the black mark on the white card also helps in detecting the bottom of the meniscus but is not as effective.

Volumetric glassware: glassware that has a calibration mark(s) that indicates a calibrated volume, as determined by the manufacturer

2. **Recording a volume.** Record the volume of a liquid in **volumetric glassware** using all certain digits (from the labeled calibration marks on the glassware) *plus* one uncertain digit (the last digit, which is the best estimate between the calibration marks). This reading provides the correct number of significant figures for the measurement. See **Data Analysis,** Part A. In Figure T.16b, the volume of solution in the buret is between the calibration marks of 3.0 and 3.1; the 3 and the 0 are certain; the 5 is the estimate between 3.0 and 3.1. The reading is 3.05 mL. Be aware that all volume readings do *not* end in 0 or 5!

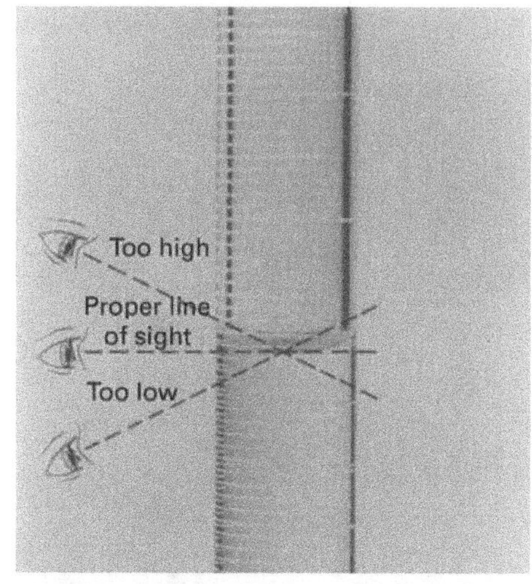

Figure T.16a Read the volume of a liquid with the eye horizontal to the bottom of the meniscus.

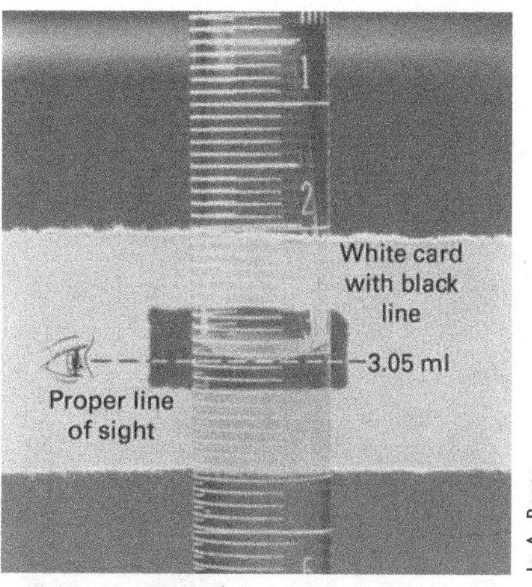

Figure T.16b Use a black line drawn on a white card to assist in pinpointing the location of the bottom of the meniscus.

B. Pipetting a Liquid

The most common type of pipet in the laboratory is labeled TD at 20ºC. A pipet labeled TD at 20ºC (to deliver at 20ºC) means that the volume of the pipet is calibrated according to the volume it delivers from gravity flow only.

A clean pipet in conjunction with the proper technique for dispensing a liquid from a pipet are important in any quantitative determination.

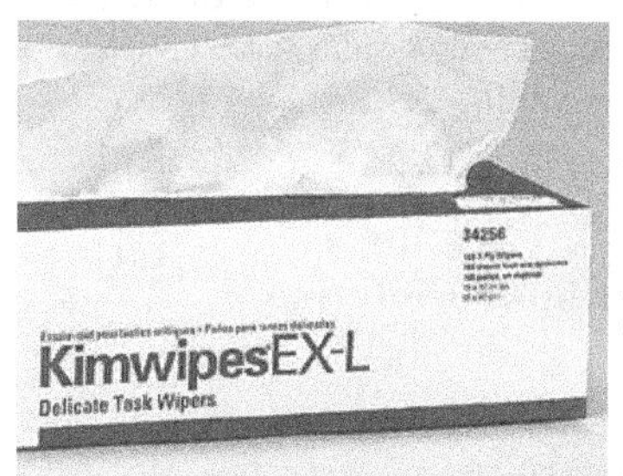

Dust/lint-free tissue.

1. **Preparation of the pipet.** See *Technique 2* for cleaning glassware. A clean pipet should have no water droplets adhering to its inner wall. Inspect the pipet to ensure it is free of chips or cracks. Transfer the liquid that you intend to pipet from the reagent bottle into a clean, dry beaker; do *not* insert the pipet tip directly into the reagent bottle (*Technique 5*). Dry the outside of the pipet tip with a clean, dust-free towel or tissue (e.g., Kimwipe). Using the suction from a collapsed rubber (pipet) bulb, draw a 2- to 3-mL portion into the pipet as a rinse. Roll the rinse around in the pipet to make certain that the liquid washes the entire surface of the inner wall. Deliver the rinse through the pipet tip into a waste beaker and discard as directed in the experiment. Repeat the rinse 2–3 times.
2. **Filling of the pipet.** Place the pipet tip well below the surface of the liquid in the beaker. Using the collapsed pipet bulb (or a pipet pump—*never* use your mouth!), draw the liquid into the pipet until the level is 2–3 cm above the calibration "mark" on the pipet (Figure T.16c, page 36). Do not "jam" the pipet bulb onto the pipet! Remove the bulb and quickly cover the top of the pipet with your index finger (*not* your thumb!). Remove the tip from the liquid and wipe off the pipet tip with a clean, dust-free towel or tissue. Holding the pipet in a *vertical* position over a waste beaker, control the delivery of the excess liquid until the level is "at the mark" in the pipet (Figure T.16d, page 36). Read the meniscus correctly. Remove any drops suspended from the pipet tip by touching it to the wall of the waste beaker. This is a technique you will need to practice.
3. **Delivery of the liquid.** Deliver the liquid to the receiving vessel (Figure T.16e, page 36) by releasing the index finger from the top of the pipet. Dispense the liquid along the wall of the receiving vessel to avoid splashing. To remove a hanging drop from the pipet tip, touch the side of the receiving flask for its removal. Do *not* blow or shake out the last bit of liquid that remains in the tip; this liquid has been included in the calibration of the pipet . . . remember this is a TD at 20ºC pipet!
4. **Cleanup.** Once it is no longer needed in the experiment, rinse the pipet with several portions of deionized water and drain each rinse through the tip.

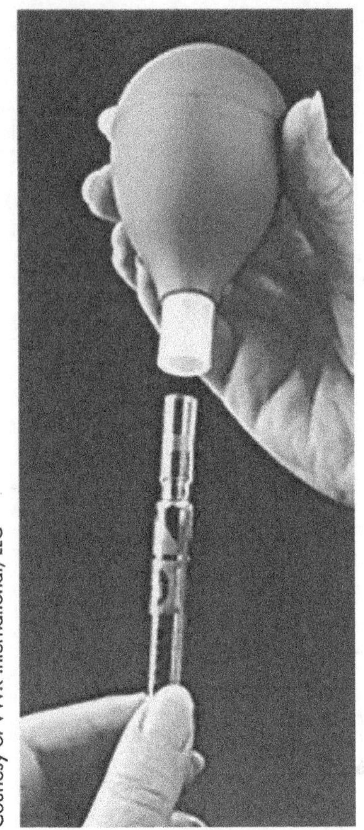
Courtesy of VWR International, LLC

Figure T.16c Draw the liquid into the pipet with the aid of a rubber pipet bulb (*not* the mouth!).

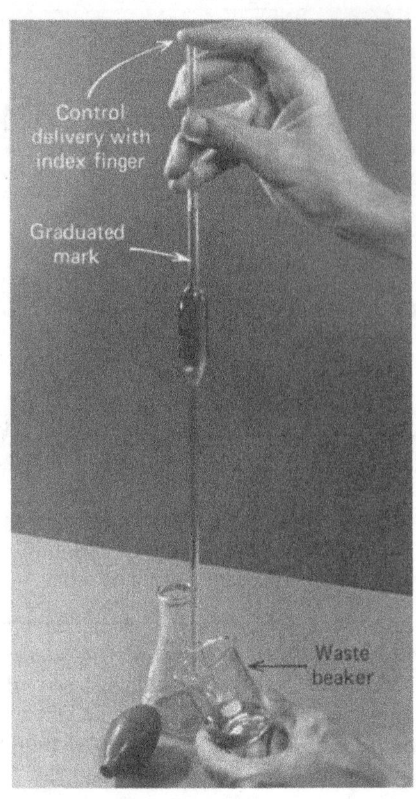

Jo A. Beran

Figure T.16d Control the delivery of the liquid from the pipet with the forefinger (*not* the thumb!).

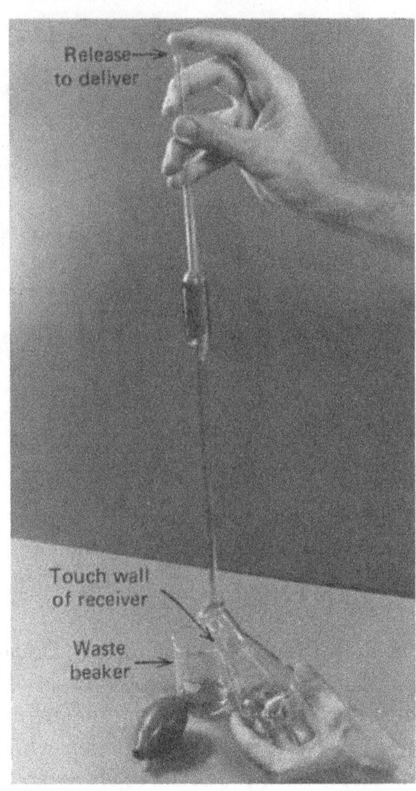

Jo A. Beran

Figure T.16e Deliver the liquid from the vertically positioned pipet with the tip touching the wall of the receiving flask.

C. Titrating a Liquid (Solution)

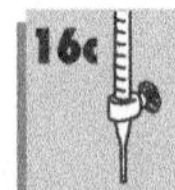

A clean buret in conjunction with the proper technique for measuring and dispensing a liquid from a buret is important in any quantitative analysis determination.

Titrant: the reagent solution in the buret to be used for the experiment

1. **Preparation of the buret.** See *Technique 2* for cleaning glassware. If a buret brush is needed, be careful to avoid scratching the buret wall with the wire handle. Once the buret is judged to be "clean," close the stopcock. Rinse the buret with several 3- to 5-mL portions of water and then **titrant.** Tilt and roll the barrel of the buret so that each rinse comes into contact with the entire inner wall. Drain each rinse through the buret tip into the waste beaker. Dispose of the rinse as advised in the experiment. Support the buret with a buret clamp (Figure T.16f).
2. **Preparation of the titrant.** Close the stopcock. With the aid of a *clean* funnel, fill the buret with the titrant to just above the zero mark. Open the stopcock briefly to release any air bubbles in the tip *and* allow the meniscus of the titrant to go below the uppermost graduation on the buret. Allow 10–15 seconds for the titrant to drain from the wall, **record the volume** (±0.02 mL, *Technique 16A.2*) of titrant in the buret. Note that the graduations on a buret *increase* in value from the top down (Figure T.16g).

Record the volume: To record the correct number of significant figures, read the volume in the buret using all certain digits (from the labeled calibration marks on the buret) plus one uncertain digit (the last digit that is the best estimate between the calibration marks).

3. **Operation of the buret.** During the addition of the titrant from the buret, operate the stopcock with your left hand (if right-handed) and swirl the Erlenmeyer flask with your right hand (Figure T.16h). This prevents the stopcock from sliding out of its barrel and allows you to maintain a normal, constant swirling motion of the reaction mixture in the receiving flask as the titrant is added. The opposite procedure, of course, is applicable if you are left-handed (Figure T.16i). Use an Erlenmeyer flask as a receiving flask in order to minimize the loss of solution due to splashing.

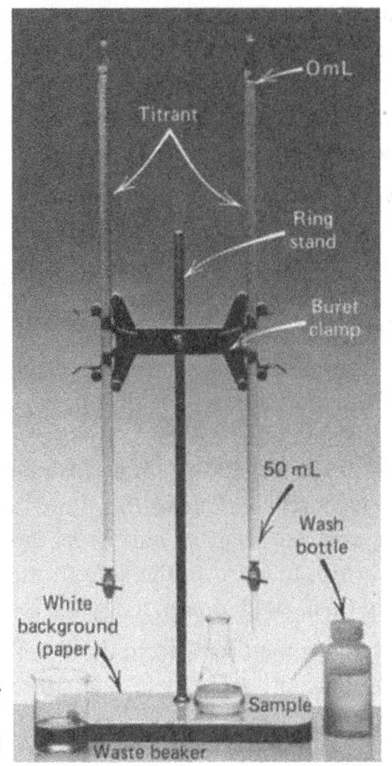

Figure T.16f Setup for a titration analysis

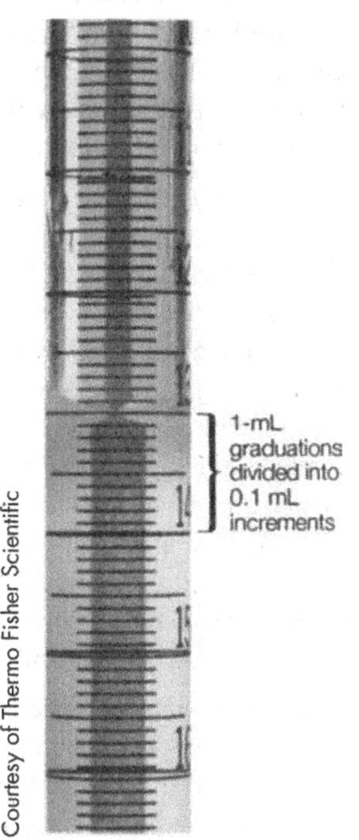

Figure T.16g A 50-mL buret is marked from top to bottom, 0 to 50 mL, with 1-mL gradations divided into 0.1-mL increments.

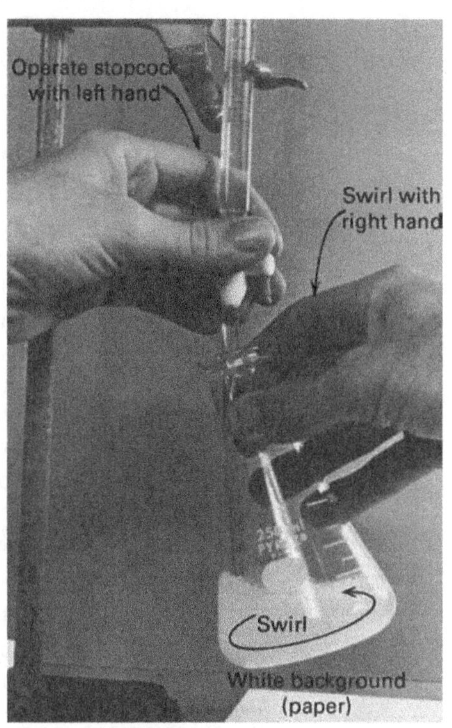

Figure T.16h Titration technique for right-handers

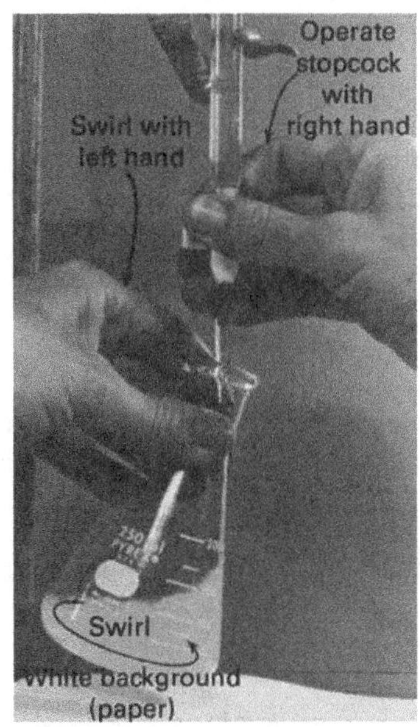

Figure T.16i Titration technique for left-handers.

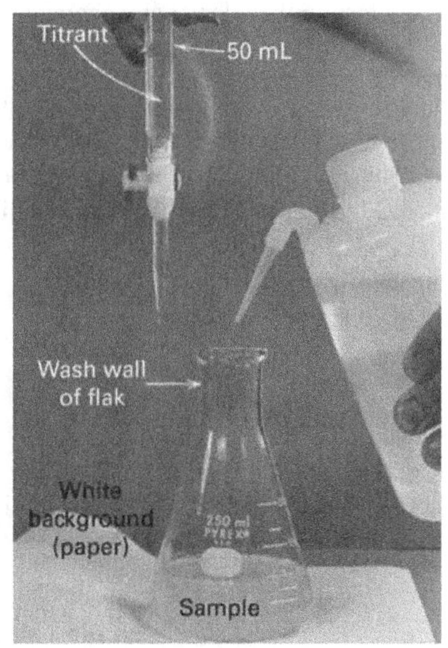

Figure T.16j Place a white background beneath the receiving flask and wash the wall of the receiving flask periodically during the titration.

Figure T.16k A slow color fade of the indicator occurs near the endpoint in the titration.

If a magnetic stirrer is used for mixing the titrant with the analyte, operate at a low speed to minimize any splashing of the reaction mixture and to minimize oxygen of the air from mixing and reacting with either the titrant or analyte. Occasionally, a beaker is used as a receiving flask, especially if a temperature probe (or thermometer) or a pH probe is required during the titration.

4. **Addition of titrant to receiving flask.** Have a white background (a piece of white paper) beneath the receiving flask to better see the endpoint for the titration (the point at which the indicator turns color). If the endpoint is a change from colorless to white, a black background is preferred. Add the titrant, from the buret to the Erlenmeyer flask as described above; periodically stop its addition and wash the inner wall of the flask with the solvent (generally deionized water) from a wash bottle (Figure T.16j, page 37). Near the endpoint (slower color fade of the indicator, Figure T.16k, page 37), slow the rate of titrant addition until a drop (or less) makes the color change of the indicator persist for 30 seconds. **Stop,** allow 10–15 seconds for the titrant to drain from the buret wall, read, and record the volume in the buret (*Technique 16A.2*).

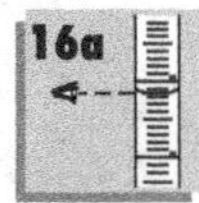

   To add less than a drop of titrant (commonly referred to as a "half-drop") to the receiving flask, suspend a drop from the buret tip, touch it to the side of the receiving flask, and wash the wall of the receiving flask (with deionized water).

5. **Cleanup.** After completing the series of titrations, drain the titrant from the buret, rinse the buret with several portions of deionized water, and drain each rinse through the tip. Discard the excess titrant and the rinses as advised in the experiment. Store the buret as advised by your laboratory instructor.

Technique 17. Quick Tests

An educated nose is an important and very useful asset to the chemist. Use it with caution, however, because some vapors induce nausea and/or are toxic. *Never* hold your nose directly over a vessel.

A. Testing for Odor

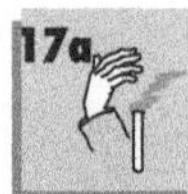

Fan some vapor toward your nose (Figure T.17a). *Always* consult your laboratory instructor before testing the odor of any chemical.

B. Testing for Acidity/Basicity

To test the acidity or basicity of a solution with test paper, insert a *clean* stirring rod into the solution, withdraw it, and touch it to the pH test paper (Figure T.17b). For litmus paper, acidic solutions turn blue litmus red; basic solutions turn red litmus blue. *Never* place the test paper directly into the solution.

Other paper-type indictors, such as pHydrion paper (Figure T.17c), are also used to gauge the acidity or basicity of a solution.

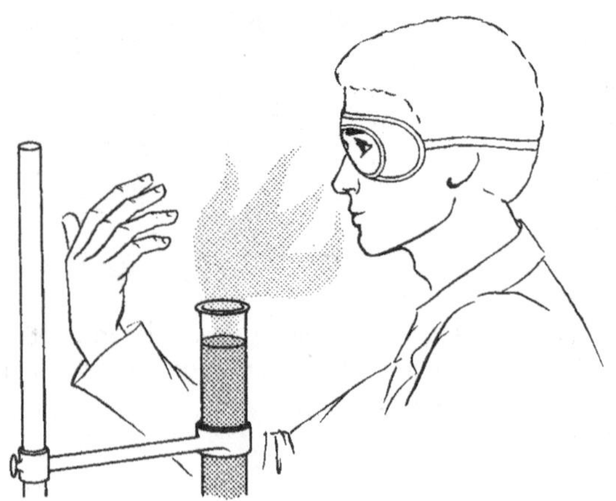

Figure T.17a Fan the vapors gently toward the nose.

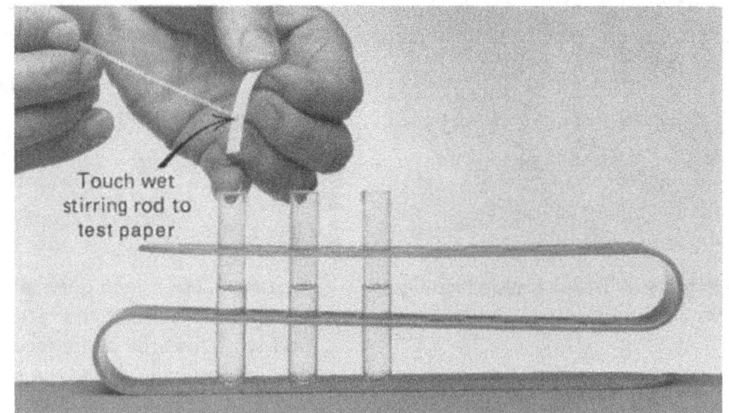

Jo A. Beran

Figure T.17b Test for acidity or basicity.

Courtesy of Micro Essential Labs

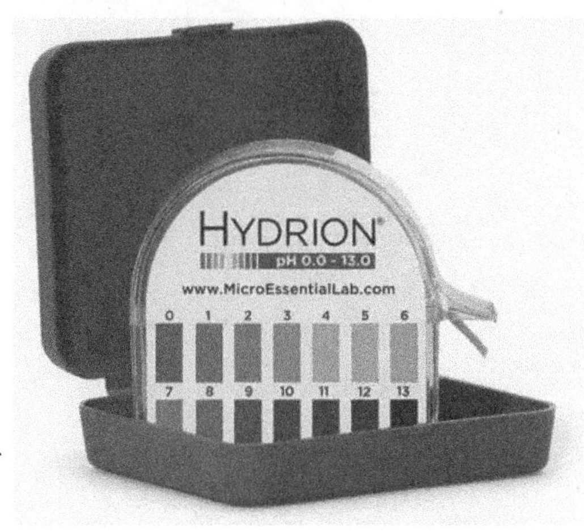

Figure T.17c Hydrion® pH test papers impregnated with a mixture of acid–base indicators can be used to measure the approximate pH of a solution.

Disclaimer: The material contained in the **Laboratory Safety and Guidelines** and **Laboratory Techniques** sections of this manual has been compiled from sources believed to be reliable and to represent the best opinions of safety in the laboratory. This manual is intended to provide basic guidelines for safe practices in the undergraduate chemistry laboratory. It cannot be assumed that all necessary warning and precautionary measures are contained in this manual, or that other or additional information or measures may not be required.

Further discussions of these and other laboratory techniques can be found on the Internet.

Notes on Laboratory Techniques

Laboratory Assignment

Laboratory Techniques

Date __________ Lab Sec. ______ Name ______________________________ Desk No. __________

Identify the Technique Icon, at left, for each of the following techniques.

	Technique Icon	*Description of technique*
1.	____________	To dispense chemicals, read the label at least twice before removing any chemical from the reagent bottle.
2.	____________	Water or glycerol should be applied to the glass tubing and the hole in the rubber stopper before inserting the glass tubing.
3.	____________	A centrifuge should be balanced with an even number of centrifuge/test tubes, placed across the rotor from one another, with equal volumes of liquid.
4.	____________	The volume of a liquid or solution in calibrated volumetric glassware should be read using all-certain digits (from the labeled calibration marks on the glassware) *plus* one uncertain digit (the last digit that is the best estimate *between* the calibration marks)—that is, to the correct number of significant figures.
5.	____________	The bowl of the funnel for gravity filtration should be always less than two-thirds full.
6.	____________	To dispense a liquid from a pipet, first draw the liquid into the pipet 2–3 cm above the calibration mark with a pipet bulb and then use the index finger to control its flow.
7.	____________	The suction created for the vacuum filtration of a precipitate is applied with an aspirator in which the water faucet is fully open.
8.	____________	To prepare a solution, always add the solid reagent or more concentrated solution to a volumetric flask that is already approximately one-third full with solvent.
9.	____________	While dispensing titrant from a buret, the stopcock should be operated with the left hand (if right-handed) and the Erlenmeyer flask should be swirled with the right hand.
10.	____________	To heat a solid to high temperatures in the absence of air, place the solid in a crucible and fully cover the crucible with the crucible lid.
11.	____________	Information on the properties and disposal of chemicals can be found in the stockroom or online from the MSDS collection.
12.	____________	A buret should be rinsed with several 3- to 5-mL portions of titrant before being filled.
13.	____________	Glassware is clean when no water droplets cling to the inner wall of the vessel.
14.	____________	For heating a liquid in a test tube, the test tube should be less than one-third full, moved continuously in and out of the "cool" flame at a 45° angle, mostly near the top of the liquid.
15.	____________	The volume of a liquid should be read at the bottom of the meniscus.
16.	____________	Small quantities of liquids in test tubes are best be heated (safely) in a hot water bath with the heat source being either a hot plate or a direct flame.
17.	____________	All chemicals must be properly disposed—either according to the Experimental Procedure or the laboratory instructor.
18.	____________	Never place reagents directly onto the weighing pan of a balance—always use weighing paper, a beaker, or some other container.
19.	____________	A hot plate (*not* an open flame) is the heat source for heating or evaporating flammable liquids.

20. ____________ The tared mass of a sample is its mass without regard to its container.

21. ____________ Transfer liquids and solutions from a reagent bottle or beaker with the aid of a stirring rod.

22. ____________ A "small" test tube has a volume of ~3 mL.

23. ____________ A litmus paper test for the acidity or basicity of a solution requires the use of a stirring rod to remove a portion of the solution to then be touched to the litmus paper.

24. ____________ After drying a hygroscopic solid in a drying oven, the solid should be cooled in a desiccator.

25. ____________ The color change of the indicator at the endpoint of a titration should persist for 30 seconds.

Answer True or False for the following statements that refer to Laboratory Techniques.

Ask your instructor to identify the questions you are to complete.

__________ **1.** All clean glassware should be air-dried naturally.

__________ **2.** While cleaning glassware, discard all washes and rinses from the delivery point of the glass vessel.

__________ **3.** To avoid waste in the use of chemicals, share the unused portion with other chemists before discarding.

__________ **4.** Never touch, taste, or smell a chemical unless specifically told to do so.

__________ **5.** A chemical with a "blue" hazard label (a number 3 rating) means that the chemical is highly reactive.

__________ **6.** If uncertain as to how to dispose of a chemical, dumping it into the sink followed by copious amount of water is a safe disposal procedure.

__________ **7.** Use a spatula to transfer solid chemicals from a reagent bottle.

__________ **8.** Most all chemicals used in experiments can be discarded into the sink.

__________ **9.** The number of significant figures used to record the mass of a chemical should correspond to the sensitivity of the balance used for the measurement.

__________ **10.** A 3-inch test tube has a volume of 3 mL; an 8-inch test tube must have a volume of 8 mL.

__________ **11.** To transfer a solution, a stirring rod touches the delivery point of the reagent vessel and the wall of the receiving vessel.

__________ **12.** The *minimum* number of centrifuge tubes placed in a centrifuge during its operation is two.

__________ **13.** A test tube should be less than one-third full when heating with a "cool" flame.

__________ **14.** Right-handed students should operate the stopcock of a buret with their left hand and swirl the Erlenmeyer (receiving) flask with the right hand.

__________ **15.** The thumb is the digit of choice on controlling the flow of liquid from a pipet.

__________ **16.** Blow out the solution remaining in the pipet tip after the solution has drained from the pipet.

__________ **17.** A buret must *always* be filled to the top (the zero mark) before every titration procedure.

__________ **18.** The volume of solution in a buret should be read and recorded 10–15 seconds after completing the titration.

__________ **19.** It is possible to add a half-drop of solution from a buret.

__________ **20.** To test the acidity of a solution with pH paper, place the pH paper directly in the solution.

__________ **21.** The odor of a chemical should not be tested unless specifically instructed to do so. The vapors of the chemical should be fanned toward the nose.

__________ **22.** One must first calculate the number of moles of solute that are required before preparing a solution of known concentration.

Summarize the *Disclaimer* in your own words.

Courtesy of Thermo Fisher Scientific

A set of standard SI mass units.

Dry Lab 1

The Laboratory and SI

Objectives

- To check into the laboratory
- To become familiar with the laboratory and the laboratory manual
- To learn the rules of laboratory safety and the necessity of practicing these rules in the laboratory
- To learn how to properly organize and record laboratory data
- To develop skills in the use of *Le Système International d'Unités* (SI Units)

Introduction

All chemical principles, tools, and techniques are developed in the laboratory. The experience of observing a chemical phenomenon and then explaining its behavior is one that simply cannot be gained by reading a textbook, listening to a lecturer, searching the Internet, or viewing a video. It is in the laboratory where chemistry comes alive, where chemical principles are learned and applied to the vast natural "chemistry laboratory" that we call our everyday environment. The objectives of a laboratory experience are to design and build apparatus, develop techniques, observe, record and interpret data, and deduce rational theories so that the real world of science is better explained and understood.

In the laboratory, you will use common equipment and safe chemicals to perform experiments. You record your experimental observations and interpret the data on the basis of sound chemical principles. A good scientist is a thinking scientist trying to account for the observed data and rationalize any contradictory data. Cultivate self-reliance and confidence in your data, even if "the data do not look right." This is how many breakthroughs in science occur.

"There is no surer way to screw up an experiment than to be certain of its outcome."

Stuart Feinstein, author "Ignorance: How It Drives Science"

In the first few laboratory sessions you will be introduced to some basic rules, equipment, and techniques and some situations where you use them. These include laboratory safety rules, *Le Système International d'Unités* (SI Units), the Bunsen burner, and the analytical balance. Additional laboratory techniques are illustrated under **Laboratory Techniques** pages 17–42; others are introduced as the need arises.

Dry Lab Procedure

Procedure Overview: Laboratory procedures are introduced. A familiarity with laboratory apparatus, the policies regarding laboratory safety, the procedures for presenting laboratory data, and an encounter with the SI units are emphasized.

A. Laboratory Check-in

At the beginning of the first laboratory period, you are assigned a lab station containing laboratory equipment. Place the laboratory equipment on the laboratory bench and, with the check-in list appearing on page 7, or one provided by your laboratory instructor, check off each piece of chemical apparatus as you return it to the drawer. If you are unsure of a name for the apparatus, refer to the list of chemical "kitchenware" on pages 7–8. Ask your instructor about any items on the check-in list that are not at your lab station.

The icon refers to Laboratory Technique 2 on page 19. Read through Laboratory Technique 2 for the proper technique of cleaning laboratory glassware.

A good scientist is always neat and well organized; keep your equipment clean and arranged in an orderly manner so that it is ready for immediate use. Have at your lab station dishwashing soap (or detergent) for cleaning glassware and paper towels or a rubber lab mat on which to set the clean glassware for drying.

Obtain your laboratory instructor's approval for the completion of the check-in procedure. Refer to Part A of the ***Report Sheet***.

B. Laboratory Safety and Guidelines

Your laboratory instructor will discuss laboratory safety and other basic laboratory procedures with you. Remember, however, that your laboratory instructor cannot practice laboratory safety for you or for those who work with you. It is your responsibility to *play it safe!*

On the inside front cover of this manual is space to list the location of some important safety equipment and important information for reference in the laboratory. Fill this out. Obtain your laboratory instructor's approval for its completion.

Read and study **Laboratory Safety and Guidelines** on pages 1–4. Complete any other laboratory safety sessions or requirements that are requested by your laboratory instructor. Answer the laboratory safety questions on the ***Report Sheet***.

C. Data Documentation

Each experiment in this manual will require you to observe, record and report data, perform calculations with the data, and then analyze and interpret the data. Scientists are careful in the procedures that are used for handling data so that the reliability and credibility of the experimental data are upheld.

It is important that these procedures are followed at the outset of your laboratory experience. Read and study **Data Documentation** on pages 5–8. Answer the laboratory data questions on the ***Report Sheet***.

D. Data Analysis

Analyzing data in the laboratory is critical in delivering the precision of experimental results. Firstly, the recorded data must be expressed according to the precision of the instruments collecting the data. This also includes the calculations associated with the data.

To do so, the correct number of significant figures is used to express this precision. The guidelines for expressing significant figures in recording and calculating data are listed in **Data Analysis**, Part A.

Once the data are listed in accordance with the correct number of significant figures, a summary of the reliability of the data can be determined by calculating the average, the standard deviation, the relative standard deviation, and the relative error of the data values. These mathematical analyses are explained in **Data Analysis**, Parts B–E.

A summary of changes in the data when parameters are changed in the experiment can often be illustrated with a well-constructed graph of the data. Guidelines for graph construction are also present in **Data Analysis**, Parts F and G.

E. *Le Système International d'Unités* (SI Units)

The SI, a modern version of the metric system, provides a logical and interconnected framework for all basic measurements. The SI, and some of its slight modifications, is used throughout the world by scientists and engineers as the international system for scientific measurements and, in most countries, for everyday measurements. For laboratory measurements, the SI base unit of mass is the **kilogram (kg)** [chemists are most familiar with the **gram (g)**, where 10^3 g = 1 kg]. The SI base unit for length is the **meter (m)** [chemists are most familiar with several subdivisions of the meter]. The SI derived unit for volume is the **cubic meter (m^3)** [chemists are most familiar with the **liter (L)**, where 1 L = 10^{-3} m^3 = 1 dm^3]. Subdivisions and multiples of each

Table D1.1 Prefixes in *Le Système International d'Unités*

Prefix	Abbreviation	Meaning (power of ten)	Example Using "grams"
femto-	f	10^{-15}	$fg = 10^{-15}$ g
pico-	p	10^{-12}	$pg = 10^{-12}$ g
nano-	n	10^{-9}	$ng = 10^{-9}$ g
micro-	μ	10^{-6}	$\mu g = 10^{-6}$ g
milli-	m	10^{-3}	$mg = 10^{-3}$ g
centi-	c	10^{-2}	$cg = 10^{-2}$ g
deci-	d	10^{-1}	$dg = 10^{-1}$ g
kilo-	k	10^{3}	$kg = 10^{3}$ g
mega-	M	10^{6}	$Mg = 10^{6}$ g
giga-	G	10^{9}	$Gg = 10^{9}$ g
tera-	T	10^{12}	$Tg = 10^{12}$ g

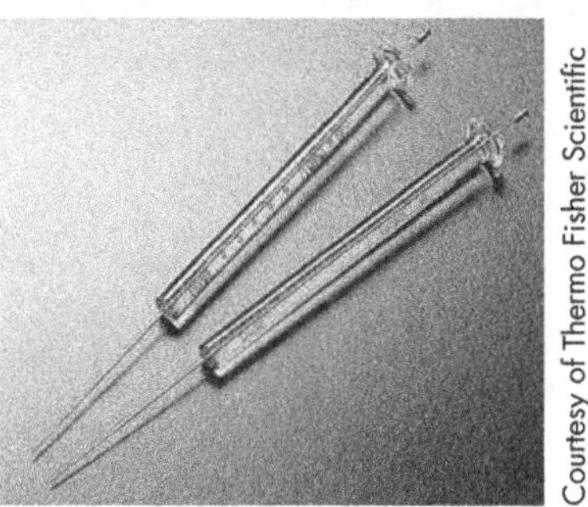
Courtesy of Thermo Fisher Scientific

A microliter syringe

unit are related to these units by a power of 10. The prefixes used to denote these subdivisions and multiples are shown in Table D1.1. Memorize these prefixes and their meanings.

In Table D1.1, *the prefix indicates the power of 10.* For example, 4.3 *milli*grams means 4.3×10^{-3} grams; *milli* has the same meaning as "$\times\ 10^{-3}$." Figure D1.1 shows representative SI measurements for mass, length, and volume.

Conversions of measurements within SI are quite simple if the definitions for the prefixes are known and unit conversion factors for problem solving are used. To illustrate the use of unit conversion factors, consider the following example.

Example D1.1 Convert 4.3 nanograms to micrograms.
Solution. From Table D1.1, note that nano- and 10^{-9} are equivalent and that micro- and 10^{-6} are equivalent. Considering mass, it also means that $ng = 10^{-9}$ g *and* $\mu g = 10^{-6}$ g. This produces two equivalent unit conversion factors for each equality:

$$\frac{10^{-9}\text{ g}}{\text{ng}}, \quad \frac{\text{ng}}{10^{-9}\text{g}} \quad \text{and} \quad \frac{10^{-6}\text{ g}}{\mu\text{g}}, \quad \frac{\mu\text{g}}{10^{-6}\text{g}}$$

These unit conversion factors have no effect on the magnitude of the mass measurement (the conversion factors = 1), only the units by which they are expressed.

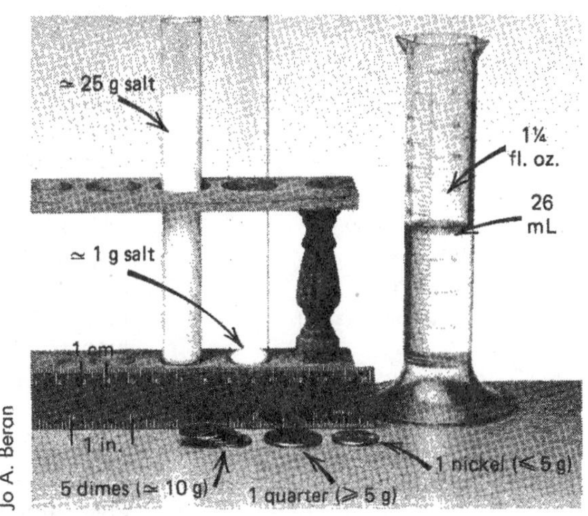

Figure D1.1 Comparisons of SI and English measurements

Beginning our solution to the problem with the measured quantity (i.e., 4.3 ng), we need to convert ng to g and g to μg using the appropriate conversion factors to obtain proper unit cancellation:

$$4.3 \text{ ng} \times \frac{10^{-9} \text{ g}}{\text{ng}} \times \frac{\mu\text{g}}{10^{-6} \text{ g}} = 4.3 \times 10^{-3} \mu\text{g}$$

ng cancel g cancel

ng → g → μg = μg

The SI is compared with the English system in Table D1.2. SI units of measurement that chemists commonly use in the laboratory are listed in brackets. Appendix A has a more comprehensive table of conversion factors. Conversions between the SI and the English system are quite valuable, especially to Americans because international science and trade communications are in SI or metric units.

Appendix A

Example D1.2 Using Tables D1.1 and D1.2, express the volume of 1.00 quart of water in terms of cubic centimeters.
Solution. As 1 cm = 10^{-2} m, then 1 cm^3 = $(10^{-2} \text{ m})^3 = (10^{-2})^3 \text{ m}^3$.
From Table D1.2, we need unit conversion factors for quarts → liters, liters → m^3, and finally m^3 → cm^3. Starting with 1.00 qt (our measured value in the problem), we have:

$$1.00 \text{ qt} \times \frac{1 \text{ L}}{1.057 \text{ qt}} \times \frac{10^{-3} \text{ m}^3}{1 \text{ L}} \times \frac{\text{cm}^3}{(10^{-2})^3 \text{ m}^3} = 946 \text{ cm}^3$$

qt cancel L cancel m^3 cancel

qt → L → m^3 → cm^3 = cm^3

Note again that the unit conversion factors in Example D1.2 do not change the magnitude of the measurement, only its form of expression.
Since 1 cm^3 = 1 mL, 1.00 quart is equivalent to 946 mL.

The ***Report Sheet***, Part E, further acquaints you with conversions within the SI and between SI and the English system. Ask your laboratory instructor which of the questions from Part E you are to complete on the ***Report Sheet***.

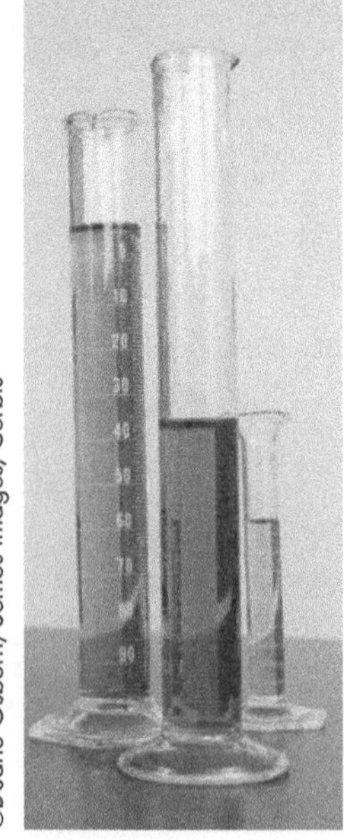
©Duane Osborn/Somos Images/Corbis

Graduated cylinders of different volumes

Table D1.2 Comparison of *Le Système International d'Unités* and English System of Measurements[†]

Physical Quantity	SI Unit	Conversion Factor
Length	meter (m)	1 km = 0.6214 mi 1 m = 39.37 in. 1 in. = 0.0254 m = 2.54 cm
Volume	cubic meter (m^3) [liter (L)][a]	1 L = 10^{-3} m^3 = 1 dm^3 = 10^3 mL 1 mL = 1 cm^3 1 L = 1.057 qt 1 oz (fluid) = 29.57 mL
Mass	kilogram (kg) [gram (g)]	1 lb = 453.6 g 1 kg = 2.205 lb
Pressure	pascal (Pa) [atmosphere (atm)]	1 Pa = 1 N/m^2 1 atm = 101.325 kPa = 760 torr 1 atm = 14.696 lb/in.^{2} (psi)
Temperature	kelvin (K) [degrees Celsius (°C)]	K = 273 + °C $°\text{C} = \frac{°\text{F} - 32}{1.8}$
Energy	joule (J)	1 cal = 4.184 J 1 Btu = 1054 J

[a]The SI units enclosed in brackets are commonly used in chemical measurements and calculations.
†For additional conversion factors, go online to www.onlineconversion.com.

Dry Lab 1 *Report Sheet*

The Laboratory and SI

Date __________ Lab Sec. ______ Name ____ Desk No. _________

A. Laboratory Check-In

Instructor's approval ____

B. Laboratory Safety and Guidelines

Instructor's approval for completion of inside front cover ______________________________

Read **Laboratory Safety and Guidelines** on pages 1–4 and answer the following as *true* or *false*.

_____ **1.** Prescription glasses, which are required by law to be "safety glasses," can be worn in place of safety goggles in the laboratory.

_____ **2.** Sleeveless blouses and tank tops are *not* appropriate attire for the laboratory.

_____ **3.** Only shoes that shed liquids are permitted in the laboratory.

_____ **4.** "I just finished my tennis class. I can wear my tennis shorts to lab just this one time, right?"

_____ **5.** Your laboratory has an eyewash fountain.

_____ **6.** "Oops! I broke a beaker containing deionized water in the sink." An accident as simple as that does not need to be reported to the laboratory instructor.

_____ **7.** A beaker containing an acidic solution has broken on the bench top and spilled onto your clothes from the waist down and it burns. Ouch! You should immediately proceed to the safety shower and flood the affected area.

_____ **8.** You received a paper cut on your finger and it is bleeding. Immediately go to the medicine cabinet to apply a disinfectant.

_____ **9.** It is good laboratory protocol to inform other students when they are not practicing good laboratory safety procedures. If they continue to not follow the safety procedures, you should "rat" on them . . . tell the laboratory instructor.

_____ **10.** Cell phones, iPods, and other electronic equipment should be turned off during the laboratory period.

_____ **11.** Your friend is a senior chemistry major and thoroughly understands the difficult experiment that you are performing. Therefore, it is advisable (even recommended) that you invite him or her into the laboratory for direct assistance.

_____ **12.** You missed lunch but brought a sandwich to the laboratory. Since you cannot eat in the lab, it is okay to leave the sandwich in the hallway and then go in and out to take bites while the laboratory experiment is ongoing.

Write a short response for the following questions.

1. What does the phrase "neck to knee to wrist" mean with regard to laboratory safety?

2. The first action after an accident occurs is:

3. You want to try a variation of the Experimental Procedure because of your chemical curiosity. What is the proper procedure for performing the experiment?

4. A chemical spill has occurred. What should be your first and second action in treating the chemical spill?

5. Describe how you will be dressed when you are about to begin an experiment in the laboratory.

Instructor's approval of your knowledge of laboratory safety. ______________________________

C. Data Documentation

Read **Data Documentation** on pages 5–8 and answer the following as *true* or *false*.

_____ 1. "Quick data," such as that of a mass measurement on a balance located at the far side of the laboratory, can be recorded on a paper scrap and then transferred to the ***Report Sheet*** at your lab station.

_____ 2. Data that has been mistakenly recorded on the ***Report Sheet*** can be erased and replaced with the correct data. This is to maintain a neat ***Report Sheet***.

_____ 3. All data should be recorded in permanent ink!

_____ 4. To discuss improvements in accessing data for your experiment, it is best to consult your classmates.

_____ 5. To compare the accuracy of your data, it is best to consult the Internet.

D. Data Analysis

Read **Data Analysis** on pages 9–16 and answer the following as *true* or *false*.

_____ 1. The laboratory instrumentation determines the number of significant figures when recording quantitative data.

_____ 2. Zeros recorded when collecting data are *never* significant figures.

_____ 3. Dividing 0.32 g of sulfur by its density of $2.07 g/cm^3$ results in an answer with three significant figures.

_____ 4. Good accuracy of data always indicates good precision.

_____ 5. Good precision of data *always* indicates good accuracy.

_____ 6. A systematic error in collected data can be corrected.

_____ 7. A random error in collected data cannot be corrected.

_____ 8. For scientific data only one data point is necessary to calculate its standard deviation.

_____ 9. For determining the relative deviation in the analysis of a data set, the standard deviation and the average of the data set must be determined.

_____ 10. The relative error is an indication of the precision of the collected data.

E. *Le Système International d'Unités* (SI Units)

Circle the questions that have been assigned. See **Data Analysis, A**

1. Complete the following table. Express all answers with the correct number of significant figures (see page 9). Show all work in completing the calculations for the conversions.

	SI Expression	Power of 10 Expression		SI Expression	Power of 10 Expression
Example	1.2 mg	1.2×10^{-3} g			
a.	3.3 gigabytes	__________	**c.**	__________	6.72×10^{-3} ampere
b.	__________	7.6×10^{-6} L	**d.**	2.16 kilowatts	__________

2. Convert each of the following using the definitions in Table D1.1 and unit conversion factors. Show the cancellation of units.

a. $4.76 \text{ pm} \times \dfrac{\rule{4cm}{0.4pt}\ \text{m}}{\text{pm}} \times \dfrac{\rule{4cm}{0.4pt}\ \mu\text{m}}{\text{m}} = \rule{4cm}{0.4pt}\ \mu\text{m}$

b. $25.0 \text{ mL} \times \rule{3cm}{0.4pt} \times \rule{3cm}{0.4pt} = \rule{4cm}{0.4pt}\ \text{cL}$

3. Determine the volume (in mL) of 1.0 teaspoon. 1 tablespoon = 3 teaspoons; 1 tablespoon = ½ fluid ounce

4. A basketball is inflated to 9.0 psi (pounds per square inch) above atmospheric pressure of 14.7 psi (a total pressure of 23.7 psi). The diameter of the basketball is 10 inches.

Slobo/iStockphoto

a. What is the pressure of the air in the basketball, expressed in atmospheres?

b. What is the volume (in liters) of the basketball? The volume of a sphere = $\frac{4}{3}\pi r^3$.

5. Hurricane Katrina, which hit the Gulf Coast of Louisiana and Mississippi on August 29, 2005, had the second lowest ever recorded barometric pressure at 0.920 mb. Convert this pressure to units of....

NASA/GSFC

a. atmospheres.

b. inches of Hg (as would appear on weather report).

6. A beaker in your laboratory drawer has an inside diameter of 6.8 cm and a height of 8.9 cm.

Using the equation $V = \pi r^2 h$, calculate the volume of the beaker, expressed in milliliters.

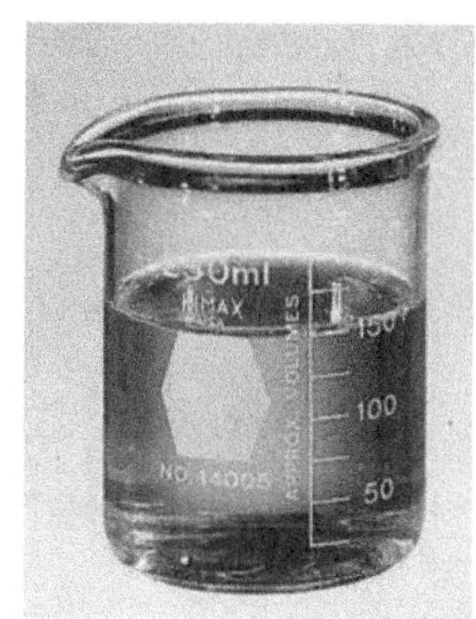

Courtesy of Thermo Fisher Scientific

7. The standard width between rails on North American and most European railroads is 4 ft 8 in. Calculate this distance in....

Skyak/iStockphoto

a. centimeters.

b. meters.

8. The heat required to raise the temperature of a large cup of water (for coffee) from room temperature to boiling is approximately 100 kJ. Express this quantity of heat in kilocalories. Show your calculations.

ALEAIMAGE/iStockphoto

9. An aspirin tablet has a mass of about 325 mg (5 grains). Calculate the total mass of aspirin tablets in a 500-tablet bottle in grams and ounces.

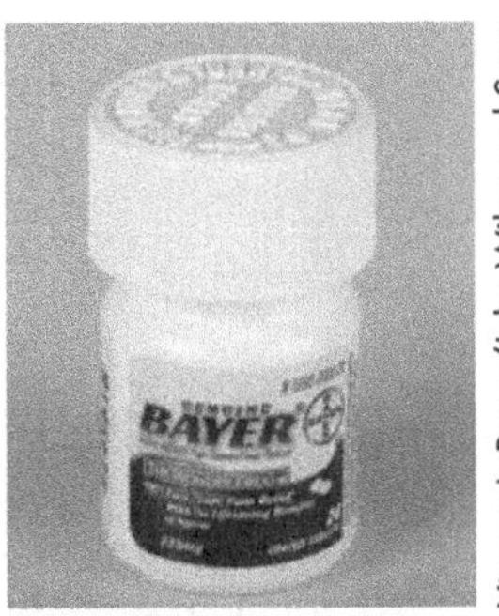

Vincent LaRussa/John Wiley and Sons

a. grams

b. ounces

10. A concrete pile from a waterfront pier was pulled from the harbor water at Port Hueneme, California. Its dimensions were 14 in. × 14 in. × 15 ft (1 in. = 2.54 cm).

Jo A. Beran

a. What is the surface area, expressed in square feet, of a single face of the pile? Exclude the ends of the pile.

b. Determine the total surface area, expressed in square meters, of the pile, including the ends of the pile.

c. How many cubic meters of concrete were used to make the pile?

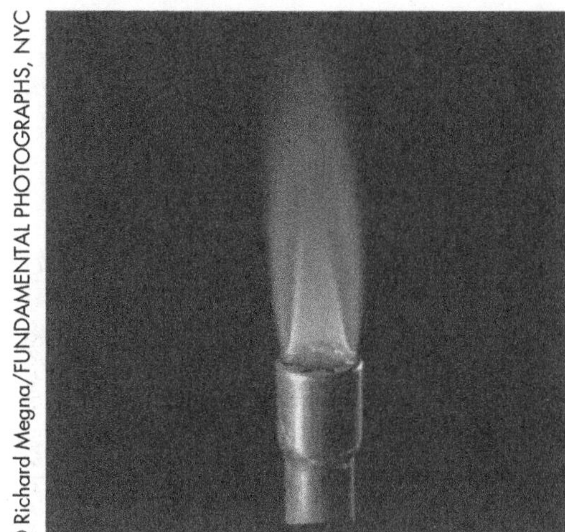

A properly adjusted Bunsen flame is a blue, nonluminous flame.

Experiment 1

Basic Laboratory Operations

Objectives

- To light and properly adjust the flame of a Bunsen burner
- To develop the skill for properly operating a balance
- To develop the technique of using a pipet
- To determine the density of an unknown substance

Techniques

The following techniques are used in the Experimental Procedure:

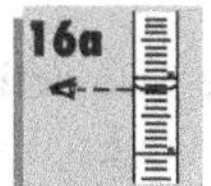

Introduction

You will use a number of techniques repeatedly throughout your laboratory experience. Seventeen principal techniques are fully described under **Laboratory Techniques** in this manual (pp. 17–42). The application of a technique in the Experimental Procedure is noted in the page margin by the corresponding technique icon. Become familiar with each technique and icon before using it in the experiment.

In this experiment, you will learn several common techniques that are used repeatedly throughout this laboratory manual. You will learn to light and adjust a Bunsen burner, to use a laboratory balance, and to use a pipet. With the skills developed in using a balance and pipet, you will determine the density of a metal and a liquid.

Bunsen Burner

Robert Bunsen, 1811–1899

Hydrocarbon: a molecule consisting of only the elements carbon and hydrogen

Nonluminous: nonglowing or nonilluminating

Incandescence: glowing with intense heat

Laboratory burners come in many shapes and sizes, but all accomplish one main purpose: A combustible gas–air mixture yields a hot, efficient flame (Figure 1.1, page 52). The combustible gas used to supply the fuel for the **Bunsen** burner in most laboratories is natural gas. Natural gas is a mixture of gaseous **hydrocarbons,** but primarily the hydrocarbon methane, CH_4. If sufficient oxygen is supplied, methane burns with a blue, **nonluminous** flame, producing carbon dioxide and water as combustion products:

$$CH_4(g) + 2O_2(g) \longrightarrow CO_2(g) + 2H_2O(g) \qquad (1.1)$$

With an insufficient supply of oxygen, small carbon particles are produced, which, when heated to **incandescence,** produce a yellow, luminous flame. The combustion products may, in addition to carbon dioxide and water, include carbon monoxide.

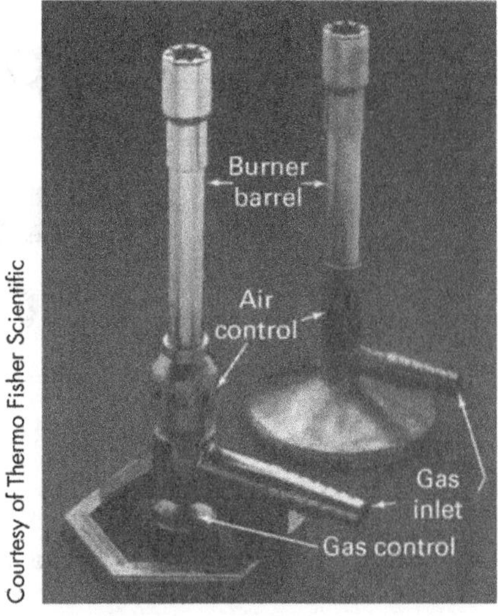

Figure 1.1 Bunsen-type burners

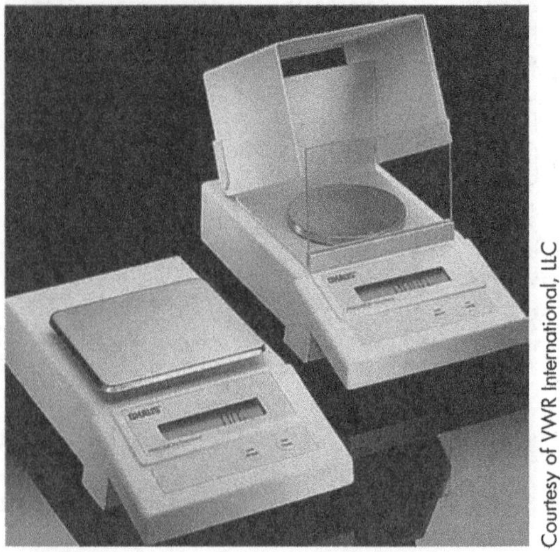

Figure 1.2 Two balances with different sensitivities

Laboratory Balances

The laboratory balance is perhaps the most often used piece of laboratory apparatus. Balances, *not* scales, are of different makes, models, and sensitivities (Figure 1.2). The selection of the appropriate balance for a mass measurement depends on the degree of precision required for the analysis. Top-loading balances are the most common.

Density

Intensive property: property independent of sample size

$$\text{density} = \frac{\text{mass}}{\text{volume}}$$

Each pure substance exhibits its own set of **intensive properties.** One such property is **density,** the mass of a substance per unit volume. In the English system, the density of water at 4°C is 8.34 lb/gal or 62.2 lb/ft^3, whereas in SI the density of water at 4°C is 1.00 g/cm^3 or 1.00 g/mL.

In this experiment, the data for the mass and the volume of water displaced (see Figure 1.5, page 54) are used to calculate the density of a water-insoluble solid; the density of an unknown liquid is calculated from separate mass and volume measurements of the liquid.

Chemists conventionally express the units for density in the SI as g/cm^3 for solids, g/mL for liquids, and g/L for gases at specified temperatures and pressures.

Experimental Procedure

Procedure Overview: A Bunsen flame is ignited, adjusted, and analyzed. Various laboratory balances are operated and used. Mass and volume data are collected to determine the density of a solid and of a liquid.

Perform the experiment with a partner. At each circled superscript (1–10) in the procedure, *stop* and record your observation on the ***Report Sheet***. Discuss your observations with your lab partner and your instructor.

The ***Report Sheet*** is formatted to enter experimental data in the "open" blanks and to only enter calculated data in the "shaded" blanks.

A. Bunsen Burner

Create an efficiently burning (nonluminous) flame by adjusting the gas-control valve and the air-control valve on the Bunsen burner. A nonluminous flame burns blue; a luminous flame burns yellow.

1. **Lighting the burner.** Properly light a burner using the following sequence.
   a. Attach the tubing from the burner to the gas outlet on the lab bench. Close the gas-control valve on the burner (see Figure 1.1) and fully open the gas valve at the outlet.

b. Close the air-control holes at the base of the burner and slightly open the gas-control valve.

c. Bring a lighted match or striker up the outside of the burner barrel until the escaping gas at the top ignites.

d. After the gas ignites, adjust the air-control valve until the flame is pale blue and has two or more distinct cones.

e. Slowly further open the gas-control valve of the burner until you hear a slight buzzing. This sound is characteristic of the hottest flame from the burner. Too much air and/or too much gas, may blow the flame out. When the flame is yellow, open the air-control valve; when the flame "jumps," close the gas-control valve. When the best adjustment is reached, the flame should exhibit three distinct cones (Figure 1.3), be less than 1.5 in. high, and be blue in color.

f. *If the flame goes out,* immediately close the gas valve at the outlet and repeat the procedure for lighting the burner.①

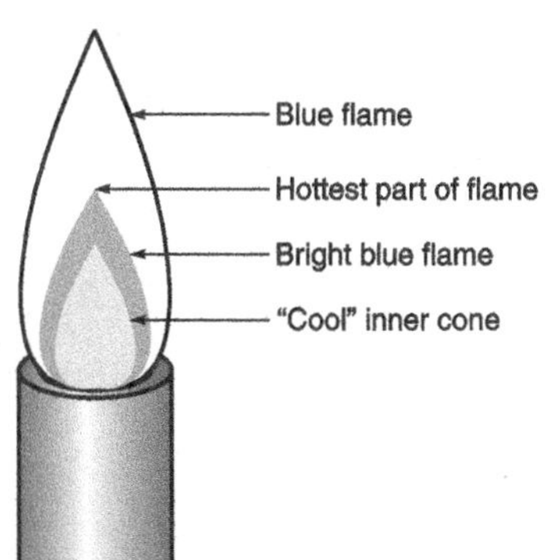

Figure 1.3 Flame of a properly adjusted Bunsen burner.

2. **Observing flame temperatures using a wire gauze.** Temperatures within the second (inner) cone of a nonluminous blue flame approach 1600°C.

a. Using crucible tongs (or forceps), hold a wire gauze parallel to the burner barrel just above the burner top (Figure 1.4). Observe the relative heat zones of the flame. Sketch a diagram of your observations on the ***Report Sheet.***②

b. *Close* (or nearly close) the air-control valve and repeat the observation with a luminous flame.③

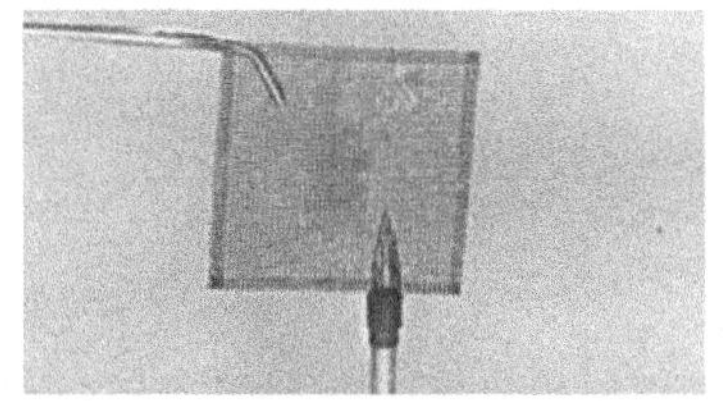

Jo A. Beran

Figure 1.4 Hold the wire gauze parallel to the burner barrel.

B. Laboratory Balances

1. **Practice using the balances.** Refer to the ***Report Sheet.*** As suggested, measure the mass of several objects. Use the top-loading balance only after the instructor explains its operation. Be sure to record the mass of the objects with the correct number of significant figures that indicates to the sensitivity of the balance.④ Refer to *Technique 6.*

2. **Precision of a measurement.**

a. Obtain a 10-mL graduated cylinder and measure and tare its mass (±0.001 g) on your assigned balance. Add 7 mL (±0.1 mL) of water and measure the combined mass.⑤ Calculate the mass of 7 mL of water. Refer to *Technique 16A* (p. 34) for reading and recording a volume.

Data Analysis, B

b. Discard the water and again fill the graduated cylinder to the 7-mL mark. Record the mass measurement on the ***Report Sheet.*** Repeat this procedure at least five times. Calculate the average mass of 7 mL of water.

C. Density

Ask your instructor which balance you are to use to determine the densities of your unknowns. Write the balance number on the ***Report Sheet.***⑥

1. **Water-insoluble solid.**

a. Obtain an unknown solid and record its number.⑦ Using the assigned balance tare the mass of a piece of weighing paper,[1] place the solid on the weighing paper and measure its mass. Record the mass according to the sensitivity of the balance.

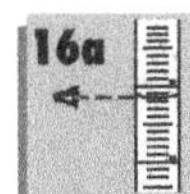

b. Half-fill a 10-mL (or larger) graduated cylinder with water and record its volume (Figure 1.5a, page 54).

c. Gently slide the known mass of solid into the graduated cylinder held at a 45° angle. Roll the solid around in the cylinder, removing any air bubbles that are trapped or that adhere to the solid. Record the new water level (Figure 1.5b, page 54). The volume of the solid is the difference between the two water levels.

[1]The balance is reset to zero *after* the weighing paper is placed on the balance pan.

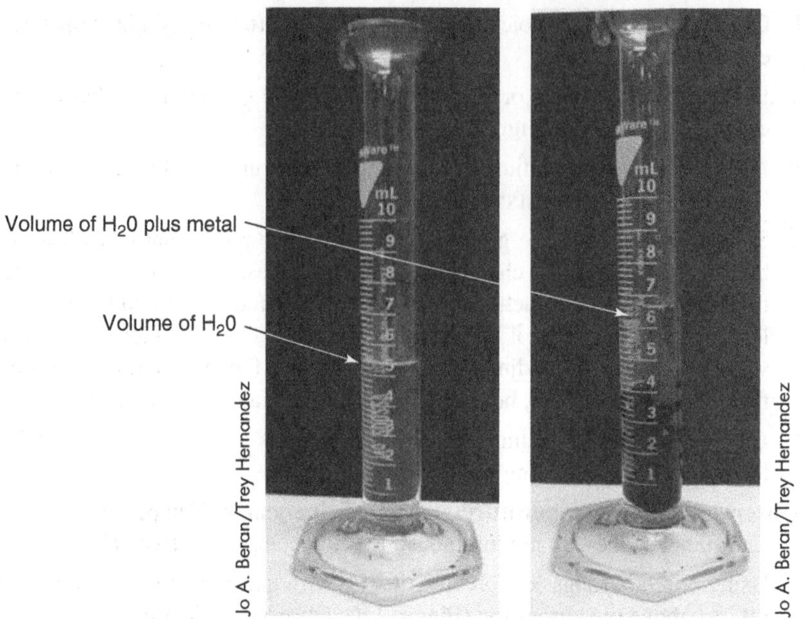

Figure 1.5 Apparatus for measuring the density of a water-insoluble solid

d. Remove the solid, dry it, and measure its volume a second time.

Disposal: Check with your instructor for the procedure of properly returning the solid sample.

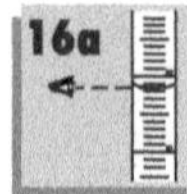

2. **Liquid, water**
   a. Clean your smallest laboratory beaker. Using your assigned balance, measure and record its mass. Pipet 5 mL of water into the beaker.
   b. Measure and record the mass of the beaker and water. Calculate the density of water from the available data. Repeat the density determination for Trial 2.⑧
   c. Collect and record the density value of water at room temperature from five additional laboratory measurements from classmates.⑨ Calculate the average density of water at room temperature.

*Refer to **Data Analysis, B** for calculating average values.*

3. **Liquid, unknown**
   a. Dry the beaker and pipet. Ask the instructor for a liquid unknown and record its number.⑩ (**Caution:** *The unknown liquid may be **flammable**. Do not inhale the fumes of the liquid; extinguish all flames.*)
   b. Rinse the pipet with two 1-mL quantities of the unknown liquid and discard. Repeat the measurements of Part C.2, substituting the unknown liquid for the water. Repeat this experiment for Trial 2. Calculate the average density of the liquid.

Flammable: capable of igniting in air (generally initiated with a flame or spark)

Disposal: Check with your instructor. Dispose of the unknown liquid and the rinses in the Waste Liquids container.

The Next Step

How might the density of an object less dense than water be determined—for example, packing peanuts, a slice of bread, a feather? How might the density of a water-soluble solid be determined?

Experiment 1 *Prelaboratory Assignment*

Basic Laboratory Operations

Date _________ Lab Sec. ______ Name ____ Desk No. _________

1. A proper fuel–air mixture is most critical in the production of an efficient, nonluminous flame. For the ignition of an efficient Bunsen flame in the laboratory, identify the (most common) fuel and the required air component.

2. **a.** What is the dominant color of a nonluminous flame from a Bunsen burner? Explain.

   b. Is the temperature of a luminous flame greater or less than that of a nonluminous flame? Explain.

3. Diagram the cross section of a graduated cylinder, illustrating *how* to read the meniscus.

16a

4. Experimental Procedure, Part B. What is the sensitivity of the *least* sensitive balance most likely to be in your laboratory?

5. A woodfire in a fireplace typically has a yellow flame whereas a (natural) gas fire (for a kitchen stove) is typically blue. Explain why the appearance of the wood flame is yellow whereas the gas flame most often appears blue.

DJClaassen/iStockphoto

6. Refer to *Technique 16B*.

   a. Remove the drop suspended from a pipet tip by . . .

   b. The finger used to control the delivery of liquid from a pipet is the . . .

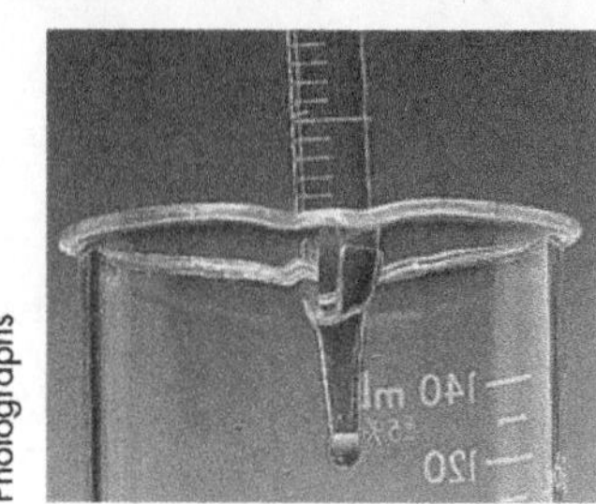

Richard Megna/Fundamental Photographs

   c. What should be done with the last bit of liquid remaining in the pipet after delivery?

   d. Most pipets are calibrated as TD 20°C. Define TD; what is its meaning regarding the volume of liquid a pipet delivers?

7. Experimental Procedure, Part C.1. The density of diamond is 3.51 g/cm^3, and the density of platinum is 21.43 g/cm^3. If equal masses of diamond and platinum are transferred to equal volumes of water in separate graduated cylinders, which graduated cylinder would have the greatest volume change? Explain or show with a sample calculation.

8. Experimental Procedure, Part C.3. The mass of a beaker is 5.333 g. After 5.00 mL of a concentrated hydrochloric acid solution is pipetted into the beaker, the combined mass of the beaker and the hydrochloric acid sample is 11.229 g. From the data, what is the measured density of the hydrochloric acid solution?

Experiment 1 *Report Sheet*

Basic Laboratory Operations

Date __________ Lab Sec. ______ Name ______________________________ Desk No. __________

A. Bunsen Burner

1. ①Instructor's Approval of a well-adjusted Bunsen flame: ______________________________

2. a. At right, draw a sketch of the heat zones for a nonluminous flame as directed with the wire gauze positioned parallel to the burner barrel. Label the "cool" and "hot" zones.②

b. What happens to the "cool" and "hot" zones of a nonluminous flame, when the air-control valve is closed (nearly closed)? Explain.③

B. Laboratory Balances

1. ④Determine the mass of the following objects on your assigned balance. Express your results with the correct sensitivity.

Balance no. ______________ Sensitivity ______________

Object	Description of Object (size or volume)	Mass (*g*)
Test tube	______________	______________
Beaker	______________	______________
Spatula	______________	______________
Graduated cylinder	______________	______________
Other (see instructor)	______________	______________

2. ⑤**Precision of Measurement.** Balance no. ______________

Mass of graduated cylinder (if not tared) ______________

	Trial 1	*Trial 2*	*Trial 3*	*Trial 4*	*Trial 5*	*Trial 6*
a. Mass of cylinder $+H_2O$ (*l*) (*g*)	________	________	________	________	________	________
b. Mass of 7 mL $H_2O(l)$ (*g*)	________	________	________	________	________	________

c. Average mass of 7 mL $H_2O(l)$ (*g*) ______________ ***Data Analysis, B***

Comment on the precision of the mass measurements for the water samples.

C. Density

⑥Balance no. ______________

1. ⑦Solid Unknown Number ______	Trial 1	Trial 2
a. Tared mass of solid (*g*)		
b. Volume of water (*cm*^{3})		
c. Volume of water and solid (*cm*^{3})		
d. Volume of solid (*cm*^{3})		
e. Density of solid (*g/cm*^{3})		
f. Average density of solid (*g/cm*^{3})		

2,3. Liquid: Water and Unknown	Water		Liquid Unknown No. ______ ⑩	
	Trial 1	*Trial 2*	*Trial 1*	*Trial 2*
a. Mass of beaker (*g*)				
b. Mass of beaker + liquid (*g*)				
c. Mass of liquid (*g*)				
d. Volume of liquid (*mL*)				
e. ⑧Density of liquid (*g/mL*)				
f. Average density of liquid (*g/mL*)				

⑨Class Data/Group	1	2	3	4	5	6
Density of Water						

Average density of water at room temperature: **Data Analysis, B**

Laboratory Questions

Circle the questions that have been assigned.

1. Part A.1. If you have a properly adjusted hot flame, which is pale blue with three distinct cones, what is observed if the gas control value is slightly closed? Explain.
2. Part A.1. If you have a properly adjusted hot flame, which is pale blue with three distinct cones, what is observed if the air-control valve is slightly closed? Explain.
3. Part A.2. A burning candle produces a luminous flame. What is the fuel for the burning candle? Why is the flame luminous?
4. Part C.1c. The solid is not completely submerged in the water. Will this technique error increase, decrease, or have no effect on the reported density of the solid? Explain.
5. Part C.2. Suppose that after delivery several drops of the water cling to the inner wall of the pipet (because the pipet wall is dirty). Will this technique error increase, decrease, or have no effect on the reported density of water? Explain. See drawing at right.
6. Part C.3. The unknown liquid is volatile. If some of the liquid evaporates between the time the liquid is delivered to the beaker and the time its mass is measured, will the reported density of the liquid be too high, too low, or unaffected? Explain.

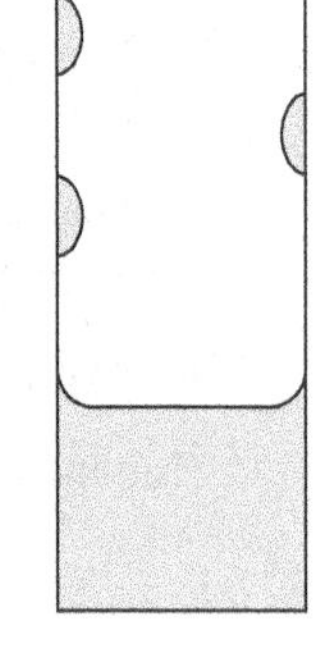

Jo A. Beran/Trey Hernandez

Experiment 2

Identification of a Compound: Chemical Properties

A potassium chromate solution added to a silver nitrate solution results in the formation of insoluble silver chromate.

OBJECTIVES

- To identify a compound on the basis of its **chemical properties**
- To design a systematic procedure for determining the presence of a particular compound in aqueous solution

Chemical property: characteristic of a substance that is dependent on its chemical environment

TECHNIQUES

The following techniques are used in the Experimental Procedure:

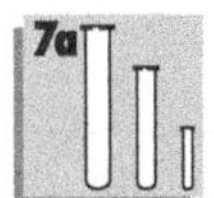

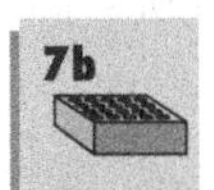

INTRODUCTION

Chemists, and scientists in general, develop and design experiments in an attempt to understand, explain, and predict various chemical phenomena. Carefully controlled (laboratory) conditions are needed to minimize the many parameters that affect the observations. Chemists organize and categorize their data and then systematically analyze the data to reach some conclusion; often, the conclusion may be to carefully plan more experiments!

It is presumptuous to believe that a chemist must know the result of an experiment before it is ever attempted; most often, an experiment is designed to determine the presence or absence of a **substance** or to determine or measure a parameter. A goal of the environmental or synthesis research chemist is, for example, to separate the substances of a reaction mixture (one generated in the laboratory or one found in nature) and then identify each substance through a systematic, or sometimes **trial-and-error,** study of their chemical and physical properties. As you will experience later, *Experiments 4, 37–39* are designed to identify a specific ion (by taking advantage of its unique chemical properties) in a mixture of ions through a systematic sequence of analyses.

Substance: a pure element or compound having a unique set of chemical and physical properties

Trial-and-error study: a method that is often used to seek a pattern in the accumulated data

In this experiment, you will observe chemical reactions that are characteristic of various compounds under controlled conditions. After collecting and organizing your data, you will be given an unknown compound, one that you have previously investigated. The interpretations of the collected data will assist you in identifying your unknown compound.

What observations will you be looking for? Chemical changes are generally accompanied by one or more of the following:

- A gas is evolved. This evolution may be quite rapid, or it may be a "fizzing" sound (Figure 2.1, page 60).

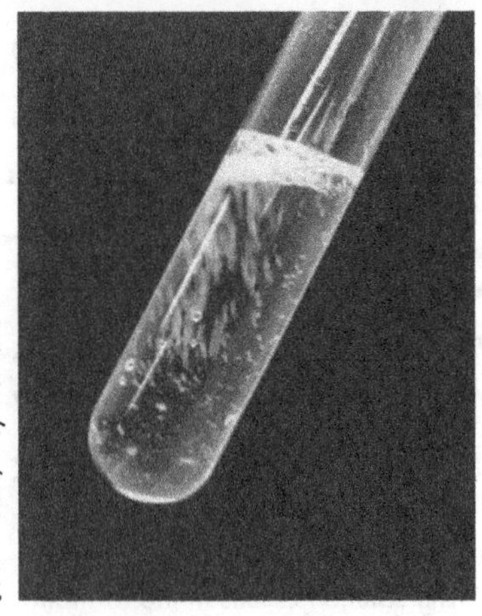

Jo A. Beran/Trey Hernandez

Figure 2.1 A reaction mixture of $NaHCO_3(aq)$ and $HCl(aq)$ produces CO_2 gas

- A *precipitate* appears (or disappears). The nature of the precipitate is important. It may be crystalline, it may have color, or it may merely cloud the solution.
- Heat may be evolved or absorbed. The reaction vessel becomes warm if the reaction is exothermic or cools if the reaction is endothermic.
- A *color change* occurs. A substance added to the system may cause a color change.
- A *change in odor* is detected. The odor of a substance may appear, disappear, or become more intense during the course of a chemical reaction.

The chemical properties of the following compounds, dissolved in water, are investigated in Part A of this experiment:

Sodium chloride	$NaCl(aq)$
Sodium carbonate	$Na_2CO_3(aq)$
Magnesium sulfate	$MgSO_4(aq)$
Ammonium chloride	$NH_4Cl(aq)$
Water	$H_2O(l)$

The following test **reagents** are used to identify and characterize these compounds:

Silver nitrate	$AgNO_3(aq)$
Sodium hydroxide	$NaOH(aq)$
Hydrochloric acid	$HCl(aq)$

Reagent: a solid chemical or a solution having a known concentration of solute

In Part B of this experiment, the chemical properties of five compounds in aqueous solutions, labeled 1 through 5, are investigated with three reagents labeled A, B, and C. Chemical tests will be performed with these eight solutions. An unknown will then be issued and matched with one of the solutions, labeled 1 through 5.

EXPERIMENTAL PROCEDURE

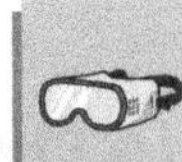

Procedure Overview: In Part A, a series of tests for the chemical properties of known compounds in aqueous solutions are conducted. A similar series of tests are conducted on an unknown set of compounds in Part B. In each case, an unknown compound is identified on the basis of the chemical properties observed.

You should discuss and interpret your observations on the known chemical tests with a partner, but each of you should analyze your own unknown compound. At each circled superscript[1–7] in the procedure, *stop* and record your observation on the ***Report Sheet***.

To organize your work, you will conduct a test on each known compound for the five aqueous solutions and the unknown compound with a single test reagent. The ***Report Sheet*** provides a "reaction matrix" for you to describe your observations. Because the space is limited, you may want to devise codes such as the following:

- pc—precipitate + color
- cc—cloudy + color
- nr—no reaction
- g—gas, no odor
- go—gas, odor

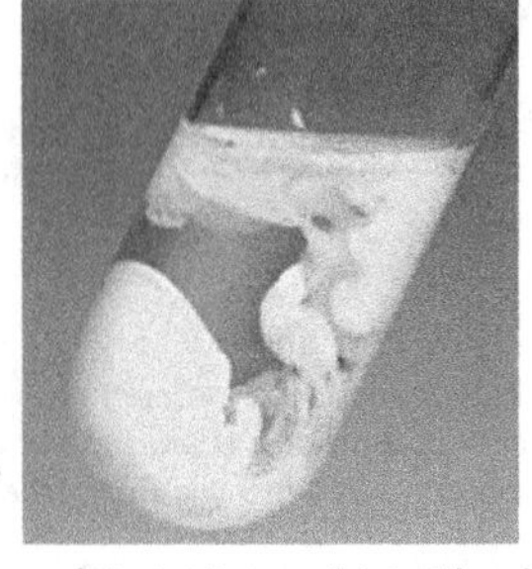

Andy Washnik

A mix of $AgNO_3$ and $NaCl$ solutions produce a white $AgCl$ precipitate.

A. Chemical Properties of Known Compounds

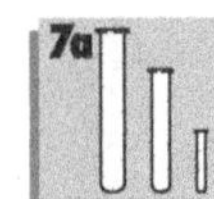

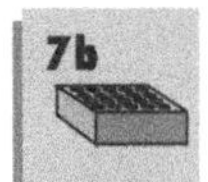

1. Observations with silver nitrate test reagent

a. Use a permanent marker to label five small, clean test tubes (Figure 2.2a) or set up a clean 24-well plate (Figure 2.2b). Ask your instructor which setup you should use. Place ~1 mL of each of the five "known" solutions into the labeled test tubes (or wells A1–A5).

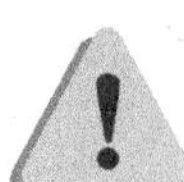

b. Use a dropper pipet (or a dropper bottle) to deliver the silver nitrate solution to each of the known solutions. (**Caution:** *$AgNO_3$ forms black stains on the skin. The stain, caused by silver metal, causes no harm.*) If after adding several drops you observe a chemical change, then add 5–10 drops to see if there are additional changes. Record your observations in the matrix on the ***Report Sheet.***[1] Save your test

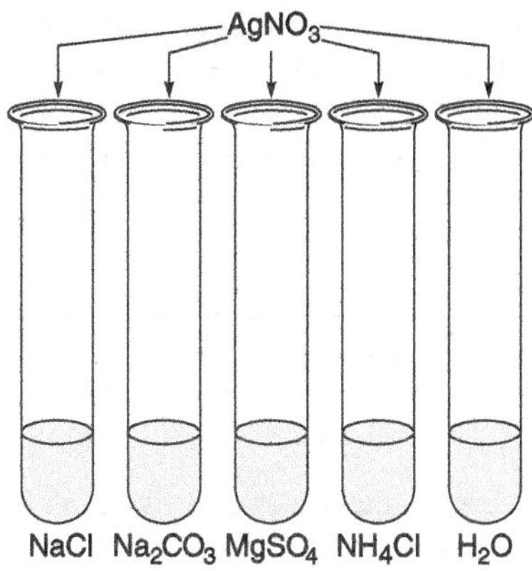

Figure 2.2a Arrangement of test tubes for testing with the silver nitrate reagent

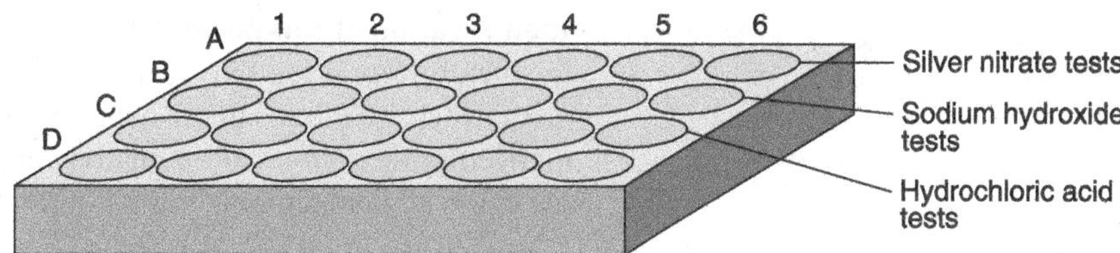

Figure 2.2b Arrangement of test solutions in the 24-well plate for testing salts

solutions for Part A.4. Write the formula for each precipitate that forms. Ask your lab instructor for assistance. For example, a mixture of NaCl(*aq*) and $AgNO_3$(*aq*) produces AgCl(*s*) as a precipitate. The insolubility of AgCl is noted in Appendix E.

Appendix E

2. **Observations with sodium hydroxide test reagent**

   a. Use a permanent marker to label five additional small, clean test tubes (Figure 2.3). Place ~1 mL of each of the five "known" solutions into this second set of labeled test tubes (or wells B1–B5, Figure 2.2b).

   b. To each of these solutions, slowly add 5–10 drops of the sodium hydroxide solution; make observations as you add the solution. Check to see if a gas evolves in any of the tests. Check for odor. What is the nature of any precipitates that form? Observe *closely*.② Save your test solutions for reference in Part A.4. Write the formula for each of the precipitates that formed.

Appendix E

3. **Observations with hydrochloric acid test reagent**

   a. Use a permanent marker to label five additional small, clean test tubes (Figure 2.4). Place ~1 mL of each of the five "known" solutions into this third set of labeled test tubes (or wells C1–C5, Figure 2.2b).

   b. Slowly add 5–10 drops of the hydrochloric test reagent to the solutions and record your observations. Check to see if any gas is evolved. Check for odor. Observe closely.③ Save your test solutions for reference in Part A.4. Write the formula for any compound that forms.

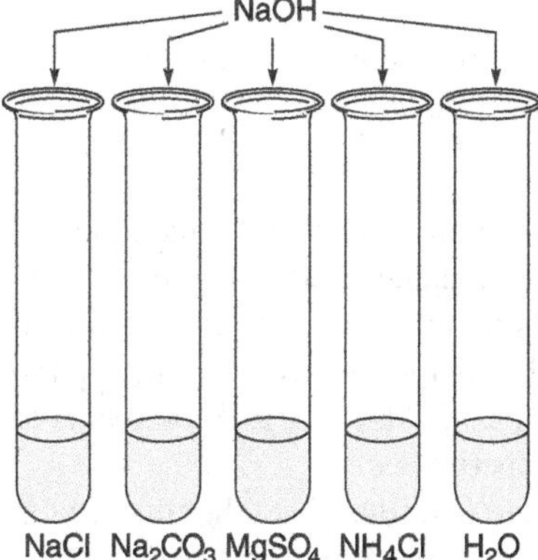

Figure 2.3 Arrangement of test tubes for testing with the sodium hydroxide reagent

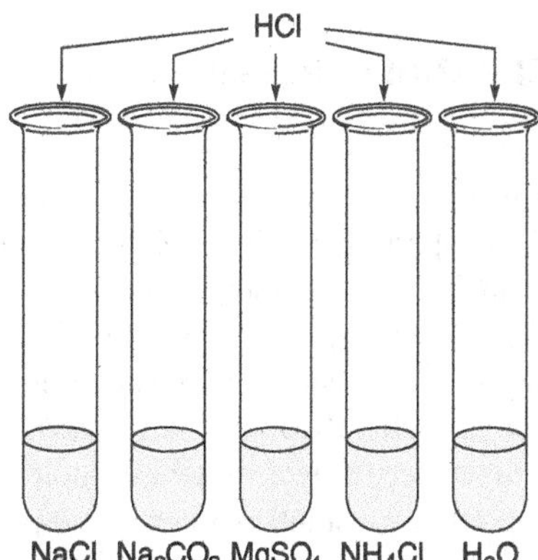

Figure 2.4 Arrangement of test tubes for testing with the hydrochloric acid reagent

4. **Identification of unknown.** Obtain an unknown for Part A from your laboratory instructor. Repeat the three tests with the reagents in Parts A.1, 2, and 3 on your unknown. On the basis of the data from the "known" solutions (collected and summarized in the ***Report Sheet*** matrix) and that of your unknown solution, identify the compound in your unknown solution.④

Disposal: Discard the test solutions in the Waste Salts container.

CLEANUP: Rinse the test tubes or well plate twice with tap water and twice with deionized water. Discard each rinse in the Waste Salts container.

B. Chemical Properties of Unknown Compounds

The design of the experiment in Part B is similar to that of Part A. Therefore, 15 clean test tubes or a clean 24-well plate is necessary.

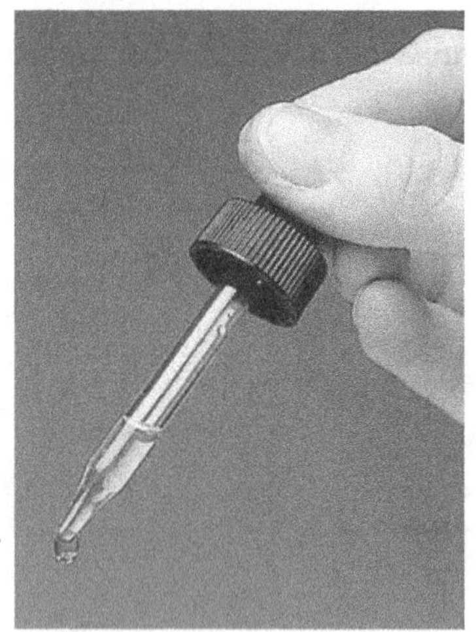

Ken Karp

A dropper pipet. 20 drops is ~1 mL of solution.

1. **Preparation of solutions.** On the reagent shelf are five solutions labeled 1 through 5, each containing a different compound. Use small clean test tubes or the well plate as your testing laboratory. About 1 mL of each test solution is necessary for analysis.
2. **Preparation of reagents.** Also on the reagent shelf are three reagents labeled A, B, and C. Use a dropper pipet (or dropper bottle) or a Beral pipet to deliver reagents A through C to the solutions.
3. **Testing the solutions**
   a. Test each of the five solutions with drops (and then excess drops) of reagent A. If, after adding several drops, you observe a chemical change, add 5–10 drops more to see if there are additional changes. Observe closely and describe any evidence of chemical change; record your observations.⑤
   b. With a fresh set of solutions 1–5 in clean test tubes (or wells), test each with reagent B.⑥ Repeat with reagent C.⑦
4. **Identification of unknown.** An unknown solution will be issued that is one of the five solutions from Part B.1. On the basis of the data in your reaction matrix and the data you have collected, identify your unknown as one of the five solutions.

Disposal: Discard the test solutions in the Waste Salts container.

CLEANUP: Rinse the test tubes or well plate twice with tap water and twice with deionized water. Discard each rinse in the Waste Salts container.

The Next Step

This experiment will enable you to better understand the importance of "separation and identification," a theme that appears throughout this manual. For example, refer to *Experiments 3, 4, 37, 38, and 39.* These experiments require good experimental techniques that support an understanding of the chemical principles involved in the separation and identification of the various compounds or ions. Additionally, the amounts of a substance of interest are also determined in other experiments.

Obtain a small (~50 cm^3) sample of soil, add water, and filter. Test the filtrate with the silver nitrate test reagent. Test a second soil sample *directly* with the hydrochloric acid test reagent. What are your conclusions?

Experiment 2 *Prelaboratory Assignment*

Identification of a Compound: Chemical Properties

Date __________ Lab Sec. ______ Name ____ Desk No. __________

1. Experimental Procedure, Part A.

a. What is the criterion for clean glassware?

2

b. What is the size and volume of a "small, clean test tube"?

7a

2. Experimental Procedure, Part A.2. Describe the technique for testing the odor of a chemical.

17a

3. Identify at least five observations that are indicative of a chemical reaction.

4. Depending upon the tip of a dropper pipet, there are approximately 20 drops per milliliter of water. The Experimental Procedure, Parts A and B, indicates the addition of 5–10 drops of each solution (Figure 2.2a) to the test tubes. Calculate the volume range in milliliters for the solution.

5. Experimental Procedure, Part A. The substances NaCl, Na_2CO_3, $MgSO_4$, and NH_4Cl, which are used for test solutions, are all soluble ionic compounds. For each substance, indicate the ions present in its respective test solution.

NaCl: ______________________________

Na_2CO_3: ______________________________

$MgSO_4$: ______________________________

NH_4Cl: ______________________________

6. Three colorless solutions in test tubes, with no labels, are in a test tube rack on the laboratory bench. Lying beside the test tubes are three labels: potassium iodide, KI; silver nitrate, $AgNO_3$; and sodium sulfide, Na_2S. You are to place the labels on the test tubes using only the three solutions present. Here are your tests:

- A portion of test tube 1 added to a portion of test tube 3 produces a yellow silver iodide precipitate.
- A portion of test tube 1 added to a portion of test tube 2 produces a black silver sulfide precipitate.

a. Your conclusions are:
Test tube 1 ______________________________

Test tube 2 ______________________________

Test tube 3 ______________________________

b. Write the balanced equation for the formation of silver iodide, AgI, from a mix of two selected solutions provided above.

c. Write the balanced equation for the formation of silver sulfide, Ag_2S, from a mix of two selected solutions provided above.

Experiment 2 *Report Sheet*

Identification of a Compound: Chemical Properties

Date _________ Lab Sec. ______ Name ______________________________ Desk No. _________

A. Chemical Properties of Known Compounds

Indicate your observations in the reaction matrix.

Test	$NaCl(aq)$	$Na_2CO_3(aq)$	$MgSO_4(aq)$	$NH_4Cl(aq)$	$H_2O(l)$	Unknown
① $AgNO_3(aq)$						
② $NaOH(aq)$						
③ $HCl(aq)$						

Write formulas for the *precipitates* that formed in Part A. (See Appendix E)

Part A.1						
Part A.2						
Part A.3						

Sample no. of unknown for Part A.4 ____________________

④Compound in unknown solution ____________________

B. Chemical Properties of Unknown Compounds

Indicate your observations in the reaction matrix.

Sample no. of unknown for Part B.4 ____________________

Solution No.	1	2	3	4	5	Unknown
⑤Reagent A						
⑥Reagent B						
⑦Reagent C						

Compound of unknown is the same as Solution No. ____________________

Laboratory Questions

Circle the questions that have been assigned.

1. Identify a chemical reagent used *in this experiment* that can be used to distinguish solid $CaCl_2$ (soluble) from solid $CaCO_3$ (insoluble). What is the distinguishing observation?

2. What test reagent used *in this experiment* will distinguish a soluble Cl^- salt from a soluble SO_4^{2-} salt? What is the distinguishing observation?

3. Predict what would be *observed* (*and why*) from an aqueous mixture for each of the following (all substances are water soluble).

   a. potassium carbonate and hydrochloric acid
   b. zinc chloride and silver nitrate
   c. magnesium chloride and sodium hydroxide
   d. ammonium nitrate and sodium hydroxide

4. Three colorless solutions in test tubes, with no labels, are in a test tube rack on the laboratory bench. Lying beside the tests tubes are three labels: 0.10 *M* Na_2CO_3, 0.10 *M* HCl, and 0.10 *M* KOH. You are to place the labels on the test tubes using only the three solutions present. Here are your tests:

   - A few drops of the solution from test tube 1 added to a similar volume of the solution in test tube 2 produces no visible reaction but the solution becomes warm.
   - A few drops of the solution from test tube 1 added to a similar volume of the solution in test tube 3 produces carbon dioxide gas.

   Identify the labels for test tubes 1, 2, and 3.

5. Three colorless solutions in test tubes, with no labels, are in a test tube rack on the laboratory bench. Lying beside the test tubes are three labels: silver nitrate, $AgNO_3$; hydrochloric acid, HCl; and sodium carbonate, Na_2CO_3. You are to place the labels on the test tubes using only the three solutions present. Here is your analysis procedure:

   - A portion of test tube 1 added to a portion of test tube 2 produces carbon dioxide gas, CO_2.
   - A portion of test tube 2 added to a portion of test tube 3 produces a white silver carbonate precipitate.

   a. On the basis of your observations how would you label the three test tubes?
   b. What would you expect to happen if a portion of test tube 1 is added to a portion of test tube 3?

6. For individual solutions of the cations Ag^+, Ba^{2+}, Mg^{2+}, and Cu^{2+}, the following experimental observations were collected:

	$NH_3(aq)$	$HCl(aq)$	$H_2SO_4(aq)$
Ag^+	No change	White ppt[a]	No change
Ba^{2+}	No change	No change	White ppt
Mg^{2+}	White ppt	No change	No change
Cu^{2+}	Blue ppt/deep blue soln with excess	No change	No change

[a]Example: When an aqueous solution of hydrochloric acid is added to a solution containing Ag^+, a white precipitate (ppt) forms.

   From these experimental observations,

   a. identify a reagent that distinguishes the chemical properties of Ag^+ and Mg^{2+}. What is the distinguishing observation?
   b. identify a reagent that distinguishes the chemical properties of HCl and H_2SO_4. What is the distinguishing observation?
   c. identify a reagent that distinguishes the chemical properties of Ba^{2+} and Cu^{2+}. What is the distinguishing observation?
   ***d.** identify a reagent that distinguishes the chemical properties of Cu^{2+} and Mg^{2+}. What is the distinguishing observation?

Experiment 3

Water Analysis: Solids

"Clear" water from streams contains small quantities of dissolved and suspended solids.

OBJECTIVES

- To determine the total, dissolved, and suspended solids in a water sample
- To determine the ions present in the solids of a water sample

TECHNIQUES

The following techniques are used in the Experimental Procedure:

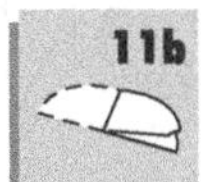

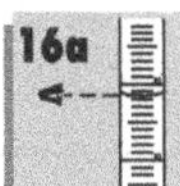

INTRODUCTION

Surface water is used as the primary drinking water source for many large municipalities. The water is piped into a water-treatment facility where impurities are removed and bacteria are killed before the water is placed into the distribution lines. The contents of the surface water must be known and predictable so that the treatment facility can properly and adequately remove these impurities. Tests are used to determine the contents of the surface water.

Dissolved Solids

Water in the environment has a large number of impurities with an extensive range of concentrations. Dissolved solids are water-soluble substances, most often salts, although some dissolved solids may come from organic sources. Naturally occurring dissolved salts generally result from the movement of water over or through mineral deposits such as limestone. These dissolved solids, characteristic of the **watershed,** generally consist of sodium, calcium, magnesium, and potassium cations and chloride, sulfate, bicarbonate, carbonate, bromide, and fluoride anions. Anthropogenic (human-related) dissolved solids include nitrates from fertilizer runoff and human wastes, phosphates from detergents and fertilizers, and organic compounds from pesticides, sewage runoff, and industrial wastes.

Watershed: the land area from which the natural drainage of water occurs

Dissolved salts can be problematic in potable water. Typical dissolved salt concentrations range from 20 to 1,000 mg/L, although most waters are less than 500 mg/L. High concentrations also indicate "hard" water (*Experiment 21*), which can clog pipes and industrial cooling systems. Also, high concentrations of dissolved salts can cause diarrhea or constipation for some people.

Salinity, a measure of the total salt content in a water sample, is expressed as the grams of dissolved salts per kilogram of water or as **parts per thousand** (ppt). The average ocean salinity is 35 ppt, whereas freshwater salinity is usually less than 0.5 ppt. Brackish water, where fresh river water meets salty ocean water, varies from 0.5 ppt to 17 ppt. For water samples with low organic levels, the salinity of a water sample approximates that of total dissolved solids (TDS) content.

Parts per thousand (ppt): 1g of substance per 1,000g (1 kg) of sample

More specifically, the anions that account for the salinity of the water are generally the carbonates and bicarbonates, CO_3^{2-} and HCO_3^-; the halides, Cl^-, Br^-, and I^-; the phosphates, PO_4^{3-}; and the sulfates, SO_4^{2-}. A qualitative testing of a water sample can determine the presence of these various ions.

Ionic equation: ionic equations, though appearing somewhat premature in this manual, are written to better illustrate the ions in solution that are involved in the chemical reactions and observations. Experiment 6 will further illustrate the use of ionic equations for chemical reactions.

To test for the presence of carbonates and bicarbonates in the water, an acid—generally nitric acid, HNO_3—is added to the sample, resulting in the evolution of carbon dioxide gas. The **ionic equation** for the reaction is

$$CO_3^{2-}(aq) + 2\,H^+(aq) + NO_3^-(aq) \rightarrow CO_2(g) + H_2O(l) + NO_3^-(aq) \quad (3.1)$$

A qualitative test for the halides is the addition of silver ion, resulting in a silver halide precipitate:

$$Ag^+(aq) + Cl^-, Br^-, I^-(aq) \rightarrow AgCl\,(s, \text{white}) + AgBr\,(s, \text{light brown}) + AgI(s, \text{dark brown}) \quad (3.2)$$

The most common cation present in "natural" waters is calcium. Calcium is the principal ion responsible for water hardness. See *Experiment 21*. A qualitative test for its presence results from the addition of oxalate ion, $C_2O_4^{2-}$, to the sample to form insoluble calcium oxalate.

$$Ca^{2+}(aq) + C_2O_4^{2-}(aq) \rightarrow CaC_2O_4(s) \quad (3.3)$$

While these tests may have interferences as performed in this experiment, a more detailed experimental and systematic procedure is presented in *Experiment 37*.

Suspended Solids

Suspended solids: solids that exhibit colloidal properties or solids that remain in the water because of turbulence

Suspended solids are very finely divided particles that are kept in suspension by the turbulent action of the moving water; they are *insoluble* in water but are filterable. Total suspended solids (TSS) is a measure of the turbidity or the clarity of the water.

High concentrations of suspended solids such as decayed organic matter, sand, silt, and clay can settle to cover (and suffocate) the existing ecosystem at the bottom of a lake, can make disinfectants for water treatment less effective, and can absorb or adsorb various organic and inorganic pollutants, resulting in an increase of their residence in the water sample.

Total Solids

Total solids (TS) are the sum of the dissolved and suspended solids in the water sample. In this experiment the total solids and the total dissolved solids (TDS) are determined directly; the total suspended solids are assumed to be the difference since

$$\text{total suspended solids (TSS)} = \text{total solids (TS)} - \text{total dissolved solids (TDS)} \quad (3.4)$$

ppm: 1 mg substance per kilogram sample = 1 part per million (ppm)

The U.S. Public Health Service recommends that drinking water not exceed 500 mg total mg solids/kg water, or 500 **ppm**. However, in some localities, the total solids content may range up to 1,000 ppm of potable water; that's 1 g/L!! An amount more than 500 ppm water does not mean the water is unfit for drinking; an excess of 500 ppm is merely not recommended.

Experimental Procedure

Filtrate: the solution that passes through the filter into a receiving flask.

Turbid sample: a cloudy suspension due to stirred sediment.

Procedure Overview: The amounts of total, dissolved, and suspended solids in a water sample are determined in this experiment. The water sample is filtered to remove the suspended solids, and the **filtrate** is evaporated to dryness to determine the total dissolved solids (TDS); evaporation of a water sample without filtration determines the total solids (TS). Each dried sample is then tested for the presence of chloride, carbonate (or bicarbonate), and calcium ions. Be aware of the number of significant figures when recording data.

Obtain 100 mL of a water sample from your instructor. The water sample may be from the ocean, a lake, a stream, or from an underground aquifer. Seek approval of your instructor. Preferably the water sample is high in **turbidity.** Record the sample number and write a short description of the sample on the ***Report Sheet***.

Figure 3.1 Wash the spattered material from the convex side of the watch glass.

Ask your instructor whether evaporating dishes or 250-mL beakers are to be used for the analysis.

Assume the density of your water sample to be 1.01 g/mL.

A. Total Dissolved Solids (TDS)

1. **Filter the water sample.** Gravity filter about 50 mL of a *thoroughly stirred or shaken* water sample into a clean, dry 100-mL beaker. While waiting for the filtration to be completed, proceed to Part B.
2. **Evaporate the filtrate to dryness**
   - **a.** Clean, dry, and measure the mass (±0.001 g) of an evaporating dish (or 250-mL beaker).
   - **b.** Pipet a 25-mL aliquot (portion) of the filtrate into the evaporating dish (250-mL beaker). Determine the combined mass of the sample and evaporating dish (250-mL beaker).
   - **c.** Use a hot plate or direct flame (Figure T.14a or T.14b) to *slowly* heat—do not boil—the mixture to dryness.
   - **d.** As the mixture nears dryness, cover the evaporating dish (beaker) with a watch glass and reduce the intensity of the heat.[1] If spattering occurs, allow the dish to cool to room temperature, rinse the adhered solids from the watch glass (see Figure 3.1), and return the rinse to the dish.
3. **A final heating to dryness.** Again heat slowly, being careful to avoid further spattering. After all of the water has evaporated, reduce the heat of the hot plate or maintain a **"cool" flame** beneath the dish for ~3 minutes. Allow the dish to cool to room temperature and determine its final mass. Cool the evaporating dish and sample in a desiccator, if available.

Cool flame: a Bunsen flame of low intensity—a slow rate of natural gas is flowing through the burner barrel.

B. Total Solids (TS) and Total Suspended Solids (TSS)

1. **Evaporate an original water sample to dryness**
   - **a.** Clean, dry, and measure the mass (±0.001 g) of a second evaporating dish (or 250-mL beaker).

[1]This reduces the spattering of the remaining solid and its subsequent loss in analysis.

b. Thoroughly stir or agitate 100 mL of the original water sample; pipet[2] a 25-mL aliquot of this sample into the evaporating dish (250-mL beaker). Record the combined mass of the water sample and evaporating dish (beaker).

c. Evaporate *slowly* the sample to dryness as described in Part A.2. Record the mass of the solids remaining in the evaporating dish.

2. **Total suspended solids.** Collect the appropriate data to determine the total suspended solids in the water sample.

C. Analysis of Data

Data Analysis A, B

1. **Precision of data?** Compare your TDS, TS, and TSS data with three other chemists in your laboratory who have analyzed the *same* water sample. Record their results on the ***Report Sheet***. Calculate the average value for the TSS in the water sample. Pay head to significant figures.

D. Chemical Tests[3]

Amounts of the dried samples may be too small for testing. Consult with your which tests (D.1, D.2, or D.3) should be completed, if any.

1. **Test for carbonates and bicarbonates.** With your spatula, loosen a small portion of the dried samples from Part A and Part B and transfer each to *separately* marked 75-mm test tubes or watchglasses. Add 1 drop of 6 *M* HNO_3 (**Caution:** *HNO_3 is corrosive and a severe skin irritant*) and *quickly and carefully* observe. What can you conclude from your observation?
2. **Test for chlorides (halides).** To each of the samples from Part D.1, add 1 drop of water, agitate the solution, and add 1–2 drops of 0.01 *M* $AgNO_3$ (**Caution:** *$AgNO_3$ is a skin irritant*) and observe. What can you conclude from your observation?

Appendix E

3. **Test for calcium ion.** With your spatula, loosen a second portion of the dried samples from Parts A and B and transfer each to *separately* marked 75-mm test tubes or watchglasses. Add about 1 drop of water, agitate or stir the solution, and add 1 drop of 1 *M* $K_2C_2O_4$ and observe. What can you conclude from your observation?

Disposal: Discard the dried salts from Part A and B and the test solutions from Part D in the Waste Salts container.

CLEANUP: Rinse the test tubes and evaporating dishes (250-mL beakers) with tap water and twice with deionized water.

The Next Step

Devise a plan to determine the changes in TSS and TDS at various points along a water source (river, stream, lake, drinking water, etc.). Explain why the values change as a result of location, rainfall, season, time of day, and so on. Test to determine the ions that are primary contributors to the TDS of the sample.

---

[2]If the solution appears to be so turbid that it may plug the pipet tip, use a 25-mL graduated cylinder to measure the water sample as accurately as possible.

[3]For each of the tests in Part D there are other ions that may show a positive test. However, the ions being tested are those most common in environmental water samples.

Experiment 3 *Prelaboratory Assignment*

Water Analysis: Solids

Date __________ Lab Sec. ______ Name ____ Desk No. __________

1. List several anions, by formula, that contribute to the salinity of a water sample.

2. Distinguish between and characterize *total dissolved solids* (TDS) and *total suspended solids* (TSS) in a water sample.

3. Experimental Procedure, Part A.2c, d. Explain why a "cool flame" is important in heating a solution to dryness.

4. a. What is an **aliquot** of a sample?

b. What is the **filtrate** in a gravity filtration procedure?

c. How full (the maximum level) should a funnel be filled with solution in a filtration procedure?

11c

5. Experimental Procedure, Part D. What observation is "expected" when:

a. an acid (nitric acid, HNO_3) is added to a solution containing carbonate or bicarbonate ions? See *Experiment 2*, Experimental Procedure, Part A.3.

b. silver ion is added to a solution containing chloride (or bromide or iodide) ions? See Appendix E and *Experiment 2*, Experimental Procedure, Part A.1.

6. A 25.0 mL aliquot of a well-shaken and filtered sample of river water is pipetted into an evaporating dish. The sample was heated to dryness. Assume the density of the river water was 1.01 g/mL. The following data were collected for Trial 1. Complete the table. (See ***Report Sheet***.) Record calculated values with the correct number of significant figures.

A. Total Dissolved Solids (TDS)

Calculation Zone

Part A.6

1. Mass of evaporating dish (*g*)	26.217
2. Mass of water sample plus evaporating dish (*g*)	51.467
3. Mass of water sample (*g*)	
4. Mass of *dried* sample plus evaporating dish (*g*)	35.291
5. Mass of dissolved solids in 25-mL aliquot of filtered sample (*g*)	
6. Mass of dissolved solids per total mass of sample (*g solids/g sample*) Show calculation.	
7. Total solids (*g solids/kg sample, ppt*)	

7. The following data were collected for determining the concentration of suspended solids in a water sample (density = 1.01 g/mL). Express all calculated data with the correct number of significant figures (see **Data Analysis, A**).

	Trial 1	*Trial 2*	*Trial 3*	*Trial 4*	*Trial 5*	*Trial 6*
Volume of sample (*mL*)	25.0	20.0	50.0	25.0	20.0	25.0
Mass of sample (*g*)						
Mass of dry solid (*g*)	10.767	8.436	21.770	10.826	8.671	10.942
Mass of solid/mass of sample (*g/g*)						

a. What is the *average* TSS in the water sample? Express this measurement in ppt (parts per thousand, g/kg). See **Data Analysis, B**.

b. Calculate the standard deviation and the relative standard deviation (% RSD) for the analyses. See **Data Analysis, C and D**.

Experiment 3 *Report Sheet*

Water Analysis: Solids

Date __________ Lab Sec. ______ Name ____ Desk No. __________

Sample Number: ____________ Describe the nature of your water sample, i.e., its color, turbidity, etc.

A. Total Dissolved Solids (TDS)	***Trial 1***	***Trial 2***
1. Mass of evaporating dish (beaker) (*g*)		
2. Mass of water sample plus evaporating dish (beaker) (*g*)		
3. Mass of water sample (*g*)		
4. Mass of *dried* sample plus evaporating dish (*g*)		
5. Mass of dissolved solids in 25-mL aliquot of filtered sample (*g*)		
6. Mass of dissolved solids per total mass of sample (*g solids/g sample*)		
7. Total dissolved solids (TDS) or salinity (*g solids/kg sample, ppt*)		
8. Average TDS of the sample		

B. Total Solids (TS) and Total Suspended Solids (TSS)		
1. Mass of evaporating dish (beaker) (*g*)		
2. Mass of water sample plus evaporating dish (beaker) (*g*)		
3. Mass of water sample (*g*)		
4. Mass of *dried* sample (*g*)		
5. Mass of total solids in 25-mL aliquot of unfiltered sample (*g*)		
6. Mass of total solids per total mass of sample (*g solids/g sample*)		
7. Total solids (TS, *g solids/kg sample, ppt*)		
8. Average TS of the sample		
9. Total suspended solids (TSS, *g solids/kg sample, ppt*)		
10. Average TSS of the sample		

C. Analysis of Data

Chemist No.	**No. 1 (you)**	**No. 2**	**No. 3**	**No. 4**
TDS (*g/kg*)				
TS (*g/kg*)				
TSS (*g/kg*)				

Average value of total suspended solids (TSS) from four chemists (x) = ____________________

D. Chemical Tests

Test	*Observation*	*Conclusion*
1. CO_3^{2-}, HCO_3^- (TDS)		
CO_3^{2-}, HCO_3^- (TS)		
2. Cl^-, Br^-, I^- (TDS)		
Cl^-, Br^-, I^- (TS)		
3. Ca^{2+} (TDS)		
Ca^{2+} (TS)		

Write a summary of your assessment of the quality of your water sample.

Laboratory Questions

Circle the questions that have been assigned.

1. Part A.1. The collected water sample is not filtered. Will this oversight result in the TDS value being reported too high or too low? Explain.
2. Part A.2. The evaporating dish was not properly cleaned of a volatile material before its mass was determined. When the sample is heated to dryness the volatile material is removed. As a result of this technique error, will the reported TDS be too high, too low, or unaffected? Explain.
3. Part A.2. Some spattering of the sample onto the watchglass does occur near dryness. In a hurry to complete the analysis, the chemist chooses not to return the spattered solids to the original sample and skips the first part of Part A.3. Will the reported TDS for the water sample be too high or too low? Explain.
4. Part A.3 and Part B.2. The sample in the evaporating dish is *not* heated to total dryness. How will this error in technique affect the reported value for TDS—too high, too low, or unaffected? Explain. TSS—too high, too low, or unaffected? Explain.
5. Part A.3. As the sample cools, moisture from the atmosphere condenses on the outside of the evaporating dish (beaker) before the mass is measured. Will the presence of the condensed moisture increase or decrease the reported TDS in the water sample? Explain.
6. Parts B.1 and B.2. The sample in the evaporating dish (beaker) is *not* heated to total dryness. As a result of this technique error, will the reported value for total solids (TS) be too high, too low, or unaffected? Explain.
7. Parts A and B. Suppose the water sample has a relatively high percent of volatile solid material. How would this have affected the reported mass of:
   a. dissolved solids—too high, too low, or unaffected? Explain.
   b. total solids—too high, too low, or unaffected? Explain.
   c. suspended solids—too high, too low, or unaffected? Explain.
8. Part D.2. When several drops of 0.010 *M* $AgNO_3$ are added to a test sample, a white precipitate forms. What can you conclude from this observation? Explain.

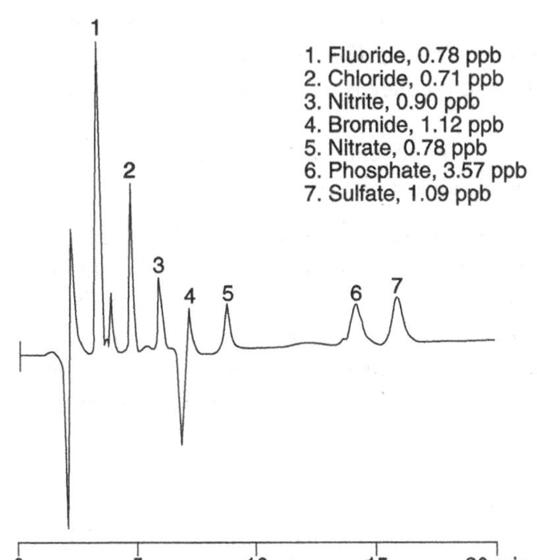

Experiment 4

Paper Chromatography

Trace levels of anions in high-purity water can be determined by chromatography.

OBJECTIVES

- To become familiar with chromatography, a technique for separating the components of a mixture
- To separate a mixture of transition metal cations by paper chromatography

TECHNIQUES

The following techniques are used in the Experimental Procedure:

INTRODUCTION

Most substances found in nature, and many prepared in the laboratory, are impure; that is, they are a part of a mixture. One goal of chemical research is to devise methods to identify and remove impurities from the chemical of interest.

A **mixture** is a physical combination of two or more pure substances wherein each substance retains its own chemical identity. For example, each component in a sodium chloride–water mixture possesses the same chemical properties as in the pure state: Water consists of H_2O molecules, and sodium chloride is sodium ions, Na^+, and chloride ions, Cl^-.

The method chosen for separating a mixture is based on the differences in the chemical and/or physical properties of the components of the mixture. Some common *physical* methods for separating the components of a mixture include:

- **Filtration:** removing a solid substance from a liquid by passing the suspension through a filter (see *Techniques 11B–E* and *Experiment 3* for details).
- **Distillation:** vaporizing a liquid from a solid (or another liquid) and condensing the vapor (see margin photo).
- **Crystallization:** forming a crystalline solid by decreasing its solubility by cooling the solution, evaporating the solvent, or adding a solvent in which the substance is less soluble (see *Experiments 15 and 19*).
- **Extraction:** removing a substance from a solid or liquid mixture by adding a solvent in which the substance is more soluble (see *Experiment 11*).

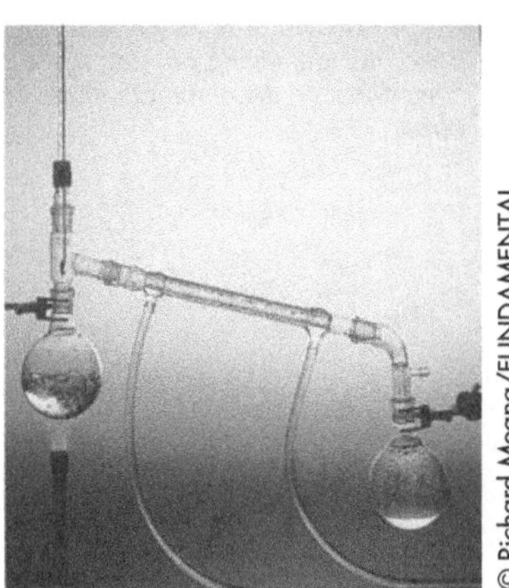
A distillation apparatus

- **Centrifugation:** removing a substance from a mixture using a centrifuge (see *Technique 11F* and *Experiments 37, 38, and 39* for details).
- **Sublimation:** vaporizing a solid and recondensing its vapor (not all solids sublime, however).
- **Chromatography:** separating the components of a mixture on the basis of their differing adsorptive tendencies on a stationary phase.

Mobile phase: the phase (generally liquid) in which the components of the mixture exist

Eluent: the solvent in which the components of the mixture are moved along the stationary phase

Stationary phase: the phase (generally solid) to which the components of the mobile phase are characteristically adsorbed

In the chromatography[1] technique, two phases are required for the separation of the components (or compounds) of a mixture: the mobile phase and the stationary phase. The **mobile phase** consists of the solute components of the mixture and the solvent—the solvent being called the **eluent** or **eluting solution** (generally a mixture of solvents of differing polarities). The **stationary phase** is an adsorbent that has an intermolecular affinity not only for the solvent[2] but also for the individual solute components of the mixture.

As the mobile phase passes over the stationary phase, the chromatogram develops. The solute components of the mobile phase have varying affinities for the stationary phase. The solute components of the mixture having a stronger affinity for the stationary phase move shorter distances, while those with a lesser affinity move greater distances along the stationary phase during the time the chromatogram is being developed. Separation, and subsequent identification, of the solute components of the mixture is thus achieved. The leading edge of the mobile phase in the chromatogram is called the **eluent front.** When the eluent front reaches the edge of the chromatographic paper, the developing of the chromatogram is stopped.

Of the different types of chromatography including, for example, gas–solid chromatography, liquid–solid chromatography, column chromatography, thin-layer chromatography, and ion chromatography, this experiment uses paper chromatography as a separation technique.

In this experiment (Figure 4.1), chromatographic paper (similar to filter paper), a paper that consists of polar cellulose molecules, is the stationary phase. The mobile phase consists of one or more of the transition metal cations, Mn^{2+}, Fe^{3+}, Co^{2+}, Ni^{2+}, and Cu^{2+} (the solute components), dissolved in an acetone–hydrochloric acid eluent.[3] The chromatographic paper is first "spotted" (and marked with a pencil *only*) with the five known solutions, one for *each* of the cations, and then for three unknown solutions, each having a mixture of the cations. The paper is then dried.

Capillary action: action by which the ions have an adhesive attraction (ion-dipole attractive forces) to the fibers of the stationary phase (paper)

Band: the identifying position of the component on the chromatography paper

The spotted chromatographic paper is then placed in contact with the eluent to form the mobile phase. By **capillary action**, the transition metal ions are transported along the paper. Each transition metal has its own (unique) adsorptive affinity for the polar, cellulose chromatographic paper; some are more strongly adsorbed than others. Also, each ion has its own solubility in the eluting solution. As a result of these two factors, some transition metal ions move further along the chromatographic paper than others to form **bands** at some distance from the origin, therefore indicating that the ions are separating.[4]

---

[1] *Chromatography* means "the graphing of colors"; historically, this technique was used to separate the various colored compounds from naturally occurring colored substances (e.g., dyes, plant pigments).

[2] This attraction is due to the similar type of intermolecular forces between the adsorbent (the stationary phase) and the solute components of the mobile phase (e.g., dipole–dipole, ion–dipole, dipole–hydrogen bonding).

[3] The eluting solution (acetone–hydrochloric acid) actually converts the transition metal ions to their chloro ions, and it is in this form that they are transported and separated along the paper.

[4] Consider, for example, a group of students moving through a cafeteria food line. The stationary phase is the food line; the mobile phase consists of students. You are well aware that some students go through the food line quickly because they are less attracted to the various food items. Others take forever to pass through the food line because they must stop to consider each item; they thus have a longer residence time in the food line.

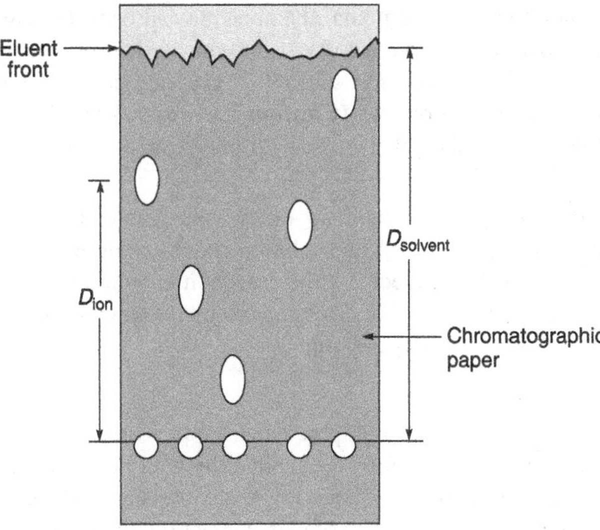

Figure 4.1 Determination of the R_f value for a transition metal ion

For a given eluting solution, stationary phase, temperature, and so on, each ion is characterized by its own R_f (ratio of fronts) factor:

$$R_{f,\,ion} = \frac{\text{distance from origin to final position of ion}}{\text{distance from origin to eluent front}} = \frac{D_{ion}}{D_{solvent}} \tag{4.1}$$

The origin of the **chromatogram** is defined as the point where the ion is "spotted" on the paper. The eluent front is defined as the most advanced point of movement of the mobile phase along the paper from the origin (Figure 4.1).

Chromatogram: the "picture" of the separated components on the chromatography paper

The next step is to identify the exact position and the specific ion for each of these bands. Some transition metal ions are already colored; for others, a characteristic reagent for each metal ion is used to enhance the metal ion's appearance and location on the stationary phase.

In this experiment, you will prepare a chromatogram for each transition metal ion, locate its characteristic band, and determine its R_f value. A chromatogram of a test solution(s) will also be analyzed to identify the transition metal ions present in a solution mixture.

EXPERIMENTAL PROCEDURE

Procedure Overview: Chromatographic paper and an eluent are used to separate an aqueous mixture of transition metal cations. An enhancement reagent is used to intensify the appearance of the metal cation band on the paper.

Obtain about 2 mL of three unknown cation mixtures from your instructor in carefully marked 75-mm test tubes. Record the number of each unknown on the second page of the ***Report Sheet***.

A. Preparation of Chromatography Apparatus

1. **Developing chamber.** Obtain a 600-mL beaker and enough plastic wrap (e.g., Saran Wrap) for a cover (Figure 4.2, page 78). In the fume hood, prepare 10 mL of an eluting solution that consists of 9 mL of acetone and 1 mL of 6 *M* HCl. (**Caution:** *Acetone is flammable; extinguish all flames; HCl is corrosive.*)

   Pour this eluent into the middle of the beaker using a stirring rod; be careful not to wet the sides of the beaker. The depth of the eluent in the beaker should be 0.75–1.25 cm but *less than* 1.5 cm. Cover the beaker with the plastic wrap for about 10 minutes.[5] Hereafter, this apparatus is called the **developing chamber.**

   Figure 4.3, page 78 shows a commercial developing chamber.

[5]The "atmosphere" in the beaker should become saturated with the vapor of the acetone–HCl eluent.

Figure 4.2 Use plastic wrap to cover the developing chamber.

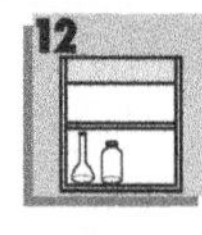

2. **Ammonia chamber.** The ammonia chamber may already be assembled in the hood. *Ask your instructor.* Obtain a dry, 1,000-mL beaker and place it in the *fume hood.* Pour 5 mL of *conc* NH_3 into a 30-mL beaker and position it at the center of the 1,000-mL beaker (Figure 4.4). (**Caution:** *Do not inhale the ammonia fumes.*) Cover the top of the 1,000-mL beaker with plastic wrap. This apparatus will be used in Part C.3.
3. **Capillary tube.** Obtain eight capillary tubes from the stockroom. When a glass capillary tube touches a solution, the solution should be drawn into the tip. When the tip is then touched to a piece of filter paper, it should deliver a microdrop of solution. Try "spotting" a piece of filter paper with a known solution or water until the diameter of the drop is only 2–4 mm.
4. **Stationary phase.**
   a. Obtain one piece of chromatographic paper (approximately 10 × 20 cm). Handle the paper only along its top 20-cm edge (by your designation) and lay it flat on a clean piece of paper, *not* directly on the lab bench. The chromatographic paper should remain dry and free of skin contact (avoiding skin oil) at all times.
   b. Draw a *pencil* line 1.5 cm from the *bottom* 20-cm edge of the paper (Figure 4.5). Starting 2 cm from the 10-cm edge and along the 1.5-cm line, make eight X's with a 2-cm separation. Use a pencil to label each X *below* the 1.5-cm line with the five cations being investigated and unknowns U1, U2, and U3.

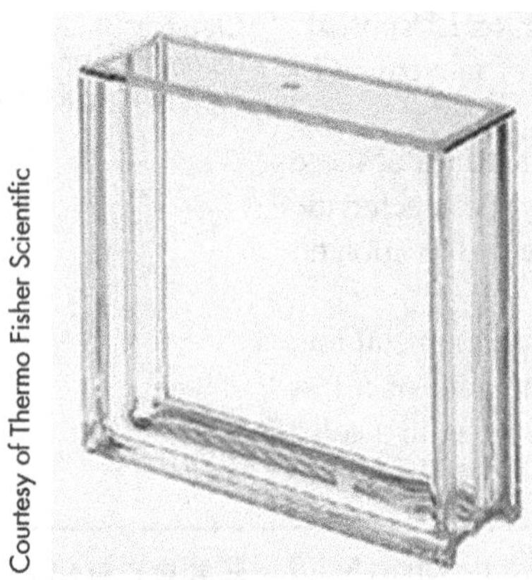

Figure 4.3 A commercial developing chamber

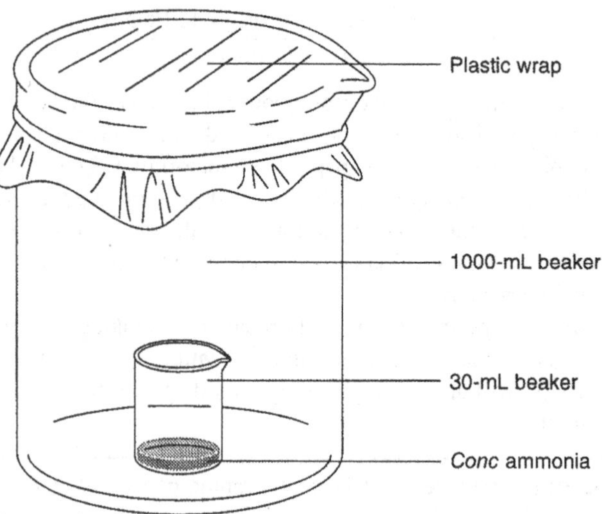

Figure 4.4 Apparatus for the ammonia chamber

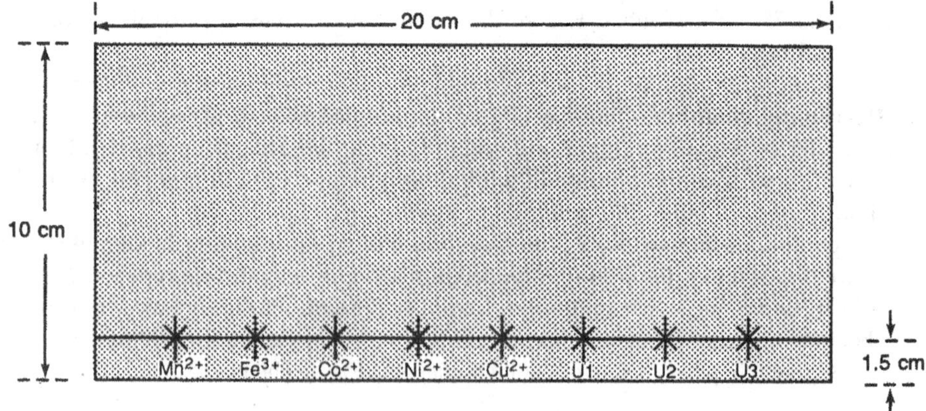

Figure 4.5 Labeling the stationary phase (the chromatographic paper) for the chromatogram

B. Preparation of the Chromatogram

1. **Spot the stationary phase with the knowns and unknown(s).** Using the capillary tubes (remember you'll need *eight* of them, one for each solution) "spot" the chromatographic paper at the marked X's with the five known solutions containing the cations and the three unknown solutions. The microdrop should be 2–4 mm in diameter. Allow the spots to dry. A heat lamp or hair dryer may be used to hasten the drying—do *not* touch the paper along this bottom edge.

   Repeat the spotting and drying procedure two more times in order to increase the amount of metal ion at the spot on the chromatographic paper. Be sure to dry the sample between applications. Dry the paper with **caution:** *The heat lamp or hair dryer is hot!*

2. **Prepare the stationary phase for elution.** Form the chromatographic paper (Figure 4.5) into a cylinder and, near the top, attach the ends with tape, a staple, or small paper clip. Do *not* allow the two ends of the paper to touch (Figure 4.6). Be sure the spots are dry and will *not* come into direct contact with the eluting solution in the developing chamber!

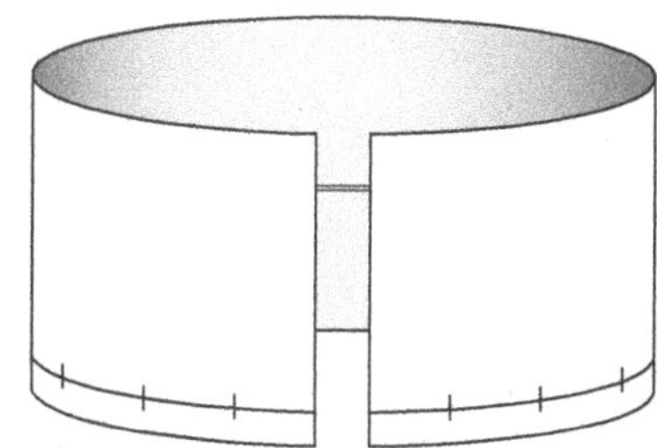

Figure 4.6 Formation of the stationary phase for placement in the developing chamber

3. **Develop the chromatogram.** Place the paper cylinder into the developing chamber (Part A.1, Figure 4.2). The entire "bottom" of the cylindrical chromatographic paper must sit on the bottom of the developing chamber. Do *not* allow the paper to touch the wall. Make certain that the eluent is *below* the 1.5-cm line. *Replace the plastic wrap.* Do not disturb the developing chamber once the paper has been placed inside.

   When the eluent front has moved to within 1.5 cm of the top of the chromatographic paper, remove the plastic wrap. Measure and record the D_{eluent} on the ***Report Sheet***.

C. Analysis of the Chromatogram

1. **Detection of bands.** Remove the paper from the developing chamber and *quickly* mark (with a pencil) the position of the *eluent front*.[6] Allow the chromatogram to air-dry or gently dry with a heat gun (Figure 4.7) set at a low temperature.

   While the chromatogram is drying, cover the developing chamber with the plastic wrap. Analyze the paper and circle (with a pencil) any colored bands, those from the solutions containing the known cations and those from the unknown solutions.[7] Record the color for each metal ion on the ***Report Sheet***.

2. **Enhancement of the chromatogram.** To enhance the appearance and locations of the bands, move the chromatogram to the fume hood. Position the paper in the ammonia chamber (Part A.2, Figure 4.4) and cover the 1,000-mL beaker with the plastic wrap.

   After the deep blue color of Cu^{2+} is evident, remove the chromatogram and circle any new transition metal ion bands that appear. Table 4.1 identifies the colors of other cations in the presence of ammonia. Mark the *center* of each band with a pencil. Allow the chromatogram to dry.

   Record the color of each metal ion in the ammonia chamber.

Courtesy of Thermo Fisher Scientific

Figure 4.7 A low temperature heat gun can accelerate the drying.

Table 4.1 Spot Solutions That Enhance the Band Positions of the Various Cations

	Cation				
	Mn^{2+}	Fe^{3+}	Co^{2+}	Ni^{2+}	Cu^{2+}
NH_3 test	Tan	Red-brown	Pink (brown)	Light blue	Blue
Spot solution	0.1 *M* $NaBiO_3$ (acidic) (purple)	0.2 *M* KSCN (blood red)	*Sat'd* KSCN in acetone (blue-green)	0.1 *M* NaHDMG (brick-red)	0.2 *M* $K_4[Fe(CN)_6]$ (red)

[6] Do this quickly because the eluent evaporates.

[7] For the unknown solutions, there will most likely be more than one band.

3. **Band enhancement.** (Optional, seek advice from your instructor.) The "exact" band positions for the known cations and those of the mixture may be better defined using a second "spot solution."

   As necessary, use a capillary tube to spot the center of each band (from the known and unknown test solutions) with the corresponding spot solution identified in Table 4.1. This technique more vividly locates the position of the band. Remember, the unknown test solution(s) may have more than one cation band.

4. **Analysis of your chromatogram.** Where is the center of each band? Mark the center of each band with a pencil.

   Measure and record the distance between the origin and the spot for each ion, D_{ion}. Calculate and record the R_f values for each transition metal ion.

5. **Composition of the unknown(s).** Look closely at the bands for your unknown(s). What is the R_f value for each band in each unknown? Which ion(s) is(are) present in your unknown(s)? Record your conclusions on the ***Report Sheet***. Submit your chromatogram to your instructor for approval.

Disposal: Dispose of the eluting solution in the Waste Organics container. Allow the *conc* NH_3 in the ammonia chamber to evaporate in the hood.

The Next Step

Ink is a mixture of dyes. (1) Research the use of a chromatographic technique for the separation of the dyes in ink. (2) Design a project to separate the components of leaves from different trees, shrubs, or grasses. (3) Design a project for the separation of amino acids in fruit juices.

ATTACH OR SKETCH THE CHROMATOGRAM THAT WAS DEVELOPED IN THE EXPERIMENT

Experiment 4 *Prelaboratory Assignment*

Paper Chromatography

Date ________ Lab Sec. ______ Name ______________________________ Desk No. ________

1. **a.** What is the function of the mobile phase for developing a chromatogram?

   b. What is the chemical composition of the mobile phase in this experiment?

2. **a.** What is the function of the stationary phase for developing a chromatogram?

   b. What is the stationary phase in this experiment?

3. **a.** What is the function of the eluent for developing a chromatogram?

   b. What is the eluent (eluting solution) in this experiment?

4. Experimental Procedure, Part A. Distinguish between the functions of the developing chamber and the ammonia chamber.

5. Experimental Procedure, Parts A.4 and B.1. Paraphrase what must be done to prepare the stationary phase for the developing chamber in this experiment, Part B.3?

6. A student developed a chromatogram and found that the eluent front traveled 94 mm and the Zn^{2+} cation traveled 24 mm. In the development of a chromatogram of a mixture of cations, the eluent front traveled 87 mm. If Zn^{2+} is a cation of the unknown mixture, where will its band appear in the chromatogram?

7. The chromatogram for the separation of amino acids using a butanoic acid/acetic eluent is sketched at right.

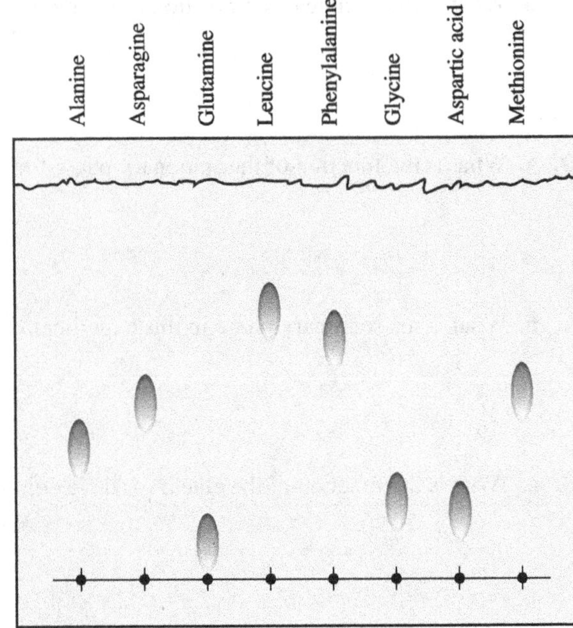

Use a ruler to determine $D_{\text{amino acid}}$ and then calculate R_f for each amino acid.

$D_{\text{solvent, eluent}}$ = ________________

Amino Acid	$D_{\text{amino acid}}$	R_f
Alanine	________	________
Asparagine	________	________
Glutamine	________	________
Leucine	________	________
Phenylalanine	________	________
Glycine	________	________
Aspartic acid	________	________
Methionine	________	________

Experiment 4 *Report Sheet*

Paper Chromatography

Date ________ Lab Sec. ______ Name ______________________________ Desk No. ________

C.4. Analysis of the Chromatogram for Individual Ions

Distance of eluent front from the origin, D_{eluent}: __________ mm

	Color (original)	**Color (with NH_3)**	**Color (with spot solution)**	**Distance (mm) Traveled, D_{ion}**	R_f
Mn^{2+}					
Fe^{3+}					
Co^{2+}					
Ni^{2+}					
Cu^{2+}					

Instructor's approval of chromatogram ______________________________

Show your calculations for R_f.

C.5. Analysis of the Chromatogram of Unknown Mixtures

Unknown number(s) U1=________ U2=________ U3=________

	Band 1		*Band 2*		*Band 3*		*Band 4*	
Unknown	**Distance (mm) Traveled, D_{ion}**	**R_f**	**Distance (mm) Traveled, D_{ion}**	**R_f**	**Distance (mm) Traveled, D_{ion}**	**R_f**	**Distance (mm) Traveled, D_{ion}**	**R_f**
U1								
U2								
U3								

Show your calculations for R_f.

Cations present in U1 ________ ________ ________ ________

Cations present in U2 ________ ________ ________ ________

Cations present in U3 ________ ________ ________ ________

Laboratory Questions

Circle the questions that have been assigned.

1. Part A.1 and Part B.3.
   a. Why is it important to keep the developing chamber covered with plastic wrap during the development of the chromatogram?
   b. The developing chamber is *not* covered with plastic wrap during the development of the chromatogram. Will the D_{ion} value for the cation be greater than or less than the actual value as a result of this technique error? Explain.
2. Part A.4. Explain how the appearance of the chromatogram might change if the chromatographic paper were initially wet with water or had come in contact with the skin.
3. Part A.4. Why was a pencil used to mark the chromatogram and not a ballpoint or ink pen?
4. Part B.1. Explain why the cation samples are repeatedly spotted and dried on the chromatographic paper.
5. Part B.3. The eluent is to be below the 1.5-cm line on the chromatographic paper. Describe the expected observation if the eluent were above the 1.5-cm line.
6. Part C.2. Explain why the *center* of the band is used to calculate the R_f value for a cation rather than the leading edge of the band.
7. Suppose two cations have the same R_f value. How might you resolve their presence in a mixture using paper chromatography?

Charles D. Winters/Science Source

Dry Lab 2A

Inorganic Nomenclature I. Oxidation Numbers

Sodium chloride salt crystals are a one-to-one combination of sodium cations and chloride anions. The sodium cation has an oxidation number of +1, and the chloride anion has an oxidation number of −1.

OBJECTIVES

- To become familiar with the oxidation numbers of various elements
- To identify the oxidation numbers of elements in compounds and ions

INTRODUCTION

You have probably noticed that members of virtually all professions have a specialized language. Chemists are no exception. For chemists to communicate internationally, some standardized technical language is required. Historically, common names for many compounds evolved and are still universally understood—for example, water, sugar (sucrose), and ammonia—but with new compounds being synthesized and isolated daily, a "familiar" system is no longer viable. Two newsworthy common names to appear in the literature are *buckminsterfullerene* (also called *bucky ball*) and *sulflower.*[1]

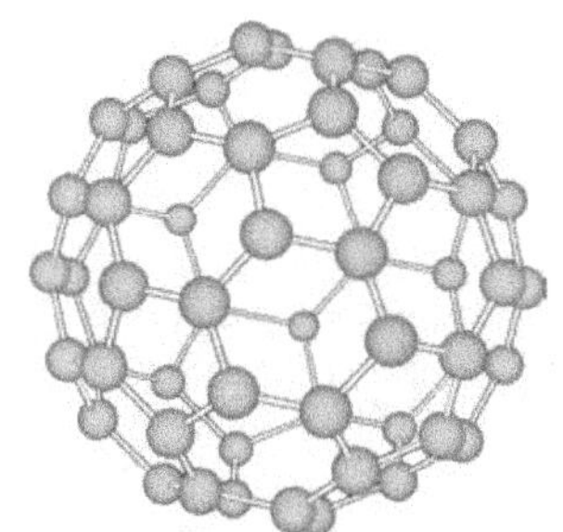

Buckminsterfullerene

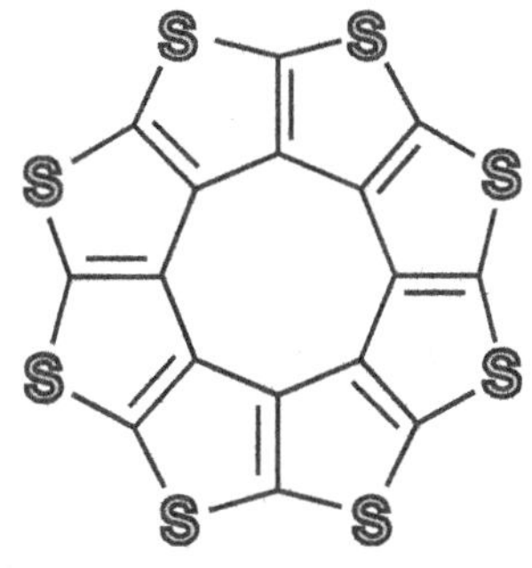

Sulflower

The Chemical Abstracts Service (CAS) of the American Chemical Society currently has more than 71 million inorganic and organic compounds registered in its database[2] with an average of 2.6 new compounds being registered per second over the past 12 months, 7 days a week, 24 hours a day! Not only does each compound have a unique name, according to a systematic method of nomenclature, but also each compound has a unique molecular structure and set of chemical and physical properties. Therefore, it has become absolutely necessary for the scientific community to properly name compounds according to a universally accepted system of nomenclature.

In the three parts of *Dry Lab 2* (A, B, and C), you will learn a few systematic rules established by the International Union of Pure and Applied Chemistry (IUPAC) for naming and writing formulas for inorganic compounds. You are undoubtedly already familiar with some symbols for the elements and the names for several common compounds. For instance, NaCl is sodium chloride. Continued practice and work in writing formulas and naming compounds will make you even more knowledgeable of the chemist's vocabulary.

Oxidation Number

Charges are conventionally written "number and charge" (e.g., 3+), but oxidation numbers are written "charge and number" (e.g., −2)

Elements or groups of chemically bonded elements (called **polyatomic** or **molecular groups**) that have **charge** are called **ions**. If the charge is positive, they are called **cations;** if negative, they are **anions.** Oftentimes elements combine to form a compound in which the elements may not have an actual charge but rather an "apparent" charge called its **oxidation number** (or oxidation state). The oxidation number, the charge an atom would have if the electrons in the bond were assigned to the more electronegative element, may be either positive or negative.

[1]An extensive listing of common chemical names appears in Appendix B.
[2]http://www.cas.org

While monoatomic and polyatomic ions have an actual charge, the charge of an atom or element within a compound is often uncertain. However, with the application of a few rules, the apparent charge or oxidation number of an atom or element in a compound can be easily determined. Thus, the use of oxidation numbers has a greater range of applicability. For example, knowledge of the oxidation numbers for a range of elements allows us to write the correct chemical formula for a large number of compounds. It is *not* necessary to simply memorize disconnected chemical formulas.

The following "rules" will only use the term *oxidation number* when considering the common charge *or* "apparent" charge for an element. Note in rule 6 that polyatomic ions have an actual charge (not an oxidation number).

1. Any element in the free state (not combined with another element) has an oxidation number of zero, regardless of the complexity of the molecule in which it occurs. Each atom in Ne, O_2, P_4 S_8, and C_{60} has an oxidation number of 0.

2. Monoatomic ions have an oxidation number equal to the charge of the ion. The ions Ca^{2+}, Fe^{3+}, and Cl^- have oxidation numbers of +2, +3, and –1, respectively.

3. Oxygen in compounds has an assigned oxidation number of –2 (except for a –1 in peroxides; e.g., H_2O_2, and +2 in OF_2). The oxidation number of oxygen is –2 in FeO, Fe_2O_3, $KMnO_4$, and KIO_3.

4. Hydrogen in compounds has an oxidation number of +1 (except for –1 in metal hydrides; e.g., NaH). Its oxidation number is +1 in HCl, $NaHCO_3$, and NH_3.

5. Some elements exhibit only one common oxidation number in certain types of compounds:

a. Group 1A elements always have an oxidation number of +1 in compounds.

b. Group 2A elements always have an oxidation number of +2 in compounds.

c. Boron and aluminum always possess an oxidation number of +3 in compounds.

Binary compounds: compounds consisting of only two elements (see Dry Lab 2B)

d. In **binary compounds** *with metals,* the nonmetallic elements of Group 6A generally exhibit an oxidation number of –2.

e. In binary compounds *with metals,* the elements of Group 7A have an oxidation number of –1.

Polyatomic ions are also called molecular ions (see Dry Lab 2C)

6. **Polyatomic ions** have a charge equal to the *sum* of the oxidation numbers of the elements of the polyatomic group. See Example D2A.2. The polyatomic ions SO_4^{2-}, NO_3^-, and PO_4^{3-} have charges of 2–, 1–, and 3–, respectively.

7. In assigning oxidation numbers to elements in a compound, the element closest to fluorine (the most electronegative element) in the periodic table is always assigned the negative oxidation number. In the compound, P_4O_{10}, oxygen has the negative oxidation number of –2.

8. **a.** For compounds, the sum of oxidation numbers of all atoms in the compound must equal zero.

Example D2A.1 For Na_2S, the sum of the oxidation numbers equals zero.

2 Na atoms, +1 for each (rule 5a) = +2

1 S atom, –2 for each (rule 5d) = –2

Sum of oxidation numbers (+2) + (–2) = 0

b. For polyatomic ions, the sum of the oxidation numbers of the elements must equal the charge of the ion.

Example D2A.2 For CO_3^{2-} the sum of the oxidation numbers of the elements equals a charge of 2–.

3 O atoms, –2 for each (rule 3) = –6

1 C atom which must be +4 = +4

so that (–6) + (+4) = 2–, the charge of the CO_3^{2-} ion.

9. Some chemical elements show more than one oxidation number, depending on the compound. The preceding rules may be used to determine their values. Consider the compounds $FeCl_2$ and $FeCl_3$. Since the chlorine atom has an oxidation number of –1 when combined with a metal (rule 5e), the oxidation numbers of iron are +2 in $FeCl_2$ and +3 in $FeCl_3$.

An extensive listing of oxidation numbers and charges for monoatomic ions and polyatomic ions are presented in *Dry Lab 2C*, Table D2C.1.

Dry Lab Procedure

Procedure Overview: The oxidation number of an element in a selection of compounds and ions is determined by application of the rules in the Introduction.

Your instructor will indicate the questions you are to complete. Answer them on a separate piece of paper. Be sure to indicate the date, your lab section, and your desk number on your ***Report Sheet***.

1. Indicate the oxidation number of carbon and sulfur in the following compounds.

a. CO	**d.** $Na_2C_2O_4$	**g.** SO_2	**j.** Na_2SO_3	**m.** SCl_2
b. CO_2	**e.** CH_4	**h.** SO_3	**k.** $Na_2S_2O_3$	**n.** Na_2S
c. Na_2CO_3	**f.** H_2CO	**i.** Na_2SO_4	**l.** $Na_2S_4O_6$	**o.** $SOCl_2$

2. Indicate the oxidation number of phosphorus, iodine, nitrogen, tellurium, and silicon in the following polyatomic ions. Remember that the sum of the oxidation numbers for a polyatomic ion must equal the charge of the ion.

a. PO_4^{3-}	**d.** $P_3O_{10}^{5-}$	**g.** IO^-	**j.** NO_2^-	**m.** $N_2O_2^{2-}$
b. PO_3^{3-}	**e.** IO_3^-	**h.** NH_4^+	**k.** NO^+	**n.** TeO_4^{2-}
c. HPO_4^{2-}	**f.** IO_2^-	**i.** NO_3^-	**l.** NO_2^+	**o.** SiO_3^{2-}

3. Indicate the oxidation number of the metallic element(s) in the following compounds. None of the compounds listed are peroxides.

a. Fe_2O_3	**g.** CrO_3	**m.** MnO_2
b. FeO	**h.** K_2CrO_4	**n.** PbO_2
c. CoS	**i.** $K_2Cr_2O_7$	**o.** Pb_3O_4
d. $CoSO_4$	**j.** $KCrO_2$	**p.** ZrI_4
e. K_3CoCl_6	**k.** $KMnO_4$	**q.** U_3O_8
f. $CrCl_3$	**l.** Mn_2O_7	**r.** UO_2Cl_2

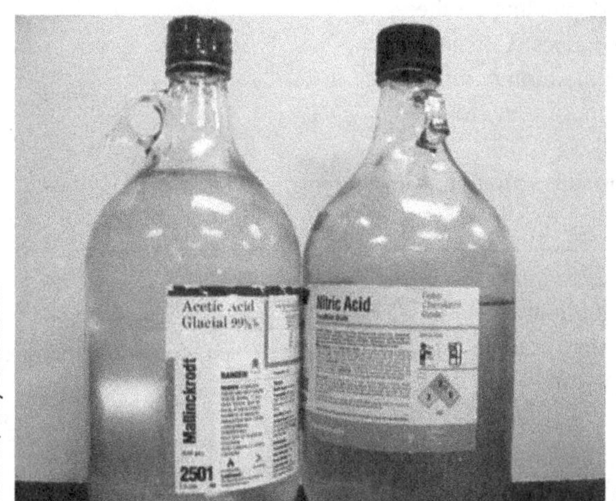

Common ternary acids (or oxoacids) in the laboratory are acetic acid and nitric acid.

Jo A. Beran/Trey Hernandez

Dry Lab 2C

Inorganic Nomenclature III. Ternary Compounds

OBJECTIVES

- To name and write formulas for salts and acids containing polyatomic anions
- To name and write formulas for acid salts

INTRODUCTION

In *Dry Lab 2B*, the naming and the writing of formulas for binary compounds, the simplest of compounds, were introduced.

Ternary compounds are generally considered as having a polyatomic anion containing oxygen. Compounds such as $KMnO_4$, $BaSO_4$, $KClO_3$, and HNO_3 are ternary compounds that have the polyatomic anions MnO_4^-, SO_4^{2-}, ClO_3^-, and NO_3^-, respectively. Ternary compounds can be categorized as salts and acids.

Metal Cation and a Polyatomic Anion Containing Oxygen—A Ternary Salt

Many polyatomic anions consist of one element (usually a nonmetal) and oxygen; the entire grouping of atoms carries a negative charge. The anion is named by using the root name of the element (not the oxygen) with the suffix *-ate.* As examples, SO_4^{2-} is the sul*fate* ion and NO_3^- is the nitr*ate* ion.

If *only two* polyatomic anions form from an element and oxygen, the polyatomic anion having the element with the higher oxidation number uses the suffix *-ate;* the polyatomic anion having the element with the lower oxidation number uses the suffix *-ite.* Examples include the following:

sulfate ion

nitrate ion

phosphate ion

Ion	Oxidation Number	Name	Ion	Oxidation Number	Name
SO_4^{2-}	S is +6	sulf*ate*	SO_3^{2-}	S is +4	sulf*ite*
NO_3^-	N is +5	nitr*ate*	NO_2^-	N is +3	nitr*ite*
PO_4^{3-}	P is +5	phosph*ate*	PO_3^{3-}	P is +3	phosph*ite*

The formulas and names of common polyatomic anions are listed in Table D2C.1.

Salts that have a polyatomic anion are named in the same manner as the binary salts: The metal cation (along with the Stock system or *-ic, -ous* distinction) is named first followed by the polyatomic anion. Some examples follow:

Salt	*Name*
Na_2SO_4	sodium sulfate
Na_2SO_3	sodium sulfite
$Fe(NO_3)_3$	iron(III) or ferric nitrate
$FeSO_4$	iron(II) or ferrous sulfate

Table D2C.1 Names and Oxidation Numbers and Charges of Common Monoatomic and Polyatomic Ions

Ion	Name	Ion	Name
A. Metallic and Polyatomic Cations			
Oxidation Number of +1; Charges of 1+			
NH_4^+	ammonium	Hg_2^{2+}	mercury(I), mercurous
Cu^+	copper(I), cuprous	K^+	potassium
H^+	hydrogen	Ag^+	silver (I)
Li^+	lithium	Na^+	sodium
Oxidation Number of +2; Charges of 2+			
Ba^{2+}	barium	Mn^{2+}	manganese(II), manganous
Cd^{2+}	cadmium	Hg^{2+}	mercury(II), mercuric
Ca^{2+}	calcium	Ni^{2+}	nickel(II)
Cr^{2+}	chromium(II), chromous	Sr^{2+}	strontium
Co^{2+}	cobalt(II), cobaltous	Sn^{2+}	tin(II), stannous
Cu^{2+}	copper(II), cupric	UO_2^{2+}	uranyl
Fe^{2+}	iron(II), ferrous	VO^{2+}	vanadyl
Pb^{2+}	lead(II), plumbous	Zn^{2+}	zinc
Mg^{2+}	magnesium		
Oxidation Number of +3; Charges of 3+			
Al^{3+}	aluminum	Co^{3+}	cobalt(III), cobaltic
As^{3+}	arsenic(III)	Fe^{3+}	iron(III), ferric
Cr^{3+}	chromium(III), chromic	Mn^{3+}	manganese(III), manganic
Oxidation Number of +4; Charges of 4+			
Pb^{4+}	lead(IV), plumbic	Sn^{4+}	tin(IV), stannic
Oxidation Number of +5; Charges of 5+			
V^{5+}	vanadium(V)	As^{5+}	arsenic(V)
B. Nonmetallic and Polyatomic Anions			
Oxidation Number of −1; Charges of 1−			
$CH_3CO_2^-$	acetate *or*	H^-	hydride
$C_2H_3O_2^-$	acetate	ClO^-	hypochlorite
Br^-	bromide	I^-	iodide
ClO_3^-	chlorate	NO_3^-	nitrate
Cl^-	chloride	NO_2^-	nitrite
ClO_2^-	chlorite	ClO_4^-	perchlorate
CN^-	cyanide	IO_4^-	periodate
F^-	fluoride	MnO_4^-	permanganate
OH^-	hydroxide		
Oxidation Number of −2; Charges of 2−			
CO_3^{2-}	carbonate	O_2^{2-}	peroxide
CrO_4^{2-}	chromate	SiO_3^{2-}	silicate
$Cr_2O_7^{2-}$	dichromate	SO_4^{2-}	sulfate
MnO_4^{2-}	manganate	S^{2-}	sulfide
O^{2-}	oxide	SO_3^{2-}	sulfite
$C_2O_4^{2-}$	oxalate	$S_2O_3^{2-}$	thiosulfate
Oxidation Number of −3; Charges of 3−			
N^{3-}	nitride	BO_3^{3-}	borate
PO_4^{3-}	phosphate	AsO_3^{3-}	arsenite
PO_3^{3-}	phosphite	AsO_4^{3-}	arsenate
P^{3-}	phosphide		

If *more than two* polyatomic anions are formed from a given element and oxygen, the prefixes *per-* and *hypo-* are added to distinguish the additional ions. This appears most often among the polyatomic anions with a halogen as the distinguishing element. The prefixes *per-* and *hypo-* are often used to identify the extremes (the high and low) in oxidation numbers of the element in the anion. Table D2C.2, page 100, summarizes the nomenclature for these and other polyatomic anions.

For example, ClO_4^- is *per*chlor*ate* because the oxidation number of Cl is +7 (the highest oxidation number of the four polyatomic anions of chlorine), whereas ClO^- is *hypo*chlor*ite* because the oxidation number of Cl is +1. Therefore, $NaClO_4$ is sodium perchlorate and NaClO is sodium hypochlorite. The name of $Co(ClO_3)_2$ is cobalt(II) chlorate because the chlorate ion is ClO_3^- (see Table D2C.1) and the oxidation number

Table D2C.2 Nomenclature of Polyatomic Anions and Ternary Acids

Name of Polyatomic Anion	Acid	4A	5A	6A	7A
		Elements of Group Number			
			Oxidation Number		
per___ate	per___ic acid	—	—	—	+7
___ate	___ic acid	+4	+5	+6	+5
___ite	___ous acid	—	+3	+4	+3
hypo___ite	hypo___ous acid	—	+1	+2	+1

of Cl is +5 (see Table D2C.2). The cobalt is Co^{2+} because two chlorate, ClO_3^-, ions are required for the neutral salt.

Ternary Acids or Oxoacids

The ternary acids (also referred to as **oxoacids**) are compounds of hydrogen and a polyatomic anion. In contrast to the binary acids, the naming of the ternary acids does not include any mention of hydrogen. The ternary acids are named by using the root of the element in the polyatomic anion and adding a suffix; if the polyatomic anion ends in *-ate,* the ternary acid is named an *-ic acid.* If the polyatomic anion ends in *-ite,* the ternary acid is named an *-ous acid.* To understand by example, the following are representative names for ternary acids.

sulfuric acid

perchloric aci

Ion	Name of Ion	Acid	Name of Acid
SO_4^{2-}	sulf*ate* ion	H_2SO_4	sulfur*ic acid*
SO_3^{2-}	sulf*ite* ion	H_2SO_3	sulfur*ous acid*
CO_3^{2-}	carbon*ate* ion	H_2CO_3	carbon*ic acid*
NO_3^-	nitr*ate* ion	HNO_3	nitr*ic acid*
ClO_4^-	perchlor*ate* ion	$HClO_4$	perchlor*ic acid*
IO^-	hypoiod*ite* ion	HIO	hypoiod*ous acid*

Acid Salts

Sodium hydrogen sulphate is also called sodium bisulfate and sodium acid sulphate. $NaHSO_4$ is commonly used to adjust the pH of home swimming pools.

lissart/iStockphoto

Acid salts are salts in which a metal cation replaces *fewer than* all of the hydrogens of an acid having more than one hydrogen (a polyprotic acid). The remaining presence of the hydrogen in the compound is indicated by inserting its name into that of the salt.

Salt	Name
$NaHSO_4$	sodium *hydrogen* sulfate (one Na^+ ion replaces one H^+ ion in H_2SO_4)
$CaHPO_4$	calcium *hydrogen* phosphate (one Ca^{2+} ion replaces two H^+ ions in H_3PO_4)
NaH_2PO_4	sodium *dihydrogen* phosphate (one Na^+ ion replaces one H^+ ion in H_3PO_4)
$NaHCO_3$	sodium *hydrogen* carbonate (one Na^+ ion replaces one H^+ ion in H_2CO_3)
NaHS	sodium *hydrogen* sulfide (one Na^+ ion replaces one H^+ ion in H_2S)

An older system of naming acid salts substitutes the prefix *bi* for a *single* hydrogen before naming the polyatomic anion. For example, $NaHCO_3$ is sodium *bi*carbonate, $NaHSO_4$ is sodium *bi*sulfate, and NaHS is sodium *bi*sulfide.

The Next Step

The naming of organic compounds also follows a set of guidelines. IUPAC regularly meets to ensure that new compounds have a systematic name. Review the nomenclature of the simple organic compounds, such as the alcohols, ethers, acids, and amines.

Dry Lab Procedure

Procedure Overview: Given the formula of the compounds, the proper names for a large number of ternary compounds are to be written. Given the name of ternary compounds, the formulas for a large number of compounds are to be written.

Your instructor will assign the exercises you are to complete. Answer them on a separate piece of paper. Be sure to indicate the date, your lab section, and your desk number on your ***Report Sheet***. Use the rules that have been described.

1. Use Table D2C.2 to name the following polyatomic anions.

a. BrO_3^-	d. $N_2O_2^{2-}$	g. IO_2^-	j. TeO_4^{2-}
b. IO_3^-	e. AsO_2^-	h. SO_3^{2-}	k. SeO_4^{2-}
c. PO_2^{3-}	f. BrO_2^-	i. SiO_3^{2-}	l. NO_2^-

2. Name the following salts of the representative elements.

a. Na_2SO_4	e. $Ca_3(PO_3)_2$	i. K_2MnO_4	m. $Li_2S_2O_3$
b. K_3AsO_4	f. Na_2SiO_3	j. $KMnO_4$	n. $Ba(NO_2)_2$
c. Li_2CO_3	g. K_2CrO_4	k. Li_2SO_3	o. $Ba(NO_3)_2$
d. $Ca_3(PO_4)_2$	h. $K_2Cr_2O_7$	l. Li_2SO_4	p. KCH_3CO_2

3. Name the following salts of the transition and post-transition elements using the Stock system.

a. $Fe(OH)_3$	e. $CuCO_3$	i. $MnSO_4$	m. $CrPO_4$
b. $FePO_4{\bullet}6H_2O$	f. $CuSO_4{\bullet}5H_2O$	j. $Mn(CH_3CO_2)_2$	n. $CrSO_4{\bullet}6H_2O$
c. $FeSO_4{\bullet}7H_2O$	g. $Sn(NO_3)_2$	k. $Hg_2(NO_3)_2$	o. $Co_2(CO_3)_3$
d. CuCN	h. $Sn(SO_4)_2$	l. $Hg(NO_3)_2{\bullet}H_2O$	p. $CoSO_4{\bullet}7H_2O$

4. Name the following ternary acids.

a. H_2SO_4	e. $HMnO_4$	i. HNO_2	m. $HClO_4$
b. H_2SO_3	f. H_2CrO_4	j. H_2CO_3	n. $HClO_3$
c. $H_2S_2O_3$	g. H_3BO_3	k. $H_2C_2O_4$	o. $HClO_2$
d. H_3PO_4	h. HNO_3	l. CH_3COOH	p. HClO

5. Name the following acid salts. Use the "older" system wherever possible.

a. $NaHCO_3$	d. NH_4HCO_3	g. $NaHSO_4{\bullet}H_2O$	j. $MgHAsO_4$
b. $Ca(HCO_3)_2$	e. NaHS	h. Li_2HPO_4	k. KH_2AsO_4
c. KHC_2O_4	f. $KHSO_3$	i. LiH_2PO_4	l. $KHCrO_4$

6. Write formulas for the following compounds.

a. potassium permanganate	l. nickel(II) nitrate hexahydrate
b. potassium manganate	m. chromous nitrite
c. calcium carbonate	n. vanadyl nitrate
d. lead(II) carbonate	o. uranyl acetate
e. ferric carbonate	p. barium acetate dihydrate
f. silver thiosulfate	q. sodium silicate
g. sodium sulfite	r. calcium hypochlorite
h. ferrous sulfate heptahydrate	s. potassium chlorate
i. iron(II) oxalate	t. ammonium oxalate
j. sodium chromate	u. sodium borate
k. potassium dichromate	v. cuprous iodate

7. Write formulas for the following acids.

a. sulfuric acid	j. phosphoric acid
b. thiosulfuric acid	k. carbonic acid
c. sulfurous acid	l. bromous acid
d. periodic acid	m. chromic acid
e. iodic acid	n. permanganic acid
f. hypochlorous acid	o. manganic acid
g. nitrous acid	p. boric acid
h. nitric acid	q. oxalic acid
i. phosphorous acid	r. silicic acid

8. Write formulas and name the hodgepodge of compounds resulting from matching all cations with all anions for each set.

Set 1		Set 2		Set 3	
Cations	Anions	Cations	Anions	Cations	Anions
Li^+	Cl^-	Fe^{3+}	PO_4^{3-}	Pb^{2+}	SiO_3^{2-}
Cd^{2+}	SO_4^{2-}	Fe^{2+}	HPO_4^{2-}	NH_4^+	S^{2-}
Na^+	NO_3^-	Al^{3+}	HCO_3^-	$H^+(aq)$*	MnO_4^-
Cu^{2+}	O^{2-}	Zn^{2+}	CN^-	Mn^{3+}	HSO_4^-
V^{5+}	CO_3^{2-}	K^+	$CH_3CO_2^-$ or $C_2H_3O_2^-$	Hg^{2+}	$Cr_2O_7^{2-}$
Mg^{2+}	I^-	VO^{2+}	IO^-	Sr^{2+}	$C_2O_4^{2-}$

*Name as acids

9. Write correct formulas for the following hodgepodge of compounds from *Dry Labs 2A, 2B, and 2C.*

a. vanadium(V) fluoride
b. stannic oxide
c. silicon tetrafluoride
d. mercuric oxide
e. lithium hypochlorite
f. iodine trifluoride
g. ferrous oxalate
h. cuprous oxide
i. copper(I) chloride
j. calcium hydride
k. cadmium iodide
l. barium acetate dihydrate
m. ammonium sulfide
n. vanadium(V) oxide
o. titanium(IV) chloride
p. scandium(III) nitrate
q. nickel(II) acetate hexahydrate
r. mercurous nitrate
s. lead(II) acetate
t. ferric phosphate hexahydrate
u. ferric chromate
v. dinitrogen tetrasulfide
w. chromous acetate
x. calcium nitride
y. ammonium dichromate
z. silver acetate

10. Write the correct formulas for the following matched common name/chemical name compound. See Appendix B.

Common Name	Chemical Name
a. acid of sugar	oxalic acid
b. aqua fortis	nitric acid
c. barium white, fixed white	barium sulfate dihydrate
d. bitter salt, Epsom salts	magnesium sulfate heptahydrate
e. blue vitrol	copper(II) sulfate pentahydrate
f. calomel	mercurous chloride
g. caustic potash	potassium hydroxide
h. Chile saltpeter, sodium nitre	sodium nitrate
i. chrome yellow	lead(IV) chromate
j. Indian red, jeweler's rouge	ferric oxide
k. lime	calcium oxide
l. oil of vitrol	sulfuric acid
m. talc or talcum	magnesium silicate
n. Glauber's salt	sodium sulfate

Scimat/Science Source

Experiment 8

Limiting Reactant

Calcium oxalate crystals contribute to the formation of kidney stones.

OBJECTIVES

- To determine the limiting reactant in a mixture of two soluble salts
- To determine the **percent composition** of each substance in a salt mixture

TECHNIQUES

The following techniques are used in the Experimental Procedure:

Percent composition: the mass ratio of a component of a mixture or compound to the total mass of the sample times 100

INTRODUCTION

Two factors affect the yield of products in a chemical reaction: (1) the amounts (moles) of starting materials (reactants) and (2) the **percent yield** of the reaction. Many experimental conditions, for example, temperature and pressure, can be adjusted to increase the yield of a desired product in a chemical reaction, but because chemicals react according to fixed mole ratios (**stoichiometrically**), only a limited amount of product can form from measured amounts of starting materials. The reactant determining the amount of product generated in a chemical reaction is called the **limiting reactant** in the chemical system.

Percent yield:

$$\left(\frac{\text{actual yield}}{\text{theoretical yield}}\right) \times 100$$

Stoichiometrically: by a study of a chemical reaction using a balanced equation

To better understand the concept of the limiting reactant, let us look at the reaction under investigation in this experiment, the reaction of calcium chloride dihydrate, $CaCl_2 \cdot 2H_2O$, and potassium oxalate monohydrate, $K_2C_2O_4 \cdot H_2O$, in an aqueous solution.

$$CaCl_2 \cdot 2H_2O(aq) + K_2C_2O_4 \cdot H_2O(aq) \longrightarrow CaC_2O_4 \cdot H_2O(s) + 2\,KCl(aq) + 2\,H_2O(l) \quad (8.1)$$

Calcium oxalate monohydrate, $CaC_2O_4 \cdot H_2O$, the product, is an insoluble compound, but is found naturally in a number of diverse locations. It is found in plants, such as rhubarb leaves, agave, and (in small amounts) spinach, and is the cause of most kidney stones. In small doses, it causes a severe reaction to the lining of the digestive tract. However, the handling of calcium oxalate in the laboratory is safe, so long as it is not transferred to the mouth.

For the reaction system in this experiment, both the calcium chloride and potassium oxalate are soluble salts, but the calcium oxalate is insoluble. The **ionic equation** for the reaction is

Ionic equation: A chemical equation that presents ionic compounds in the form in which they exist in aqueous solution. See Experiment 6.

$$Ca^{2+}(aq) + 2\,Cl^-(aq) + 2\,K^+(aq) + C_2O_4^{2-}(aq) + 3\,H_2O(l) \longrightarrow CaC_2O_4 \cdot H_2O(s) + 2\,Cl^-(aq) + 2\,K^+(aq) + 2\,H_2O(l) \quad (8.2)$$

Spectator ions: cations or anions that do not participate in any observable or detectable chemical reaction

Net ionic equation: an equation that includes only those ions that participate in the observed chemical reaction, also presented in Experiment 6.

Presenting only the ions that show evidence of a chemical reaction (i.e., the formation of a precipitate) and by removing the **spectator ions** (i.e., no change of ionic form during the reaction), we have the **net ionic equation** for the observed reaction:

$$Ca^{2+}(aq) + C_2O_4^{2-}(aq) + H_2O(l) \longrightarrow CaC_2O_4 \cdot H_2O(s) \qquad (8.3)$$

Calcium oxalate monohydrate is thermally stable below ~90°C but forms the anhydrous salt, CaC_2O_4, at temperatures above 110°C.

Therefore, one mole of Ca^{2+} (from one mole of $CaCl_2 \cdot 2H_2O$, molar mass = 147.02 g/mol) reacts with one mole of $C_2O_4^{2-}$ (from one mole of $K_2C_2O_4 \cdot H_2O$, molar mass = 184.24 g/mol) to produce one mole of $CaC_2O_4 \cdot H_2O$ (molar mass = 146.12 g/mol). If the calcium oxalate is heated to temperatures greater than 110°C for drying, then anhydrous CaC_2O_4 (molar mass = 128.10 g/mol) is the product.

In Part A of this experiment the solid reactant salts $CaCl_2 \cdot 2H_2O$ and $K_2C_2O_4 \cdot H_2O$ form a heterogeneous mixture of unknown composition. The mass of the solid mixture is measured and then added to water—insoluble $CaC_2O_4 \cdot H_2O$ forms. The $CaC_2O_4 \cdot H_2O$ precipitate is collected via gravity filtration and dried, and its mass is measured.

The percent composition of the salt mixture is determined by first testing for the limiting reactant. In Part B, the limiting reactant for the formation of solid calcium oxalate monohydrate is determined from two precipitation tests of the final reaction mixture from Part A: (1) the mixture is tested for an excess of calcium ion with an oxalate reagent—observed formation of a precipitate indicates the presence of an excess of calcium ion (and a limited amount of oxalate ion) in the salt mixture; (2) the mixture is also tested for an excess of oxalate ion with a calcium reagent—observed formation of a precipitate indicates the presence of an excess of oxalate ion (and a limited amount of calcium ion) in the salt mixture.

Calculations

The calculations for the analysis of the salt mixture require some attention. "How do I proceed to determine the percent composition of a salt mixture of $CaCl_2 \cdot 2H_2O$ and $K_2C_2O_4 \cdot H_2O$ by measuring only the mass of the $CaC_2O_4 \cdot H_2O$ precipitate?"

Example: A 0.538-g sample of the salt mixture is added to water and after drying (to less than 90°C) 0.194 g of $CaC_2O_4 \cdot H_2O$ is measured. Tests reveal that $K_2C_2O_4 \cdot H_2O$ is the limiting reactant. What is the percent composition of the salt mixture? Since $K_2C_2O_4 \cdot H_2O$ is the limiting reactant, how many grams of the excess $CaCl_2 \cdot 2H_2O$ were in the salt mixture?

Solution: Since $K_2C_2O_4 \cdot H_2O$ is the limiting reactant, then, according to equation 8.1, the moles of $K_2C_2O_4 \cdot H_2O$ in the salt mixture equals the moles of $CaC_2O_4 \cdot H_2O$ formed. Therefore, the calculated mass of $K_2C_2O_4 \cdot H_2O$ in the original salt mixture is

Data Analysis, A

$$\text{grams } K_2C_2O_4 \cdot H_2O = 0.194 \text{ g } CaC_2O_4 \cdot H_2O \times \frac{1 \text{ mol } CaC_2O_4 \cdot H_2O}{146.12 \text{ g } CaC_2O_4 \cdot H_2O}$$

$$\times \frac{1 \text{ mol } K_2C_2O_4 \cdot H_2O}{1 \text{ mol } CaC_2O_4 \cdot H_2O} \times \frac{184.24\ K_2C_2O_4 \cdot H_2O}{1 \text{ mol } K_2C_2O_4 \cdot H_2O}$$

$$= 0.245 \text{ g } K_2C_2O_4 \cdot H_2O \text{ in the salt mixture.}$$

The percent by mass of $K_2C_2O_4 \cdot H_2O$ in the original salt mixture is

$$\%\ K_2C_2O_4 \cdot H_2O = \frac{0.245 \text{ g } K_2C_2O_4 \cdot H_2O}{0.538 \text{ g sample}} \times 100 = 45.5\%\ K_2C_2O_4 \cdot H_2O$$

The mass of the $CaCl_2 \cdot 2H_2O$ in the salt mixture is the difference between the mass of the sample and the mass of $K_2C_2O_4 \cdot H_2O$ or (0.538 g – 0.245 g =) 0.293 g. The percent by mass of $CaCl_2 \cdot 2H_2O$ in the original salt mixture is

$$\%\ CaCl_2 \cdot 2H_2O = \frac{0.538 \text{ g} - 0.245 \text{ g}}{0.538 \text{ g sample}} \times 100 = 54.5\%\ CaCl_2 \cdot 2H_2O$$

According to equation 8.1, the moles of $CaCl_2 \cdot 2H_2O$ that react equals the moles of $K_2C_2O_4 \cdot H_2O$ (the limiting reactant) that react equals the moles of $CaC_2O_4 \cdot H_2O$ that precipitate. Therefore, the mass of $CaCl_2 \cdot 2H_2O$ (the *excess* reactant) that reacts is

$$\text{mass } CaCl_2 \cdot 2H_2O = 0.194 \text{ g } CaC_2O_4 \cdot H_2O \times \frac{1 \text{ mol } CaC_2O_4 \cdot H_2O}{146.12 \text{ g } CaC_2O_4 \cdot H_2O}$$

$$\times \frac{1 \text{ mol } CaCl_2 \cdot 2H_2O}{1 \text{ mol } CaC_2O_4 \cdot H_2O} \times \frac{147.02 \text{ g } CaCl_2 \cdot 2H_2O}{1 \text{ mol } CaCl_2 \cdot 2H_2O}$$

$$= 0.195 \text{ g } CaCl_2 \cdot 2H_2O \text{ reacted}$$

Since 0.293 g $CaCl_2 \cdot 2H_2O$ were calculated present in the original salt mixture, then the mass of *excess* $CaCl_2 \cdot 2H_2O$ is (0.293 g – 0.195 g =) 0.098 g *xs* $CaCl_2 \cdot 2H_2O$.

Experimental Procedure

Procedure Overview: In Part A, a measured mass of a solid $CaCl_2 \cdot 2H_2O/K_2C_2O_4 \cdot H_2O$ salt mixture of unknown percent composition is added to water. The precipitate that forms is digested, filtered, and dried, and its mass is measured. Observations from tests on the **supernatant** solution in Part B determine which salt in the mixture is the limiting reactant. An analysis of the data provides the determination of the percent composition of the salt mixture.

Supernatant: the clear solution that exists after the precipitate has settled

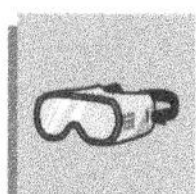

Two trials are recommended for this experiment. To hasten the analyses, measure the mass of duplicate unknown solid salt mixtures in *clean* 150- or 250-mL beakers and simultaneously follow the procedure for each. Label the beakers accordingly for Trial 1 and Trial 2 to avoid the intermixing of samples and solutions.

Obtain about 2–3 g of an unknown $CaCl_2 \cdot 2H_2O/K_2C_2O_4 \cdot H_2O$ salt mixture.

Be aware of the number of significant figures when recording data.

A. Precipitation of $CaC_2O_4 \cdot H_2O$ from the Salt Mixture

Data Analysis, A

1. **Prepare the salt mixture.**
   a. *Mass of salt mixture.* Measure the mass (±0.001 g) of beaker 1 and record on the ***Report Sheet*** for Trial 1. Transfer ~1 g of the salt mixture to the beaker, measure, and record the combined mass. Repeat for Trial 2, beaker 2.
   b. *Adjust pH of deionized water.* Fill a 400-mL beaker with deionized water. Test with pH paper. If the water is acidic, adjust it to be *just* basic with drops of 6 *M* NH_3. If already basic to pH paper, then no addition of NH_3 is necessary.[1]
   c. *Mix deionized water and salt.* Add ~150 mL of the deionized water from Part A.1b to the salt mixture in beaker 1. Stir the mixture with a stirring rod for 2–3 minutes and then allow the precipitate to settle. Leave the stirring rod in the beaker. Repeat for Trial 2.
2. **Digest the precipitate.**[2]
   a. *Heat.* Cover the beaker with a watch glass and warm the solution on a hot plate (Figure 8.1, page 126) to a temperature not to exceed 75°C for ~15 minutes. Periodically stir the solution and, in the meantime, proceed to Part A.3.
   b. *Cool.* After ~15 minutes, remove the heat and allow the precipitate to settle; the solution does *not* need to cool to room temperature.

[1] Calcium oxalate does *not* precipitate in an acidic solution because of the formation of $H_2C_2O_4^-$, an ion that does not precipitate with Ca^{2+}.

[2] Digesting a precipitate in warm water promotes the dissolving of the smaller precipitate particles followed by their re-precipitating onto the existing larger particles. The result is a more efficient filtering process.

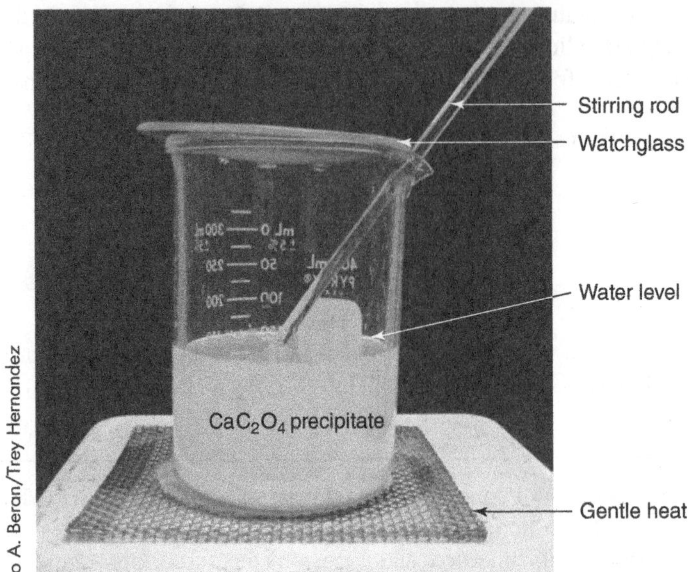

Figure 8.1 Warming and digesting the precipitate

c. *Wash water.* While the precipitate is settling, heat (70–80°C) ~30 mL of deionized water for use as wash water in Part A.5.

3. **Set up a gravity (or vacuum[3]) filtering apparatus.** Place your initials (in pencil) and "Trial 1" on a piece of Whatman No. 42 or Fisherbrand Q2 filter paper,[4] fold, and tear off its corner. Measure and record its mass (±0.001 g). Seal the filter paper into the filter funnel with a small amount of deionized water. Discard the deionized water from the receiving flask. Have your instructor inspect your apparatus before continuing. Return to Part A.2b.

4. **Withdraw and save supernatant.** Once the precipitate has settled and the supernatant has cleared in Part A.2b, use a dropping pipet to withdraw enough supernatant to half-fill two 75-mm test tubes labeled "1" and "2." Save for Part B.

Rubber policeman: a spatula-like rubber tip attached to a stirring rod

5. **Filter the $CaC_2O_4 \cdot H_2O$ precipitate.** While the remaining solution of the salt mixture from Part A.4 is still warm, quantitatively transfer the precipitate to the filter (Figure 8.2). Transfer any precipitate on the wall of the beaker to the filter with the aid of a **rubber policeman**; wash any remaining precipitate onto the filter with three or four 5-mL volumes of warm water (from Part A.2c).

6. **Dry and measure the amount of $CaC_2O_4 \cdot H_2O$ precipitate.** Remove the filter paper and precipitate from the filter funnel. Air-dry the precipitate on the filter paper until the next laboratory period or dry in a <110°C constant temperature drying oven for at least 1 hour or overnight. Determine the combined mass (±0.001 g) of the precipitate and filter paper. Record. Repeat for Trial 2.

7. **Formula of the precipitate.** If the precipitate is air-dried, the precipitate is $CaC_2O_4 \cdot H_2O$; if oven-dried at ≥110°C, the precipitate is the anhydrous CaC_2O_4. Enter the mass of the dried precipitate on the ***Report Sheet***.

[3]A vacuum filtering apparatus (*Technique 11E*) can also be used; the filtering procedure will be more rapid, but more precipitate may pass through the filter paper.
[4]Whatman No. 42 and Fisherbrand Q2 filter papers are both fine-porosity filter papers; a fine-porosity filter paper is used to reduce the amount of precipitate passing through the filter.

Ken Karp

Figure 8.2 Gravity filtration is used to filter finely divided precipitates.

B. Determination of the Limiting Reactant

From the following two tests (Figure 8.3) you can determine the limiting reactant in the original salt mixture. Some cloudiness may appear in both tests, but one will show a definite formation of precipitate.

1. **Clarify the supernatant.** Centrifuge the two collected supernatant samples from Part A.4.
2. **Test for *excess* $C_2O_4^{2-}$.** Add two drops of (test reagent) 0.5 *M* $CaCl_2$ to the supernatant liquid in test tube 1. If a precipitate forms, the $C_2O_4^{2-}$ is *in excess* and Ca^{2+} is the limiting reactant in the original salt mixture.
3. **Test for *excess* Ca^{2+}.** Add two drops of (test reagent) 0.5 *M* $K_2C_2O_4$ to the supernatant liquid in test tube 2. If a precipitate forms, the Ca^{2+} is *in excess* and $C_2O_4^{2-}$ is the limiting reactant in the original salt mixture.

An obvious formation of precipitate should appear in only one of the tests.
Repeat for Trial 2.

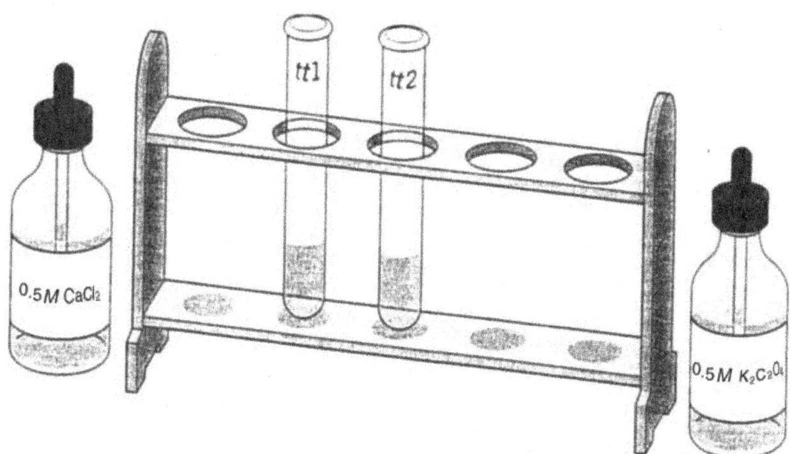

Figure 8.3 Testing for the excess (and the limiting) reactant

Disposal: Dispose of the calcium oxalate, including the filter paper, in the Waste Solids container. Dispose of the waste solutions in the Waste Liquids container.

CLEANUP: Rinse each beaker with small portions of warm water and discard in the Waste Liquids container. Rinse twice with tap water and twice with deionized water and discard in the sink.

The Next Step

All reactions other than decomposition reactions have limiting reactants! From the combustion of fossil fuels to the many integrated chemical processes of biochemical reactions in living organisms, there is one reactant that limits the process. For examples, what is the limiting reactant in the combustion of gasoline in the cylinder of an engine? What is the limiting reactant in the eutrophication of a body of water? What is the limiting reactant in making bread rise? What is the limiting reactant in the precipitation of a salt? Research the limiting reactant concept in upcoming experiments.

Notes and Calculations

Experiment 8 *Prelaboratory Assignment*

Limiting Reactant

Date ________ Lab Sec. ______ Name ________________________________ Desk No. ________

1. The limiting reactant is determined in this experiment.
   a. What are the reactants (and their molar masses) in the experiment?

   b. How is the limiting reactant determined in the experiment?

2. Experimental Procedure, Part A.2. What is the procedure and purpose of "digesting the precipitate"?

3. Two special steps in the Experimental Procedure are incorporated to reduce the loss of the calcium oxalate precipitate. Identify the steps in the procedure and the reason for each step.

4. a. A sample of a $CaCl_2 \cdot 2H_2O/K_2C_2O_4 \cdot H_2O$ solid salt mixture is dissolved in ~150 mL of deionized water previously adjusted to a pH that is basic. The precipitate, after having been filtered, was air-dried and weighed. Data for Trial 1 were obtained as shown. Complete the following table. (See ***Report Sheet.***) Record calculated values with the correct number of significant figures.

A. Precipitation of $CaC_2O_4 \cdot H_2O$ from the Salt Mixture		***Calculation Zone***
3. Mass of salt mixture (*g*)	0.879	***Data Analysis, 1.***
4. Mass of filter paper (*g*)	1.896	
5. Mass of filter paper and $CaC_2O_4 \cdot H_2O$ (*g*)	2.180	
6. Mass of air-dried $CaC_2O_4 \cdot H_2O$ (*g*)		
B. Determination of Limiting Reactant		***Data Analysis, 3.***
1. Limiting reactant in salt mixture	$CaCl_2 \cdot 2H_2O$	
2. Excess reactant in salt mixture		
Data Analysis		
1. Moles of $CaC_2O_4 \cdot H_2O$ precipitated (*mol*) Show calculation.		***Data Analysis, 4.***
2. Moles of limiting reactant in salt mixture (*mol*) See equation 8.1.		
3. Mass of limiting reactant in salt mixture (*g*) Show calculation.		
4. Mass of excess reactant in salt mixture (*g*) Equals mass of salt mixture minus mass of limiting reactant. Show calculation.		***Data Analysis, 5.***
5. Percent limiting reactant in salt mixture (%) Show calculation.		
6. Percent excess reactant in salt mixture (%)		

4. b. For Trials 2 and 3, the percent $CaCl_2 \cdot 2H_2O$ in the mixture was 39.7% and 28.4% respectively.

a. What is the average percent of $CaCl_2 \cdot 2H_2O$ in the sample? **Data Analysis, B.**

b. What are the standard deviation and the relative standard deviation (%RSD) for the percent of $CaCl_2 \cdot 2H_2O$ in the sample? **Data Analysis, C and D.**

Experiment 8 *Report Sheet*

Limiting Reactant

Date __________ Lab Sec. ______ Name ____________________________________ Desk No. _________

A. Precipitation of $CaC_2O_4 \cdot H_2O$ from the Salt Mixture

Unknown number ______________	*Trial 1*	*Trial 2*
1. Mass of beaker (*g*)		
2. Mass of beaker and salt mixture (*g*)		
3. Mass of salt mixture (*g*)		
4. Mass of filter paper (*g*)		
5. Mass of filter paper and product after air-dried or oven-dried (*g*)		
6. Mass of dried product (*g*)		
7. Formula of dried product		

B. Determination of Limiting Reactant

1. Limiting reactant in salt mixture (write complete formula) ______________

2. Excess reactant in salt mixture (write complete formula) ______________

Data Analysis

	Trial 1	*Trial 2*
1. Moles of $CaC_2O_4 \cdot H_2O$ (or CaC_2O_4) precipitated (*mol*)	*	
2. Moles of limiting reactant in salt mixture (*mol*) • formula of limiting hydrate ______________		
3. Mass of limiting reactant in salt mixture (*g*)		
4. Mass of excess reactant in salt mixture (*g*) • formula of excess hydrate ______________		
5. Percent limiting reactant in salt mixture (%)		
6. Percent excess reactant in salt mixture (%)		
7. Mass of excess reactant that reacted (*g*)		
8. Mass of excess reactant, unreacted (*g*)		

*Show calculations for Trial 1 on next page.

Show all calculations fot Trial 1. See **Data Analysis, A**

Laboratory Questions

Circle the questions that have been assigned.

1. Part A.2. If the step for digesting the precipitate were omitted, will the reported "percent limiting reactant" in the salt mixture be too high, too low, or unaffected? Explain.
2. Part A.3. A couple of drops of water were accidentally placed on the properly folded filter paper before its mass was measured. However, in Part A.6, the $CaC_2O_4{\cdot}H_2O$ precipitate and the filter paper were dry. As a result of this sloppy technique, will the mass of the limiting reactant be reported too high, too low, or remain unaffected? Explain.
3. Part A.5. Because of the porosity of the filter paper some of the $CaC_2O_4{\cdot}H_2O$ precipitate passes through the filter paper. Will the reported percent of the limiting reactant in the original salt mixture be reported too high or too low? Explain.
4. Part A.5. Excessive quantities of wash water are added to the $CaC_2O_4{\cdot}H_2O$ precipitate. Will the mass of the $CaC_2O_4{\cdot}H_2O$ be reported too high, too low, or remain unaffected? Explain.
5. Part A.6. The $CaC_2O_4{\cdot}H_2O$ precipitate is not completely air-dried when its mass is determined. Will the reported mass of the limiting reactant in the original salt mixture be reported too high or too low? Explain.
6. Part A.6, 7. The drying oven, although thought (and assumed) to be set at 125°C, had an inside temperature of 84°C. How will this error affect the reported percent by mass of the limiting reactant in the salt mixture . . . too high, too low, or unaffected? Explain.
7. Part A.4 and Part B. In a hurry to complete the experiment, Anna withdrew two volumes of solution from Part A.2 before the precipitate had settled. As a result, what dilemma might she have encountered in Part B? Explain.
8. Part B.2. A reagent bottle on the shelf labeled 0.5 *M* NaCl was used in place of the 0.5 *M* $CaCl_2$. Assuming $C_2O_4^{2-}$ to be in excess, what would be observed as a result of using this wrong reagent in this test? Explain.

Michael Watson

Experiment 9

A Volumetric Analysis

A titrimetric analysis requires the careful addition of titrant.

OBJECTIVES

- To prepare and standardize a sodium hydroxide solution
- To determine the molar concentration of a strong acid

TECHNIQUES

The following techniques are used in the Experimental Procedure:

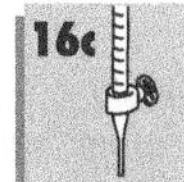

INTRODUCTION

A chemical analysis that is performed primarily with the aid of volumetric glassware (e.g., pipets, burets, volumetric flasks) is called a **volumetric analysis.** For a volumetric analysis procedure, a known quantity or a carefully measured amount of one substance reacts with a to-be-determined amount of another substance with the reaction occurring in aqueous solution. The volumes of all solutions are carefully measured with volumetric glassware.

The known amount of the substance for an analysis is generally measured and available in two ways:

1. As a **primary standard**—An accurate mass (and thus, moles) of a solid substance is measured on a balance, dissolved in water, and then reacted with the substance being analyzed.
2. As a **standard solution**—A measured number of moles of substance is present in a measured volume of solution, generally expressed as the molar concentration (or molarity) of the substance. A measured volume of the standard solution then reacts with the substance being analyzed.

Primary standard: a substance that has a known high degree of purity, a relatively large molar mass, is nonhygroscopic, and reacts in a predictable way

Standard solution: a solution having a very well known concentration of a solute

The reaction of the known substance with the substance to be analyzed, occurring in aqueous solution, is generally conducted by a titration procedure.

The titration procedure requires a buret to dispense a liquid, called the **titrant,** into a flask containing the **analyte** (Figure 9.1*a*, page 134). For the acid–base titration studied in Part B of this experiment, the titrant is a standard solution of sodium hydroxide and the analyte is an acid.

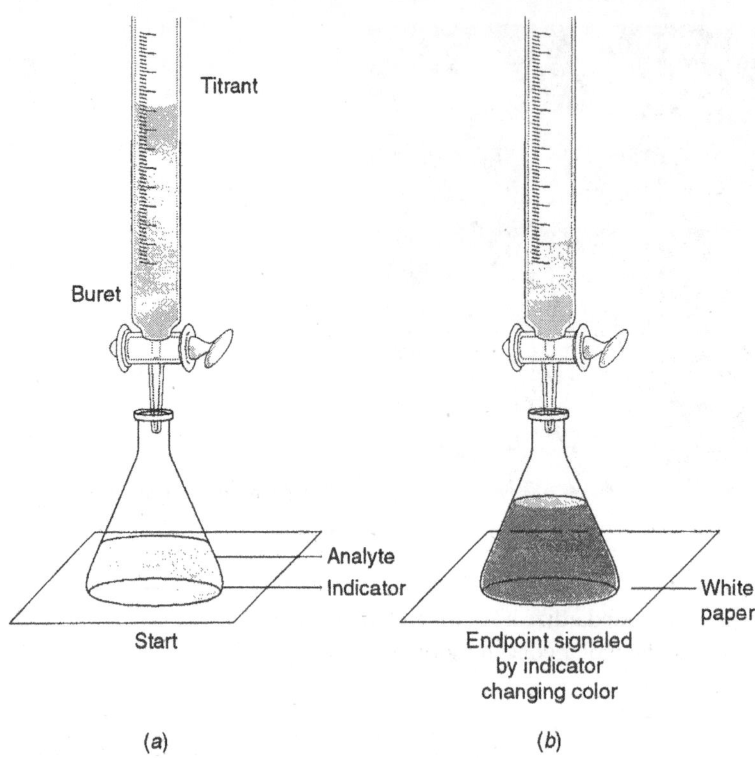

Figure 9.1 (a) Titrant in the buret is dispensed into the analyte until (b) the indicator changes color at its endpoint.

Stoichiometric amounts: amounts corresponding to the mole ratio of the balanced equation

Acid–base indicator: a substance having an acidic structure with a different color than its basic structure

pH: the negative logarithm of the molar concentration of H_3O^+, pH = $-\log[H_3O^+]$. Refer to Experiment 6.

A reaction is complete when **stoichiometric amounts** of the reacting substances are combined. In a titration this is the **stoichiometric point.**[1] In this experiment, the stoichiometric point for the acid–base titration is detected using a phenolphthalein **indicator.** Phenolphthalein is colorless in an acidic solution but pink in a basic solution. The point in the titration at which the phenolphthalein changes color is called the **endpoint** of the indicator (Figure 9.1*b*). Indicators are selected so that the stoichiometric point in the titration coincides (at approximately the same **pH**) with the endpoint of the indicator.

Standardization of a Sodium Hydroxide Solution

Hygroscopic: able to absorb water vapor readily

Solid sodium hydroxide is very **hygroscopic;** therefore, its mass cannot be measured to prepare a solution with an accurately known molar concentration (a primary standard solution). To prepare a NaOH solution with a very well known molar concentration, it must be standardized with an acid that *is* a primary standard.

In Part A of this experiment, *dry* potassium hydrogen phthalate, $KHC_8H_4O_4$, is used as the **primary acid standard** for determining the molar concentration of a sodium hydroxide solution. Potassium hydrogen phthalate is a white, crystalline, acidic solid. It has the properties of a primary standard because of its high purity, relatively high molar mass, and because it is only *very slightly* hygroscopic. The moles of $KHC_8H_4O_4$ used for the analysis is calculated from its measured mass and molar mass (204.23 g/mol):

COOH
COO^-K^+
potassium hydrogen phthlate

$$\text{mass}(g)\ KHC_8H_4O_4 \times \frac{\text{mol } KHC_8H_4O_4}{204.23 \text{ g } KHC_8H_4O_4} = \text{mol } KHC_8H_4O_4 \qquad (9.1)$$

From the balanced equation for the reaction, one mole of $KHC_8H_4O_4$ reacts with one mole of NaOH according to the equation:

$$KHC_8H_4O_4(aq) + NaOH(aq) \longrightarrow H_2O(l) + NaKC_8H_4O_4(aq) \qquad (9.2)$$

[1]The stoichiometric point is also called the **equivalence point**, indicating the point at which stoichiometrically equivalent quantities of the reacting substances are combined.

In Part A.3 of the Experimental Procedure, an accurately measured mass of dry potassium hydrogen phthalate is dissolved in deionized water. A prepared NaOH solution in Part A.2 is then dispensed from a buret into the $KHC_8H_4O_4$ solution until the stoichiometric point is reached, signaled by the colorless to pink change of the phenolphthalein indicator. At this point, the dispensed volume of NaOH is noted and recorded.

The molar concentration of the NaOH solution is calculated by determining the number of moles of NaOH used in the reaction (equation 9.2) and the volume of NaOH dispensed from the buret.

$$\text{molar concentration } (M) \text{ of NaOH } (mol/L) = \frac{\text{mol NaOH}}{\text{L of NaOH solution}} \tag{9.3}$$

Once the molar concentration of the sodium hydroxide is calculated, the solution is said to be "standardized," and the sodium hydroxide solution is called a **secondary standard** solution.

Molar Concentration of an Acid Solution

In Part B, an unknown molar concentration of an acid solution is determined. The standardized NaOH solution is used to titrate an accurately measured volume of the acid to the stoichiometric point. By knowing the volume and molar concentration of the NaOH, the number of moles of NaOH used for the analysis is

$$\text{volume } (L) \times \text{molar concentration } (mol/L) = \text{mol NaOH} \tag{9.4}$$

From the stoichiometry of the reaction, the moles of acid neutralized in the reaction can be calculated. If your acid of unknown concentration is a monoprotic acid, HA [as is $HCl(aq)$], then the mole ratio of acid to NaOH will be 1:1 (equation 9.5). However, if your acid is diprotic, H_2A (as is H_2SO_4), then the mole ratio of acid to NaOH will be 1:2 (equation 9.6). Your instructor will inform you of the acid type: HA or H_2A.

$$HA(aq) + NaOH(aq) \longrightarrow NaA(aq) + H_2O(l) \tag{9.5}$$

$$H_2A(aq) + 2\,NaOH(aq) \longrightarrow Na_2A(aq) + 2\,H_2O(l) \tag{9.6}$$

From the moles of the acid that react and its measured volume, its molar concentration is calculated:

$$\text{molar concentration of the acid } (mol/L) = \frac{\text{mol acid}}{\text{volume of acid } (L)} \tag{9.7}$$

EXPERIMENTAL PROCEDURE

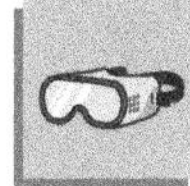

Procedure Overview: A NaOH solution is prepared with an approximate concentration. A more accurate molar concentration of the NaOH solution (as the titrant) is determined using dry potassium hydrogen phthalate as a primary standard. The NaOH solution, now a secondary standard solution, is then used to determine the "unknown" molar concentration of an acid solution.

Check with your laboratory instructor; stockroom personnel may have completed Parts A.1, and/or A.2 (or all of Part A). Begin the Experimental Procedure with the steps that follow those already completed by the stockroom personnel.

Be aware of the number of significant figures when recording data.

A. The Standardization of a Sodium Hydroxide Solution

You are to complete at least three good trials (±1% reproducibility) in standardizing the NaOH solution. Prepare three clean 125-mL or 250-mL Erlenmeyer flasks for the titration.

You will need to use approximately one liter of boiled, deionized water for this experiment. Start preparing that first.[2]

[2]Boiling the water removes traces of CO_2 that would react with the sodium hydroxide in solution.

1. **Dry the primary standard acid.** Dry 2–3 g of $KHC_8H_4O_4$ at 110°C for several hours in a constant-temperature drying oven. Cool the sample in a desiccator.
2. **Prepare an approximate 0.15 *M* NaOH solution.** Calculate and measure on a balance (±0.01g) the mass of NaOH required to prepare 500 mL of a 0.15 *M* NaOH solution. Show the calculation on the ***Report Sheet***. Fill a 500 mL polyethylene bottle about 1/3 full with previously boiled, deionized water cooled to room temperature. Add the solid NaOH in the 500 mL polyethylene bottle (Figure 9.2). *Swirl* the solution (do not shake!).[3] Finally, dilute the volume to ~500 mL with the previously boiled, deionized water. Cap the polyethylene bottle to prevent the absorption of CO_2 and label the bottle.

3. **Prepare the primary standard acid.**
   a. Calculate the mass of $KHC_8H_4O_4$ that will require about 15–20 mL of your diluted NaOH solution to reach the stoichiometric point. See ***Prelaboratory Assignment***, question 5 and show the calculation on the ***Report Sheet***.
   b. Measure this mass (±0.001 g) of $KHC_8H_4O_4$ on a **tared** piece of weighing paper (Figure 9.3) and transfer it to a clean, labeled Erlenmeyer flask. Complete the preparation of all three samples while you are occupying the balance. Dissolve the $KHC_8H_4O_4$ in about 50 mL of previously boiled, deionized water and add 2 drops of phenolphthalein.

Tared mass: mass of a sample without regard to its container

Data Analysis, A

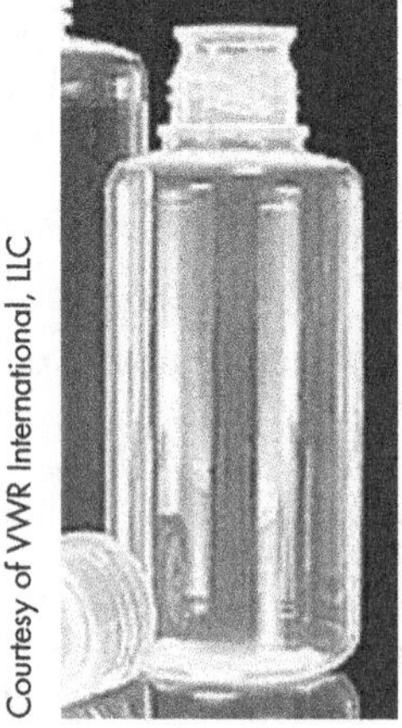

Courtesy of VWR International, LLC

Figure 9.2 A 500-mL polyethylene bottle for the NaOH solution

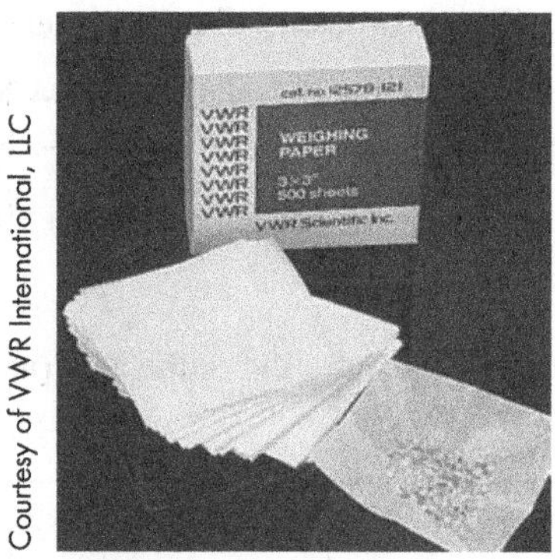

Courtesy of VWR International, LLC

Figure 9.3 Weighing paper for the $KHC_8H_4O_4$ measurements

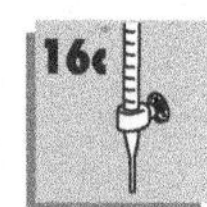

4. **Prepare a clean buret.** Wash a 50-mL buret and funnel thoroughly with soap and water using a long buret brush. Flush the buret with tap water and rinse several times with deionized water. Rinse the buret with three 5-mL portions of the diluted NaOH solution, making certain that the solution wets the entire inner surface. Drain each rinse through the buret tip. Discard each rinse in the Waste Bases container. Have the instructor approve your buret and titration setup before continuing.

[3]Carbon dioxide, CO_2, from the atmosphere is an **acidic anhydride** (meaning that when CO_2 dissolves in water, it forms an acidic solution). The acid CO_2 reacts with the base NaOH to form the less soluble salt, Na_2CO_3.

$$CO_2(g) + 2\,NaOH(aq) \longrightarrow Na_2CO_3(s) + H_2O(l)$$

5. **Fill the buret.** Using a clean funnel, fill the buret with the NaOH solution.[4] After 10–15 seconds, read the volume by viewing the bottom of the meniscus with the aid of a black line drawn on a white card or see Figure 9.4 (the buret can be removed from the stand or moved up or down in the buret clamp to simplify this reading; don't stand on a lab stool to read the meniscus). Record this initial volume according to the guideline in *Technique 16A.2*, using all certain digits (from the labeled calibration marks on the glassware) *plus* one uncertain digit (the last digit which is the best estimate between the calibration marks). Place a sheet of white paper beneath the Erlenmeyer flask.

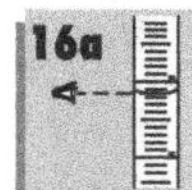

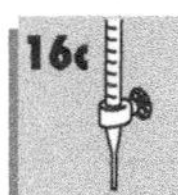

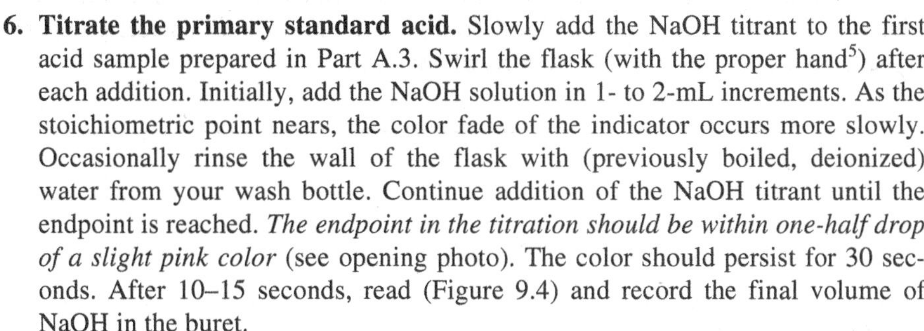

6. **Titrate the primary standard acid.** Slowly add the NaOH titrant to the first acid sample prepared in Part A.3. Swirl the flask (with the proper hand[5]) after each addition. Initially, add the NaOH solution in 1- to 2-mL increments. As the stoichiometric point nears, the color fade of the indicator occurs more slowly. Occasionally rinse the wall of the flask with (previously boiled, deionized) water from your wash bottle. Continue addition of the NaOH titrant until the endpoint is reached. *The endpoint in the titration should be within one-half drop of a slight pink color* (see opening photo). The color should persist for 30 seconds. After 10–15 seconds, read (Figure 9.4) and record the final volume of NaOH in the buret.

Figure 9.4 Read the volume of titrant with a black background.

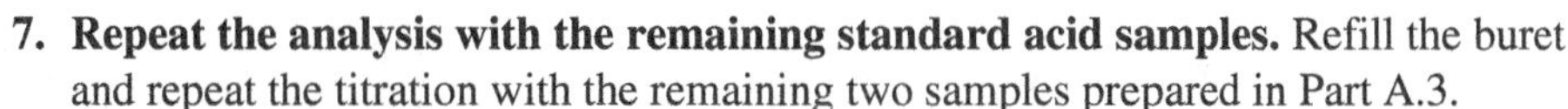

7. **Repeat the analysis with the remaining standard acid samples.** Refill the buret and repeat the titration with the remaining two samples prepared in Part A.3.
8. **Do the calculations.** Calculate the molar concentration of the diluted NaOH solution. The molar concentrations of the NaOH solution from the three analyses should be within ±1%. Place a corresponding label on the 500-mL polyethylene bottle.

Data Analysis, A

> *Disposal:* Dispose of the neutralized solutions in the Erlenmeyer flasks in the Waste Acids container.

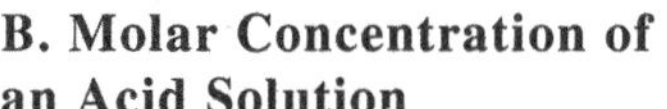

B. Molar Concentration of an Acid Solution

Three samples of the acid having an unknown concentration are to be analyzed. Ask your instructor for the acid type of your unknown (i.e., HA or H_2A). Prepare three *clean* 125- or 250-mL Erlenmeyer flasks for this determination.

1. **Prepare the acid samples of unknown concentration.** In an Erlenmeyer flask, pipet 25.00 mL of the acid solution. Add 2 drops of phenolphthalein.
2. **Fill the buret and titrate.** Refill the buret with the (now) standardized NaOH solution and, after 10–15 seconds, read and record the initial volume. Refer to Parts A.5 and A.6. Titrate the acid sample to the phenolphthalein endpoint. Read and record the final volume of titrant.

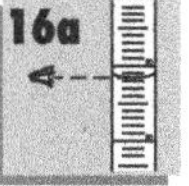

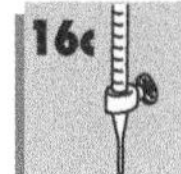

3. **Repeat.** Similarly titrate the remaining samples of the acid solution.
4. **Calculations.** Calculate the average molar concentration of your acid unknown.

Data Analysis, A

> **Save.** Save your standardized NaOH solution in the *tightly capped* 500-mL polyethylene bottle for *Experiments 10, 17, 18, and/or 19.* Consult with your instructor.

> *Disposal:* Dispose of the neutralized solutions in the Waste Acids container. Consult with your instructor.

---

[4]Be certain all air bubbles are removed from the buret tip.
[5]Check *Technique 16C.3* for this procedure.

CLEANUP: Rinse the buret and pipet several times with tap water and discard through the tip into the sink. Rinse twice with deionized water. Similarly clean the Erlenmeyer flasks.

Check and clean the balance area. All of the solid $KHC_8H_4O_4$ should be discarded in the Waste Solid Acids container.

The Next Step

What are the acid concentrations for various noncarbonated soft drinks? the acid of vinegar (*Experiment 10*), the acids used for treating swimming pools? the acid of fruit juices? the antacids (*Experiment 17*), of aspirin (*Experiment 19*). Specifically, what are those acids? Design a procedure for determining the acidity for a select grouping of foods, drinks, or other familiar commercial products.

NOTES AND CALCULATIONS

Experiment 9 *Prelaboratory Assignment*

A Volumetric Analysis

Date ________ Lab Sec. ______ Name ______________________________ Desk No. ________

1. a. What is the titrant for this experiment?

b. Is the indicator generally added to the titrant or the analyte in a titration?

2. a. What is the primary standard used in this experiment (name and formula)? Define a primary standard.

b. What is the secondary standard used in this experiment (name and formula)? Define a secondary standard.

3. Distinguish between a stoichiometric point and an endpoint in an acid–base titration.

4. a. When rinsing a buret after cleaning it with soap and water, should the rinse be dispensed through the buret tip or the top opening of the buret? Explain. 16c

b. Experimental Procedure, Part A.4. In preparing the buret for titration, the final rinse is with the NaOH titrant rather than with deionized water. Explain.

5. Part A.3. Calculate the mass of $KHC_8H_4O_4$ (molar mass = 204.23 g/mol) that reacts with 15 mL of the 0.15 *M* NaOH solution prepared in Part A.2. Express this mass $KHC_8H_4O_4$ to the correct number of significant figures and record the calculation on the ***Report Sheet***.

6. **a.** Complete the following table of Trial 1 (See ***Report Sheet***) for determining the molar concentration of a standard NaOH solution, followed by the determination of the molar concentration of a monoprotic acid solution according to the experimental procedure. Record calculated values with the correct number of significant figures.

A. Standardization of a Sodium Hydroxide Solution — *Calculation Zone*

1. Tared mass of $KHC_8H_4O_4$ (*g*)	0.411	*Part A.3*
2. Molar mass of $KHC_8H_4O_4$ (g/mol)	204.44	
3. Moles of $KHC_8H_4O_4$ (mol) Show calculation.		
4. Buret reading, *initial* (*mL*)	4.20	
5. Buret reading, *final* (*mL*)	19.90	
6. Volume of NaOH dispensed (*mL*)		*Part A.7*
7. Molar concentration of NaOH solution (*mol/L*) Show calculation.		

B. Molar Concentration of an Acid Solution

		Part B.6
1. Volume of acid solution (*mL*)	25.0	
2. Buret reading, *initial* (*mL*)	3.70	
3. Buret reading, *final* (*mL*)	20.47	
4. Volume of NaOH dispensed (*mL*)		
5. Molar concentration of NaOH solution (*mol/L*)		*Part B.7*
6. Moles of NaOH dispensed (*mol*) Show calculation.		
7. Molar concentration of acid solution (*mol/L*) Show calculation.		

6. **b.** For Trials 2 and 3, the molar concentration of the acid was 0.922 *M* and 0.856 *M* respectively.

a. What is the average molar concentration of the acid solution? **Data Analysis, B.**

b. What are the standard deviation and the relative standard deviation (%RSD) for the molar concentration of the acid solution? **Data Analysis, C and D.**

Experiment 9 *Report Sheet*

A Volumetric Analysis

Date ________ Lab Sec. _____ Name ______________________________ Desk No. ________

Maintain at least three significant figures when recording data and performing calculations.

A. Standardization of a Sodium Hydroxide Solution

Calculate the approximate mass of NaOH required to prepare 500 mL of a 0.15 *M* NaOH solution (Part A.2).

Calculate the approximate mass of $KHC_8H_4O_4$ for the standardization of the NaOH solution (Part A.3).

	Trial 1	*Trial 2*	*Trial 3*
1. Tared mass of $KHC_8H_4O_4$ (*g*)	________	________	________
2. Molar mass of $KHC_8H_4O_4$		204.23 g/mol	
3. Moles of $KHC_8H_4O_4$ (*mol*)	________	________	________
Titration apparatus approval		________________	
4. Buret reading of NaOH, *initial* (*mL*)	________	________	________
5. Buret reading of NaOH, *final* (*mL*)	________	________	________
6. Volume of NaOH dispensed (*mL*)	________	________	________
7. Molar concentration of NaOH (*mol/L*)	________	________	________
8. Average molar concentration of NaOH (*mol/L*)		________________	***Data Analysis, B***
9. Standard deviation of molar concentration		________________	***Data Analysis, C***
10. Relative standard deviation of molar concentration (*%RSD*)		________________	***Data Analysis, B***

B. Molar Concentration of an Acid Solution

Acid type, HA or H_2A: ________ Unknown No. ________

Balanced equation for neutralization of acid with NaOH.

	Sample 1	Sample 2	Sample 3
1. Volume of acid solution (*mL*)	25.0	25.0	25.0
2. Buret reading of NaOH, *initial* (*mL*)			
3. Buret reading of NaOH, *final* (*mL*)			
4. Volume of NaOH dispensed (*mL*)			
5. Molar concentration of NaOH (*mol/L*), Part A			
6. Moles of NaOH dispensed (*mol*)			
7. Molar concentration of acid solution (*mol/L*)			
8. Average molar concentration of acid solution (*mol/L*)			**Data Analysis, B**
9. Standard deviation of molar concentration			**Data Analysis, C**
10. Relative standard deviation of molar concentration (*%RSD*)			**Data Analysis, D**

Laboratory Questions

Circle the questions that have been assigned.

1. Part A.1. Pure potassium hydrogen phthalate is used for the standardization of the sodium hydroxide solution. Suppose that the potassium hydrogen phthalate is *not* completely dry. Will the reported molar concentration of the sodium hydroxide solution be too high, too low, or unaffected because of the moistness of the potassium hydrogen phthalate? Explain.
2. Part A.2. The student forgot to prepare any boiled, deionized water for the preparation of the NaOH solution and *then* forgot to cap the bottle. Will the concentration of the NaOH solution be greater than, less than, or unaffected by this carelessness? Explain.
3. Part A.6. A drop of the NaOH titrant adheres to the side of the buret (because of a dirty buret) between the initial and final readings for the titration. As a result of the "clean glass" error, will the molar concentration of the NaOH solution be reported as too high or too low? Explain.
4. Part A. The mass of $KHC_8H_4O_4$ is measured to the nearest milligram; however, the volume of water in which it is dissolved is *never* of concern—water is even added to the wall of the Erlenmeyer flask during the titration. Explain why water added to the $KHC_8H_4O_4$ has no effect on the data, whereas water added to the NaOH solution may drastically affect the data.
5. Part B.2. The wall of the Erlenmeyer flask is occasionally rinsed with water from the wash bottle (see Part A.6) during the analysis of the acid solution. Will this technique result in the molar concentration of the acid solution being reported as too high, too low, or unaffected? Explain.
6. Parts A.6 and B.2. For the standardization of the NaOH solution in Part A.6, the endpoint was consistently reproduced to a faint pink color. However, the endpoint for the titration of the acid solution in Part B.2 was consistently reproduced to a dark pink color. Will the reported molar concentration of the acid solution be too high, too low, or unaffected by the differences in the colors of the endpoints. Explain.

Richard Megna/Fundamental Photographs

Vinegar is a 4–5% (by mass) solution in acetic acid.

Experiment 10

Vinegar Analysis

Objective

- To determine the percent by mass of acetic acid in vinegar

Techniques

The following techniques are used in the Experimental Procedure:

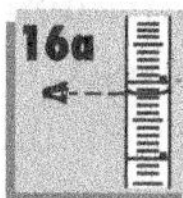

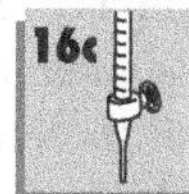

Introduction

Household vinegar is a 4–5% (by mass) acetic acid, CH_3COOH, solution (4% is the minimum federal standard). Generally, caramel flavoring and coloring are also added to make the product aesthetically more appealing.

$CH_3C(=O)OH$

acetic acid

A volumetric analysis using the titration technique is the method used for determining the percent by mass of acetic acid in vinegar. A measured mass of vinegar is titrated to the phenolphthalein endpoint with a measured volume of a standardized sodium hydroxide solution. Since the volume and molar concentration of the standardized NaOH solution are known, the moles of NaOH used for the analysis are also known.

$$\text{mol NaOH} = \text{L NaOH solution} \times \frac{\text{mol NaOH}}{\text{L NaOH solution}} \tag{10.1}$$

From the balanced equation:

$$CH_3COOH(aq) + NaOH(aq) \longrightarrow NaCH_3CO_2(aq) + H_2O(l) \tag{10.2}$$

$$\text{mol } CH_3COOH = \text{mol NaOH} \tag{10.3}$$

The mass of CH_3COOH in the vinegar is calculated from the measured moles of CH_3COOH neutralized in the reaction and its molar mass, 60.05 g/mol:

$$\text{mass}(g) \text{ of } CH_3COOH = \text{mol } CH_3COOH \times \frac{60.05 \text{ g } CH_3COOH}{\text{mol } CH_3COOH} \tag{10.4}$$

Finally, the percent by mass of CH_3COOH in vinegar is calculated:

$$\% \text{ by mass of } CH_3COOH = \frac{\text{mass } (g) \text{ of } CH_3COOH}{\text{mass } (g) \text{ of vinegar}} \times 100 \tag{10.5}$$

Experimental Procedure

Procedure Overview: Samples of one or two vinegars are analyzed for the amount of acetic acid in the sample. A titration setup is used for the analysis, using a standardized NaOH solution as the titrant and phenolphthalein as the indicator.

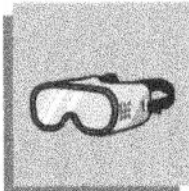

A standardized NaOH solution was prepared in *Experiment 9*. If that solution was saved, it is to be used for this experiment. If the solution was not saved, you either must again prepare and standardize the solution (*Experiment 9*, Part A) or obtain about 150 mL of a standardized NaOH solution prepared by stockroom personnel. Your instructor will advise you.

Be aware of the number of significant figures when recording data.

A. Preparation of Vinegar Sample

Check with your laboratory instructor to determine if you are to analyze one or two vinegars. Either obtain 15 mL of a single vinegar or 10 mL of each of two vinegars in separate 10-mL graduated cylinders. Clean at least two 125- or 250-mL Erlenmeyer flasks.

1. **Calculate the volume of vinegar.** Calculate the volume of vinegar that would be needed for the neutralization of 25 mL of the standardized NaOH solution. Assume the vinegar has a density of 1 g/mL and a percent acetic acid of 5% by mass, and the standardized NaOH solution is 0.1 *M* NaOH. Show the calculation on the ***Report Sheet*** (see ***Prelaboratory Assignment***, question 1).

Data Analysis, A

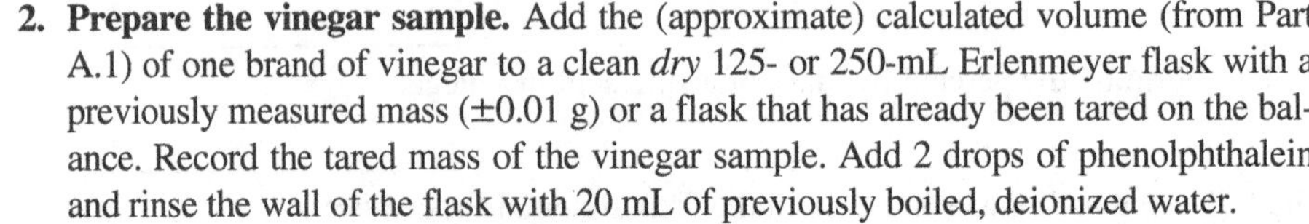

2. **Prepare the vinegar sample.** Add the (approximate) calculated volume (from Part A.1) of one brand of vinegar to a clean *dry* 125- or 250-mL Erlenmeyer flask with a previously measured mass (±0.01 g) or a flask that has already been tared on the balance. Record the tared mass of the vinegar sample. Add 2 drops of phenolphthalein and rinse the wall of the flask with 20 mL of previously boiled, deionized water.

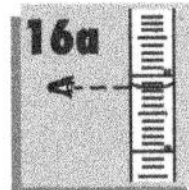

3. **Prepare the buret and titration setup.** Rinse twice a clean 50-mL buret with ~5 mL of the standardized NaOH solution, making certain no drops cling to the inside wall. Fill the buret with the standardized NaOH solution, eliminate all air bubbles in the buret tip, and, after 10–15 seconds, read and record the initial volume (see *Technique 16C.2*). Place a sheet of white paper beneath the flask containing the vinegar sample.

B. Analysis of Vinegar Sample

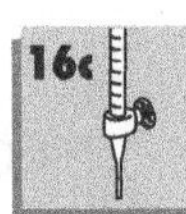

Record the *exact* molar concentration of the NaOH solution on the ***Report Sheet***, B.4.

1. **Titrate the vinegar sample.** Slowly add the NaOH solution from the buret to the acid, swirling the flask (with the proper hand[1]) after each addition. Occasionally, rinse the wall of the flask with previously boiled, deionized water from your wash bottle. Continue addition of the NaOH titrant until the endpoint is reached.[2] See *Technique 16C.4*. After 10–15 seconds, read (Figure 10.1) and record the final volume of NaOH titrant in the buret (see *Technique 16A.2*).
2. **Repeat with the same vinegar.** Refill the buret and repeat the titration *at least* once more with another sample of the same vinegar.
3. **Consult with your instructor.** You are to complete Parts A and B for a second vinegar to determine its average percent acetic acid *or* complete a third and/or fourth analysis of your original vinegar. For the additional analyses, revise the ***Report Sheet*** accordingly.
4. **Calculations.** Determine the average percent by mass of acetic acid in the vinegar(s).

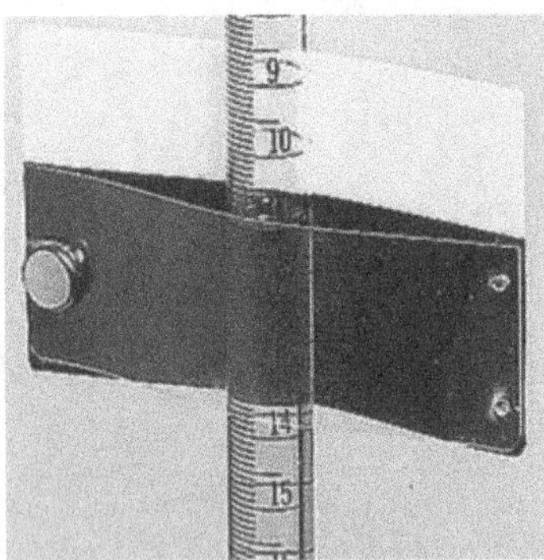

Courtesy of Thermo Fisher Scientific

Figure 10.1 Read the volume of titrant with a black background.

> *Disposal:* All test solutions and the NaOH solution in the buret can be discarded in the Waste Bases container.

CLEANUP: Rinse the buret twice with tap water and twice with deionized water, discarding each rinse through the buret tip into the sink. Similarly, rinse the flasks.

---

[1]Review *Technique 16C.3* for this procedure.

[2]The endpoint (and the stoichiometric point) is near when the color fade of the phenolphthalein indicator occurs more slowly with each successive addition of smaller volumes of NaOH solution to the vinegar.

Experiment 10 *Prelaboratory Assignment*

Vinegar Analysis

Date __________ Lab Sec. ______ Name ____ Desk No. __________

1. Assuming the density of a 5% acetic acid by mass solution is 1.0 g/mL, determine the volume of the acetic acid solution necessary to neutralize 25.0 mL of 0.10 *M* NaOH. Also record this calculation on your ***Report Sheet***.

2. **a.** A chemist often uses a white card with a black mark to aid in reading the meniscus of a clear liquid. How does this technique make the reading more accurate? Explain.

   16a

   b. A chemist should wait 10–15 seconds after dispensing a volume of titrant before a reading is made. Explain why the wait is good laboratory technique.

   16c

   c. The color change at the endpoint should persist for 30 seconds. Explain why the time lapse is a good titration technique.

3. Lemon juice has a pH of about 2.5. *Assuming* that the acidity of lemon juice is due solely to citric acid, that citric acid is a monoprotic acid, and that the density of lemon juice is 1.0 g/mL, then the citric acid concentration calculates to 0.5% by mass. Estimate the volume of 0.0100 *M* NaOH required to neutralize a 3.71-g sample of lemon juice. The molar mass of citric acid is 190.12 g/mol.

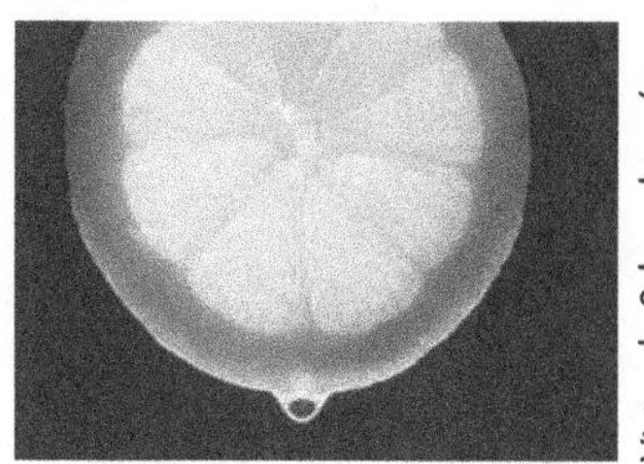

Victor de Schwanberg/
Science Source

4. Explain why it is quantitatively *not* acceptable to titrate each of the vinegar samples with the NaOH titrant to the same *dark pink* endpoint.

5. a. A commercial vinegar is analyzed for the percent acetic acid present. The data for Trial 1 is listed in the table below. Complete the table to determine the percent. (See ***Report Sheet.***) Record calculated values with the correct number of significant figures.

A. Preparation of Vinegar Sample			<u>*Calculation Zone*</u>
1. Mass of vinegar (*g*)	3.06	*Part B.5*	
B. Analysis of Vinegar Sample			
1. Buret reading, *initial* (*mL*)	3.70		
2. Buret reading, *final* (*mL*)	25.40	*Part B.6*	
3. Volume of NaOH used (*mL*)			
4. Molar concentration of NaOH solution (*mol/L*)	0.0940		
5. Moles of NaOH added (*mol*) Show calculation.		*Part B.7*	
6. Moles of CH_3COOH in vinegar (*mol*) Show calculation.			
7. Mass of CH_3COOH in vinegar (*g*) Show calculation.			
8. Percent by mass of CH_3COOH in vinegar (%) Show calculation.		*Part B.8*	

5. b. For Trials 2 and 3, the percent CH_3COOH in vinegar was 5.01% and 4.66% respectively.
a. What is the average percent of CH_3COOH in the vinegar sample? **Data Analysis, B.**

b. What are the standard deviation and the relative standard deviation (%RSD) for the percent of CH_3COOH in the vinegar sample? **Data Analysis, C and D.**

Experiment 10 *Report Sheet*

Vinegar Analysis

Date ________ Lab Sec. ______ Name ________________________________ Desk No. ________

A. Preparation of Vinegar Sample

Calculate the approximate volume of the vinegar sample needed for the analyses (Part A.1).

Brand of vinegar or unknown no.	________		________	
	Trial 1	*Trial 2*	*Trial 1*	*Trial 2*
1. Mass of flask (*g*)	______	______	______	______
2. Mass of flask + vinegar (*g*)	______	______	______	______
3. Mass of vinegar (*g*)	______	______	______	______
B. Analysis of Vinegar Sample				
1. Buret reading of NaOH, *initial* (*mL*)	______	______	______	______
2. Buret reading of NaOH, *final* (*mL*)	______	______	______	______
3. Volume of NaOH used (*mL*)	______	______	______	______
4. Molar concentration of NaOH (*mol/L*)	______________		______________	
5. Moles of NaOH added (*mol*)	______*	______	______	______
6. Moles of CH_3COOH in vinegar (*mol*)	______	______	______	______
7. Mass of CH_3COOH in vinegar (*g*)	______	______	______	______
8. Percent by mass of CH_3COOH in vinegar (%)	______	______	______	______
9. Average percent by mass of CH_3COOH in vinegar (%)	______________		______________	

*Calculations for Trial 1 of the first vinegar sample on next page.

Calculations for Trial 1.

Discuss briefly a comparison of the two vinegars *or* for an analysis of a single vinegar, calculate the standard deviation and the relative standard deviation. **Data Analysis C and D.**

Laboratory Questions

Circle the questions that have been assigned.

1. Part A.2. A 20-mL volume of previously boiled, deionized water is added to the Erlenmeyer flask to prepare the sample for titration. Explain why this volume is not critical to the analysis.
2. Part A.2. Previously boiled, deionized water is unavailable. In a hurry to pursue the analysis, deionized water (not boiled) is added. How does this attempt to expedite the analysis affect the reported percent acetic acid in vinegar: too high, too low, or unaffected? Explain.
3. Part A.2 and B.1. The 20 mL of water added to the Erlenmeyer flask is to be *previously boiled*, deionized water. Since water does absorb CO_2 from the atmosphere and since CO_2 dissolved in water causes it to be slightly acidic, will the use of deionized water that has *not* been previously boiled cause the mass of acetic acid in the vinegar to be calculated as too high or too low? Explain.
4. Part A.2
   a. In determining the percent acetic acid in vinegar, the mass of each vinegar sample is measured rather than the volume. Explain.
   b. If the vinegar were measured volumetrically (e.g., a pipet), what additional piece of data would be needed to complete the calculations for the experiment?
5. Part A.3. The buret is filled with the NaOH titrant and the initial volume reading is immediately recorded without waiting the recommended 10–15 seconds. However in Part B.1, the 10–15 second time lapse does occur before the reading is made. Does this technique error result in an increase, a decrease, or have no effect on the reported percent acetic acid in the vinegar? Explain.
6. Part B.1. The endpoint of the titration is overshot! Does this technique error result in an increase, a decrease, or have no effect on the reported percent acetic acid in the vinegar? Explain.
7. Part B.1. The wall of the flask is periodically rinsed with the previously boiled, deionized water from the wash bottle. Does this titrimetric technique result in an increase, a decrease, or have no effect on the reported percent acetic acid in the vinegar? Explain.
8. Part B.1. A drop of NaOH titrant, dispensed from the buret, adheres to the wall of the Erlenmeyer flask but is not washed into the vinegar with the wash bottle. Does this error in technique result in the reported percent of acetic acid being too high, too low, or unaffected? Explain.

triggermouse/iStockphoto

Dry Lab 3

Atomic and Molecular Structure

Metallic cations heated to high temperatures produce characteristic colors that appear in the starbursts.

OBJECTIVES

- To view and calibrate visible line spectra
- To identify an element from its visible line spectrum
- To identify a compound from its infrared spectrum
- To predict the three-dimensional structure of molecules and molecular ions

INTRODUCTION

Visible light, as we know it, is responsible for the colors of nature—blue skies, green trees, red roses, orange-red rocks, and brown deer. Our eyes are able to sense and distinguish the subtleties and the intensities of those colors through a complex naturally designed detection system—our eyes. The beauty of nature is a result of the interaction of sunlight with matter. Since all matter consists of atoms and molecules, it is obvious that sunlight, in some way, interacts with them to produce nature's colors.

Within molecules of compounds are electrons, vibrating bonds, and rotating atoms, all of which can absorb energy. Because every compound is different, every molecule of a given compound possesses its own unique set of electronic, vibrational, and rotational **energy states,** which are said to be **quantized.** When incident electromagnetic (EM) radiation falls on a *molecule,* the radiation absorbed (the absorbed light) is an energy equal to the difference between two energy states, placing the molecule in an excited state. The remainder of the EM radiation passes through the molecule unaffected.

Energy state: the amount of energy confined within an atom or molecule, which can be changed by the absorption or emission of discrete (quantized) amounts of energy

Quantized: only a definitive amount (of energy)

Atoms of elements interact with EM radiation in much the same way, except there are no bonds to vibrate or atoms to rotate. Only electronic energy states are available for energy absorption.

EM radiation is energy as well as light, and light has wavelengths and frequencies. The relationship between the energy, E, and its **wavelength,** λ, and **frequency,** ν, is expressed by the equations:

Wavelength: the distance between two crests of a wave

Frequency: the number of crests that pass a given point per second

$$E = \frac{hc}{\lambda} = h\nu \qquad \text{(D3.1)}$$

where h is Planck's constant, 6.63×10^{-34} J•s/photon; c equals the velocity of the EM radiation, 3.00×10^{8} m/s; λ is the wavelength of the EM radiation in meters; and ν (pronounced "new") is its frequency in reciprocal seconds (s^{-1}).

EM radiation includes not only the wavelengths of the visible region (400 to 700 nm) but also those that are shorter (e.g., the ultraviolet and X-ray regions) and longer (e.g., the infrared, microwave, and radio wave regions). See Figure D3.1, page 162. From Equation D3.1, shorter wavelength EM radiation has higher energy.

When an atom or molecule absorbs EM radiation from the visible region of the spectrum, it is usually an electron that is excited from a lower to a higher energy state.

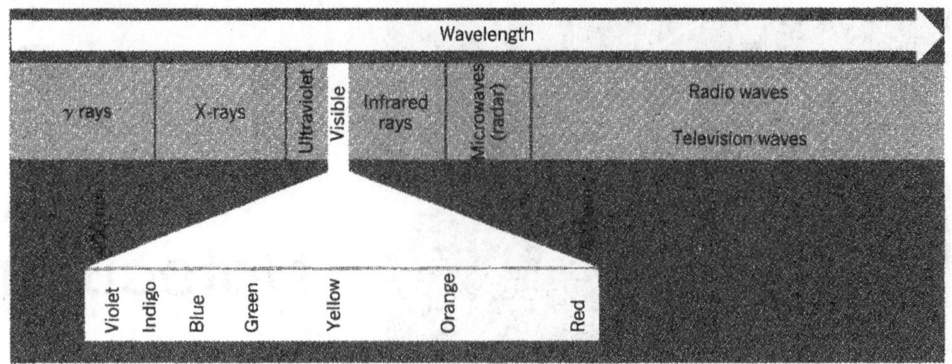

Figure D3.1 Visible light (400–700 nm) is a small part of the electromagnetic spectrum.

White light: EM radiation containing all wavelengths of visible light

Spectrophotometer: an instrument used to detect and monitor the interaction of electromagnetic radiation with matter. The instrument has an EM radiation source, a grating to sort wavelengths, a sample cell, and an EM radiation detector. See Figures 34.1 and 34.2.

When **white light** passes through a sample, our eyes (and the EM detector of a **spectrophotometer**) detect the wavelengths of visible light *not* absorbed—that is, the transmitted light. Therefore, the colors we see are *complementary* to the ones absorbed. If, for example, the atom or molecule absorbs energy exclusively from the violet region of the visible spectrum, the transmitted light (and the substance) appears yellow (violet's complementary color) (Figure D3.2) In reality, atoms and molecules of a substance absorb a range of wavelengths, some wavelengths more so than others, resulting in a mix of transmitted colors leading to various shades of colors.

Table D3.1 lists the colors corresponding to wavelength regions of light (and their complements) in the visible region of the EM spectrum.

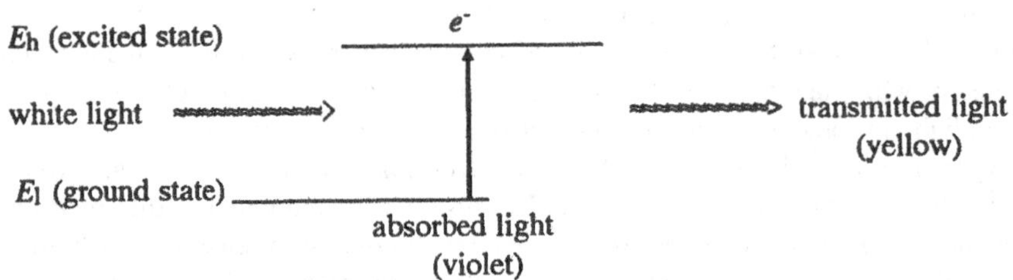

Figure D3.2 White light that is *not* absorbed is the transmitted light that we detect with our eyes.

Atomic Structure

Photon: a particlelike quantity of electromagnetic radiation, often associated with electron transitions

When an atom of an element absorbs EM radiation in the visible region, it is the electrons that absorb energy to reach excited states. When the electrons return to the lowest energy state (the **ground state**) by various pathways, the same amount of energy absorbed is now emitted as **photons.**[1] The photons have unique energies and wavelengths that represent the difference in the energy states of the atom.

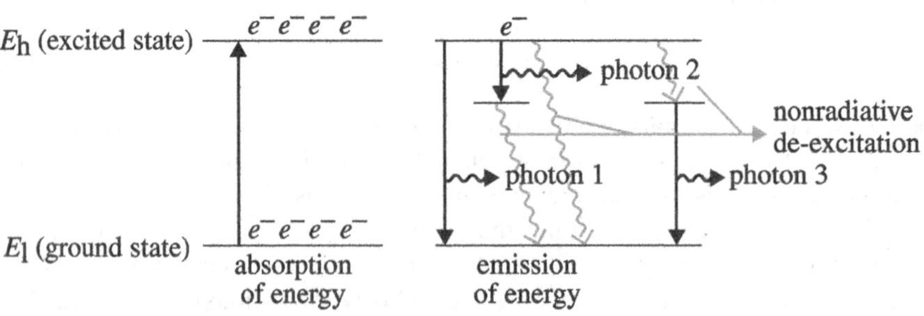

[1]Many electrons "de-excite" to the ground state by only nonradiative pathways, others through a combination of photons *and* nonradiative pathways.

Table D3.1 Color and Wavelengths in the Visible Region of the Electromagnetic Spectrum

Color Absorbed	Wavelength (*nm*)	Color Transmitted
Red	750–610	Green-blue
Orange	610–595	Blue-green
Yellow	595–580	Violet
Green	580–500	Red-violet
Blue	500–435	Orange-yellow
Violet	435–380	Yellow

Because electrons can have a large number of excited states, a large collection of excited-state electrons returning to the ground state produces an array of photons. When these emitted photons pass through a prism, an emission **line spectrum** is produced; each line in the spectrum corresponds to photons of fixed energy and wavelength. The line spectrum for hydrogen is shown in Figure D3.3.

Each element exhibits its own characteristic line spectrum because of the unique electronic energy states in its atoms. For example, the 11 electrons in sodium have a different set of electron energy states than do the 80 electrons in mercury. Therefore, when an electron in an excited state of a sodium atom moves to a lower energy state, the emitted photon has a different energy and wavelength from one that is emitted when an electron de-excites (i.e., moves to a lower energy state) in a mercury atom.

The different wavelengths of the emitted photons produce different yet characteristic colors of light. Light emitted from an excited sodium atom is characteristically yellow-orange, but mercury emits a blue light. Flame tests (*Experiment 38*) and exploding aerial fireworks attest to the uniqueness of the electronic energy states of the atoms for different elements.

Much of the modern theory of atomic structure, which we call *quantum theory* or *quantum mechanics*, is based on the emission spectra of the elements.

Molecular Structure

The structures of molecules are much more complex than those of atoms. Molecules may contain thousands of atoms, each in a unique (energy and three-dimensional) environment. Since each molecule is unique, so must be its energy levels for EM

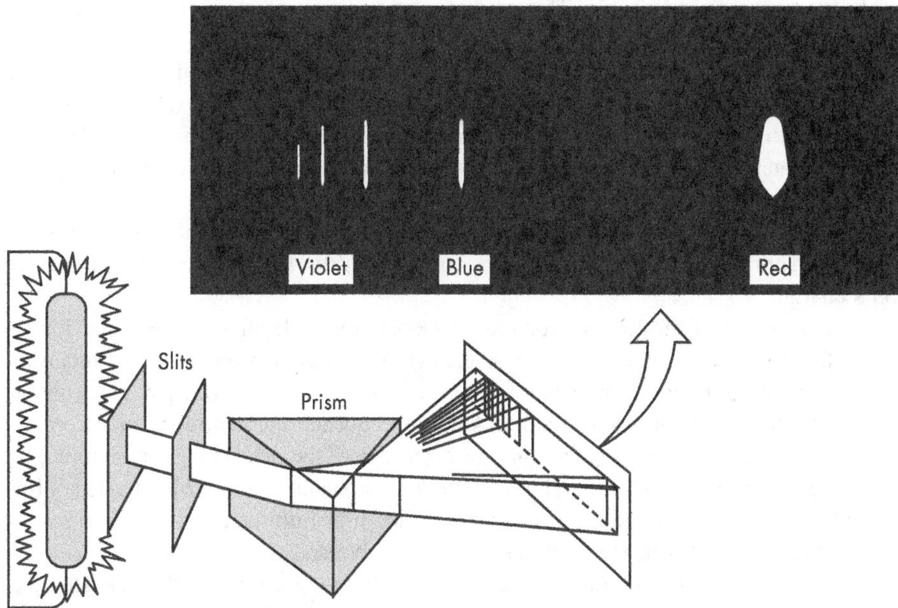

Figure D3.3 Formation of the line spectrum for hydrogen

Table D3.2 Infrared Absorption Bands for Specific Atoms in Bond Arrangements in Molecules

Atoms in Bonds	Wavenumbers	Wavelengths
O—H	3,700 to 3,500 cm^{-1}	2.7 to 2.9 μm
C—H	3,000 to 2,800 cm^{-1}	3.3 to 3.6 μm
C=O	1,800 to 1,600 cm^{-1}	5.6 to 6.2 μm
C—O	1,200 to 1,050 cm^{-1}	8.3 to 9.5 μm
C—C	1,670 to 1,640 cm^{-1}	6.0 to 6.1 μm

absorption. Using EM radiation to elucidate the three-dimensional structure of a molecule can be painstakingly tedious, especially for the structures of the "living" (biochemical) molecules, such as DNA and hemoglobin. Oftentimes, EM radiation is only one of many tools used to determine the molecular structure of a compound.

Infrared EM radiation is used as a probe for the identification of specific atom arrangements in molecules. For example, the O—H bond, as in water and alcohols, absorbs infrared radiation for a principal vibrational energy transition between 3,700 and 3,500 **cm^{-1}** or wavelengths of 2.7 to 2.9 μm. Other characteristic infrared absorption bands for specific atom arrangements in molecules are listed in Table D3.2.

cm^{-1}: Infrared spectroscopists often indicate absorption bands in units of reciprocal centimeters, called ***wavenumbers,*** *rather than as wavelengths.*

A first view of an infrared spectrum of a molecule seems confusing as more absorption bands appear than what might be anticipated from looking at the structure of the molecule and Table D3.2. Other absorptions occur as a result of multiatom interactions (stretches, bends, etc.) or orientations, but the primary bands appear as expected. Therefore, in an analysis of an infrared spectrum, a search of the primary bands in Table D3.2 is first and foremost.

For other molecules and molecular ions, other regions of EM radiation are most effective. For example, the $FeNCS^{2+}$ ion has a major absorption of radiation at 447 nm, and this property is used to measure its concentration in an aqueous solution in *Experiments 34 and 35*—the higher the concentration, the more EM radiation that is absorbed.

Lewis Theory

Valence electrons: electrons in the highest energy state (outermost shell) of an atom in the ground state

Isoelectronic: two atoms are isoelectronic if they have the same number of valence electrons.

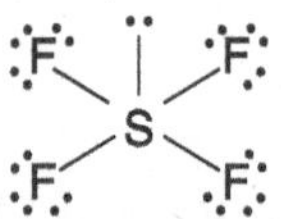

Courtesy Library of Congress

Gilbert Newton Lewis (1875–1946)

In 1916, G. N. Lewis developed a theory that focused on the significance of **valence electrons** in chemical reactions and in bonding. He proposed the **octet rule** in which atoms form bonds by losing, gaining, or sharing valence electrons until each atom of the molecule has the same number of valence electrons (eight, two for helium) as the nearest noble gas in the periodic table. The resulting arrangement of atoms formed the Lewis structure of the compound.

The Lewis structure for water shows that by sharing the one valence electron on each of the hydrogen atoms with the six valence electrons on the oxygen atom, all three atoms obtain the same number of valence electrons as the nearest noble gas. Thus, in water the hydrogen atoms are **isoelectronic** with helium atoms and the oxygen atom is isoelectronic with the neon atom.

The Lewis structures for ions are written similarly, except that electrons are removed from (for cations) or added to (for anions) the structure to account for the ion's charge.

An extension of the Lewis structure also exists for molecules or molecular ions in which the central atom is of Period 3 or greater. While the peripheral atoms retain the noble gas configuration, the central atom often extends its valence electrons to accommodate additional electron pairs. As a consequence the central atom accommodates more than eight valence electrons, an extension of the octet rule. For example, the six valence electrons of sulfur bond to four fluorine atoms in forming SF_4. To do so, four of the six valence electrons on sulfur share with the four fluorine atoms and two remain nonbonding—now 10 valence electrons exist for the bonded sulfur atom.

Although a Lewis structure accounts for the bonding based on the valence electrons on each atom, it does not predict the three-dimensional structure for a molecule. The development of the valence shell electron pair repulsion (VSEPR) theory provides insight into the three-dimensional structure of the molecule.

Valence Shell Electron Pair Repulsion (VSEPR) Theory of the Structures of Molecules and Molecular Ions

VSEPR theory proposes that the three-dimensional (3-D) structure of a molecule is determined by the repulsive interaction of electron pairs in the valence shell of its central atom. The three-dimensional orientation is such that the distance between the electron pairs is maximized so that the electron pair interactions are minimized. A construction of the Lewis structure of a molecule provides the first link in predicting the molecular structure.

Methane, CH_4, has four bonding electron pairs in the valence shell of its carbon atom (the central atom in the molecule). Repulsive interactions between these four electron pairs are minimized when the electron pairs are positioned at the vertices of a tetrahedron (3-D structure) with H—C—H bond angles of 109.5°. On the basis of the VSEPR theory, one can generalize that *all* molecules (or molecular ions) having four electron pairs in the valence shell of its central atom have a tetrahedral arrangement of these electron pairs with *approximate* bond angles of 109.5°. The nitrogen atom in ammonia, NH_3, and the oxygen atom in water, H_2O, also have four electron pairs in their valence shell!

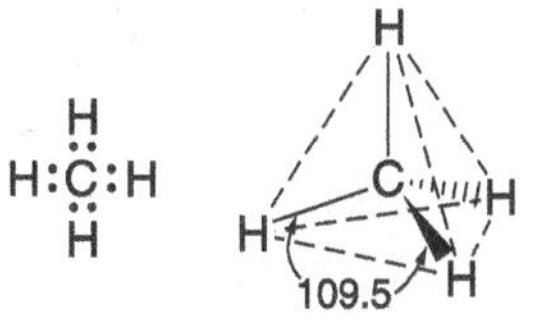

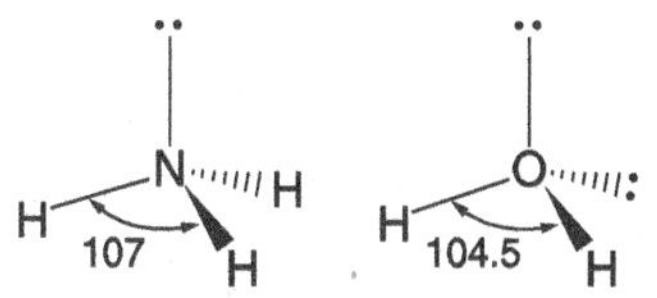

The preferred arrangement of the bonding and nonbonding electron pairs around the central atom gives rise to the corresponding structure of a molecule. The three-dimensional structures for numerous molecules and molecular ions can be grouped into a few basic structures. Based on a correct Lewis structure, a VSEPR formula summarizes the number and type (bonding and nonbonding) of electron pairs in the compound or ion. The VSEPR formula uses the following notations:

A refers to the central atom.

X_m refers to *m* number of *bonding* pairs of electrons on A.

E_n refers to *n* number of *nonbonding* pairs of electrons on A.

If a molecule has the formula AX_mE_n, it means there are $m + n$ electron pairs in the valence shell of A, the central atom of the molecule; *m* are bonding and *n* are nonbonding electron pairs. For example, CH_4, SiF_4, $GeCl_4$, PH_4^+, and PO_4^{3-} all have a VSEPR formula of AX_4. Thus, they all have the same three-dimensional structure, that of a tetrahedral structure. Water has a VSEPR formula of AX_2E_2

It should be noted here that valence electrons on the central atom contributing to a multiple bond do *not* affect the geometry of a molecule. For example in SO_2, the VSEPR formula is AX_2E, and the geometric shape of the molecule is V-shaped. See Table D3.3. Further applications are presented in more advanced chemistry courses.[2]

Table D3.3 VSEPR and Geometric Shapes of Molecules and Molecular Ions

Valence Shell Electron Pairs	Bonding Electron Pairs	Nonbonding Electron Pairs	VSEPR Formula	Three-Dimensional Structure	Bond Angle	Geometric Shape	Examples
2	2	0	AX_2	 :—A—:	180°	Linear	$HgCl_2$, $BeCl_2$
3	3	0	AX_3		120°	Planar triangular	BF_3, $In(CH_3)_3$
	2	1	AX_2E		<120°	V-shaped	$SnCl_2$, $PbBr_2$
4	4	0	AX_4	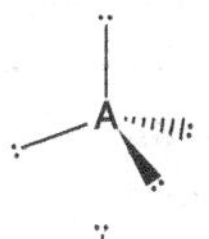	109.5°	Tetrahedral	CH_4, $SnCl_4$
	3	1	AX_3E		<109.5°	Trigonal pyramidal	NH_3, PCl_3, H_3O^+
	2	2	AX_2E_2		<109.5°	Bent	H_2O, OF_2, SCl_2
5	5	0	AX_5	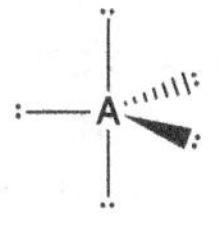	90°/120°	Trigonal bipyramidal	PCl_5, $NbCl_5$
	4	1	AX_4E		>90°	Irregular tetrahedral	SF_4, $TeCl_4$
	3	2	AX_3E_2		<90°	T-shaped	ICl_3
	2	3	AX_2E_3		180°	Linear	ICl_2^-, XeF_2
6	6	0	AX_6	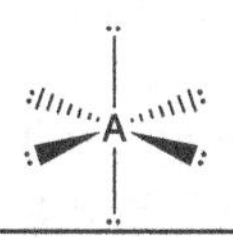	90°	Octahedral	SF_6
	5	1	AX_5E		>90°	Square pyramidal	BrF_5
	4	2	AX_4E_2		90°	Square planar	ICl_4^-, XeF_4

[2]For more information on VSEPR theory and structure, go to http://winter.group.shef.ac.uk/vsepr.

Table D3.3 presents a summary of the VSEPR theory for predicting the geometric shape and approximate bond angles of a molecule or molecular ion based on the five basic VSEPR three-dimensional structures of molecules and molecular ions.

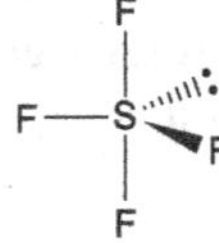

Let us refer back to SF_4, the molecule with the extended valence shell on the central atom. The sulfur atom has four bonding electron pairs (m = 4) and one nonbonding pair (n = 1). This gives a VSEPR formula of AX_4E_1, predicting a geometric shape of irregular tetrahedral (sometimes also called *seesaw*) with bond angles greater than 90°. Molecular models will enable you to envision these properties of SF_4.

Dry Lab Procedure

In Part A, the visible emission spectra of a number of elements are studied (see color plate on back cover of this manual). The wavelengths of the spectra are set relative to the mercury spectrum at the bottom of color plate. The most intense lines of the mercury spectrum are listed in Table D3.4.

In Part B, a spectrum from the color plate will be assigned, and, with reference to Table D3.5, the element producing the line spectrum will be identified.

In Part C, a molecule will be assigned and, with reference to Table D3.2, a spectra will be matched to the molecule.

In Part D, a number of simple molecules and molecular ions will be assigned, and their three-dimensional structure and approximate bond angles will be determined. The Lewis structure and the VSEPR adaptation of the Lewis structure are used for analysis.

Discuss with your instructor which parts of the Dry Lab Procedure are to be completed and by when. If there is no advanced preparation and you are to complete all parts, you may be rushed for time.

A. The Mercury Spectrum

1. **The color plate.** Notice the various experimental emission line spectra on the color plate (back cover). A continuous spectrum appears at the top, the line spectra for various elements appear in the middle, and the Hg spectrum appears at the bottom.
2. **Set the spectra of the color plate.** The wavelength scale has been set relative to the dominant wavelengths of the mercury spectrum (Table D3.4) appearing at the bottom of the color plate.

   Use a ruler to align the bottom linear wavelength scale with the top wavelength scale of the color plate. A wax marker or a "permanent" felt tip pen may be required to connect the wavelength scales. As a result, a wavelength grid is now set for calibrating all of the emission spectra on the color plate.

   Have your instructor approve your wavelength grid of the spectra on the color plate. See the ***Report Sheet***.

Table D3.4 Wavelengths of the Visible Lines in the Mercury Spectrum

Violet	404.7 nm
Violet	407.8 nm
Blue	435.8 nm
Yellow	546.1 nm
Orange	577.0 nm
Orange	579.1 nm

B. The Spectra of Elements

1. **Hydrogen spectrum.** Use Figure D3.3, page 163, to identify which of the emission spectra on the color plate on the back cover is that of hydrogen. Justify your selection.
2. **Unknown spectra.** Your instructor will assign to you one or two emission spectra from the color plate. Analyze each spectrum by locating the most intense wavelengths in the assigned emission spectrum. Compare the wavelengths of the most intense lines with the data in Table D3.5. Identify the element having the assigned spectrum.

C. Infrared Spectra of Compounds

1. **Match of molecule with infrared spectrum.** Your instructor will assign one or more compounds on page 168 for which you are to determine its infrared spectrum. The absorption bands characteristic of atoms in bonds are listed in Table D3.2, page 164, to assist in the match.

Table D3.5 Wavelengths and Relative Intensities of the Emission Spectra of Several Elements

Element	Wavelength (*nm*)	Relative Intensity
Cadmium	467.8	200
	479.9	300
	508.6	1,000
	610.0	300
	643.8	2,000
Cesium	455.5	1,000
	459.3	460
	546.6	60
	566.4	210
	584.5	300
	601.0	640
	621.3	1,000
	635.5	320
	658.7	490
	672.3	3,300
Helium	388.9	500
	396.5	20
	402.6	50
	412.1	12
	438.8	10
	447.1	200
	468.6	30
	471.3	30
	492.2	20
	501.5	100
	587.5	500
	587.6	100
	667.8	100
Neon	585.2	500
	587.2	100
	588.2	100
	594.5	100
	596.5	100
	597.4	100
	597.6	120
	603.0	100
	607.4	100
	614.3	100
	616.4	120
	618.2	250
	621.7	150
	626.6	150
	633.4	100
	638.3	120
	640.2	200
	650.7	150
	660.0	150
Potassium	404.4	18
	404.7	17
	536.0	14
	578.2	16
	580.1	17
	580.2	15
	583.2	17
	691.1	19
Rubidium	420.2	1,000
	421.6	500
	536.3	40
	543.2	75
	572.4	60
	607.1	75
	620.6	75
	630.0	120
Sodium	466.5	120
	466.9	200
	497.9	200
	498.3	400
	568.2	280
	568.8	560
	589.0	80,000
	589.6	40,000
	616.1	240
Thallium	377.6	12,000
	436.0	2
	535.0	18,000
	655.0	16
	671.4	6
Zinc	468.0	300
	472.2	400
	481.1	400
	507.0	15
	518.2	200
	577.7	10
	623.8	8
	636.2	1,000
	647.9	10
	692.8	15

D. Structure of Molecules and Molecular Ions

1. **Five basic structures.** Using an appropriate set of molecular models, construct the five basic three-dimensional structures shown in Table D3.3, page 165. Because of the possible limited availability of molecular models, some sharing with other chemists may be necessary. Consult with your laboratory instructor.
2. **Determine three-dimensional structures.** On the ***Report Sheet*** are selections of suggested molecules and molecular ions for which their three-dimensional structures (geometric shapes) and approximate bond angles are to be determined. Ask your instructor which are to be completed. Set up the table as suggested on the ***Report Sheet*** for your assigned molecules/molecular ions. Refer to your "built" five basic VSEPR structures as you analyze each molecule/molecular ion.

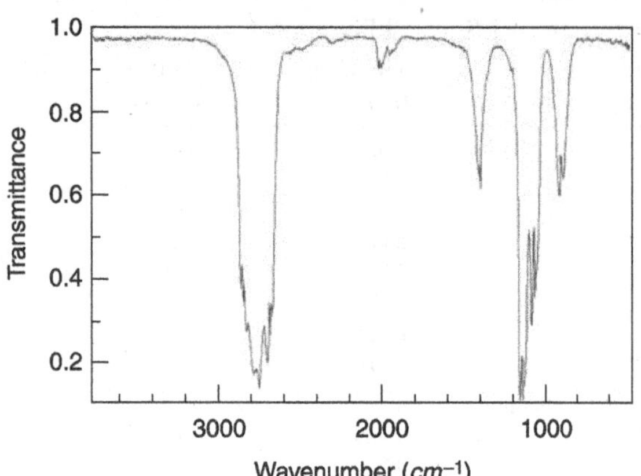

Figure D3.5A

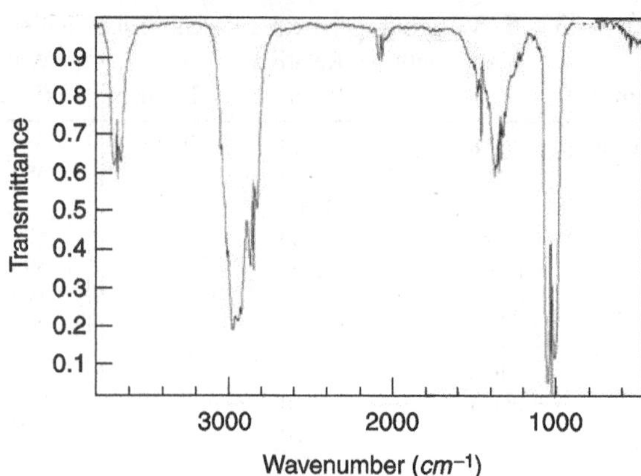

Figure D3.5B

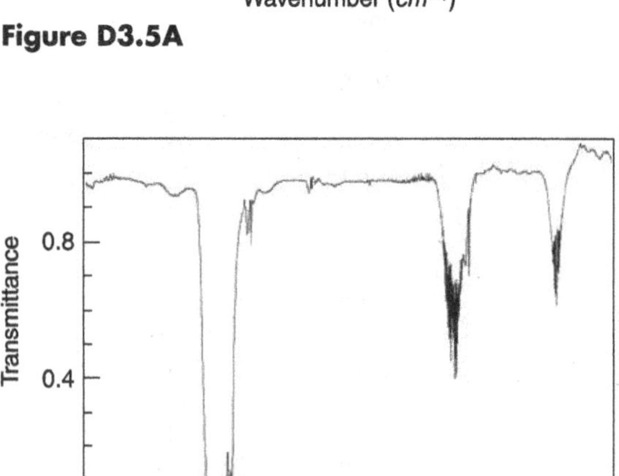

Figure D3.5C

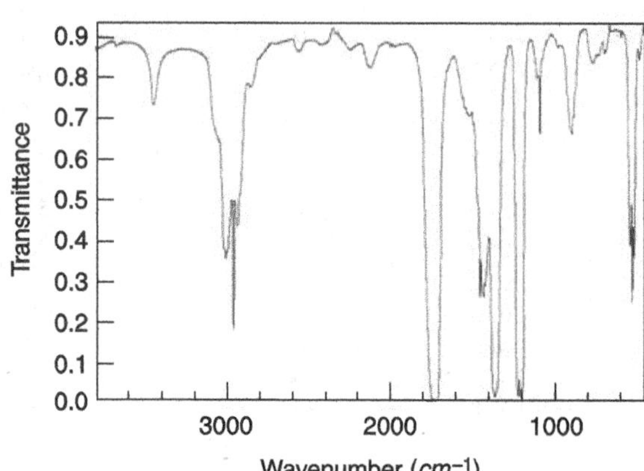

Figure D3.5D

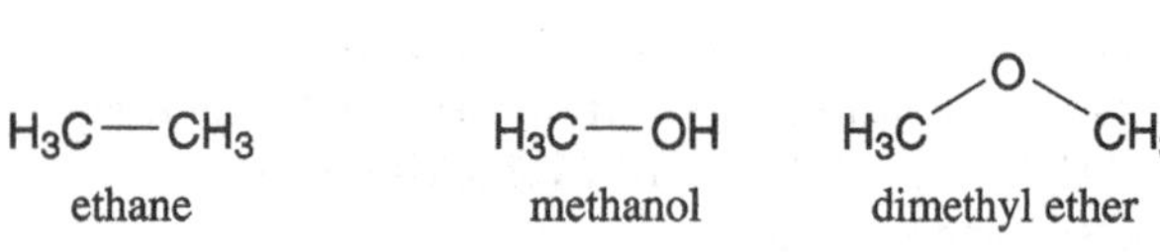

O
C
H_3C CH_3
acetone

The Next Step

What you complete in this experiment are techniques/tools for atomic and molecular structural analysis. Chemists, biologists, and biochemists are very interested in the identification and structures of compounds. Electromagnetic radiation is just one of those avenues for determination.

Dry Lab 3 *Report Sheet*

Atomic and Molecular Structure

Date _________ Lab Sec. ______ Name ______________________________ Desk No. _________

A. The Mercury Spectrum

Instructor's approval of the wavelength grid of the spectra on the color plate (back cover): ____________________

B. The Spectra of Elements

1. Spectrum number _____ is the emission line spectrum for hydrogen on the color plate.

   What are the wavelengths and colors of the emission lines of the visible spectrum of hydrogen?

2. Identification of Spectra
   a. Spectrum number _____

   Intense lines in the spectrum: _____ nm; _____ nm; _____ nm; _____ nm; _____ nm; _____ nm; _____ nm

   Element producing the spectrum ____________________

   b. Spectrum number _____

   Intense lines in the spectrum: _____ nm; _____ nm; _____ nm; _____ nm; _____ nm; _____ nm; _____ nm

   Element producing the spectrum ____________________

C. Match of Molecule with Infrared Spectrum

Complete the following table.

Molecule Assigned	Atom-in-Bond Arrangements	Absorption Bands (cm^{-1})	Infrared Spectrum Figure No.
______	______	______	______
______	______	______	______
______	______	______	______

D. Structure of Molecules and Molecular Ions

On a separate sheet of paper, set up the following table (with eight columns) for each of the molecules/molecular ions that are assigned to you/your group. The central atom of the molecule/molecular ion is italicized.

Molecule or Molecular Ion	Lewis Structure	Valence Shell Electron Pairs	Bonding Electron Pairs	Nonbonding Electron Pairs	VSEPR Formula	Approx. Bond Angle	Geometric Shape
1. $\mathit{C}H_4$	H H:C:H H	4	4	0	AX_4	109.5°	tetrahedral
2. $\mathit{S}F_4$							
3. $H_2\mathit{O}$							

1. Complete the table (as outlined above) for the following molecules/molecular ions, all of which obey the Lewis octet rule. Complete those that are assigned by your laboratory instructor.

- **a.** $H_3\mathit{O}^+$
- **b.** $\mathit{N}H_3$
- **c.** $\mathit{N}H_4^+$
- **d.** $\mathit{C}H_3^-$
- **e.** $\mathit{Sn}H_4$
- **f.** $\mathit{B}F_4^-$
- **g.** $\mathit{P}O_4^{3-}$
- **h.** $\mathit{P}F_3$
- **i.** $\mathit{As}H_3$
- **j.** $\mathit{Si}F_4$
- **k.** $H_2\mathit{S}$
- **l.** $\mathit{N}H_2^-$

2. Complete the table (as outlined above) for the following molecules/molecular ions, *none* of which obey the Lewis octet rule. Complete those that are assigned by your laboratory instructor.

- **a.** $\mathit{Ga}I_3$
- **b.** $\mathit{P}Cl_2F_3$
- **c.** $\mathit{Br}F_3$
- **d.** $\mathit{Xe}F_2$
- **e.** $\mathit{Xe}F_4$
- **f.** $\mathit{Xe}OF_2$
- **g.** $\mathit{Xe}OF_4$
- **h.** $\mathit{Sb}F_6^-$
- **i.** $\mathit{S}F_6$
- **j.** $\mathit{Sn}F_6^{2-}$
- **k.** $\mathit{I}F_4^-$
- **l.** $\mathit{I}F_4^+$

3. Complete the table (as outlined above) for the following molecules/molecular ions. No adherence to the Lewis octet rule is indicated. Complete those that are assigned by your laboratory instructor.

- **a.** $\mathit{As}F_3$
- **b.** $\mathit{Cl}O_2^-$
- **c.** $\mathit{C}F_3Cl$
- **d.** $\mathit{Sn}F_2$
- **e.** $\mathit{Sn}F_4$
- **f.** $\mathit{P}F_4^+$
- **g.** $\mathit{P}F_5$
- **h.** $\mathit{S}O_4^{2-}$
- **i.** $\mathit{C}N_2^{2-}$
- **j.** $\mathit{Kr}F_2$
- **k.** $\mathit{Te}F_6$
- **l.** $\mathit{As}F_5$

4. Complete the table (as outlined above) for the following molecules/molecular ions. For molecules or molecular ions with two or more atoms considered as central atoms, consider each atom separately in the analysis according to Table D3.3. Complete those that are assigned by your laboratory instructor.

- **a.** $O\mathit{P}Cl_3$
- **b.** $H_2\mathit{CC}H_2$
- **c.** $\mathit{C}H_3\mathit{N}H_3^+$
- **d.** $Cl_3\mathit{CC}F_3$
- **e.** $Cl_2\mathit{O}$
- **f.** $Cl\mathit{C}N$
- **g.** $\mathit{C}OCl_2$
- **h.** $O\mathit{CCC}O$
- **i.** $\mathit{C}O_2$
- **j.** O_3
- **k.** $\mathit{N}O_3^-$
- **l.** $\mathit{Te}F_2(CH_3)_4$

Dry Lab Questions

Circle the questions that have been assigned.

1. What experimental evidence leads scientists to believe that only quantized electronic energy states exist in atoms?

2. a. What is the wavelength range of the visible spectrum for electromagnetic radiation?

   b. What is the color of the short wavelength region of the visible spectrum?

   c. If a substance absorbed the wavelengths from the short wavelength region of the visible spectrum, what would be its color?

3. Explain why "roses are red and violets are blue."

4. a. Is the energy absorption associated with bands in an infrared spectrum of higher or lower energy than the lines appearing in a visible line spectrum? Explain.

   b. Identify the type of energy transition occurring in a molecule that causes a band to appear in an infrared spectrum.

   c. Identify the type of energy transition occurring in an atom that causes a line to appear in a visible line spectrum.

5. Since $FeNCS^{2+}$ has an absorption maximum at 447 nm, what is the color of the $FeNCS^{2+}$ ion in solution?

6. a. Write the Lewis structure for XeF_4.

b. Write the VSEPR formula for XeF_4.

c. Sketch (or describe) the three-dimensional structure (or geometric shape) of XeF_4.

d. What are the approximate F–Xe–F bond angles in XeF_4?

7. Glycine, the simplest of the amino acids, has the formula, $CH_2(NH_2)COOH$, and the Lewis structure at right.

a. Write the VSEPR formula for the nitrogen atom as the central atom in glycine.

```
    H   :O:
    |   ||
H—C—C—Ö—H
    |       ¨
   :N—H
    |
    H
```

b. Based on VSEPR theory, what is the approximate C—N—H bond angle in glycine? Explain.

c. What is the approximate O—C—O bond angle in glycine? Explain.

d. Identify at least two absorption bands (and corresponding cm^{-1}) that would likely appear in the infrared spectrum of glycine.

Courtesy of Thermo Fisher Scientific

A thermometer is secured with a thermometer clamp to guard against breakage.

Experiment 14

Molar Mass of a Solid

Objectives

- To observe and measure the effect of a solute on the freezing point of a solvent
- To determine the molar mass (molecular weight) of a nonvolatile, nonelectrolyte solute

Techniques

The following techniques are used in the Experimental Procedure:

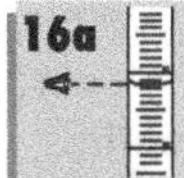

Introduction

A pure liquid, such as water or ethanol, has characteristic physical properties: the melting point, boiling point, density, vapor pressure, viscosity, surface tension, and additional data listed in handbooks of chemistry. The addition of a soluble solute to the liquid forms a homogeneous mixture called a **solution.** The solvent of the solution assumes physical properties that are no longer definite but dependent on the amount of solute added. The vapor pressure of the solvent decreases, the freezing point of the solvent decreases, the boiling point of the solvent increases, and the osmotic pressure of the solvent increases. The degree of the change depends on the *number* of solute particles that have dissolved, *not* on the chemical identity of the solute. These four physical properties that depend on the number of solute particles dissolved in a solvent are called **colligative properties.**

For example, one mole of glucose or urea (neither of which dissociates in water) lowers the freezing point of one kilogram of water by 1.86°C; whereas one mole of sodium chloride lowers the freezing point of one kilogram of water by nearly twice that amount (~3.72°C) because, when dissolved in water, it dissociates into Na^+ and Cl^- providing *twice* as many moles of solute particles per mole of solute as do glucose or urea.

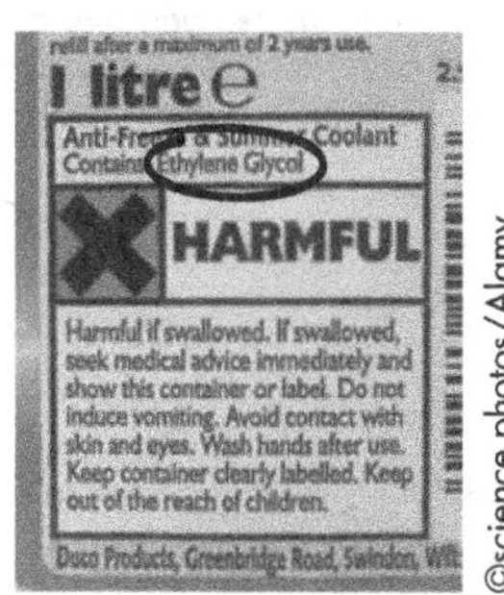

©science photos/Alamy

Figure 14.1 Ethylene glycol is a major component of most antifreeze solutions.

When freezing ice cream at home, a salt–ice water mixture provides a lower temperature bath than an ice/water mixture alone. Antifreeze (ethylene glycol, Figure 14.1) added to the cooling system of an automobile reduces the probability of freeze-up in the winter and boiling over in the summer because the antifreeze/water solution has a lower freezing point and a higher boiling point than pure water.

Colligative properties: properties of a solvent that result from the presence of the number of solute particles in the solution and not their chemical composition

These changes in the properties of pure water that result from the presence of a **nonvolatile solute** are portrayed by the phase diagram in Figure 14.2, page 190, a plot of vapor pressure versus temperature. The solid lines refer to the equilibrium conditions between the respective phases for pure water; the dashed lines represent the same conditions for an aqueous solution.

Nonvolatile solute: a solute that does not have a measurable vapor pressure

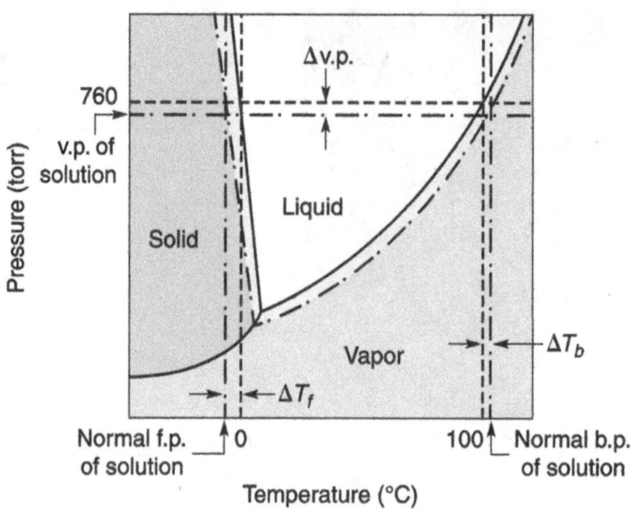

Figure 14.2 Phase diagram (not shown to scale) for water (—) and for an aqueous solution (–·–·–).

Vapor pressure: pressure exerted by a vapor when the vapor is in a state of dynamic equilibrium with its liquid

The **vapor pressure** of water is 760 torr at its boiling point of 100°C. When a nonvolatile solute dissolves in water to form a solution, solute molecules occupy a part of the surface area. This inhibits movement of some water molecules into the vapor state, causing a **vapor pressure lowering** of the water ($\Delta v.p.$ in Figure 14.2), lower than 760 torr. With the vapor pressure less than 760 torr, the solution (more specifically, the water in the solution) no longer boils at 100°C. For the solution to boil, the vapor pressure must be increased to 760 torr; boiling can resume only if the temperature is increased above 100°C. This **boiling point elevation** (ΔT_b in Figure 14.2) of the water is due to the presence of the solute.

Boiling point: the temperature at which the vapor pressure of a liquid equals atmospheric pressure

A solute added to water also affects its freezing point. The normal freezing point of water is 0°C, but in the presence of a solute, the temperature must be lowered below 0°C before freezing occurs (the energy of the water molecules must be lowered to increase the magnitude of the intermolecular forces so that the water molecules "stick" together to form a solid); this is called a **freezing point depression** of the water (ΔT_f in Figure 14.2).

Freezing point: the temperature at which the liquid and solid phases of a substance coexist

The changes in the freezing point, ΔT_f, and the boiling point, ΔT_b, are directly proportional to the molality, m, of the solute in solution. The proportionality is a constant, characteristic of the actual solvent. For water, the freezing point constant, k_f, is 1.86°C • kg/mol, and the boiling point constant, k_b, is 0.512°C • kg/mol.

$$\Delta T_f = |T_{f,\text{ solvent}} - T_{f,\text{ solution}}| = k_f m \tag{14.1}$$

$$\Delta T_b = |T_{b,\text{ solvent}} - T_{b,\text{ solution}}| = k_b m \tag{14.2}$$

In equations 14.1 and 14.2, T_f represents the freezing point and T_b represents the boiling point of the respective system. $|T_{f,\text{ solvent}} - T_{f,\text{ solution}}|$ represents the absolute temperature difference in the freezing point change. **Molality** is defined as

$$\text{molality, } m = \frac{\text{mol solute}}{\text{kg solvent}} = \frac{\text{(mass/molar mass)}}{\text{kg solvent}} \tag{14.3}$$

k_f and k_b values for various solvents are listed in Table 14.1.

In this experiment, the freezing points of a selected pure solvent and of a solute–solvent mixture are measured. The freezing point lowering (difference), the k_f data from Table 14.1 for the solvent, and equations 14.1 and 14.3 are used to calculate the moles of solute dissolved in solution and, from its measured mass, the molar mass of the solute.

Cooling curve: a data plot of temperature versus time showing the rate of cooling of a substance before, during, and after its phase changes

Experimentally, the freezing points of the solvent and the solution are obtained from a **cooling curve**—a plot of temperature versus time. An ideal plot of the data appears in Figure 14.3. The cooling curve for a pure solvent reaches a plateau at its freezing point: Extrapolation of the plateau to the temperature axis determines

Table 14.1 Molal Freezing Point and Boiling Point Constants for Several Solvents

Substance	Freezing Point (°C)	$k_f\left(\frac{°C \cdot kg}{mol}\right)$	Boiling Point (°C)	$k_b\left(\frac{°C \cdot kg}{mol}\right)$
H_2O	0.0	1.86	100.0	0.512
Cyclohexane	—	20.0	80.7	2.69
Naphthalene	80.2	6.9	—	—
Camphor	179	39.7	—	—
Acetic acid	17	3.90	118.2	2.93
t-Butanol	25.5	9.1	—	—

its freezing point. The cooling curve for the solution does *not* reach a plateau but continues to decrease slowly as the solvent freezes out of solution. Its freezing point is determined at the intersection of two straight lines drawn through the data points above and below the freezing point (Figure 14.3).

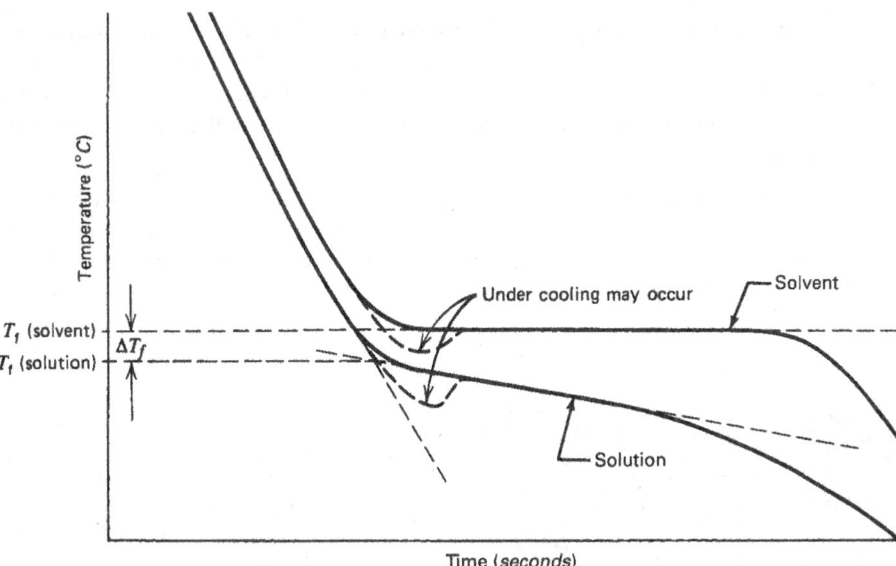

Figure 14.3 Cooling curves for a solvent and solution

Experimental Procedure

Procedure Overview: Cyclohexane is the solvent selected for this experiment although other solvents may be just as effective for the determination of the molar mass of a solute. Another solvent[1] may be used at the discretion of the laboratory instructor. Consult with your instructor. The freezing points of pure cyclohexane and a cyclohexane *solution* are determined from plots of temperature versus time. The mass of the solute is measured before it is dissolved in a known mass of cyclohexane.

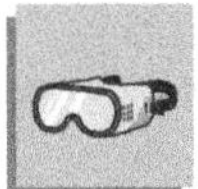

Obtain about 15 mL of cyclohexane. You'll use the cyclohexane throughout the experiment. Your laboratory instructor will issue you ~1 g of unknown solute. Record the unknown number of the solute on the ***Report Sheet***.

Be aware of the number of significant figures when recording data.

The cooling curve to be plotted in Part A.4 can be established by using a thermal probe that is connected directly to either a calculator or computer with the appropriate software. If this thermal sensing/recording apparatus is available in the laboratory, consult with your instructor for its use and adaptation to the experiment. The probe merely replaces the glass or digital thermometer in Figure 14.4, page 192.

[1] *t*-Butanol is a suitable substitute for cyclohexane in this experiment.

A. Freezing Point of Cyclohexane (Solvent)

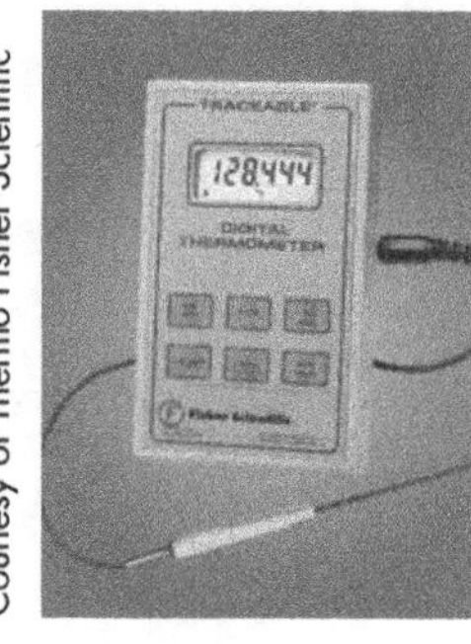

Courtesy of Thermo Fisher Scientific

A modern digital thermometer

Data Analysis, A

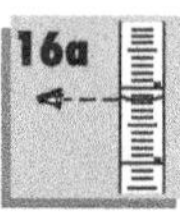

Data Analysis, F

1. **Prepare the ice–water bath.** Assemble the apparatus shown in Figure 14.4. A 400-mL beaker is placed inside a 600-mL beaker, the latter being an outside insulating beaker. You may want to place a paper towel between the beakers to further insulate the ice–water bath. Place about 300 mL of an ice–water slurry into the 400-mL beaker.[2]

   Obtain a digital or glass thermometer, mount it with a thermometer clamp to the ring stand, and position the thermometer in the test tube. (**Caution:** *If the thermometer is a glass thermometer, handle the thermometer carefully. If the thermometer is accidentally broken, notify your instructor immediately.*)

2. **Prepare the cyclohexane.** Determine the mass (±0.01 g)[3] of a *clean, dry* 200-mm test tube in a 250-mL beaker (Figure 14.5). Add approximately 12 mL of cyclohexane (**Caution:** *Cyclohexane is flammable—keep away from flames; cyclohexane is a mucous irritant—do not inhale*) to the test tube. Place the test tube containing the cyclohexane into the ice–water bath (Figure 14.4). Secure the test tube with a utility clamp. Insert the thermometer probe and a wire stirrer into the test tube. *Secure the thermometer* so that the thermometer bulb or thermal sensor is completely submerged into the cyclohexane.

3. **Record data for the freezing point of cyclohexane.** While stirring with the wire stirrer, record the temperature at timed intervals (15 or 30 seconds) on the second page of the ***Report Sheet***. The temperature remains virtually constant at the freezing point until the solidification is complete. Continue collecting data until the temperature begins to drop again.

4. **Plot the data.** On linear graph paper or by using appropriate software, plot the temperature (°*C*, vertical axis) versus time (*sec*, horizontal axis) to obtain the cooling curve for cyclohexane. Have your instructor approve your graph.

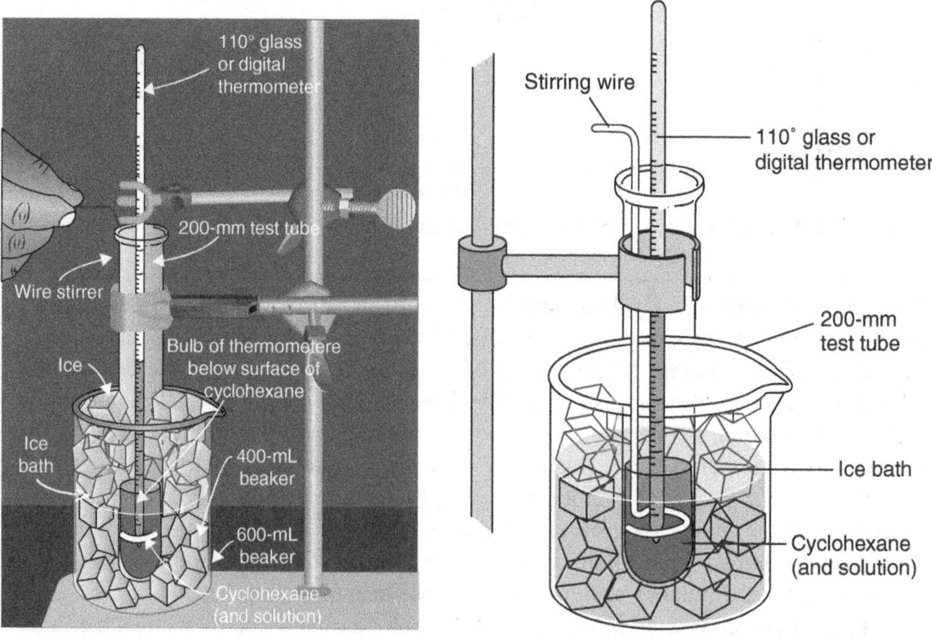

Figure 14.4 Freezing point apparatus

[2]Rock salt may be added to further lower the temperature of the ice–water bath.
[3]Use a balance with ±0.001 g sensitivity, if available.

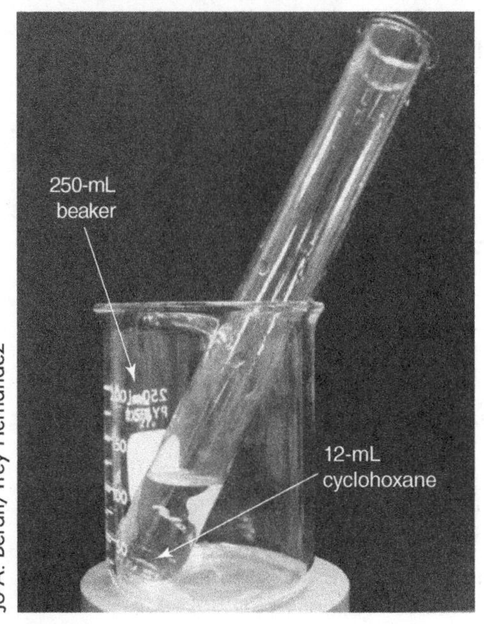

Figure 14.5 Determining the mass of beaker and test tube before (Part A.2) and after adding cyclohexane (Part B.1)

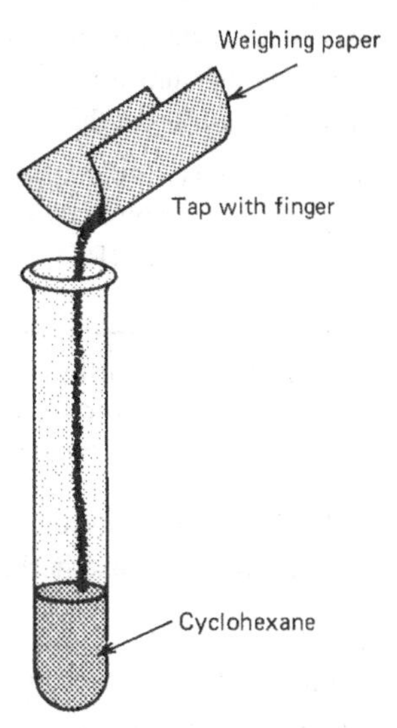

Figure 14.6 Transfer of the unknown solid solute to the test tube containing cyclohexane

B. Freezing Point of Cyclohexane plus Unknown Solute

Three freezing point trials for the cyclohexane solution are to be completed. Successive amounts of unknown sample are added to the cyclohexane in Parts B.4 and B.5.

1. **Measure the mass of solvent and solid solute.** Dry the outside of the test tube containing the cyclohexane and measure its mass in the same 250-mL beaker. On weighing paper, tare the mass of 0.1–0.3 g (±0.001g) of unknown solid solute (ask your instructor for the approximate mass to use) and record. Quantitatively transfer the solute to the cyclohexane in the 200-mm test tube (Figure 14.6).[4]
2. **Record data for the freezing point of solution.** Determine the freezing point of this solution in the same way as that of the solvent (Part A.3). Record the time and temperature data on page 2 of the ***Report Sheet***. When the solution nears the freezing point of the pure cyclohexane, record the temperature at more frequent time intervals (~15 seconds). A "break" in the curve occurs as the freezing begins, although it may not be as sharp as that for the pure cyclohexane.
3. **Plot the data on the same graph.** Plot the temperature versus time data on the *same* graph (and same coordinates) as those for the pure cyclohexane (Part A.4). Draw straight lines through the data points above and below the freezing point (see Figure 14.3); the intersection of the two straight lines is the freezing point of the solution.

Data Analysis, F

4. **Repeat with additional solute.** Remove the test tube and solution from the ice–water bath. Add an additional 0.1–0.3 g (±0.001g) of unknown solid solute using the *same procedure* as in Part B.1. Repeat the freezing-point determination and again plot the temperature versus time data on the same graph (Parts B.2 and B.3). The total mass of solute in solution is the sum from the first and second trials.
5. **Again. Repeat with additional solute.** Repeat Part B.4 with an additional 0.1–0.2 g (±0.001g) of unknown solid solute, using the *same procedure* as in Part B.1. Repeat the freezing-point determination and again plot the temperature

[4]In the transfer, be certain that *none* of the solid solute adheres to the test tube wall. If some does, roll the test tube until the solute dissolves.

versus time data on the same graph (Parts B.2–4). The total mass of solute in solution is the sum for the masses added in Parts B.1, B.4 and B.5. You now should have four plots on the same graph.

6. **Obtain instructor's approval.** Have your instructor approve the three temperature versus time graphs (Parts B.3–5) that have been added to your first temperature versus time graph (Part A.4) for the pure cyclohexane.

Disposal: Dispose of the waste cyclohexane and cyclohexane solution in the Waste Organic Liquids container.

CLEANUP: Safely store and return the thermometer. Rinse the test tube once with acetone; discard the rinse in the Waste Organic Liquids container.

C. Calculations

Data Analysis, A

1. From the plotted data, determine ΔT_f for Trial 1, Trial 2, and Trial 3. Refer to the plotted cooling curves (see Figure 14.3).
2. From k_f (Table 14.1), the mass (in kg) of the cyclohexane, and the measured ΔT_f, calculate the moles of solute for each trial. See equations 14.1 and 14.3.
3. Determine the molar mass of the solute for each trial (remember the mass of the solute for each trial is different).
4. What is the average molar mass of your unknown solute?

Data Analysis, B, C, and D

5. Calculate the standard deviation and the relative standard deviation (%RSD) for the molar mass of the solute.

The Next Step

Salts dissociate in water. (1) Design an experiment to determine the percent dissociation for a selection of salts in water—consider various concentrations of the salt solutions. Explain your data. (2) Determine the total concentration of dissolved solids in a water sample using this technique and compare your results to the data in *Experiment 3*.

Notes and Calculations

Experiment 14 *Prelaboratory Assignment*

Molar Mass of a Solid

Date ________ Lab Sec. ______ Name ______________________________ Desk No. ________

1. This experiment is more about understanding the colligative properties of a solution rather than the determination of the molar mass of a solid.
   a. Define colligative properties.

   b. Which of the following solutes has the greatest effect on the colligative properties for a given mass of pure water? Explain.
   (i) 0.01 mol of $CaCl_2$ (an electrolyte)
   (ii) 0.01 mol of KNO_3 (an electrolyte)
   (iii) 0.01 mol of $CO(NH_2)_2$ (a nonelectrolyte)

2. Explain why ice cubes formed from water of a glacier freeze at a higher temperature than ice cubes formed from water of an underground aquifer.

Photodynamic/iStockphoto

3. Two solutions are prepared using the *same* solute:
   Solution A: 0.14 g of the solute dissolves in 15.4 g of *t*-butanol
   Solution B: 0.17 g of the solute dissolves in 12.7 g of cyclohexane
   Which solution has the greatest freezing point change? Show calculations and explain.

4. Experimental Procedure.

a. How many (total) data plots are to be completed for this experiment? Account for each.

b. What information is to be extracted from each data plot?

5. **a.** Data were collected for Trial 1 to determine the molar mass of a nonvolatile solid solute when dissolved in cyclohexane. Complete the table for the analysis (See ***Report Sheet***). Record calculated values with the correct number of significant figures.

B. Freezing Point of Cyclohexane plus Unknown Solute			***Calculation Zone***
2. Mass of cyclohexane (*g*)	10.14	*Part C.4*	
3. Mass of added solute (*g*)	0.255		
C. Calculations			
1. k_f for cyclohexane (*°C • kg/mol*)	20.0		
2. Freezing point change, ΔT_f (*°C*)	3.04	*Part C.6*	
3. Mass of cyclohexane in solution (*kg*)			
4. Moles of solute, total (*mol*) Show calculation.			
5. Mass of solute in solution, total (*g*)			
6. Molar mass of solute (*g/mol*) Show calculation.			

5. **b.** For Trials 2 and 3, the molar mass of the solute was 151 g/mol and 143 g/mol respectively.

a. What is the average molar mass of the solute ?

b. What are the standard deviation and the relative standard deviation (%RSD) for the molar mass of the solute ?

Experiment 14 *Report Sheet*

Molar Mass of a Solid

Date ________ Lab Sec. ______ Name ______________________________ Desk No. ________

A. Freezing Point of Cyclohexane (Solvent)

1. Mass of beaker, test tube (g) ____________

2. Freezing point, from cooling curve (°C) ____________

3. Instructor's approval of graph ____________

B. Freezing Point of Cyclohexane plus Unknown Solute

Unknown solute no. ________	*Trial 1 (Parts B.1, B.3)*	*Trial 2 (Part B.4)*	*Trial 3 (Part B.5)*
1. Mass of beaker, test tube, cyclohexane (g)		____________	
2. Mass of cyclohexane (g)		____________	
3. Tared mass of added solute (g)	________	________	________
4. Freezing point, from cooling curve (°C)	________	________	________
5. Instructor's approval of graph		____________	

Calculations

1. k_f for cyclohexane (°C • kg/mol)		20.0	
2. Freezing-point *change*, ΔT_f (°C)	________	________	________
3. Mass of cyclohexane in solution (kg)	________	________	________
4. Moles of solute, *total* (mol)	________	________	________
5. Mass of solute in solution, *total* (g)	________	________	________
6. Molar mass of solute (g/mol)	________	________*	________
7. Average molar mass of solute (g/mol)		____________	**Data Analysis, B**
8. Standard deviation of molar mass		____________	**Data Analysis, C**
9. Relative standard deviation of molar mass (%RSD)		____________	**Data Analysis, D**

*Show calculation(s) for Trial 2 on the next page.

*Calculations for Trial 2.

A. Cyclohexane		B. Cyclohexane + Unknown Solute					
Time	Temp	*Trial 1*		*Trial 2*		*Trial 3*	
		Time	Temp	Time	Temp	Time	Temp

Continue recording data on your own paper and submit it with the ***Report Sheet***.

Laboratory Questions

Circle the questions that have been assigned.

1. Part A.3. Some of the cyclohexane solvent vaporized during the temperature versus time measurement. Will this loss of cyclohexane result in its freezing point being recorded as too high, too low, or unaffected? Explain.
2. Part A.3. The digital thermometer is miscalibrated by +0.15°C over its entire range. If the same thermometer is used in Part B.2, will the reported moles of solute in the solution be too high, too low, or unaffected? Explain.
3. Part B.1. Some of the solid solute adheres to the side of the test tube during the freezing point determination of the solution in Part B.2. As a result of the oversight, will the reported molar mass of the solute be too high, too low, or unaffected? Explain.
4. Part B.2. Some of the cyclohexane solvent vaporized during the temperature versus time measurement. Will this loss of cyclohexane result in the freezing point of the solution being recorded as too high, too low, or unaffected? Explain.
5. Part B.2. The solute dissociates slightly in the solvent. How will the slight dissociation affect the reported molar mass of the solute—too high, too low, or unaffected? Explain.

*6. Part B.3, Figure 14.3. The temperature versus time data plot (Figure 14.3) shows no change in temperature at the freezing point for a pure solvent; however, the temperature at the freezing point for a solution steadily decreases until the solution has completely solidified. Account for this decreasing temperature.

7. Part C.1. Interpretation of the data plots consistently shows that the freezing points of three solutions are too high. As a result of this "misreading of the data," will the reported molar mass of the solute be too high, too low, or unaffected? Explain.

$2\,CrO_4^{2-}(aq) + 2H^+(aq) \rightleftharpoons Cr_2O_7^{2-}(aq) + H_2O(l)$

Jo A. Beran/Trey Hernandez

Experiment 16

LeChâtelier's Principle; Buffers*

The chromate ion (left) is yellow, and the dichromate ion (right) is orange. An equilibrium between the two ions is affected by changes in pH.

OBJECTIVES

- To study the effects of concentration and temperature changes on the position of equilibrium in a chemical system
- To study the effect of strong acid and strong base addition on the pH of buffered and unbuffered systems
- To observe the common-ion effect on a dynamic equilibrium

The following techniques are used in the Experimental Procedure:

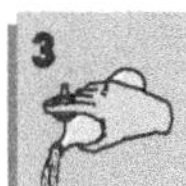

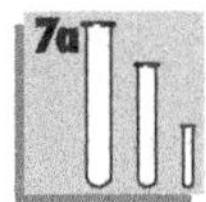

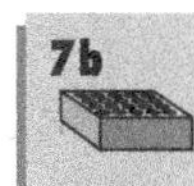

INTRODUCTION

Most chemical reactions do not produce a 100% yield of product, not because of experimental technique or design, but rather because of the chemical characteristics of the reaction. The reactants initially produce the expected products, but after a period of time the concentrations of the reactants and products *stop* changing.

This apparent cessation of the reaction before a 100% yield is obtained implies that the chemical system has reached a state where the reactants combine to form the products at a rate equal to that of the products re-forming the reactants. This condition is a state of **dynamic equilibrium** and is characteristic of all reversible reactions.

For the reaction

$$2\,NO_2(g) \rightleftharpoons N_2O_4(g) + 58\text{ kJ} \tag{16.1}$$

chemical equilibrium is established when the rate at which two NO_2 molecules react equals the rate at which one N_2O_4 molecule dissociates (Figure 16.1).

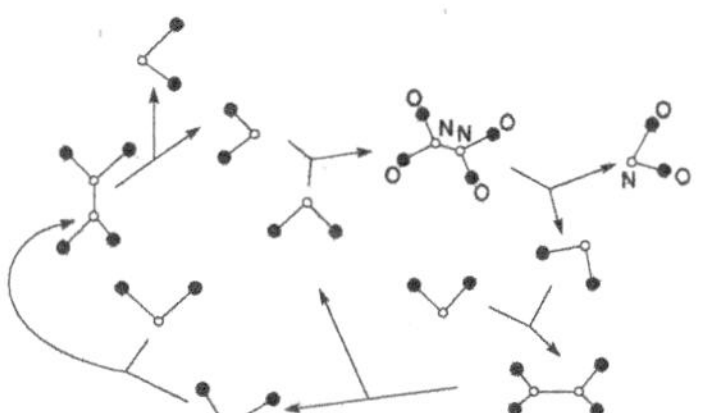

Figure 16.1 A dynamic equilibrium exists between reactant NO_2 molecules and product N_2O_4 molecules.

If the concentration of one of the species in the equilibrium system changes, or if the temperature changes, the equilibrium tends to *shift* in a way that compensates for the change. For example, assuming the system represented by equation 16.1 is in a state of dynamic equilibrium, if more NO_2 is added, the probability of its reaction with other NO_2 molecules increases. As a result, more N_2O_4 forms, and the reaction shifts to the *right,* until equilibrium is reestablished.

A general statement governing all systems in a state of dynamic equilibrium follows:

> *If an external stress (change in concentration, temperature, etc.) is applied to a system in a state of dynamic equilibrium, the equilibrium shifts in the direction that minimizes the effect of that stress.*

*Numerous online Web sites discuss LeChâtelier's principle.

This is **LeChâtelier's principle,** proposed by Henri Louis LeChâtelier in 1888.

Often the equilibrium concentrations of all species in the system can be determined. From this information, an equilibrium constant can be calculated; its magnitude indicates the relative position of the equilibrium. This constant is determined in *Experiments 22, 26, and 34.*

Two factors affecting equilibrium position are studied in this experiment: changes in concentration and changes in temperature.

Changes in Concentration

Metal–Ammonia Ions. Aqueous solutions of copper ions and nickel ions appear sky blue and green, respectively. The colors of the solutions change, however, in the presence of added ammonia, NH_3. Because the metal–ammonia bond is stronger than the metal–water bond, ammonia substitution occurs and the following equilibria shift *right,* forming the metal–ammonia **complex ions:**[1]

Complex ion: a metal ion bonded to a number of Lewis bases. The complex ion is generally identified by its enclosure with brackets, [ ].

$$[Cu(H_2O)_4]^{2+}(aq) + 4\,NH_3(aq) \rightleftharpoons [Cu(NH_3)_4]^{2+}(aq) + 4\,H_2O(l) \qquad (16.2)$$

$$[Ni(H_2O)_6]^{2+}(aq) + 6\,NH_3(aq) \rightleftharpoons [Ni(NH_3)_6]^{2+}(aq) + 6\,H_2O(l) \qquad (16.3)$$

Addition of strong acid, H^+, affects these equilibria by its reaction with ammonia (a base) on the left side of the equations:

$$NH_3(aq) + H^+(aq) \longrightarrow NH_4^+(aq) \qquad (16.4)$$

The ammonia being removed from the equilibria causes the reactions to shift *left* to relieve the stress caused by the removal of the ammonia, re-forming the aqueous Cu^{2+} (sky blue) and Ni^{2+} (green) solutions. For copper ions, this equilibrium shift may be represented as

$[Cu(H_2O)_4]^{2+}$ is a sky-blue color (left), but $[Cu(NH_3)_4]^{2+}$ is a deep-blue color (right).

$$\overset{\longleftarrow}{[Cu(H_2O)_4]^{2+}(aq) + 4\,NH_3(aq) \rightleftharpoons [Cu(NH_3)_4]^{2+}(aq) + 4\,H_2O(l)} \qquad (16.5)$$

$$\downarrow 4\,\boldsymbol{H^+(aq)}$$

$$\mathbf{4\,NH_4^+(aq)}$$

Multiple Equilibria with the Silver Ion

Many salts are only slightly soluble in water. Silver ion, Ag^+, forms a number of these salts. Several equilibria involving the relative solubilities of the silver salts of the carbonate, CO_3^{2-}, chloride, Cl^-, iodide, I^-, and sulfide, S^{2-}, anions are investigated in this experiment.

Silver Carbonate Equilibrium. The first of the silver salt equilibria observed in this experiment is that of a saturated solution of silver carbonate, Ag_2CO_3, in dynamic equilibrium with its silver and carbonate ions in solution.

$$Ag_2CO_3(s) \rightleftharpoons 2\,Ag^+(aq) + CO_3^{2-}(aq) \qquad (16.6)$$

Nitric acid, HNO_3, dissolves silver carbonate: H^+ ions react with (and remove) the CO_3^{2-} ions on the right; the system, in trying to replace the CO_3^{2-} ions, shifts to the *right.* The Ag_2CO_3 dissolves, and carbonic acid, H_2CO_3, forms.

$$\overset{\longrightarrow}{Ag_2CO_3(s) \rightleftharpoons 2\,Ag^+(aq) + CO_3^{2-}(aq)} \qquad (16.7)$$

$$\downarrow \mathbf{2}\,\boldsymbol{H^+(aq)}$$

$$\mathbf{H_2CO_3(aq)} \longrightarrow H_2O(l) + CO_2(g) \qquad (16.8)$$

The carbonic acid, being unstable at room temperature and pressure, decomposes to water and carbon dioxide. The silver ion and nitrate ion (from HNO_3) remain in solution.

[1]A further explanation of complex ions appears in *Experiment 36.*

Silver Chloride Equilibrium. Chloride ion precipitates silver ion as AgCl. Addition of chloride ion (from HCl) to the above solution containing Ag^+ causes the formation of a silver chloride, AgCl, precipitate, now in dynamic equilibrium with its Ag^+ and Cl^- ions (Figure 16.2).

Ken Karp

Figure 16.2 Solid AgCl quickly forms when solutions containing Ag^+ and Cl^- are mixed.

$$Ag^+(aq) + Cl^-(aq) \rightleftharpoons AgCl(s) \qquad (16.9)$$

Aqueous ammonia, NH_3, "ties up" (i.e., it forms a complex ion with) silver ion, producing the soluble diamminesilver(I) ion, $[Ag(NH_3)_2]^+$. The addition of NH_3 removes silver ion from the equilibrium in equation 16.9, shifting its equilibrium position to the *left* and causing AgCl to dissolve:

$$\begin{array}{l} Ag^+(aq) + Cl^-(aq) \overset{\longleftarrow}{\rightleftharpoons} AgCl(s) \\ \quad \uparrow\downarrow \mathbf{2\,\mathit{NH_3(aq)}} \\ \mathbf{[Ag(NH_3)_2]^+(\mathit{aq})} \end{array} \qquad (16.10)$$

Adding acid, H^+, to the solution again frees silver ion to recombine with chloride ion and re-forms solid silver chloride. This occurs because H^+ reacts with the NH_3 (see equation 16.4) in equation 16.10, restoring the presence of free Ag^+ to combine with the free Cl^- to form AgCl(*s*) shown in equation 16.9.

$$\begin{array}{l} \mathbf{Ag^+(\mathit{aq})} + Cl^-(aq) \overset{\longrightarrow}{\rightleftharpoons} AgCl(s) \\ \quad \uparrow 2\,NH_3(aq) + 2\,\mathbf{\mathit{H^+(aq)}} \longrightarrow 2\,NH_4^+(aq) \\ [Ag(NH_3)_2]^+(aq) \end{array} \qquad (16.11)$$

Silver Iodide Equilibrium. Iodide ion, I^- (from KI), added to the $Ag^+(aq) + 2\,NH_3(aq) \rightleftharpoons Ag(NH_3)_2{}^+(aq)$ equilibrium in equation 16.10 results in the formation of solid silver iodide, AgI.

$$\begin{array}{l} Ag^+(aq) + 2\,NH_3(aq) \overset{\longleftarrow}{\rightleftharpoons} [Ag(NH_3)_2]^+(aq) \\ \quad \downarrow \mathbf{\mathit{I^-(aq)}} \\ \mathbf{AgI(\mathit{s})} \end{array} \qquad (16.12)$$

The iodide ion removes the silver ion, causing a dissociation of the $[Ag(NH_3)_2]^+$ ion and a shift of the equilibrium to the *left*.

Silver Sulfide Equilibrium. Silver sulfide, Ag_2S, is less soluble than silver iodide, AgI. Therefore, an addition of sulfide ion (from Na_2S) to the $AgI(s) \rightleftharpoons Ag^+(aq) + I^-(aq)$ dynamic equilibrium in equation 16.12 removes silver ion; AgI dissolves, but solid silver sulfide forms.

$$\begin{array}{l} AgI(s) \overset{\longrightarrow}{\leftrightarrows} Ag^+(aq) + I^-(aq) \\ \qquad\quad \downarrow \mathbf{\tfrac{1}{2}\,\mathit{S^{2-}(aq)}} \\ \qquad \mathbf{\tfrac{1}{2}\,Ag_2S(\mathit{s})} \end{array} \qquad (16.13)$$

Buffers

In many areas of research, chemists need an aqueous solution that resists a pH change when small amounts of acid or base are added. Biologists often grow cultures that are very susceptible to changes in pH and therefore a buffered medium is required (Figure 16.3, page 210).

A buffer solution must be able to consume small additions of H_3O^+ and OH^- without undergoing large pH changes. Therefore, it must have present a basic component that can react with added H_3O^+ *and* an acidic component that can react with added OH^-. Such a buffer solution consists of a weak acid and its conjugate base (or weak base and its conjugate acid). This experiment shows that the acetic acid–acetate buffer system can minimize large pH changes:

$$CH_3COOH(aq) + H_2O(l) \rightleftharpoons H_3O^+(aq) + CH_3CO_2^-(aq) \qquad (16.14)$$

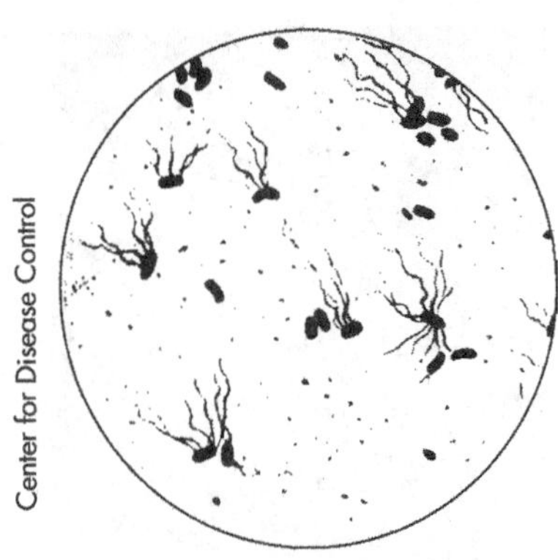

Figure 16.3 Bacteria cultures survive in media that exist over a narrow pH range. Buffers are used to control large changes in pH.

The addition of OH^- shifts the buffer equilibrium, according to LeChâtelier's principle, to the *right* because of its reaction with H_3O^+, forming H_2O. The shift right is by an amount that is essentially equal to the moles of OH^- added to the buffer system. Thus, the amount of $CH_3CO_2^-$ increases, and the amount of CH_3COOH decreases by an amount equal to the moles of OH^- added:

$$\overrightarrow{CH_3COOH(aq) + H_2O(l) \rightleftharpoons H_3O^+(aq) + CH_3CO_2^-(aq)} \quad (16.15)$$
$$\downarrow \boldsymbol{OH^-(aq)}$$
$$\mathbf{2\,H_2O}(l)$$

Conversely, the addition of H_3O^+ from a strong acid to the buffer system causes the equilibrium to shift *left*, the H_3O^+ combines with the acetate ion (a base) to form more acetic acid, an amount (moles) equal to the amount of H_3O^+ added to the system.

$$\overleftarrow{CH_3COOH(aq) + H_2O(l) \rightleftharpoons H_3O^+(aq) + CH_3CO_2^-(aq)} \quad (16.16)$$
$$\uparrow \boldsymbol{H_3O^+(aq)}$$

As a consequence of the addition of strong acid, the amount of CH_3COOH increases, and the amount of $CH_3CO_2^-$ decreases by an amount equal to the moles of strong acid added to the buffer system.

This experiment compares the pH changes of a buffered solution to those of an unbuffered solution when varying amounts of strong acid or base are added to each.

Common-Ion Effect

The effect of adding an ion or ions common to those already present in a system at a state of dynamic equilibrium is called the **common-ion effect.** The effect is observed in this experiment for the following equilibrium:

$$4\,Cl^-(aq) + [Co(H_2O)_6]^{2+}(aq) \rightleftharpoons [CoCl_4]^{2-}(aq) + 6\,H_2O(l) \quad (16.17)$$

Ligand: a Lewis base that donates a lone pair of electrons to a metal ion, generally a transition metal ion (see Experiment 36).

Equation 16.17 represents an equilibrium of the **ligands** Cl^- and H_2O bonded to the cobalt(II) ion—the equilibrium is shifted because of a change in the concentrations of the chloride ion and water.

Changes in Temperature

Referring again to equation 16.1,

$$2\,NO_2(g) \rightleftharpoons N_2O_4(g) + 58\text{ kJ} \quad \text{(repeat of 16.1)}$$

Exothermic: characterized by energy release from the system to the surroundings

The reaction for the formation of colorless N_2O_4 is **exothermic** by 58 kJ. To favor the formation of N_2O_4, the reaction vessel should be kept cool (Figure 16.4 right); removing heat from the system causes the equilibrium to replace the removed heat and the equilibrium therefore shifts *right.* Added heat shifts the equilibrium in the direction that absorbs heat; for this reaction, a shift to the left occurs with addition of heat.

Coordination sphere: all ligands of the complex ion (collectively with the metal ion they are enclosed in square brackets when writing the formula of the complex ion). See Experiment 36.

This experiment examines the effect of temperature on the system described by equation 16.17. This system involves an equilibrium between the **coordination spheres,** the water versus the Cl^- about the cobalt(II) ion; the equilibrium is concentration *and* temperature dependent. The tetrachlorocobaltate(II) ion, $[CoCl_4]^{2-}$, is more stable at higher temperatures.

EXPERIMENTAL PROCEDURE

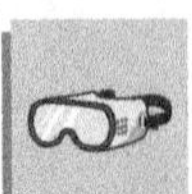

Procedure Overview: A large number of qualitative tests and observations are performed. The effects that concentration changes and temperature changes have on a system at equilibrium are observed and interpreted using LeChâtelier's principle. The functioning of a buffer system and the effect of a common ion on equilibria are observed.

Figure 16.4 NO_2, a red-brown gas (left), is favored at higher temperatures; N_2O_4, a colorless gas (right), is favored at lower temperatures. See equation 16.1.

Perform this experiment with a partner. At each circled superscript(1–21) in the procedure, *stop* and record your observations on the ***Report Sheet***. Discuss your observations with your lab partner and instructor. Account for the changes in appearance of the solution after each addition in terms of LeChâtelier's principle.

Ask your instructor which parts of the Experimental Procedure are to be completed. Prepare a hot water bath for Part E.

A. Metal-Ammonia Ions

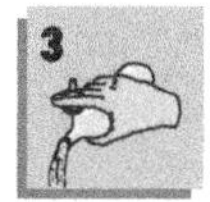

1. **Formation of metal–ammonia ions.** Place ~1 mL (<20 drops) of 0.1 *M* $CuSO_4$ (or 0.1 *M* $NiCl_2$) in a small, clean test tube.(1) Add drops of *conc* NH_3 (**Caution:** *strong odor, do not inhale*) until a color change occurs and the solution is clear (*not* colorless).(2)
2. **Shift of equilibrium.** Add drops of 1 *M* HCl until the color again changes.(3)

B. Multiple Equilibria with the Silver Ion

1. **Silver carbonate equilibrium.** In a 150-mm test tube (Figure 16.5) add ~½ mL (≤10 drops) of 0.01 *M* $AgNO_3$ to ~½ mL of 0.1 *M* Na_2CO_3.(4) Add drops of 6 *M* HNO_3 (**Caution: 6 *M* HNO_3** *reacts with the skin!*) to the precipitate until evidence of a chemical change occurs.(5)
2. **Silver chloride equilibrium.** To the clear solution from Part B.1, add ~5 drops of 0.1 *M* HCl.(6) Add drops of *conc* NH_3 (**Caution!** *avoid breathing vapors and avoid skin contact*) until evidence of a chemical change.*(7) Reacidify the solution with 6 *M* HNO_3 (**Caution!**) and record your observations.(8) What happens if excess *conc* NH_3 is again added? Try it.(9)
3. **Silver iodide equilibrium.** After trying it, add drops of 0.1 *M* KI.(10)
4. **Silver sulfide equilibrium.** To the mixture from Part B.3, add drops of 0.1 *M* Na_2S† until evidence of chemical change has occurred.(11)

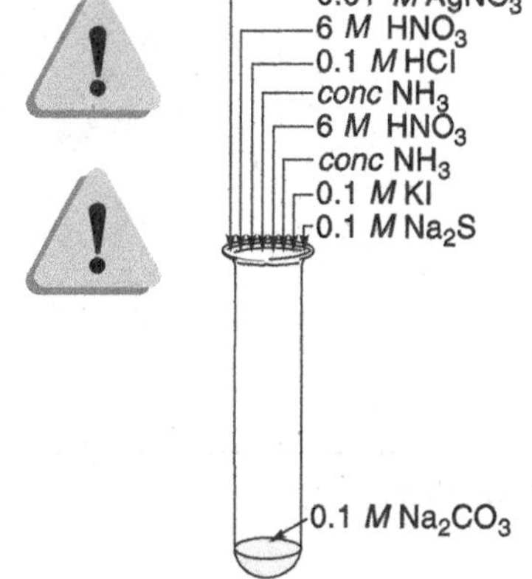

Figure 16.5 Sequence of added reagents for the study of silver ion equilibria.

*At this point, the solution should be "clear and colorless."
†The Na_2S solution should be freshly prepared.

Disposal: Dispose of the waste silver salt solutions in the Waste Silver Salts container.

CLEANUP: Rinse the test tube twice with tap water and discard in the Waste Silver Salts container. Rinse twice with deionized water and discard in the sink.

C. A Buffer System

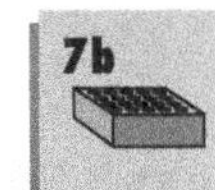

The use of a well plate is recommended. Appropriately labeled 75-mm test tubes are equally useful for performing the experiments.

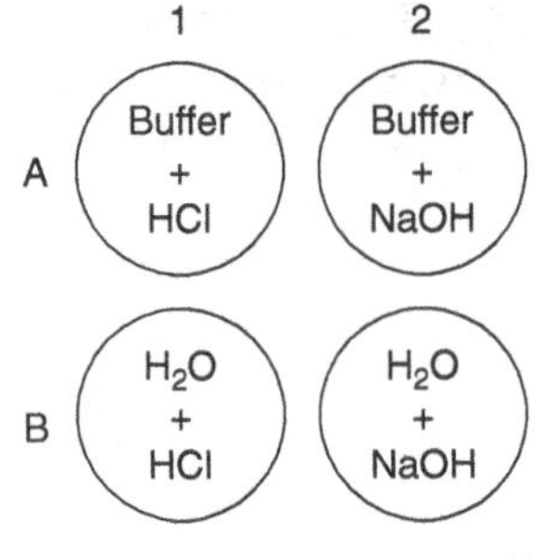

1. **Preparation of buffered and unbuffered systems.** Transfer 10 drops of 0.10 *M* CH_3COOH to wells A1 and A2 of a 24-well plate, (or appropriately labeled 75-mm test tubes), add 3 drops of universal indicator,† and note the color.[12] Compare the color of the solution with the pH color chart for the universal indicator.[12] Now add 10 drops of 0.10 *M* $NaCH_3CO_2$ to each well.[13]

   Place 20 drops of deionized water into wells B1 and B2 and add 3 drops of universal indicator.[14]
2. **Effect of strong acid.** Add 5–6 drops of 0.10 *M* HCl to wells A1 and B1, estimate the pH, and record each pH *change.*[15]
3. **Effect of strong base.** Add 5–6 drops of 0.10 *M* NaOH to wells A2 and B2, estimate the pH, and record each pH *change.*[16]
4. **Effect of a buffer system.** Explain the observed pH change for a buffered system (as compared with an unbuffered system) when a strong acid or strong base is added to it.[17]

D. $[Co(H_2O)_6]^{2+}$, $[CoCl_4]^{2-}$ Equilibrium (Common-Ion Effect)

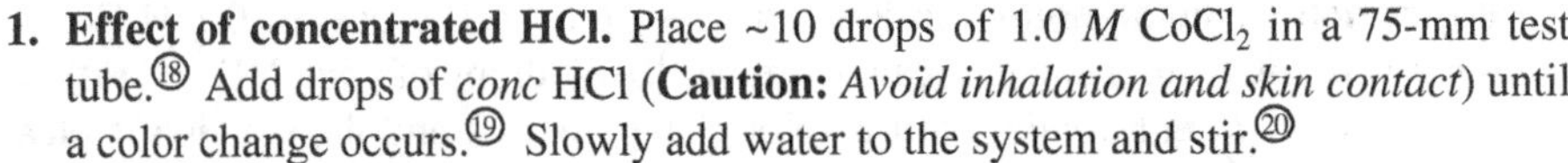

1. **Effect of concentrated HCl.** Place ~10 drops of 1.0 *M* $CoCl_2$ in a 75-mm test tube.[18] Add drops of *conc* HCl (**Caution:** *Avoid inhalation and skin contact*) until a color change occurs.[19] Slowly add water to the system and stir.[20]

E. $[Co(H_2O)_6]^{2+}$, $[CoCl_4]^{2-}$ Equilibrium (Temperature Effect)

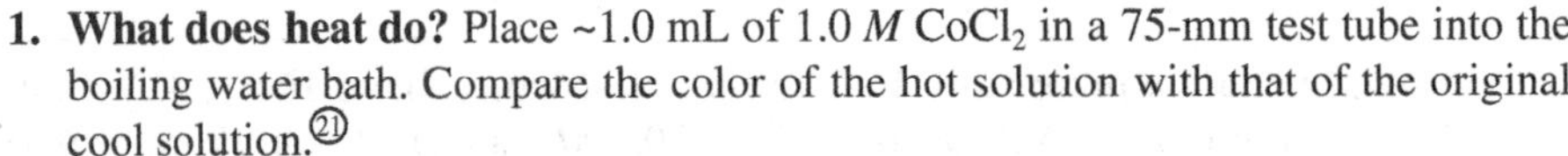

1. **What does heat do?** Place ~1.0 mL of 1.0 *M* $CoCl_2$ in a 75-mm test tube into the boiling water bath. Compare the color of the hot solution with that of the original cool solution.[21]

Disposal for Parts A, C, D, and E: Dispose of the waste solutions in the Waste Salt Solutions container.

CLEANUP: Rinse the test tubes and 24-well plate twice with tap water and discard in the Waste Salt Solutions container. Do two final rinses with deionized water and discard in the sink.

The Next Step

Buffers are vital to biochemical systems. (1) What is the pH of blood and what are the blood buffers that maintain that pH? (2) Natural waters (rivers, oceans, etc.) are buffered for the existence of plant and animal life (*Experiment 20*). What are those buffers? Experimentally, see how they resist pH changes with the additions of strong acid and/or strong base. (3) Equilibria also account for the existence of hard waters (*Experiment 21*).

†pH indicator paper may be substituted for the universal indicator to measure the pH of the solutions.

Experiment 16 *Prelaboratory Assignment*

LeChâtelier's Principle; Buffers

Date __________ Lab Sec. ______ Name ________________________________ Desk No. ________

1. **a.** Describe the *dynamic* equilibrium that exists between the two water tanks at right.

   b. Explain how LeChâtelier's principle applies when the faucet on the right tank is opened.

   c. Explain how LeChâtelier's principle applies when water is added to the right tank.

2. **a.** Experimental Procedure. Cite the reason for each of the five cautions in the experiment.

   b. Experimental Procedure, Part E. How is "bumping" avoided in the preparation of a hot water bath?

13a

3. The following chemical equilibria are studied in this experiment. To become familiar with their behavior, indicate the direction, left or right, of the equilibrium shift when the accompanying stress is applied to the system.

   a. $NH_3(aq)$ is added to $Ag^+(aq) + Cl^-(aq) \rightleftharpoons AgCl(s)$ ______________

   b. $HNO_3(aq)$ is added to $Ag_2CO_3(s) \rightleftharpoons Ag^+(aq) + CO_3^{2-}(aq)$ ______________

   c. $KI(aq)$ is added to $Ag^+(aq) + 2\ NH_3(aq) \rightleftharpoons [Ag(NH_3)_2]^+(aq)$ ______________

   d. $Na_2S(aq)$ is added to $AgI(s) \rightleftharpoons Ag^+(aq) + I^-(aq)$ ______________

   e. $KOH(aq)$ is added to $CH_3COOH(aq) + H_2O(l) \rightleftharpoons H_3O^+(aq) + CH_3CO_2^-(aq)$ ______________

   f. $HCl(aq)$ is added to $4\ Cl^-(aq) + Co(H_2O)_6^{2+}(aq) \rightleftharpoons CoCl_4^{2-}(aq) + 6\ H_2O(l)$ ______________

4. Note the dynamic equilibrium in the opening photo. Which solution changes color when the pH of both solutions is increased? Explain.

5. Experimental Procedure, Part C.1. Will the addition of $NaC_2H_3O_2$ to a CH_3COOH solution cause the pH to increase or decrease? Explain. See equation 16.14.

6. A state of dynamic equilibrium, $Ag_2CO_3(s) \rightleftharpoons 2Ag^+(aq) + CO_3^{2-}(aq)$, exists in solution.

a. What shift, if any, occurs in the equilibrium if more $Ag_2CO_3(s)$ is added to the system?

b. What shift, if any, occurs in the equilibrium if $AgNO_3(aq)$ is added to the system?

c. After water is added to the system and equilibrium is reestablished:

(i) what change in the number of moles of $Ag^+(aq)$ occurs in the system? Explain.

(ii) what change in the concentration of $Ag^+(aq)$ occurs in the system? Explain.

***d.** What shift occurs in the equilibrium if $HCl(aq)$ is added to the system? Explain.

Experiment 16 *Report Sheet*

LeChâtelier's Principle; Buffers

Date ________ Lab Sec. ______ Name ________________________________ Desk No. ________

A. Metal–Ammonia Ions

	$CuSO_4(aq)$ or $NiCl_2(aq)$	**$[Cu(NH_3)_4]^{2+}$ or $[Ni(NH_3)_6]^{2+}$**	**HCl Addition**
Color	① ______________________	② ______________________	③ ______________________

Account for the effects of $NH_3(aq)$ and $HCl(aq)$ on the $CuSO_4$ or $NiCl_2$ solution. Use equations 16.2–5 in your explanation.

B. Multiple Equilibria with the Silver Ion

④Observation and net ionic equation for reaction. Use equation 16.6 to account for your observation.

⑤Account for the observed chemical change from HNO_3 addition. Use equations 16.7–8 to account for your observation.

⑥Observation from HCl addition and net ionic equation for the reaction. Use equation 16.9 to account for your observation.

⑦Effect of *conc* NH_3. Use equation 16.10 to account for your observation.

⑧What does the HNO_3 do? Use equation 16.11 to account for your observation.

⑨What result does excess NH_3 produce?

⑩Effect of added KI. Use equation 16.12 to account for your observation. Explain.

⑪Effect of Na_2S and net ionic equation for the reaction. Use equation 16.13 to account for your observation.

C. A Buffer System

⑫Write the Brønsted acid equation for $CH_3COOH(aq)$.

Color of universal indicator in CH_3COOH ______________________ pH _____

⑬Color of universal indicator after addition of $NaCH_3CO_2$ ______________________ pH _____

Effect of $NaCH_3CO_2$ on the equilibrium. Use equation 16.14 to account for your observation.

⑭Color of universal indicator in water ______________________ pH _____

	Buffer System		Water	
	Well A1 (or test tube)	Well A2 (or test tube)	Well B1 (or test tube)	Well B2 (or test tube)
Approximate pH of ...	______	...	______	...
⑮Color after 0.10 *M* HCl addition	______	...	______	...
Approximate pH	______	...	______	...
Approximate ΔpH	______	...	______	...
Approximate pH of ...	...	______	...	______
⑯Color after 0.10 *M* NaOH addition	...	______	...	______
Approximate pH	...	______	...	______
Approximate ΔpH	...	______	...	______

⑰Discuss in detail the magnitude of the changes in pH that are observed in wells A1 and A2 relative to those observed in wells B1 and B2. Incorporate equations 16.15–16 into your discussion.

D. $[Co(H_2O)_6]^{2+}$, $[CoCl_4]^{2-}$ Equilibrium (Common-Ion Effect)

⑱Color of $CoCl_2(aq)$

⑲Observation from *conc* HCl addition and net ionic equation for the reaction. Use equation 16.17 to account for your observation.

⑳Account for the observation resulting from the addition of water.

E. $[Co(H_2O)_6]^{2+}$, $[CoCl_4]^{2-}$ Equilibrium (Temperature Effect)

(21) Effect of heat. What happens to the equilibrium? Incorporate equation 16.17 into your discussion.

Laboratory Questions

Circle the questions that have been assigned.

1. Part A.1. NH_3 is a weak base; NaOH is a strong base. Predict what would appear in the solution if NaOH had been added to the $CuSO_4$ solution instead of the NH_3. (*Hint:* See Appendix E.)
2. Part B.1
   a. HNO_3, a strong acid, is added to shift the Ag_2CO_3 equilibrium (equation 16.6) to the right. Explain why the shift occurs.
   ***b.** What would have been observed if HCl (also a strong acid) had been added instead of the HNO_3?
3. Part B.2. Suppose a solution of NaOH (a strong base) had been substituted for the NH_3 (a weak base) in the procedure. Predict the appearance of the solution as a result. Explain. See Appendix E.
4. Part B.3, 4. Suppose Parts B.3 and B.4 had been reversed in the procedure; that is, Na_2S had been added *before* the addition of KI.
   a. What would be the appearance of the solution after the addition of the Na_2S to the solution in Part B.2? Explain.
   b. What would be the appearance of the solution after the addition of the KI to the solution containing the Na_2S? Explain.
5. Part C. HCl(*aq*) is a much stronger acid that CH_3COOH(*aq*). However, when 5 drops of 0.10 *M* HCl(*aq*) is added to 20 drops of a buffer solution that is 0.10 *M* CH_3COOH and 0.10 *M* $CH_3CO_2^-$ only a very small change in pH occurs. Explain.
6. Part C. Explain why equal volumes of 0.1 *M* CH_3COOH and 0.1 *M* $NaCH_3CO_2$ function as a buffer solution, but equal volumes of 0.1 *M* HCl and 0.1 *M* NaOH do not.

***7.** Part C. At what point is a buffer solution no longer effective in resisting a pH change when a strong acid is added?

8. Part E. Consider the following endothermic equilibrium reaction system in aqueous solution:

$$4\,Cl^-(aq) + [Co(H_2O)_6]^{2+}(aq) \rightleftharpoons [CoCl_4]^{2-}(aq) + 6\,H_2O(l)$$

If the equilibrium system were stored in a vessel (with no heat transfer into or out of the vessel from the surroundings), predict what would happen to the temperature reading on a thermometer placed in the solution when hydrochloric acid is added. Explain.

Ken Karp

As weak bases, all antacids, reduce the acidity of the stomach.

Experiment 17

Antacid Analysis

OBJECTIVE

- To determine the neutralizing effectiveness per gram of a commercial **antacid**

TECHNIQUES

The following techniques are used in the Experimental Procedure:

INTRODUCTION

Various commercial antacids claim to be the "most effective" for relieving acid indigestion. All antacids, regardless of their claims or effectiveness, have one purpose—to neutralize the *excess* hydrogen ion in the stomach to relieve acid indigestion.

Antacid: Dissolved in water, it forms a basic solution

The **pH** of the gastric juice in the stomach ranges from 1.0 to 2.0. This acid, primarily hydrochloric acid, is necessary for the digestion of foods. Acid is continually secreted while eating; consequently, overeating may lead to an excess of stomach acid, leading to acid indigestion and a pH lower than normal. An excess of acid can, on occasion, cause an irritation of the stomach lining, particularly the upper intestinal tract, causing "heartburn." An antacid reacts with the hydronium ion to relieve the symptoms. Excessive use of antacids can cause the stomach to have a pH greater than 2, which stimulates the stomach to excrete additional acid, a potentially dangerous condition.

pH: negative logarithm of the molar concentration of hydronium ion, $-\log [H_3O^+]$ (see Experiment 6)

Appendix B

The most common bases used for over-the-counter antacids are:

aluminum hydroxide, $Al(OH)_3$	magnesium hydroxide, $Mg(OH)_2$
calcium carbonate, $CaCO_3$	sodium bicarbonate, $NaHCO_3$
magnesium carbonate, $MgCO_3$	potassium bicarbonate, $KHCO_3$

Milk of magnesia (Figure 17.1), an aqueous suspension of magnesium hydroxide, $Mg(OH)_2$, and sodium bicarbonate, $NaHCO_3$, commonly called *baking soda*, are simple antacids (and thus, bases) that neutralize hydronium ion, H_3O^+:

$$Mg(OH)_2(s) + 2\ H_3O^+(aq) \longrightarrow Mg^{2+}(aq) + 4\ H_2O(l) \quad (17.1)$$

$$NaHCO_3(aq) + H_3O^+(aq) \longrightarrow Na^+(aq) + CO_2(g) + 2\ H_2O(l) \quad (17.2)$$

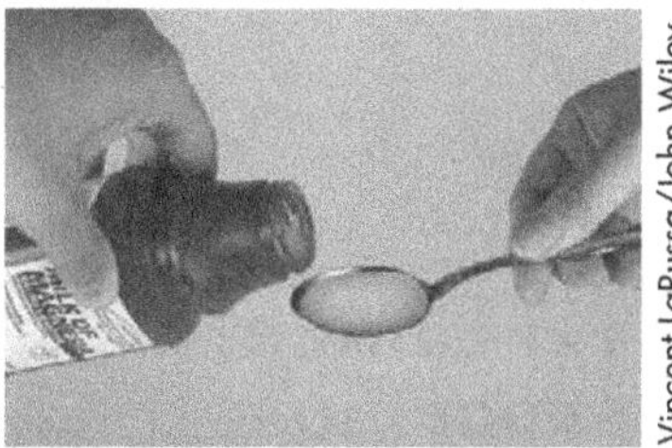

Vincent LaRussa/John Wiley and Sons

Figure 17.1 Milk of magnesia is an aqueous suspension of slightly soluble magnesium hydroxide.

The release of carbon dioxide gas from the action of sodium bicarbonate on hydronium ion (equation 17.2) causes one to "belch."

To decrease the possibility of the stomach becoming too basic from the antacid, **buffers** are often added as part of the formulation of some antacids. The more common, "faster relief" commercial antacids that buffer the pH of the stomach are those

Buffers: substances in an aqueous system that are present for the purpose of resisting changes in acidity or basicity

Table 17.1 Common Antacids

Principal Active Ingredient(s)	Formulation	Commercial Antacid
$CaCO_3$	Tablet	Tums, Titralac, Chooz, Maalox
$CaCO_3$, $Mg(OH)_2$	Tablet	Rolaids, Di-Gel, Mylanta
$MgCO_3$, $Al(OH)_3$	Tablet	Gaviscon Extra Strength
$Mg(OH)_2$, $Al(OH)_3$	Tablet	Gelasil, Tempo
$NaHCO_3$, citric acid, aspirin	Tablet	Alka-Seltzer
$Mg(OH)_2$	Tablet	Phillips' Milk of Magnesia
$Mg(OH)_2$	Liquid	Phillips' Milk of Magnesia
$Mg(OH)_2$, $Al(OH)_3$	Liquid	Mylanta Extra Strength
$MgCO_3$, $Al(OH)_3$	Liquid	Gaviscon Extra Strength

containing calcium carbonate, $CaCO_3$, and/or sodium bicarbonate. A HCO_3^-/CO_3^{2-} buffer system[1] is established in the stomach with these antacids:

$$CO_3^{2-}(aq) + H_3O^+(aq) \longrightarrow HCO_3^-(aq) + H_2O(l) \quad (17.3)$$

$$HCO_3^-(aq) + H_3O^+(aq) \longrightarrow CO_2(g) + 2\,H_2O(l) \quad (17.4)$$

Rolaids is an antacid that consists of a combination of $Mg(OH)_2$ and $CaCO_3$ in a mass ratio of 1:5, thus providing the effectiveness of the hydroxide base and the carbonate–bicarbonate buffer. Some of the more common over-the-counter antacids and their major active antacid ingredient(s) are listed in Table 17.1.

In this experiment, the neutralizing power of several antacids is determined using a strong acid–strong base titration. To obtain the quantitative data for the analysis, which requires a well-defined **endpoint** in the titration, the buffer action is eliminated.

Endpoint: the point in the titration when an indicator changes color

The buffering component of the antacid is eliminated when an *excess* of standardized hydrochloric acid, HCl, is added to the antacid solution; this addition drives the HCO_3^-/CO_3^{2-} reactions in equations 17.3 and 17.4 far to the right. The solution is then heated to remove carbon dioxide. At this point, *all* moles of base in the antacid (whether or not a buffer is present) have reacted with the standardized HCl solution.

The *unreacted* HCl is then titrated with a standardized sodium hydroxide, NaOH, solution.[2] This analytical technique is referred to as a **back titration.**

Back titration: an analytical procedure by which the analyte is "swamped" with an excess of a standardized neutralizing agent; the excess neutralizing agent is, in return, neutralized to a final stoichiometric point

The number of moles of monoprotic base in the antacid of the commercial sample *plus* the number of moles of NaOH used in the back titration equals the number of moles of HCl added to the original antacid sample:

$$\text{moles}_{\text{base, antacid}} + \text{moles}_{\text{NaOH}} = \text{moles}_{\text{HCl}} \quad (17.5)$$

A rearrangement of the equation provides the moles of base in the antacid in the sample:

$$\text{moles}_{\text{base, antacid}} = \text{moles}_{\text{HCl}} - \text{moles}_{\text{NaOH}} \quad (17.6)$$

The moles of base in the antacid per gram of antacid provide the data required for a comparison of the antacid effectiveness of commercial antacids.

Experimental Procedure

Procedure Overview: The amount of base in an antacid sample is determined. The sample is dissolved, and the buffer components of the antacid are eliminated with the addition of an excess of standardized HCl solution. The unreacted HCl is back titrated with a standardized NaOH solution.

[1]A buffer system resists large changes in the acidity of a solution. To analyze for the amount of antacid in this experiment, we want to *remove* this buffering property to determine the total effectiveness of the antacid. See *Experiment 16.*

[2]A standardized NaOH solution is one in which the concentration of NaOH has been very carefully determined.

At least two analyses should be completed per antacid if two antacids are to be analyzed to compare their neutralizing powers. If only one antacid is to be analyzed, then complete three trials.

Be aware of the number of significant figures when recording data.

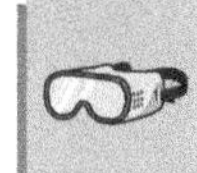

A. Dissolving the Antacid

1. **Determine the mass of antacid for analysis.** If your antacid is a tablet, pulverize and/or grind the antacid tablet with a mortar and pestle. Measure and record the mass (±0.001 g) of a 250-mL Erlenmeyer flask. Add no more than 0.2 g of the pulverized commercial antacid (or 0.2 g of a liquid antacid) to the flask and measure and record the combined mass (±0.001 g).

Data Analysis, A

2. **Prepare the antacid for analysis.** Pipet 25.0 mL of a standardized 0.1 *M* HCl solution (stomach acid equivalent) into the flask and swirl.[3] Record the actual molar concentration of the HCl on the ***Report Sheet***. Warm the solution to a very *gentle* boil and maintain the heat for ~1 minute to remove dissolved CO_2 using a hot plate (Figure 17.2a) or a direct flame and a gentle swirl (Figure 17.2b). Add 4–8 drops of bromophenol blue indicator.[4] If the solution is blue, pipet an additional 10.0 mL of 0.1 *M* HCl into the solution and boil again. Repeat as often as necessary. Record the *total* volume of HCl that is added to the antacid.

B. Analyzing the Antacid Sample

Obtain about 75 mL of a standardized 0.1 *M* NaOH solution. The solution may have been previously prepared by the stockroom personnel. If not, prepare a standardized 0.1 *M* NaOH solution as described in *Experiment 9*. Consult with your laboratory instructor.

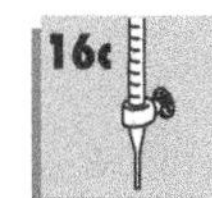

1. **Prepare the buret for titration.** Prepare a *clean* buret. Rinse the clean buret with two 3- to 5-mL portions of the standardized NaOH solution and drain through the buret tip. Record the actual molar concentration of the NaOH on the ***Report Sheet***. Fill the buret with the NaOH solution; be sure no air bubbles are in the buret tip. Wait for 10–15 seconds, then read and record its initial volume, using all certain digits *plus* one uncertain digit.

Read Technique 16c closely.

Read the buret to the correct number of significant figures.

Jo A. Beran

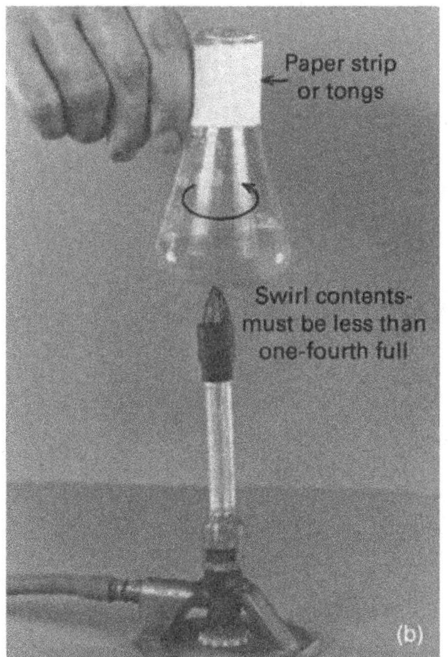

Jo A. Beran

Figure 17.2 Gently heat the sample to remove CO_2 gas.

[3] If the sample is a tablet, swirl to dissolve. Some of the *inert* ingredients—fillers and binding agents used in the formulation of the antacid tablet—may not dissolve.

[4] Bromophenol blue is yellow at a pH less than 3.0 and blue at a pH greater than 4.6.

2. **Titrate the sample.** Once the antacid solution has cooled (Part A.2), titrate the sample with the NaOH solution to a faint blue endpoint. Watch closely; the endpoint may appear after only a few milliliters of titrant, depending on the concentration of the antacid in the sample. When a single drop (or half-drop) of NaOH solution changes the sample solution from yellow to blue, **stop.** Wait for 10–15 seconds and then read and record the final volume of NaOH solution in the buret.

Be constantly aware of the use of significant figures that reflect the precision of your measuring instrument

3. **Repeat the titration of the same antacid.** Refill the buret and repeat the experiment, starting at Part A.1.
4. **Analyze another antacid.** Perform the experiment, in duplicate, for a second antacid or complete a third trial for the same antacid. Record all data on the ***Report Sheet***.

Disposal: Dispose of the test solutions as directed by your instructor.

CLEANUP: Discard the remaining NaOH titrant as directed by your instructor. Flush the buret several times with tap water and dispense through the buret tip, followed by several portions of deionized water. Dispose of all buret washings in the sink.

C. Calculations

1. Determine the number of moles of HCl added to the antacid sample.
2. How many moles of NaOH titrant were required to neutralize the *unreacted* acid?
3. Calculate the number of moles of base in the antacid sample.
4. Calculate the number of moles of base in the antacid sample *per gram* of sample.

Data Analysis, A

NOTES AND CALCULATIONS

Experiment 17 *Prelaboratory Assignment*

Antacid Analysis

Date __________ Lab Sec. ______ Name ____ Desk No. __________

1. Write a balanced equation for the reaction of the active ingredient in Tums with excess acid. See Table 17.1.

2. Identify the two most common anions present in antacids.

3. a. How much time should be allowed for the titrant to drain from the buret wall before a reading is made?

b. Experimental Procedure, Part B.2. Bromophenol blue is the indicator used in detecting the endpoint for the antacid analysis in this experiment. What is the expected color change at the endpoint?

4. a. How many moles of stomach acid would be neutralized by one tablet of Tums Ultra 1000 that contains 1000 mg of calcium carbonate?

$CaCO_3(aq) + 2\ H_3O^+(aq) \longrightarrow Ca^{2+}(aq) + CO_2(g) + 3\ H_2O(l)$

b. Assuming the volume of the stomach to be 1.0 L, what will be the pH change of the stomach acid resulting from the ingestion of one Tums ultra 1000 tablet that contains 1000 mg of calcium carbonate.

Jo A. Beran/Trey Hernandez

5. **a.** A commercial antacid was analyzed to determine the amount of antacid present in the sample. Complete the following table for Trial 1 of the analysis. (See ***Report Sheet***.) Record calculated values with the correct number of significant figures.

A. Dissolving the Antacid — ***Calculation Zone***

3. Mass of antacid sample (*g*)	0.204	*Part C.1*
4. Total volume of HCl added (*mL*)	25.0	
5. Molar concentration of HCl (*mol/L*)	0.0978	

B. Analyzing the Antacid Sample

1. Molar concentration of NaOH (*mol/L*)	0.0902	*Part C.2*
2. Buret reading, *initial* (*mL*)	3.85	
3. Buret reading, *final* (*mL*)	10.60	
4. Volume of NaOH added (*mL*)	______	

C. Calculations — *Part C.3*

1. Moles of HCl added, total (*mol*) ______
   Show calculation.
2. Moles of NaOH added (*mol*) ______
   Show calculation.
3. Moles of base in antacid sample (*mol*) ______ — *Part C.4*
   Show calculation.
4. $\frac{\text{mol base in antacid}}{\text{mass of antacid sample}}$ (*mol/g*) ______
   Show calculation.

5. **b.** For Trials 2 and 3, the $\frac{\text{mol base in antacid}}{\text{mass of antacid sample}}$ were 8.22×10^{-3} and 1.05×10^{-2} respectively.

a. What is the average $\frac{\text{mol base in antacid}}{\text{mass of antacid sample}}$ of the antacid sample?

b. What are the standard deviation and the relative standard deviation (%RSD) for $\frac{\text{mol base in antacid}}{\text{mass of antacid sample}}$ of the antacid sample?

Experiment 17 *Report Sheet*

Antacid Analysis

Date ________ Lab Sec. ______ Name ______________________________ Desk No. ________

	Trial 1	*Trial 2*	*Trial 1*	*Trial 2*
A. Dissolving the Antacid				
1. Mass of flask (*g*)				
2. Mass of flask + antacid sample (*g*)				
3. Mass (or tared mass) of antacid sample (*g*)				
4. Total volume of HCl added (*mL*)				
5. Molar concentration of HCl (*mol/L*)				
B. Analyzing the Antacid Sample				
1. Molar concentration of NaOH (*mol/L*)				
2. Buret reading, *initial* (*mL*)				
3. Buret reading, *final* (*mL*)				
4. Volume of NaOH (*mL*)				
C. Calculations				
1. Moles of HCl added, *total* (*mol*)				
2. Moles of NaOH added (*mol*)				
3. Moles of base in antacid sample (*mol*)				
4. $\frac{\text{mol base in antacid}}{\text{mass of antacid sample}}$ (*mol/g*)	*		*	
5. Average $\frac{\text{mol base in antacid}}{\text{mass of antacid sample}}$ (*mol/g*)				

*Show calculation(s) for Trial(s) 1 on the next page.

Calculations for Trial(s) 1:

Laboratory Questions

Circle the questions that have been assigned.

1. Part A.1. The antacid tablet for analysis was not finely pulverized before its reaction with hydrochloric acid. Will this technique error increase or decrease the reported amount of antacid in the sample? Explain.
2. Part A.2. The HCl(*aq*) solution has a lower concentration than what is indicated on the reagent bottle. Will this result indicate the presence of more or fewer moles of base in the antacid? Explain.
3. Part A.2. All of the CO_2 is not removed by gentle boiling after the addition of HCl. Will the reported amount of antacid in the sample be too high, too low, or unaffected? Explain. *Hint:* Remember that $CO_2(g)$ is an acidic anhydride.
4. Part A.2. "If the solution is blue, pipet an additional 10.0 mL of 0.1 *M* HCI into the solution and boil again. Repeat as often as necessary." Explain why the solution would be blue and, if it is, why more HCl must be added.
5. Part B.1. An air bubble was initially trapped in the buret but was dispensed during the back titration of the unreacted HCl (Part B.2). As a result of this technique error, will the reported amount of antacid in the sample be too high or too low? Explain.
6. Part B.2. The bromophenol blue endpoint is surpassed in the back titration of the excess HCl with the sodium hydroxide titrant. As a result of this technique error, will the reported amount of antacid in the sample be too high or too low? Explain.

*7. A few of the "newer" antacids contain sodium citrate, $Na_3C_6H_5O_7$, as the effective, but more mild antacid ingredient.
   a. Write a balanced equation representing the antacid effect of the citrate ion, $C_6H_5O_7^{3-}$. Assume that the H_3O^+ completely neutralizes (protonates) the citrate ion, $C_6H_5O_7^{3-}$.
   b. Will 500 mg of $Na_3C_6H_5O_7$ (258.1 g/mol) or 500 mg of $Mg(OH)_2$ (58.32 g/mol) neutralize more moles of hydronium ion? Show calculations.

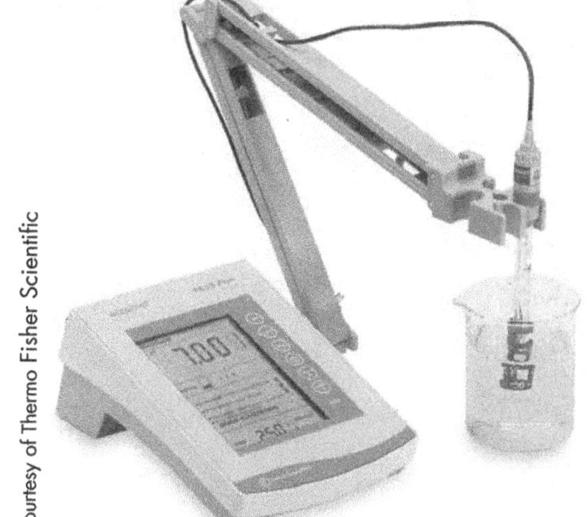

Courtesy of Thermo Fisher Scientific

A modern pH meter with a combination electrode

Experiment 18

Potentiometric Analyses

OBJECTIVES

- To operate a pH meter
- To graphically determine a stoichiometric point
- To determine the molar concentration of a weak acid solution
- To determine the molar mass of a solid weak acid
- To determine the pK_a of a weak acid

TECHNIQUES

The following techniques are used in the Experimental Procedure:

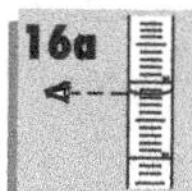

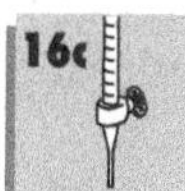

INTRODUCTION

A probe connected to an instrument that provides a direct reading of the concentration of a particular substance in an aqueous system is a convenient form of analysis. Such convenience is particularly advantageous when a large number of samples needs to be analyzed. The probe, or electrode, senses a difference in concentrations between the substance in solution and the substance in the probe itself. The concentration difference causes a voltage (or potential difference), which is recorded by an instrument called a **potentiometer.**

Potentiometer: an instrument that measures a potential difference—often called a voltmeter. See Experiment 32.

Such a potentiometer is a powerful, convenient instrument for determining the concentrations of various ions in solution. To list only a few, the molar concentrations of the cations H^+, Li^+, Na^+, K^+, Ag^+, Ca^{2+}, Cu^{2+}, Pb^{2+}; the anions F^-, Cl^-, Br^-, I^-, CN^-, SO_4^{2-}; and the gases O_2, CO_2, NH_3, SO_2, H_2S, NO_x can be measured directly using an electrode specifically designed for their measurement (a specific selective electrode).

The H^+ concentration of a solution is measured with a potentiometer called a **pH meter,** an instrument that measures a potential difference (or voltage) caused by a difference in the hydrogen concentration of the test solution relative to that of the 0.1 *M* HCl reference solution contained within the electrode. The electrode, called a *combination electrode*, is shown in Figure 18.1, page 228.

pH meter: an instrument that measures the pH of a solution

The measured voltage recorded by the potentiometer, E_{cell}, is a function of the pH of the solution at 25°C by the equation

$$E_{cell} = E' + 0.0592\ \text{pH} \tag{18.1}$$

E' is a cell constant, an internal parameter that is characteristic of the pH meter and its electrode.

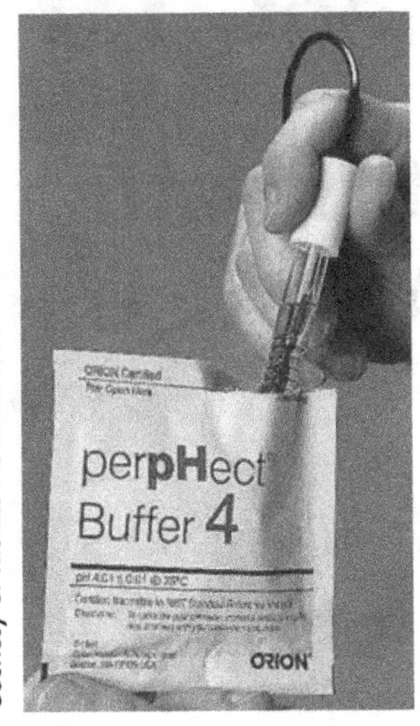

Courtesy of Thermo Fisher Scientific

Buffer solutions are used to calibrate pH meters.

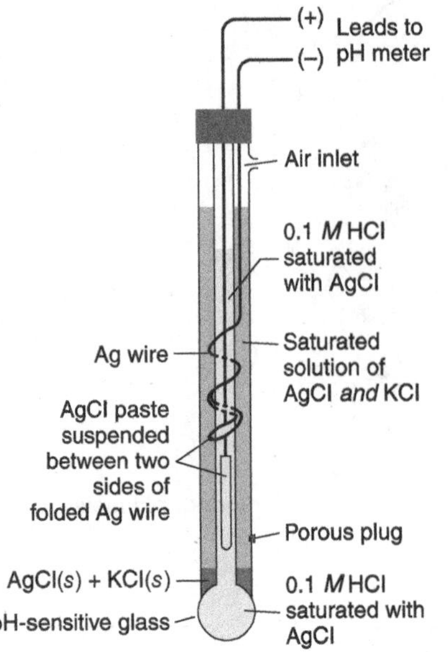

Figure 18.1 A combination electrode for measuring pH

Buffer solution: a solution that maintains a relatively constant, reproducible pH

Before any pH measurements are made, the pH meter is calibrated (that is, E' is set experimentally). The electrode is placed into a **buffer solution** of known pH (see margin photo), and the E_{cell}, the potential difference between the $[H^+]$ of the glass electrode and the $[H^+]$ of the buffer, is manually adjusted to read the pH of the buffer—this adjustment sets E'.

The readout of the pH meter is E_{cell}, expressed in volts, but since E_{cell} is directly proportional to pH (equation 18.1), the meter for the readout is expressed directly in pH units.

Indicators and pH of a Weak Acid Solution

A Stoichiometric point is often referred to as the equivalence point.

The selection of an indicator for the titration of a strong acid with a strong base is relatively easy in that the color change at the **stoichiometric point** always occurs at a pH of 7 (at 25°C). Usually, phenolphthalein can be used because its color changes at a pH close to 7. However, when a weak acid is titrated with a strong base, the stoichiometric point is at a pH greater than 7, and a different indicator may need to be selected.[1] If the weak acid is an unknown acid, then the proper indicator cannot be selected because the pH at the stoichiometric point cannot be predetermined. The color change of a selected indicator may *not* occur at (or even near) the pH of the stoichiometric point for the titration. To better detect a stoichiometric point for the titration of an unknown weak acid, a pH meter is more reliable.

Molar Concentration of a Weak Acid Solution

Titrimetric analysis: a titration procedure that is chosen for an analysis

Titration curve: a data plot of pH versus volume of titrant

In Part A of this experiment, a **titrimetric analysis** is used to determine the molar concentration of a weak acid solution. A pH meter is used to detect the stoichiometric point of the titration. An acid–base indicator will *not* be used. A standardized sodium hydroxide solution is used as the titrant.[2]

The pH of a weak acid solution increases as the standardized NaOH solution is added. A plot of the pH of the weak acid solution as the strong base is being added, pH versus V_{NaOH}, is called the **titration curve** (Figure 18.2) for the reaction. The inflection

[1]The pH is greater than 7 at the stoichiometric point for the titration of a weak monoprotic acid because of the basicity of the conjugate base, A^-, of the weak acid, HA:

$$A^-(aq) + H_2O(l) \rightarrow HA(aq) + OH^-(aq)$$

[2]The procedure for preparing a standardized NaOH solution is described in *Experiment 9*.

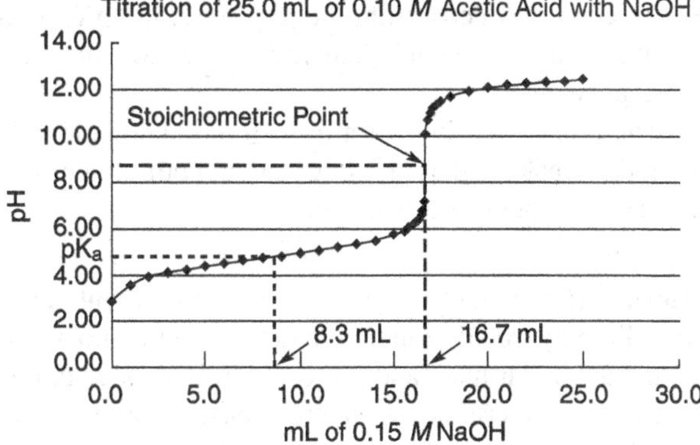

Figure 18.2 Titration curve for 25.0 mL of 0.10 *M* CH_3COOH with 0.15 *M* NaOH

point in the sharp vertical portion of the plot (about midway on the vertical rise) is the stoichiometric point.

The moles of NaOH used for the analysis equals the volume of NaOH, dispensed from the buret, times its molar concentration:

$$\text{moles NaOH } (mol) = \text{volume } (L) \times \text{molar concentration } (mol/L) \qquad (18.2)$$

For a **monoprotic acid,** HA, one mole of OH^-, neutralizes one mole of acid:

Monoprotic acid: a substance capable of donating a single proton, H^+

$$HA(aq) + OH^-(aq) \longrightarrow H_2O(l) + A^-(aq) \qquad (18.3)$$

The molar concentration of the acid is determined by dividing its number of moles of acid in solution by the volume (in liters) of the acid example:

$$\text{molar concentration HA } (mol/L) = \frac{\text{mol HA}}{\text{volume HA}(L)} \qquad (18.4)$$

For a **diprotic acid,** H_2X, 2 mol of OH^- neutralizes 1 mol of acid:

Diprotic acid: a substance capable of donating two protons

$$H_2X(aq) + 2\ OH^-(aq) \longrightarrow 2\ H_2O(l) + X^{2-}(aq) \qquad (18.5)$$

Molar Mass of a Weak Acid

In Part B, the molar mass and the pK_a of an unknown *solid* weak acid are determined. The standardized NaOH solution is used to titrate a carefully measured mass of the *dissolved* acid to the stoichiometric point. A plot of pH versus V_{NaOH} is required to define the stoichiometric point.

The moles of acid is determined as described in equations 18.2 and 18.3.

The molar mass of the acid is calculated from the moles of the solid acid neutralized at the stoichiometric point and its measured mass:

$$\text{molar mass } (g/mol) = \frac{\text{mass of solid acid}(g)}{\text{moles of solid acid}} \qquad (18.6)$$

pK_a of a Weak Acid

A weak acid, HA, in water undergoes only partial ionization:

$$HA(aq) + H_2O(l) \rightleftharpoons H_3O^+(aq) + A^-(aq) \qquad (18.7)$$

At equilibrium conditions, the mass action expression for the weak acid system equals the equilibrium constant.

$$K_a = \frac{[H_3O^+][A^-]}{[HA]} \qquad (18.8)$$

When one-half of the weak acid is neutralized by the NaOH titrant in a titration, mol HA = mol A^- and also [HA] = $[A^-]$. Since [HA] = $[A^-]$ at this point in the titration, then $K_a = [H_3O^+]$. If one takes the negative logarithm of both sides of this equality, then

pK_a = pH. As pH is recorded directly from the pH meter, the pK_a of the weak acid is readily obtained at the "halfway point" (halfway to the stoichiometric point) in the titration (Figure 18.2, page 229).

The stoichiometric point is again determined from the complete titration curve of pH versus V_{NaOH}. If the weak acid is diprotic and if both stoichiometric points are detected, then pK_{a1} and pK_{a2} can be determined.

EXPERIMENTAL PROCEDURE

Procedure Overview: The pH meter is used in conjunction with a titration apparatus and a standardized sodium hydroxide solution to determine the molar concentration of a weak acid solution and the molar mass and pK_a of a solid, weak acid. Plots of pH versus volume of NaOH are used to determine the stoichiometric point of each titration.

The number of pH meters in the laboratory is limited. You may need to share one with a partner or with a larger group. Ask your instructor for details of the arrangement. Consult with your instructor for directions on the proper care and use of the pH meter. Also inquire about the calibration of the pH meter.

Because of time and equipment constraints, it may be impossible to do all parts of the experiment in one laboratory period. Time is required not only to collect and graph the data but also to interpret the data and complete the calculations. Discuss the expectations from the experiment with your instructor.

The pH versus V_{NaOH} curves to be plotted in Parts A.6 and B.3 can be established by using a pH probe that is connected directly to either a calculator or computer with the appropriate software. If this pH sensing/recording apparatus is available in the laboratory, consult with your instructor for its use and adaptation to the experiment. The probe merely replaces the pH electrode in Figure 18.3. However, volume readings from the buret will still need to be recorded.

Be aware of the number of significant figures when recording data.

A. Molar Concentration of a Weak Acid Solution

Obtain about 90 mL of an acid solution with an unknown concentration from your instructor. Your instructor will advise you as to whether your acid is monoprotic or diprotic. Record the sample number on the ***Report Sheet***. Clean three 250-mL beakers.

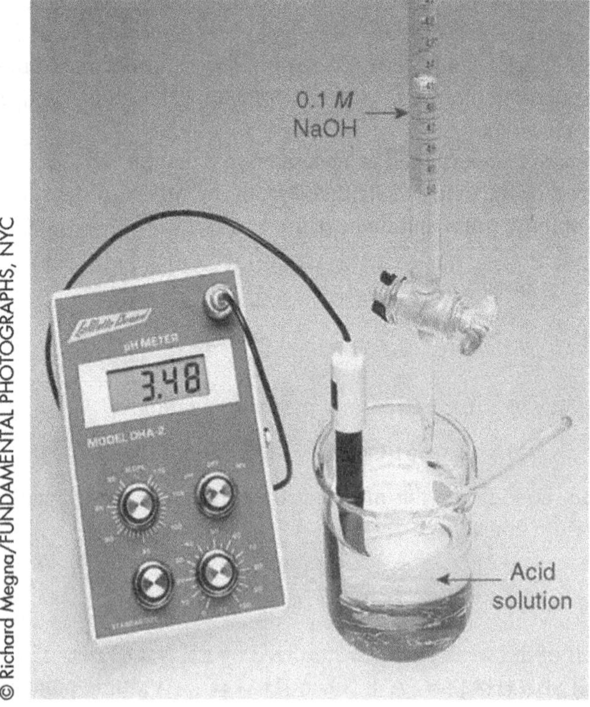

Figure 18.3 The setup for a potentiometric titration. Use a stirring rod or magnetic stirrer to stir the solution.

1. **Obtain a standardized NaOH solution.** A standardized (~0.1 *M*) NaOH solution was prepared in *Experiment 9*. If that solution was saved, it is to be used for this experiment. If the solution was not saved, you must either again prepare and standardize the solution (*Experiment 9*, Part A) or obtain about 200 mL of a standardized NaOH solution prepared by stockroom personnel. Be precise in recording the *exact* molar concentration of the NaOH solution on the ***Report Sheet***. Your instructor will advise you.

Data Analysis, A

2. **Prepare the buret with the standardized NaOH solution.** Properly clean a buret; rinse twice with tap water, twice with deionized water, and finally with three 5-mL portions of the standardized 0.1 *M* NaOH. Drain each rinse through the tip of the buret. Fill the buret with the 0.1 *M* NaOH. After 10–15 seconds, properly read[3] and **record** the volume of solution, using all certain digits *plus* one uncertain digit.

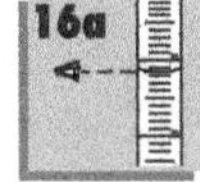

Record the volume to the correct number of significant figures

3. **Prepare the weak acid solution for analysis.** Pipet 25 mL of the unknown weak acid solution into each of three *labeled* 250-mL beakers; add 50 mL of deionized water to each.

   Set up the titration apparatus as shown in Figure 18.3. Remove the electrode from the deionized water, and touch-dry the electrode with lint-free paper (Kimwipes). Immerse the electrode about one-half inch deep into the solution of beaker 1. Swirl or stir the solution and read and record the initial pH.[4]

Courtesy of Thermo Fisher Scientific

16c

4. **Titrate the weak acid solution.** Add the NaOH titrant, initially in 1- to 2-mL increments, and swirl or stir the solution. After each addition, allow the pH meter to stabilize; read and record the pH and buret readings (pH vs. V_{NaOH}) on a *self-designed* data sheet. Repeat the additions until the stoichiometric point is near,[5] then slow the addition. When the stoichiometric point is imminent, add the NaOH titrant dropwise.[6] Use a *minimum* volume of deionized water from a wash bottle to rinse the wall of the beaker or to add half-drop volumes of NaOH. Dilution affects pH readings.

5. **Titrate beyond the stoichiometric point.** After reaching the stoichiometric point, first add drops of NaOH, then 1 mL, and finally 2- to 3-mL **aliquots** until at least 10 mL of NaOH solution have been added beyond the stoichiometric point. Read and record the pH and buret readings after each addition.

Aliquot: an undefined, generally small, volume of a solution

6. **Plot the data.** Manually or use appropriate software, such as Excel, to plot the data for the titration curve, pH vs. V_{NaOH}. Draw a smooth curve through the data points (do not connect the dots!). Properly label your graph and obtain your instructor's approval.

   From the plotted data, determine the volume of NaOH titrant added to reach the stoichiometric point.

Data Analysis, F

7. **Repeat the analysis.** Repeat the titration of the samples of weak acid in beakers 2 and 3. Determine the average molar concentration of the acid.

B. Molar Mass and the pK_a of a Solid Weak Acid

Three samples of the solid weak acid are to be analyzed. Prepare three clean 250-mL beakers for this determination. Obtain an unknown solid acid from your instructor and record the sample number; your instructor will advise you as to whether your unknown acid is monoprotic or diprotic.

[3]Remember to read the bottom of the meniscus with the aid of a black mark drawn on a white card.
[4]A magnetic stirrer and magnetic stirring bar may be used to swirl the solution during the addition of the titrant. Ask your instructor.
[5]The stoichiometric point is near when larger changes in pH occur with smaller additions of the NaOH titrant.
[6]Suggestion: It may save time to quickly titrate a test sample to determine an approximate volume to reach the stoichiometric point.

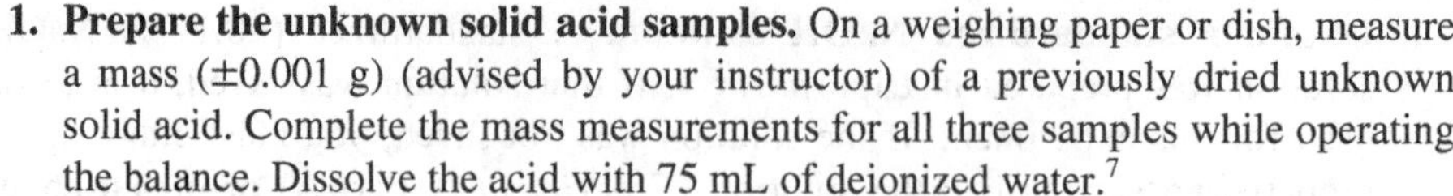

1. **Prepare the unknown solid acid samples.** On a weighing paper or dish, measure a mass (±0.001 g) (advised by your instructor) of a previously dried unknown solid acid. Complete the mass measurements for all three samples while operating the balance. Dissolve the acid with 75 mL of deionized water.[7]

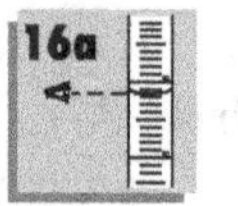
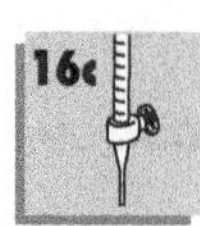

2. **Fill the buret and titrate.** Refill the buret with the standardized NaOH solution and, after 10–15 seconds, read and record the initial volume and the initial pH. Refer to Parts A.4 and A.5. Titrate each sample to 10 mL beyond the stoichiometric point.

Data Analysis, F

3. **Plot and interpret the data.** Manually or use appropriate software, such as Excel, to plot the data for a titration curve, pH vs. V_{NaOH}. From the plot, determine the volume of NaOH used to reach the stoichiometric point of the titration. Obtain your instructor's approval.

4. **Calculate the molar mass *and* the pK_a of the weak acid**
   a. Calculate the molar mass of the weak acid.
   b. Note the volume of NaOH titrant required to reach the stoichiometric point. Determine the pH (and therefore pK_a of the weak acid) at the point where one-half of the acid was neutralized.
5. **Repeat.** Similarly titrate the other unknown solid acid samples and handle the data accordingly.

Disposal: Dispose of all test solutions as directed by your instructor.

CLEANUP: Discard the sodium hydroxide solution remaining in the buret as directed by your instructor. Rinse the buret twice with tap water and twice with deionized water, discarding each rinse through the buret tip into the sink.

Data Analysis, C and D

6. **Collect the data.** Calculate the standard deviation and the relative standard deviation (%RSD) for the pK_a measurement for the acid for your three trials.

The Next Step

While most common for the determination of hydrogen ion concentrations (and pH), potentiometric titrations are also utilized for the determination of any ion's concentration where a specific ion electrode is available (see Introduction). Develop a plan or procedure for determining the concentration of an ion in solution potentiometrically, using a specific ion electrode.

For example, a chloride specific ion electrode would read pCl directly. What would be the *x*-axis label in the titration curve?

NOTES AND CALCULATIONS

[7]The solid acid may be relatively insoluble, but with the addition of the NaOH solution from the buret, it will gradually dissolve and react. The addition of 10 mL of ethanol may be necessary to dissolve the acid. Consult with your instructor.

Experiment 18 *Prelaboratory Assignment*

Potentiometric Analyses

Date __________ Lab Sec. ______ Name ______________________________ Desk No. __________

1. **a.** For a weak acid (e.g., CH_3COOH) that is titrated with a strong base (e.g., NaOH), what species (ions/molecules) are present in the solution at the stoichiometric point?

   b. For a weak acid (e.g., CH_3COOH) that is titrated with a strong base (e.g., NaOH), what species (ions/molecules) are present in the solution at the halfway point in the titration toward the stoichiometric point?

2. Briefly explain how the pK_a for a weak acid is determined in this experiment.

3. A 23.74-mL volume of 0.0981 *M* NaOH was used to titrate 25.0 mL of a weak monoprotic acid solution to the stoichiometric point. Determine the molar concentration of the weak acid solution. Express your answer to the correct number of significant figures.

4. Data in the following table were obtained for the titration of a 0.297-g sample of a solid, monoprotic weak acid with a 0.150 *M* NaOH solution. Plot (at right) pH (ordinate) vs. V_{NaOH} (abscissa).

   a. To determine the molar mass and the pK_a of a solid, monoprotic weak acid, a titration of the weak acid with a standardized NaOH solution provided the following data in the table.

V_{NaOH} added (mL)	pH
0.00	1.96
2.00	2.22
4.00	2.46
7.00	2.77
10.00	3.06
12.00	3.29
14.00	3.60
16.00	4.26
17.00	11.08
18.00	11.67
20.00	12.05
25.00	12.40

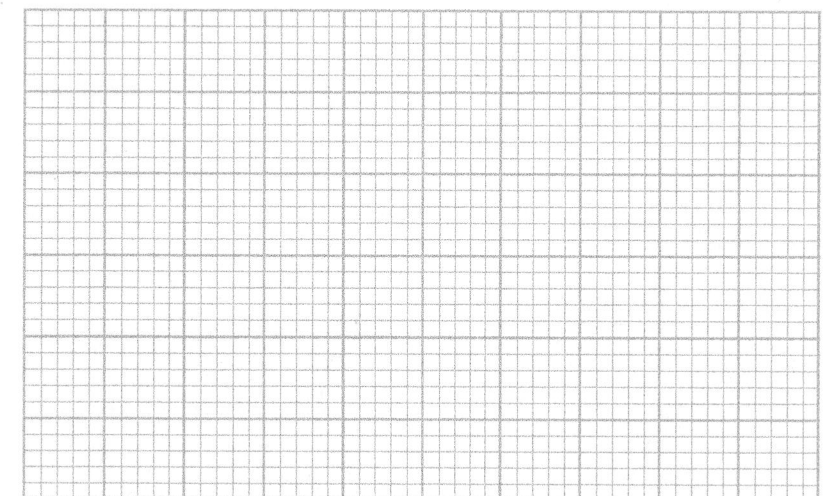

4. b. Complete the following table and show the calculations for the determinations for Trial 1 (see ***Report Sheet***). Record all calculated data to the correct number of significant figures.

<u>*Calculation Zone*</u>

1. Mass of dry, solid acid (*g*)	0.297	*Part 7*
2. Molar concentration of NaOH(*mol/L*)	0.150	
3. Buret reading of NaOH, *initial* (*mL*)	0.00	
4. Buret reading of NaOH at stoichiometric point, *final* (*mL*)		
5. Volume of NaOH dispensed at stoichiometric point (*mL, from graph*)		*Part 8*
7. Moles of NaOH to the stoichiometric point (*mol*) Show calculation.		
8. Moles of acid (*mol*) Show calculation.		
9. Molar mass of acid (*g/mol*) Show calculation.		*Part 9*
11. Volume of NaOH halfway to the stoichiometric point (*mL, from graph*)		
12. pK_a of weak acid (*from graph*)		

5. b. For Trials 2 and 3, the molar mass of the weak acid was determined to be 123 g/mol and 121 g/mol respectively.

a. What is the average molar mass of the weak acid?

b. What are the standard deviation and the relative standard deviation (%RSD) for the molar mass data of the weak acid?

Experiment 18 *Report Sheet*

Potentiometric Analyses

Date ________ Lab Sec. ______ Name ________________________________ Desk No. ________

A. Molar Concentration of a Weak Acid Solution

Sample no. ______________ Monoprotic or diprotic acid? ______________

	Trial 1	*Trial 2*	*Trial 3*
1. Molar concentration of NaOH (*mol/L*)		________	
2. Volume of weak acid (*mL*)	________	________	________
3. Buret readng of NaOH, *initial* (*mL*)	________	________	________
4. Buret reading NaOH at stoichiometric point, *final* (*mL*)	________	________	________
5. Volume of NaOH dispensed (*mL*)	________	________	________
6. Instructor's approval of pH vs. V_{NaOH} graph	________	________	________
7. Moles of NaOH to stoichiometric point (*mol*)	________	________	________
8. Moles of acid (*mol*)	________	________	________
9. Molar concentration of acid (*mol/L*)	________	________	________
10. Average molar concentration of acid (*mol/L*)		________	

B. Molar Mass and the pK_a of a Solid Weak Acid

Sample no. ______________ Monoprotic or diprotic acid? ______________ Suggested mass ______________

	Trial 1	*Trial 2*	*Trial 3*
1. Mass of dry, solid acid (*g*)	________	________	________
2. Molar concentration of NaOH (*mol/L*)		________	
3. Buret readng of NaOH, *initial* (*mL*)	________	________	________
4. Buret reading NaOH at stoichiometric point, *final* (*mL*)	________	________	________
5. Volume of NaOH dispensed (*mL*)	________	________	________
6. Instructor's approval of pH versus V_{NaOH} graph	________	________	________
7. Moles of NaOH to stoichiometric point (*mol*)	________	________	________
8. Moles of acid (*mol*)	________	________	________
9. Molar mass of acid (*g/mol*)	________ *	________	________
10. Average molar mass of acid (*g/mol*)		________	
11. Volume of NaOH halfway to stoichiometric point (*mL*)	________	________	________
12. pK_{a1} of weak acid (from graph)	________	________	________
13. Average pK_{a1}		________	

*Show calculations for Trial 1 on the next page.

*Calculations for Trial 1.

Standard deviation and the relative standard deviation (%RSD) for the pK_a of an acid from the trials of your data as from class data. **Data Analysis, C, D**

Laboratory Questions

Circle the questions that have been assigned.

1. The pH meter was not properly calibrated.
   a. How does this experimental error affect the precision of your data? Explain.
   b. How does this experimental error affect the accuracy of your data? Explain.
2. The pH meter was mistakenly calibrated to be 1.0 pH unit higher than the buffer.
   a. Part A. Will this miscalibration result in a reported molar concentration of the weak acid being too high, too low, or unaffected? Explain.
   b. Part B. Is the determined pK_a of the weak acid too high, too low, or unaffected by the miscalibration? Explain.
3. **a.** Part A.4. The pH reading is taken before the pH meter stabilizes. As a result, the pH reading may be too low. Explain.
   b. Part A.4. Explain why it is good technique to slow the addition of NaOH titrant near the stoichiometric point.
   c. Part A.5. While not absolutely necessary, why is it good technique to add NaOH titrant beyond the stoichiometric point?
4. Part B.1. The solid acid is dissolved in 100 mL of deionized water, followed by 10 mL of ethanol. How does this added volume affect the reported molar mass of the weak acid—too high, too low, or unaffected? Explain.
5. Part B.4. As a result of adding the NaOH titrant too rapidly and an unwillingness to allow the pH meter to equilibrate before reading its pH, the stoichiometric point is ill defined. As a result of this technique error,
   a. will the molar mass of the weak acid be reported as too high or too low? Explain.
   b. will the pK_a of the weak acid be reported as too high or too low? Explain.
6. Ideally, how many stoichiometric points would be observed on a pH titration curve for a diprotic acid? Sketch the appearance of its titration curve and explain.

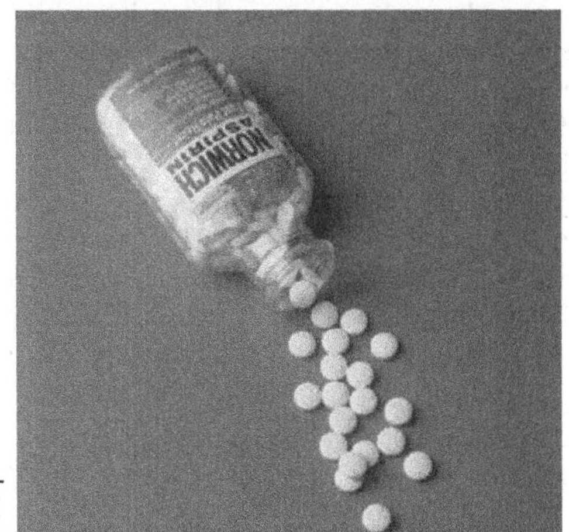

Ken Karp

Experiment 19

Aspirin Synthesis and Analysis

Aspirin is a leading commercial pain reliever, first synthesized in a pure and stable form by Felix Hoffman in 1897.

OBJECTIVES

- To synthesize aspirin
- To determine the purity of the synthesized aspirin or a commercial aspirin tablet

TECHNIQUES

The following techniques are used in the Experimental Procedure:

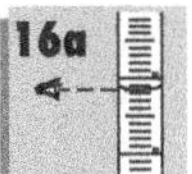

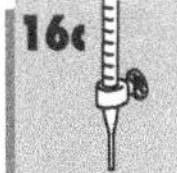

INTRODUCTION

Pure aspirin, chemically called *acetylsalicylic acid*, is both an organic **ester** and an **organic acid.** It is used extensively as a painkiller (analgesic) and as a fever-reducing drug (antipyretic). When ingested, acetylsalicylic acid remains intact in the acidic stomach, but in the basic medium of the upper intestinal tract, it forms the salicylate and acetate ions.

Ester: a –C(=O)–O– *grouping of atoms in a molecule*

Organic acid: a –C(=O)–O–H *grouping of atoms in a molecule*

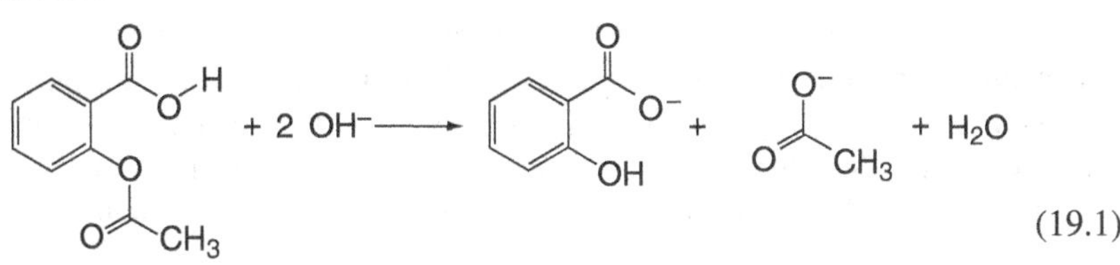

Aspirin (acetylsalicylic acid)   Salicylate ion   Acetate ion

The analgesic action of aspirin is undoubtedly due to the salicylate ion; however, its additional physiological effects and biochemical reactions are still not thoroughly understood. It is known that **salicylic acid** has the same therapeutic effects as aspirin; however, due in part to the fact that it is an acid, salicylic acid causes a more severe upset stomach than does aspirin.

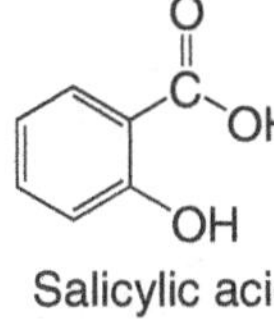

Salicylic acid

Aspirin (molar mass of 180.2 g/mol) is prepared by reacting salicylic acid (molar mass of 138.1 g/mol) with acetic anhydride (molar mass of 102.1 g/mol). Aspirin, like many other organic acids, is a weak **monoprotic acid.**

Monoprotic acid: a molecule that provides one proton for neutralization

Salicylic acid + Acetic anhydride ⟶ Aspirin (acetylsalicylic acid) + Acetic acid (H_3C–COOH)   (19.2)

Qualitatively, the purity of an aspirin sample can be determined from its melting point. The melting point of a substance is essentially independent of atmospheric pressure, but it is always lowered by the presence of impurities (a colligative property of pure substances—see *Experiment 14*). The degree of lowering of the melting point depends on the nature and the concentration of the impurities.

Quantitatively, the purity of an aspirin sample can be determined by a simple acid–base titration, Part C, or spectrophotometrically as suggested in The Next Step. For the acid–base titration, the acetylsalicylic acid reacts with hydroxide ion, from a standardized sodium hydroxide solution, accordingly.

$$C_6H_4(OCOCH_3)COOH + OH^- \longrightarrow C_6H_4(OCOCH_3)COO^- + H_2O \qquad (19.3)$$

Phenolphthalein: an acid–base indicator that is colorless at a pH less than 8.2 and pink at a pH greater than 10.0

A standardized NaOH solution titrates the acetylsalicylic acid to the **phenolphthalein** endpoint, where

$$\text{volume of NaOH } (L) \times \text{molar concentration of NaOH } (mol/L) = \text{mol NaOH} \qquad (19.4)$$

According to equation 19.3, one mole of OH^- reacts with one mole of acetylsalicylic acid; thus, the moles and mass of acetylsalicylic acid in the prepared sample are calculated. Knowing the calculated mass of the acid and the measured mass of the aspirin sample, the percent purity of the aspirin sample can be calculated:

$$\text{mol acetylsalicylic acid} \times \frac{180.2 \text{ g}}{\text{mol}} = \text{g acetylsalicylic acid} \qquad (19.5)$$

$$\% \text{ purity} = \frac{\text{g acetylsalicylic acid}}{\text{g aspirin sample}} \times 100 \qquad (19.6)$$

In Part C, the analysis for the percent acetylsalicylic acid in an aspirin sample is determined for the aspirin prepared in Part A *or* for a commercial aspirin tablet.

Experimental Procedure

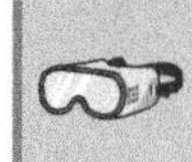

Procedure Overview: Crystalline aspirin is synthesized and then purified by the procedure of recrystallization. The melting point and the percent purity of the aspirin are determined, the latter by titration with a standardized NaOH solution.

Be aware of the number of significant figures when recording data.

A. Preparation of Aspirin

It is safest to prepare the aspirin in a fume hood. Set up a boiling water bath in a 400-mL beaker. Prepare about 100 mL of deionized ice water. Also set up an ice bath.

1. **Mix the starting materials and heat.** Measure ~2 g (±0.01 g) of salicylic acid (**Caution:** *This is a skin irritant*) in a *dry* 125-mL Erlenmeyer flask. Cover the crystals with 4–5 mL of acetic anhydride. (**Caution:** *Acetic anhydride is a severe eye irritant—avoid skin and eye contact.*) Swirl the flask to wet the salicylic acid crystals. Add 5 drops of *conc* H_2SO_4 (**Caution:** *H_2SO_4 causes severe skin burns.*) to the mixture and gently heat the flask in a boiling water bath (Figure 19.1[1]) for 5–10 minutes.
2. **Cool to crystallize the aspirin.** Remove the flask from the hot water bath and, to the reaction mixture, add ~10 mL of deionized *ice* water to decompose any excess acetic anhydride. Chill the solution in an ice bath until crystals of aspirin no longer form, stirring occasionally to decompose residual acetic anhydride. *If* an "oil" appears instead of a solid, reheat the flask in the hot water bath until the oil disappears and again cool.

[1]A Bunsen flame may be substituted for the hot plate.

3. **Separate the solid aspirin from the solution.** Set up a vacuum filtration apparatus and turn it on. Seal the filter paper with water in the Büchner funnel. *Decant* the liquid from Part A.2 onto the filter paper; minimize any transfer of the solid aspirin. Some aspirin, however, may be inadvertently transferred to the filter; *that's okay.*
4. **Filter, wash, and transfer the aspirin.** Add 15 mL of *ice* water to the flask, swirl, chill briefly, and decant onto the filter. Repeat until the transfer of the crystals to the vacuum filter is complete; maintain the vacuum to dry the crystals as best possible. Wash the aspirin crystals on the filter paper with 10 mL of ice water. Keep all of the filtrate until the aspirin has been transferred to the filter.

   If aspirin forms in the filtrate, transfer this filtrate and aspirin to a beaker, chill in an ice bath, and vacuum filter as before, using a new piece of filter paper.

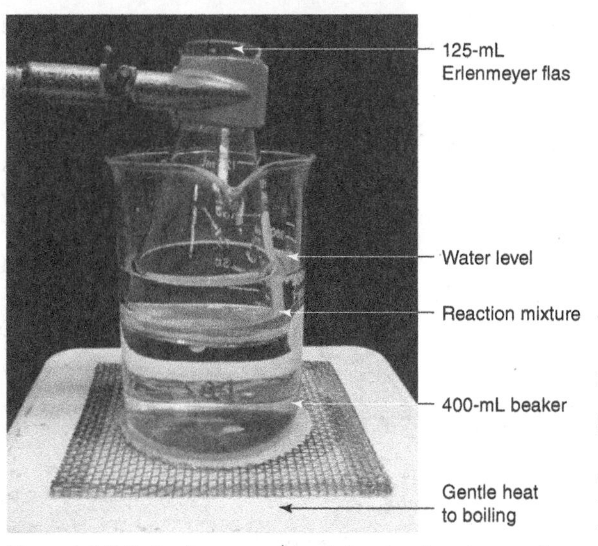

Figure 19.1 Boiling water bath for the dissolution of the acetylsalicylic acid crystals

Disposal: Dispose of the "final" filtrate as directed by your laboratory instructor.

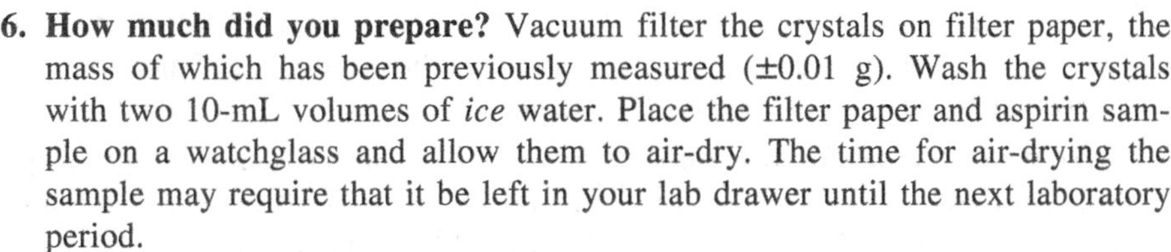

5. **Recrystallize the aspirin.** Transfer the crystals from the filter paper(s) to a 100-mL beaker. Add repetitive small volumes of ethanol (e.g., 3-mL volumes) to the aspirin until the crystals *just* dissolve (~10 mL is required). Warm the mixture in a 60°C water bath (**Caution:** *No flame—use a hot plate or a hot water bath*). Pour ~50 mL of ~60°C water into the solution. If a solid forms, continue warming until the solid dissolves but do not boil. Add more water to dissolve if necessary.

   Cover the beaker with a watchglass, remove it from the heat, and set it aside to cool slowly to room temperature. Then set the beaker in an ice bath. Beautiful needlelike crystals of acetylsalicylic acid form.

6. **How much did you prepare?** Vacuum filter the crystals on filter paper, the mass of which has been previously measured (±0.01 g). Wash the crystals with two 10-mL volumes of *ice* water. Place the filter paper and aspirin sample on a watchglass and allow them to air-dry. The time for air-drying the sample may require that it be left in your lab drawer until the next laboratory period.

   Determine the mass of the dry filter paper and sample. Dispose of the filtrate as directed by your laboratory instructor.

7. **Correct for residual solubility.** The solubility of acetylsalicylic acid is ~0.25 g per 100 mL of water. Correcting for this inherent loss of product due to the wash water in Part A.6, calculate the percent yield.
8. **What do you do with it?** Don't use it for a headache! Place the sample in a properly labeled test tube, stopper, and submit it along with your ***Report Sheet*** to your laboratory instructor at the conclusion of the experiment.

B. Melting Point of the Aspirin Sample

The melting point of the aspirin sample can be determined with either a commercial melting-point apparatus (Figure 15.5) or with the apparatus shown in Figure 19.2, page 240 and described in Part B.1. Consult with your instructor.

1. **Prepare the sample.** Fill a capillary melting-point tube to a depth of 1 cm with the recrystalized aspirin prepared in Part A.6. See Figures 15.3 and 15.4. Attach the tube to a 360°C glass or digital thermometer with a rubber band (or band of rubber

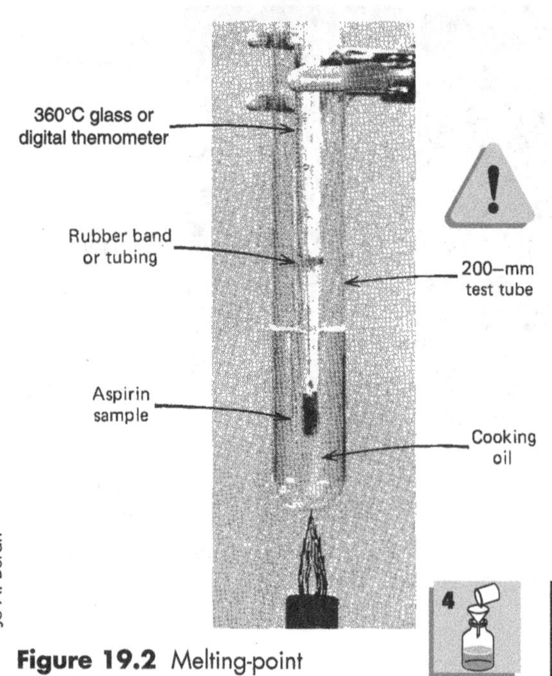

Figure 19.2 Melting-point apparatus for aspirin

tubing). Place the sample alongside the thermometer bulb (Figure 19.2) or thermal sensor. As the melting point for aspirin is greater than 100°C, a cooking oil must be used for the heating bath.

2. **Determine the melting point.** *Slowly* and *gently* heat the oil bath at a rate of ~5°C per minute until the aspirin melts. (**Caution:** *The oil bath is at a temperature greater than 100°C—do not touch!*) Cool the bath and aspirin to just below this approximate melting point until the aspirin in the tube solidifies; at a slower ~1°C per minute rate, heat again until it melts; this is the melting point of your prepared aspirin.
3. **A purity check of the sample.** If the melting point of your prepared aspirin sample is less than 130°C, repeat Part A.5 to recrystallize the sample for the purpose of increasing its purity. After the recrystallization, repeat Parts B.1 and B.2.
4. **Repeat the melting-point measurement.** Again, cool the bath and aspirin to just below the melting point until the aspirin in the tube solidifies; at a 1°C per minute rate; heat again until it melts.

Disposal: Ask your instructor about the proper disposal of the oil. Be sure the oil is cool when handling it. Dispose of the capillary tube in the Waste Glass container.

C. Percent Acetylsalicylic Acid in the Aspirin Sample

Three trials are to be completed in the analysis of the aspirin. Prepare three clean 125- or 250-mL Erlenmeyer flasks and determine the mass of three aspirin samples while occupying the balance. Obtain a 50-mL buret.

Data Analysis, A

1. **Prepare the aspirin sample for analysis.** *Assuming* 100% purity of your aspirin sample, calculate the mass of aspirin that requires 20 mL of 0.1 *M* NaOH to reach the stoichiometric point. See ***Prelaboratory Assignment*** question 5a and show the calculation on the ***Report Sheet***. On weighing paper, measure the calculated mass (±0.001 g) of the aspirin you have just prepared (or a crushed commercial aspirin tablet) and transfer it to the flask. Add 10 mL of 95% ethanol, followed by about 50 mL of deionized water, and swirl to dissolve the aspirin. Add 2 drops of phenolphthalein indicator. Repeat for trials 2 and 3.

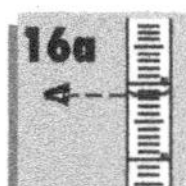

2. **Prepare the buret for titration.** Prepare a clean buret, rinse, and fill it with a standardized 0.1 *M* NaOH solution.[2] Be sure that no air bubbles are present in the buret tip. After 10–15 seconds, read and record the volume, and the *actual* molar concentration of the NaOH solution. Be precise!

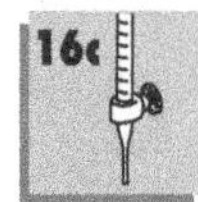

3. **Titrate the sample.** Slowly add the NaOH solution from the buret to the dissolved aspirin sample until the endpoint is reached. The endpoint in the titration should be within one-half drop of a faint pink color. The color should persist for 30 seconds. Read and record the final volume of NaOH in the buret.

Disposal: Discard the test solution in the Waste Acids container or as advised by your instructor.

CLEANUP: Discard the NaOH titrant into a properly labeled bottle; rinse the buret with several 5-mL volumes of tap water, followed by two 5-mL volumes of deionized water.

The Next Step

The purity of an aspirin sample can also be determined spectrophotometrically. Research the Internet for the procedure and refer to *Experiment 35* for details.

[2]You may need to prepare the 0.1 *M* NaOH solution using the procedure in *Experiment 9*, or the stockroom personnel may have it already prepared.

Experiment 19 *Prelaboratory Assignment*

Aspirin Synthesis and Analysis

Date __________ Lab Sec. ______ Name ____ Desk No. __________

1. Experimental Procedure, Part A.1. In the experiment, 2.00 g of salicylic acid (molar mass = 138.1 g/mol) reacts with an excess amount of acetic anhydride
   a. Calculate the theoretical yield of acetylsalicylic acid (molar mass = 180.2 g/mol) for this synthesis.

   b. After completing the Experimental Procedure, a mass of 1.78 g of acetylsalicylic acid was recovered. What is the experimental yield for its synthesis? Express the yield with the correct number of significant figures.

2. Experimental Procedure, Part A.5. Recrystallizing the aspirin removes some (or all) of the impurities in the sample. Explain how the recrystallization process performs this function.

3. Experimental Procedure, Part B.3. The melting point of the prepared aspirin in this experiment will most likely be less than (but not greater than) that of pure aspirin. Explain. See *Experiment 14*.

4. Identify the five **cautions** cited in the Experimental Procedure for this experiment.

5. Experimental Procedure, Part C.1

a. Determine the number of grams of acetylsalicylic acid that will react with 20.0 mL of 0.100 *M* NaOH. Show calculation here and on the ***Report Sheet***.

b. An aspirin sample was synthesized and analyzed. The data for the analysis for Trial 1 is in the table below. (See ***Report Sheet***.) From the data determine the percent purity of the aspirin sample. Record calculated values with the correct number of significant figures.

		Calculation Zone
1. Mass of weighing paper (*g*)	0.032	***Part 5b.8***
2. Mass of weighing paper plus aspirin sample (*g*)	1.414	
3. Mass of aspirin sample (*g*)		
4. Molar concentration of the NaOH solution (*mol/L*)	0.103	***Part 5b.10***
5. Buret reading, *initial* (*mL*)	2.05	
6. Buret reading, *final* (*mL*)	20.55	
7. Volume of NaOH added (*mL*)		
8. Moles of NaOH added (*mol*) Show calculation.		***Part 5b.11***
9. Moles of acetylsalicylic acid (*mol*)		
10. Mass of acetylsalicylic acid (*g*) Show calculation.		
11. Percent purity of aspirin sample (%) Show calculation.		

c. For Trials 2 and 3, the percent purity was determined to be 94.5% and 93.9% respectively.

a. What is the average percent purity of the aspirin sample?

b. What are the standard deviation and the relative standard deviation (%RSD) for the percent purity of the aspirin sample?

Experiment 19 *Report Sheet*

Aspirin Synthesis and Analysis

Date __________ Lab Sec. ______ Name ______________________________ Desk No. __________

A. Preparation of Aspirin

1. Mass of salicylic acid (*g*) __________
2. Theoretical yield of aspirin (*g*) __________
3. Experimental yield of aspirin (*g*) __________
4. *Total* volume of solutions in contact with aspirin in Part A.6 (*mL*) __________
5. Mass loss due to residual solubility (*g*) __________
6. Experimental yield, corrected for solubility (*g*) __________
7. Percent yield (%) __________

B. Melting Point of the Aspirin Sample

1. Melting-point measurements (°*C*) __________ __________ __________
2. Average melting point of aspirin (°*C*) __________

C. Percent Acetylsalicylic Acid in the Aspirin Sample

Calculation for the mass of aspirin for the titrimetric analysis. See Part C.1.

	Trial 1	*Trial 2*	*Trial 3*
1. Mass of weighing paper (*g*)			
2. Mass of weighing paper plus aspirin sample (*g*)			
3. Mass of aspirin sample (*g*)			
4. Molar concentration of the NaOH solution (*mol/L*)			
5. Buret reading, *initial* (*mL*)			
6. Buret reading, *final* (*mL*)			
7. Volume of NaOH added (*mL*)			

	Trial 1	Trial 2	Trial 3
8. Moles of NaOH added (*mol*)			
9. Moles of acetylsalicylic acid (*mol*)			
10. Mass of acetylsalicylic acid (*g*)			
11. Percent purity of aspirin sample (%)			
12. Average percent purity of aspirin sample (%)			
13. Calculate the standard deviation for the percent acetylsalicylic acid in aspirin.			
14. Calculate the relative standard deviation (%RSD).			

Laboratory Questions

Circle the questions that have been assigned.

1. Part A.1. According to LeChâtelier's principle, explain why it is necessary to add the *conc* H_2SO_4 during the preparation of the acetylsalicylic acid. Also see equation 19.1.
2. Part A.1. *Anhydride* means "without water." Suppose 1 *M* H_2SO_4 were substituted for the *conc* H_2SO_4. Would the yield of acetylsalicylic acid be increased, decreased, or unaffected by the substitution? Explain.
3. Part A.2. The acetic anhydride has been in the stockroom for several years and was not tightly sealed. As a result of the storage, will the yield of acetylsalicylic acid be reported as too high, too low, or unaffected? Explain.
4. Part A.2. All washings of the acetylsalicylic acid are with deionized ice water. What is the purpose of washing the acetylsalicylic acid with ice water rather than room temperature water?
5. Part A.4. Some of the aspirin passed through the filter into the filtrate. How does the aspirin in the filtrate differ from that collected on the filter paper?
6. Part A.5. The product crystals are dissolved in a minimum volume of ethanol. Is acetylsalicylic acid more soluble in ethanol or water? Explain.
7. Part B.2. Would the product isolated after Part A.4 have a higher or lower melting point than that isolated after Part A.6? Explain.
8. Part C.2. The molar concentration of the NaOH solution is recorded as being 0.1 *M* instead of the actual molar concentration of 0.151 *M*. If the recorded concentration is used to calculate the purity of the aspirin sample, will the percent purity be reported too high or too low? Explain.

Astrid & Hanns-Frieder Michler/Science Source

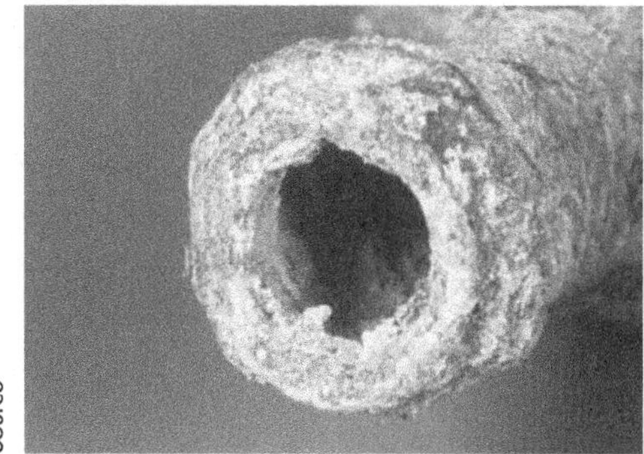

Experiment 21

Hard Water Analysis

Deposits of hardening ions (generally calcium carbonate deposits) can reduce the flow of water in plumbing.

OBJECTIVES

- To learn the cause and effects of hard water
- To determine the hardness of a water sample

TECHNIQUES

The following techniques are used in the Experimental Procedure:

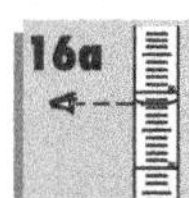

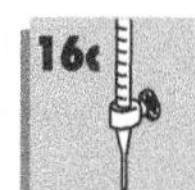

INTRODUCTION

Hardening ions present in natural waters are the result of slightly acidic rainwater flowing over mineral deposits of varying compositions; the acidic rainwater[1] reacts with the *very* slightly soluble carbonate salts of calcium and magnesium and with various iron-containing rocks. A partial dissolution of these salts releases the ions into the water supply, which may be **surface water** or groundwater.

Surface water: water that is collected from a watershed—for example, lakes, rivers, and streams

$$CO_2(aq) + H_2O(l) + CaCO_3(s) \longrightarrow Ca^{2+}(aq) + 2\ HCO_3^-(aq) \quad (21.1)$$

Hardening ions such as Ca^{2+}, Mg^{2+}, and Fe^{2+} (and other divalent, 2^+, ions) form insoluble compounds with soaps and cause many detergents to be less effective. Soaps, which are sodium salts of fatty acids such as sodium stearate, $C_{17}H_{35}CO_2^-Na^+$, are very effective cleansing agents so long as they remain soluble; the presence of the hardening ions however causes the formation of a gray, insoluble soap scum such as $(C_{17}H_{35}CO_2)_2Ca$:

$$2\ C_{17}H_{35}CO_2^-Na^+(aq) + Ca^{2+}(aq) \longrightarrow (C_{17}H_{35}CO_2)_2Ca(s) + 2\ Na^+(aq) \quad (21.2)$$

This gray precipitate appears as a bathtub ring and also clings to clothes, causing white clothes to appear gray. Dishes and glasses may have water spots, shower stalls and lavatories may have a sticky film, clothes may feel rough and scratchy, hair may be dull and unmanageable, and your skin may be irritated and sticky because of hard water.

Hard water is also responsible for the appearance and undesirable formation of "boiler scale" on tea kettles and pots used for heating water. The boiler scale is a poor conductor of heat and thus reduces the efficiency of transferring heat. Boiler scale also builds on the inside of hot water pipes, causing a decrease in the flow of water (see opening photo); in extreme cases, this buildup causes the pipe to burst.

Boiler scale consists primarily of the carbonate salts of the hardening ions and is formed according to

$$Ca^{2+}(aq) + 2\ HCO_3^-(aq) \xrightarrow{\Delta} CaCO_3(s) + CO_2(g) + H_2O(l) \quad (21.3)$$

---

[1] CO_2 dissolved in rainwater makes rainwater slightly acidic:

$$CO_2(g) + 2\ H_2O(l) \longrightarrow H_3O^+(aq) + HCO_3^-(aq)$$

The greater the $CO_2(g)$ levels in the atmosphere due to fossil fuel combustion, the more acidic will be the rainwater.

Bortner/National Audobon Society/Science Source

Figure 21.1 Stalactite and stalagmite formations are present in regions having large deposits of limestone, a major contributor of hardening ions. Colored formations are often due to trace amounts of Fe^{2+}, Mn^{2+}, or Sr^{2+}, also hardening ions.

Table 21.1 Hardness Classification of Water*

Hardness (*ppm* $CaCO_3$)	Classification
<17.1 ppm	Soft water
17.1 ppm–60 ppm	Slightly hard water
60 ppm–120 ppm	Moderately hard water
120 ppm–180 ppm	Hard water
>180 ppm	Very hard water

*U.S. Department of Interior and the Water Quality Association

Notice that this reaction is just the reverse of the reaction for the formation of hard water (equation 21.1). The same two reactions are also key to the formation of stalactites and stalagmites for caves located in regions with large limestone deposits (Figure 21.1).

Because of the relatively large natural abundance of limestone deposits and other calcium minerals, such as gypsum, $CaSO_4{\bullet}2H_2O$, it is not surprising that Ca^{2+} ion, in conjunction with Mg^{2+}, is a major component of the dissolved solids in hard water.

Hard water, however, is not a health hazard. In fact, the presence of Ca^{2+} and Mg^{2+} in hard water can be considered dietary supplements to the point of providing their recommended daily allowance (RDA). Some research studies (though disputed) have also indicated a positive correlation between water hardness and decreased heart disease.

The concentration of the hardening ions in a water sample is commonly expressed as though the hardness is due exclusively to $CaCO_3$. Hardness is commonly expressed as mg $CaCO_3$/L, which is also ppm $CaCO_3$,[2]—or grains per gallon, gpg $CaCO_3$, where 1 gpg $CaCO_3$ = 17.1 mg $CaCO_3$/L. A general classification of hard waters is listed in Table 21.1.

Theory of Analysis

Complex ion: generally a cation of a metal ion to which is bonded a number of molecules or anions (see Experiment 36)

Titrant: the solution placed in the buret in a titrimetric analysis

Analyte: the solution containing the substance being analyzed, generally in the receiving flask in a titration setup

Na_2H_2Y

In this experiment, a titration technique is used to measure the combined hardening divalent ion concentrations (primarily Ca^{2+} and Mg^{2+}) in a water sample. The titrant is the disodium salt of ethylenediaminetetraacetic acid (abbreviated Na_2H_2Y).[3]

In aqueous solution, Na_2H_2Y dissociates into Na^+ and H_2Y^{2-} ions. The H_2Y^{2-} ion reacts with the hardening ions, Ca^{2+} and Mg^{2+}, to form very stable **complex ions,** especially in a solution buffered at a pH of about 10. An ammonia–ammonium ion buffer is often used for this pH adjustment in the analysis.

As H_2Y^{2-} **titrant** is added to the **analyte,** it complexes with the "free" Ca^{2+} and Mg^{2+} of the water sample to form the respective complex ions:

$$Ca^{2+}(aq) + H_2Y^{2-}(aq) \longrightarrow [CaY]^{2-}(aq) + 2\,H^+(aq) \quad (21.4a)$$

$$Mg^{2+}(aq) + H_2Y^{2-}(aq) \longrightarrow [MgY]^{2-}(aq) + 2\,H^+(aq) \quad (21.4b)$$

From the 1:1 mole ratio of the balanced equations, it is apparent that once the molar concentration of the Na_2H_2Y solution is known, the moles of hardening ions in a water sample can be calculated:

$$\text{volume } H_2Y^{2-} \times \text{molar concentration of } H_2Y^{2-} = \text{moles } H_2Y^{2-} = \text{moles hardening ions} \quad (21.5)$$

The hardening ions, for reporting purposes, are assumed to be exclusively Ca^{2+} from the dissolving of $CaCO_3$. Since one mole of Ca^{2+} forms from one mole of $CaCO_3$, the hardness of the water sample expressed as mg $CaCO_3$ per liter of sample is

$$\text{moles hardening ions} = \text{moles } Ca^{2+} = \text{moles of } CaCO_3 \quad (21.6)$$

$$\text{ppm } CaCO_3 \left(\frac{mg\ CaCO_3}{L\ sample}\right) = \frac{\text{mol } CaCO_3}{\text{L sample}} \times \frac{100.1 \text{ g } CaCO_3}{\text{mol}} \times \frac{\text{mg}}{10^{-3}\text{g}} \quad (21.7)$$

[2]ppm means "parts per million"—1 mg of $CaCO_3$ in 1,000,000 mg (or 1 kg) solution is 1 ppm $CaCO_3$. Assuming the density of the solution is 1 g/mL (or 1 kg/L), then 1,000,000 mg solution = 1 L solution. Therefore, 1 mg/L is also an expression of ppm.

[3]**E**thylene**d**iamine**t**etr**a**acetic acid is often simply referred to as EDTA with an abbreviated formula of H_4Y.

The Indicator for the Analysis

A special indicator is used to detect the endpoint in the titration. Called Eriochrome Black T (EBT),[4] it forms complex ions with the Ca^{2+} and Mg^{2+} ions, but binds more strongly to Mg^{2+} ions. Because only a small amount of EBT is added, only Mg^{2+} complexes; no Ca^{2+} ion complexes to EBT—therefore, most all of the hardening ions remain "free" in solution to combine with H_2Y^{2-}. The EBT indicator is sky blue in solution but forms a wine-red complex with Mg^{2+}:

$$\underset{\text{sky-blue}}{Mg^{2+}(aq) + EBT(aq)} \rightleftharpoons \underset{\text{wine-red}}{[Mg\text{-}EBT]^{2+}(aq)} \tag{21.8}$$

HO, HO, N=N, NO_2, SO_3^-

Eriochrome Black T

Therefore, before any H_2Y^{2-} titrant is added for the analysis, the analyte is wine-red because of the $[Mg\text{-}EBT]^{2+}$ complex ion.

As the H_2Y^{2-} titrant is added, all of the "free" Ca^{2+} and Mg^{2+} ions in the water sample become complexed just prior to the endpoint; thereafter, the H_2Y^{2-} removes the trace amount of Mg^{2+} from the wine-red $[Mg\text{-}EBT]^{2+}$ complex. At this point, the solution changes from the wine-red color back to the original sky-blue color of the EBT indicator to reach the endpoint. All hardening ions have been complexed with H_2Y^{2-}:

$$\underset{\text{wine-red}}{[Mg^{2+}\text{-}EBT]^{2+}(aq)} + H_2Y^{2-}(aq) \longrightarrow [MgY]^{2-}(aq) + 2\,H^+(aq) + \underset{\text{sky-blue}}{EBT(aq)} \tag{21.9}$$

Therefore, the presence of Mg^{2+} in the sample is a must in order for the color change from wine-red to sky-blue to be observed. To ensure the appearance of the endpoint, oftentimes a small amount of Mg^{2+} as $[MgY]^{2-}$ is initially added to the analyte along with the EBT indicator to form the wine-red color of $[Mg\text{-}EBT]^{2+}$.

> The mechanism for the process of adding both $[MgY]^{2-}$ and EBT is as follows: The $[MgY]^{2-}$ dissociates in the analyte because the Y^{4-} (as H_2Y^{2-} in water) is more strongly bonded to the Ca^{2+} of the sample; the "freed" Mg^{2+} then combines with the EBT to form the wine-red color (equation 21.8). The complexing of the "free" Ca^{2+} and Mg^{2+} with the H_2Y^{2-} titrant continues until both are depleted. At that point, the H_2Y^{2-} reacts with the $[Mg\text{-}EBT]^{2+}$ in the sample until the sky-blue endpoint is reached (equation 21.9).
>
> Because Mg^{2+} and Y^{4-} (as H_2Y^{2-}) are freed initially from the added $[MgY]^{2-}$, but later consumed at the endpoint, no additional H_2Y^{2-} titrant is required for the analysis of hardness in the water sample.

A Standard Na_2H_2Y Solution

The standardization of a Na_2H_2Y solution is determined by its reaction with a known amount of calcium ion in a (primary) standard Ca^{2+} solution (equation 21.4a). The measured aliquot of the standard Ca^{2+} solution is buffered to a pH of 10 and titrated with the Na_2H_2Y solution to the Eriochrome Black T *sky-blue* endpoint (equation 21.9). To achieve the endpoint, a small amount of Mg^{2+} in the form of $[MgY]^{2-}$ is added to the standard Ca^{2+} solution.

Note that the standardization of the Na_2H_2Y solution with a standard Ca^{2+} solution in Part A is reversed in Part B, where the (now) standardized Na_2H_2Y solution is used to determine the concentration of Ca^{2+} (and other hardening ions) in a sample.

Experimental Procedure

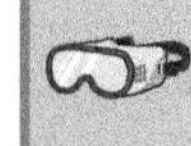

Procedure Overview: A (primary) standard solution of Ca^{2+} is used to standardize a prepared ~0.01 *M* Na_2H_2Y solution. The (secondary) standardized Na_2H_2Y solution is subsequently used to titrate the hardening ions of a water sample to the Eriochrome Black T (or calmagite) indicator endpoint.

Be aware of the number of significant figures when recording data.

A. A Standard 0.01 *M* Disodium Ethylenediaminetetraacetate, Na_2H_2Y, Solution

The standardized Na_2H_2Y solution may have already been prepared by stockroom personnel. If so, obtain 100 mL of the solution and proceed to Part B. Consult with your instructor.

Three trials are to be completed for the standardization of the ~0.01 *M* Na_2H_2Y solution. Initially prepare three clean 125-mL Erlenmeyer flasks for Part A.3.

[4]Calmagite may be substituted for Eriochrome Black T as an indicator. The same wine-red to sky-blue endpoint is observed. Ask your instructor.

1. **Measure the mass for the Na_2H_2Y solution.** Calculate the mass of $Na_2H_2Y{\cdot}2H_2O$ (molar mass = 372.24 g/mol) required to prepare 250 mL of a 0.01 *M* Na_2H_2Y solution. See ***Prelaboratory Assignment*** question 2 and show this calculation on the ***Report Sheet***. Measure this mass on weighing paper, transfer it to a 250-mL volumetric flask containing 100 mL of deionized water, swirl to dissolve, and dilute to the mark (slight heating may be required).

Read and record the volume in the buret to the correct number of significant figures.

2. **Prepare a buret for titration.** Rinse a *clean* buret with the Na_2H_2Y solution several times and then fill. Record the volume of the titrant using all certain digits plus one uncertain digit.

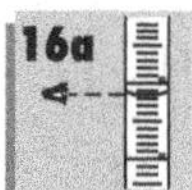

3. **Prepare the standard Ca^{2+} solution.** Obtain ~80 mL of a standard Ca^{2+} solution and record its exact molar concentration (~0.01 *M*). Pipet 25.0 mL of the standard Ca^{2+} solution into a 125-mL Erlenmeyer flask, add 1 mL of buffer (pH = 10) solution, and 2 drops of EBT indicator (containing a small amount of $[MgY]^{2-}$). Repeat for Trials 2 and 3.

Data Analysis, A

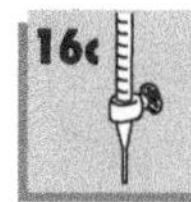

4. **Titrate the standard Ca^{2+} solution.** Titrate the standard Ca^{2+} solution with the Na_2H_2Y titrant; swirl continuously. Near the endpoint, slow the rate of addition to drops; the last few drops should be added at 3–5-second intervals. The solution changes from wine-red to purple to sky-blue—no tinge of the wine-red color should remain; the solution is *blue* at the endpoint. Record the final volume in the buret.

5. **Repeat the titration with the standard Ca^{2+} solution.** Repeat the titrations on the remaining two samples. Calculate the molar concentration of the Na_2H_2Y solution. Save the standard Ca^{2+} solution for Part B.

B. Analysis of Water Sample

Complete three trials for your analysis. The first trial is an indication of the hardness of your water sample. You may want to adjust the volume of water for the analysis of the second and third trials.

1. **Obtain the water sample for analysis**
   a. Obtain about 100 mL of a water sample from your instructor. You may use your own water sample or simply the tap water in the laboratory.
   b. If the water sample is from a lake, stream, or ocean, you will need to gravity filter the sample before the analysis.
   c. If your sample is acidic, add 1 *M* NH_3 until it is basic to litmus (or pH paper).
2. **Prepare the water sample for analysis.** Pipet 25.0 mL of your (filtered, if necessary) water sample[5] into a 125-mL Erlenmeyer flask, add 1 mL of the buffer (pH = 10) solution, and 2 drops of EBT indicator.
3. **Titrate the water sample.** Titrate the water sample with the standardized Na_2H_2Y until the *blue* endpoint appears (as described in Part A.4). Repeat (twice) the analysis of the water sample to determine its hardness.

Disposal: Dispose of the analyzed solutions in the Waste EDTA container.

The Next Step

(1) Because hardness of a water source varies with temperature, rainfall, seasons, water treatment, and so on design a systematic study of the hardness of a water source as a function of one or more variables. (2) Compare the incoming versus the outgoing water hardness of a continuous water supply. (3) Compare the water hardness of drinking water for adjacent city and county water supplies and account for the differences.

[5]If your water sample is known to have a high hardness, decrease its volume proportionally until it takes about 15 mL of Na_2H_2Y titrant for your second and third trials. Similarly, if your water sample is known to have a low hardness, increase its volume proportionally.

Experiment 21 *Prelaboratory Assignment*

Hard Water Analysis

Date ________ Lab Sec. ______ Name ________________________________ Desk No. ________

1. What cations are responsible for water hardness?

2. Experimental Procedure, Part A.1. Calculate the mass of disodium ethylenediaminetetraacetate (molar mass = 372.24 g/mol) required to prepare 250 mL of a 0.010 *M* solution. Show the calculation here and on the ***Report Sheet***. Express the mass to the correct number of significant figures.

3. Experimental Procedure, Part A.3. A 24.8 mL volume of a prepared Na_2H_2Y solution titrates 25.0 mL of a standard 0.0107 *M* Ca^{2+} solution to the Eriochrome Black T endpoint. What is the molar concentration of the Na_2H_2Y solution?

4. a. Which hardening ion, Ca^{2+} or Mg^{2+}, binds more tightly to (forms a stronger complex ion with) the Eriochrome Black T indicator used for today's analysis?

b. What is the expected color change at the endpoint in this experiment?

5. a. A naturally occurring water sample was collected and analyzed to determine its hardness. The data below is from Trial 1. (See ***Report Sheet***.) Complete the table to determine the hardness of the sample. Record the calculated values with the correct number of significant figures.

B. Analysis of Water Sample

Calculation Zone

1. Sample volume (*mL*)	50.00	***Part B.5***
2. Buret reading, *initial* (*mL*)	1.73	
3. Buret reading, *final* (*mL*)	19.25	
4. Volume of Na_2H_2Y titrant (*mL*)		
Molar concentration of Na_2H_2Y titrant (*mol/L*)	0.00940	***Part B.6***
5. Moles of Na_2H_2Y = moles of hardening ions, Ca^{2+} and Mg^{2+} (*mol*) Show calculation.		
6. Mass of equivalent $CaCO_3$ (*g*) Show calculation.		***Part B.7***
7. ppm $CaCO_3$ (*mg $CaCO_3$/L sample*) Show calculation.		

5. b. For Trials 2 and 3, the hardness of the water sample (mg $CaCO_3$/L sample) was determined to be 339 ppm $CaCO_3$ and 322 ppm $CaCO_3$ respectively.

a. What is the average hardness of the water sample?

b. What are the standard deviation and the relative standard deviation (%RSD) for the hardness (ppm $CaCO_3$) of the water sample?

5. c. Water hardness is also commonly expressed in units of grains/gallon, where 1 grain/gallon equals 17.1 ppm $CaCO_3$. Express the hardness of this water sample in grains/gallon.

5. d. Classify the hardness of this water according to Table 21.1.

Experiment 21 *Report Sheet*

Hard Water Analysis

Date __________ Lab Sec. ______ Name ______________________________ Desk No. __________

A. A Standard 0.01 *M* Disodium Ethylenediaminetetraacetate, Na_2H_2Y, Solution

Calculate the mass of $Na_2H_2Y \cdot 2H_2O$ required to prepare 250 mL of a 0.01 *M* Na_2H_2Y solution. See Part A.1.

	Trial 1	*Trial 2*	*Trial 3*
1. Volume of standard Ca^{2+} solution (*mL*)	25.0	25.0	25.0
2. Concentration of standard Ca^{2+} solution (*mol/L*)			
3. Mol Ca^{2+} = mol Na_2H_2Y (*mol*)			
4. Buret reading, *initial* (*mL*)			
5. Buret reading, *final* (*mL*)			
6. Volume of Na_2H_2Y titrant (*mL*)			
7. Molar concentration of Na_2H_2Y solution (*mol/L*)			
8. Average molar concentration of Na_2H_2Y solution (*mol/L*)			

B. Analysis of Water Sample

	Trial 1	*Trial 2*	*Trial 3*
1. Sample volume (*mL*)			
2. Buret reading, *initial* (*mL*)			
3. Buret reading, *final* (*mL*)			
4. Volume of Na_2H_2Y titrant (*mL*)			

5. Mol Na_2H_2Y = mol hardening ions, Ca^{2+} and Mg^{2+} (*mol*) ________ ________ ________

6. Mass of equivalent $CaCO_3$ (*g*) ________ ________ ________

7. ppm $CaCO_3$ (*mg* $CaCO_3$/*L sample*) ________ ________ ________

8. Average ppm $CaCO_3$ ________

9. Average gpg $CaCO_3$ ________ ***Data Analysis, B***

10. Standard deviation of ppm $CaCO_3$ ________ ***Data Analysis, C***

11. Relative standard deviation of ppm $CaCO_3$ (*%RSD*) ________ ***Data Analysis, D***

Laboratory Questions

Circle the questions that have been assigned.

1. Part A.3. State the purpose for the 1 mL of buffer (pH = 10) being added to the standard Ca^{2+} solution.
2. Part A.3. The Eriochrome Black T indicator is mistakenly omitted. What is the color of the analyte (standard Ca^{2+} solution)? Describe the appearance of the analyte with the continued addition of the Na_2H_2Y solution. Explain.

*3. Part A.3. The buffer solution is omitted from the titration procedure, the Eriochrome Black T indicator and a small amount of Mg^{2+} are added, and the standard Ca^{2+} solution is acidic.
   a. What is the color of the solution? Explain.
   b. The Na_2H_2Y solution is dispensed from the buret. What color changes are observed? Explain.

4. Part A.4. Deionized water from the wash bottle is used to wash the side of the Erlenmeyer flask. How does this affect the reported molar concentration of the Na_2H_2Y solution—too high, too low, or unaffected? Explain.
5. Part A.4. The dispensing of the Na_2H_2Y solution from the buret is discontinued when the solution turns purple. Because of this technique error, will the reported molar concentration of the Na_2H_2Y solution be too high, too low, or unaffected? Explain.
6. Part B.3. The dispensing of the Na_2H_2Y solution from the buret is discontinued when the solution turns purple. Because of this technique error, will the reported hardness of the water sample be too high, too low, or unaffected? Explain.
7. Part A.4 and Part B.3. The dispensing of the Na_2H_2Y solution from the buret is discontinued when the solution turns purple. However in Part B.3, the standardized Na_2H_2Y solution is then used to titrate a water sample to the (correct) *sky-blue* endpoint. Will the reported hardness of the water sample be too high, too low, or unaffected? Explain.

*8. Washing soda, $Na_2CO_3 \cdot 10H_2O$ (molar mass = 286 g/mol), is often used to "soften" hard water—that is, to remove hardening ions. Assuming hardness is due to Ca^{2+}, the CO_3^{2-} ion precipitates the Ca^{2+}:

$$Ca^{2+}(aq) + CO_3^{2-}(aq) \longrightarrow CaCO_3(s)$$

How many grams and pounds of washing soda are needed to remove the hardness from 500 gallons of water having a hardness of 200 ppm $CaCO_3$ (see Appendix A for conversion factors)?

Jo A. Beran/Trey Hernandez

Experiment 23

Factors Affecting Reaction Rates

The reaction rate of zinc metal decreases (left to right) with decreasing concentration of hydrochloric acid.

OBJECTIVE

- To study the various factors that affect the rates of chemical reactions

TECHNIQUES

The following techniques are used in the Experimental Procedure:

INTRODUCTION

Nanosecond: 1×10^{-9} second

Chemical kinetics is the study of chemical reaction rates, how reaction rates are controlled, and the pathway or mechanism by which a reaction proceeds from its reactants to its products.

Reaction rates vary from the very fast, in which the reaction, such as the explosion of a hydrogen–oxygen mixture, is essentially complete in microseconds or even **nanoseconds,** to the very slow, in which the reaction, such as the setting of concrete, requires years to complete.

The rate of a chemical reaction may be expressed as a *change* in the concentration of a reactant (or product) as a function of time (e.g., per second)—the greater the change in the concentration per unit of time, the faster the rate of the reaction. Other parameters that can follow the change in concentration of a **species** as a function of time in a chemical reaction are color (expressed as absorbance, Figure 23.1), temperature, pH, gas evolution (see opening photo), odor, and conductivity. The parameter chosen for following the rate of a particular reaction depends on the nature of the reaction and the species of the reaction.

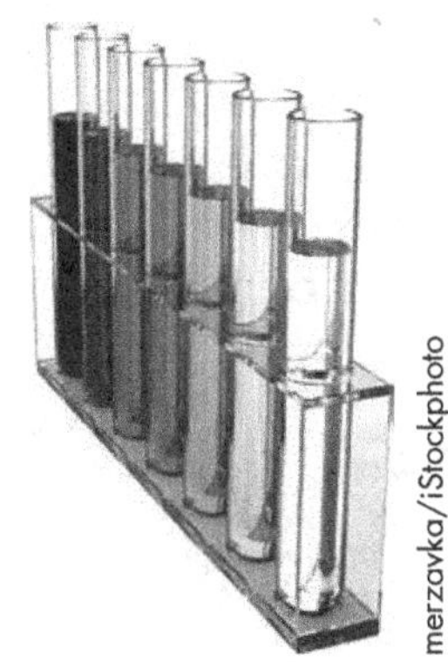

merzavka/iStockphoto

Figure 23.1 The higher concentration of light-absorbing species, the more intense is the color of the solution.

Species: any atom, molecule, or ion that may be a reactant or product of a chemical reaction

We will investigate four of five factors that can be controlled to affect the rate of a chemical reaction. The first four factors listed below are systematically studied in this experiment:

- Nature of the reactants
- Temperature of the chemical system
- Presence of a catalyst
- Concentration of the reactants
- Surface area of the reactants

Nature of the Reactants

Sodium metal and water: the reaction releases $H_2(g)$ which ignites with the oxygen in the air to produce a yellow/blue flame, the yellow resulting from the presence of Na^+ in the flame

Some substances are naturally more reactive than others and therefore undergo rapid chemical changes. For example, the reaction of **sodium metal and water** is a very rapid, exothermic reaction (see *Experiment 11*, Part F), whereas the corrosion of iron is much slower. Plastics, reinforced with fibers such as carbon or glass, are now being substituted for iron and steel in specialized applications where corrosion has historically been a problem.

Temperature of the Chemical System

Internal energy: the energy contained within the molecules/ions when they collide

As a rule of thumb, a 10°C rise in temperature doubles (increases by a factor of 2) the rate of a chemical reaction. The added heat not only increases the number of collisions[1] between reactant molecules but also, and more importantly, increases their kinetic energy. On collision of the reactant molecules, this kinetic energy is converted into an **internal energy** that is distributed throughout the collision system. This increased internal energy increases the probability for the weaker bonds to be broken and the new bonds to be formed.

Presence of a Catalyst

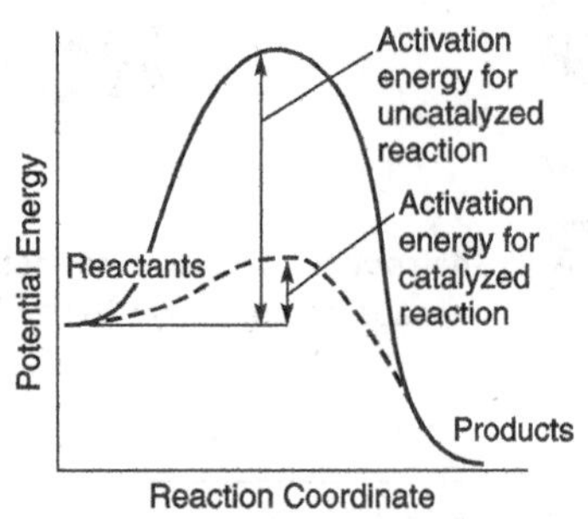

Figure 23.2 Reaction profiles of an uncatalyzed and a catalyzed reaction

A **catalyst** increases the rate of a chemical reaction without undergoing any *net* chemical change. Some catalysts increase the rate of only one specific chemical reaction without affecting similar reactions. Other catalysts are more general and affect an entire set of similar reactions. Catalysts generally reroute the pathway of a chemical reaction so that this "alternate" path, although perhaps more circuitous, has a lower activation energy for reaction than the uncatalyzed reaction (Figure 23.2).

Concentration of the Reactants

An increase in the concentration of a reactant generally increases the reaction rate. See the opening photo. The larger concentration of reactant molecules increases the probability of an "effective" collision between reacting molecules for the formation of product. On occasion, such an increase may have no effect or may even decrease the reaction rate. A quantitative investigation on the effect of concentration changes on reaction rate is undertaken in *Experiment 24*.

Surface Area of the Reactants

Generally speaking, the greater the exposed surface area of the reactant, the greater the reaction rate. For example, a large piece of coal burns very slowly, but coal *dust* burns rapidly, a consequence of which can lead to a disastrous coal mine explosion; solid potassium iodide reacts very slowly with solid lead nitrate, but when both are dissolved in solution, the formation of lead iodide is instantaneous.

EXPERIMENTAL PROCEDURE

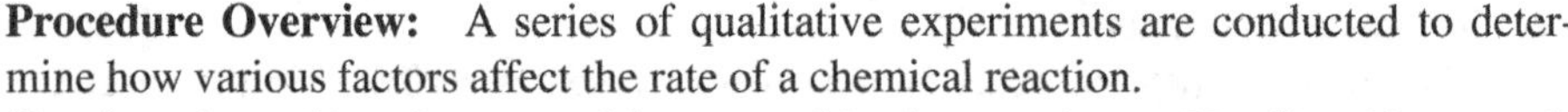

Procedure Overview: A series of qualitative experiments are conducted to determine how various factors affect the rate of a chemical reaction.

Caution: *A number of strong acids are used in the experiment. Handle with care; do not allow them to touch the skin or clothing.*

Perform the experiment with a partner. At each circled superscript(1–19) in the procedure, *stop* and record your observation on the ***Report Sheet***. Discuss your observations with your lab partner and your instructor.

Ask your instructor which parts of the Experimental Procedure you are to complete. Use a 250-mL beaker to prepare an ice water bath for Part B.3 and the hot water baths for Parts B.4 and C.3, 4.

A. Nature of the Reactants

1. **Different acids affect reaction rates.** Half-fill a set of four labeled small test tubes (Figure 23.3) with 3 *M* H_2SO_4, 6 *M* HCl, 6 *M* CH_3COOH, and 6 *M* H_3PO_4, respectively in a test tube rack. (**Caution:** *Avoid skin contact with the acids.*) Submerge a 1-cm strip of magnesium ribbon into each test tube. Compare the reaction rates and record your observations.(1)
2. **Different metals affect reaction rates.** Half-fill a set of three labeled small test tubes (Figure 23.4) with 6 *M* HCl. Submerge 1-cm strips of zinc, magnesium, and copper separately into the test tubes. Compare the reaction rates of each metal in HCl and record your observations.(2) Match the relative reactivity of the metals with the photos in Figure 23.5.(3)

[1] A 10°C temperature rise only increases the collision frequency between reactant molecules by a factor of 1.02—nowhere near the factor of 2 that is normally experienced in a reaction rate.

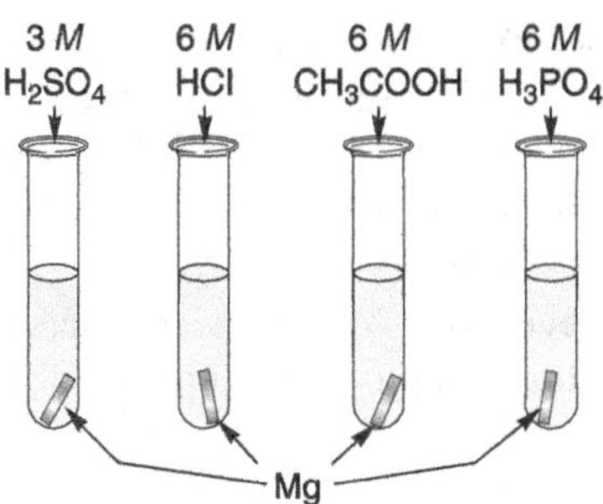

Figure 23.3 Setup for the effect of acid type on reaction rate

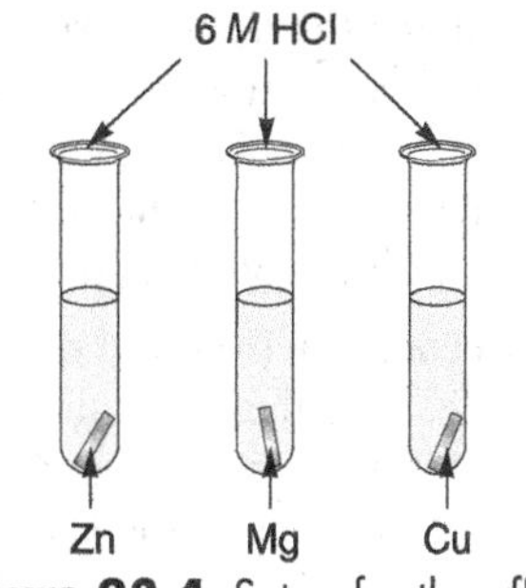

Figure 23.4 Setup for the effect of metal type on reaction rate

Courtesy of Thermo Fisher Scientific

Test Tube Rack

Jo A. Beran/Trey Hernandez

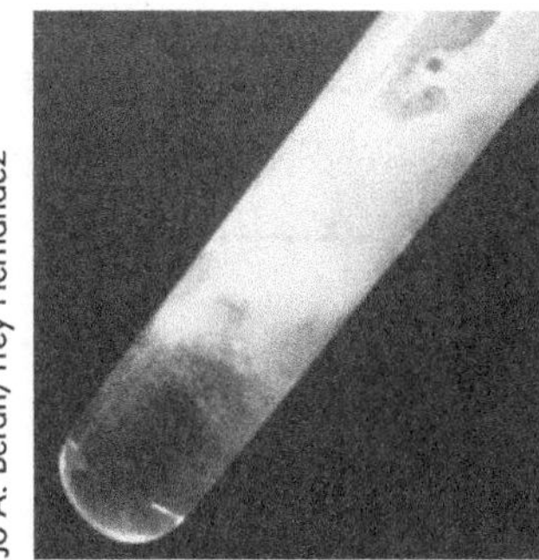

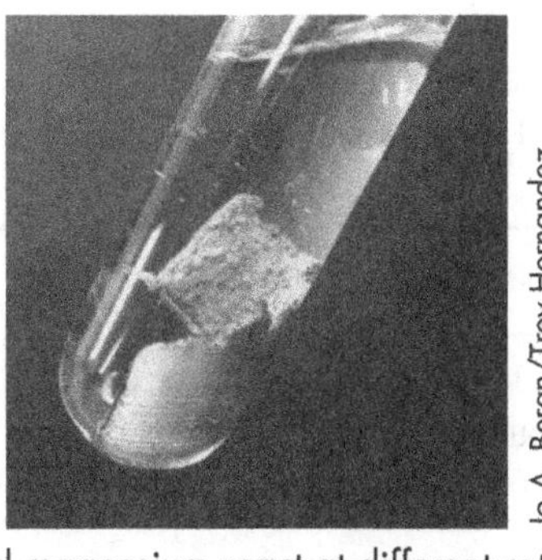

Jo A. Beran/Trey Hernandez

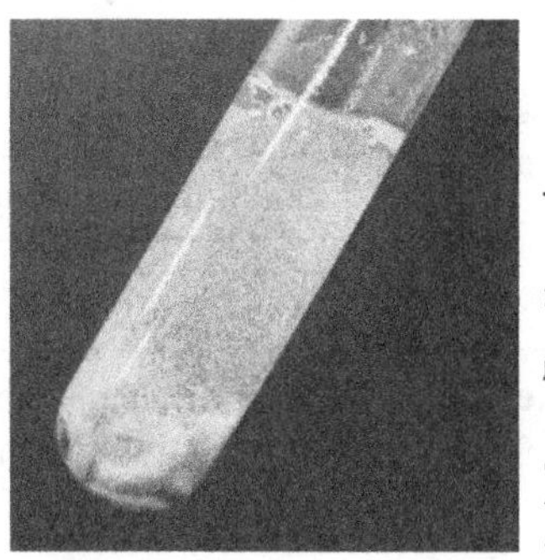

Jo A. Beran/Trey Hernandez

Figure 23.5 Zinc, copper, and magnesium react at different rates with 6 M HCl. Identify the metals in the photo according to their reactivity.③

> *Disposal:* Dispose of the reaction solutions in the Waste Inorganic Test Solutions container.

B. Temperature of the Reaction: Hydrochloric Acid–Sodium Thiosulfate Reaction System

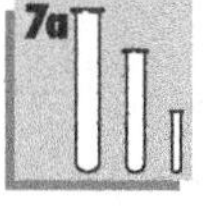

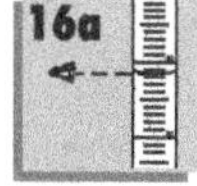

Ask your instructor to determine if *both* Parts B and C are to be completed. You should perform the experiment with a partner; as one student combines the test solutions, the other notes the time.

The oxidation–reduction reaction that occurs between hydrochloric acid and sodium thiosulfate, $Na_2S_2O_3$, produces insoluble sulfur as a product.

$$2\,HCl(aq) + Na_2S_2O_3(aq) \longrightarrow S(s) + SO_2(g) + 2\,NaCl(aq) + H_2O(l) \quad (23.1)$$

The time required for the cloudiness of sulfur to appear is a measure of the reaction rate. Measure each volume of reactant with separate graduated pipets.

1. **Prepare the solutions.** Pipet 2 mL of 0.1 *M* $Na_2S_2O_3$ into each of a set of three 150-mm, *clean* test tubes. Into a second set of three 150-mm test tubes, pipet 2 mL of 0.1 *M* HCl. Label each set of test tubes.

   The first pair of $Na_2S_2O_3$–HCl pair test tubes is to be combined at room temperature in Part B.2. Place a second pair of $Na_2S_2O_3$–HCl pair test tubes in an ice water bath for Part B.3. and a third pair of $Na_2S_2O_3$–HCl pair test tubes in a warm water bath (<60°C) for Part B.4. Allow each pair of test tubes to establish thermal equilibrium (~5 minutes) before continuing to Parts B.3, and 4.

2. **Record the time for reaction at room temperature.** Be prepared to start time for monitoring the reaction rate. Combine the first pair of $Na_2S_2O_3$–HCl pair test tubes and START TIME. Agitate the mixture for several seconds. STOP TIME when the cloudiness of the sulfur appears. Record the time lapse and room temperature, using all certain digits *plus* one uncertain digit.

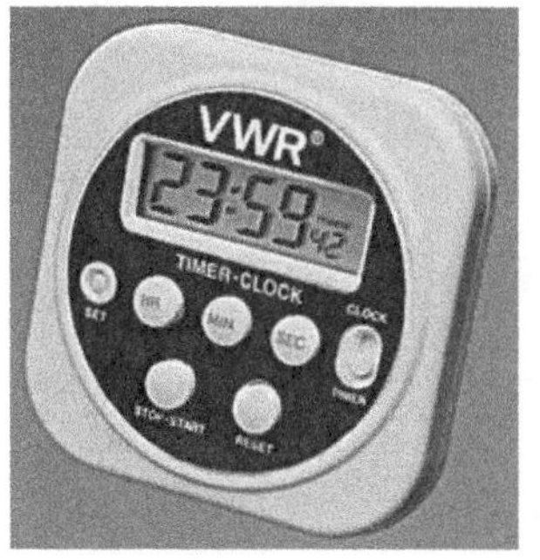

Courtesy of VWR International, LLC

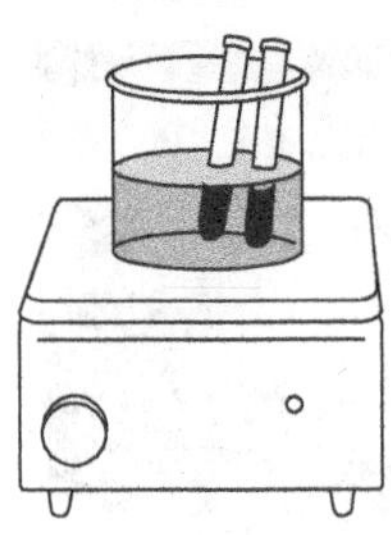

3. **Record the time for reaction at the lower temperature.** From the ice bath, pour the HCl solution into the $Na_2S_2O_3$ solution, START TIME. Agitate the mixture for several seconds, and return the reaction mixture to the ice bath. STOP TIME when the cloudiness of the sulfur appears. Record the time lapse for the reaction and the temperature of the bath, using all certain digits *plus* one uncertain digit.④
4. **Record the time for reaction at the higher temperature.** From the warm water bath, pour the HCl solution into the $Na_2S_2O_3$ solution and proceed as in Parts B.2 and B.3. Record the appropriate data.⑥

   Repeat any of the above reactions as deemed necessary.

Data Analysis, F

5. **Plot the data.** Plot temperature (y-axis) versus time (x-axis) on one-half of a sheet of linear graph paper or by using appropriate software for the three data points. Have the instructor approve your graph.⑦ Further interpret your data as suggested on the ***Report Sheet***.

Disposal: Dispose of the reaction solutions in the Waste Inorganic Test Solutions container.

C. Temperature of the Reaction: Oxalic Acid–Potassium Permanganate Reaction System

The reaction rate for the oxidation–reduction reaction between oxalic acid, $H_2C_2O_4$, and potassium permanganate, $KMnO_4$, is measured by recording the time elapsed for the (purple) color of the permanganate ion, MnO_4^-, to *disappear* in the reaction:

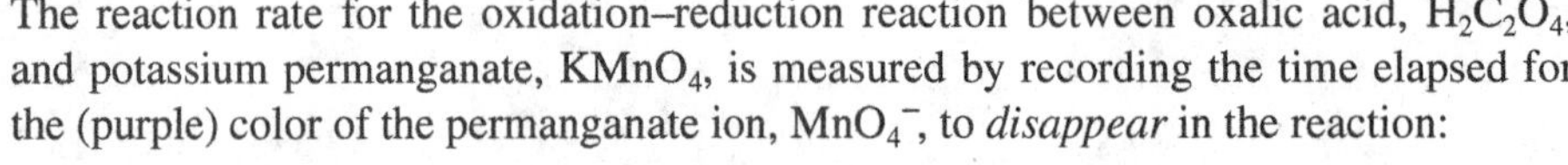

$$5\ H_2C_2O_4(aq) + 2\ KMnO_4(aq) + 3\ H_2SO_4(aq) \longrightarrow 10\ CO_2(g) + 2\ MnSO_4(aq) + K_2SO_4(aq) + 8\ H_2O(l) \quad (23.2)$$

Measure the volume of each solution with separate *clean* graduated pipets. As one student pours the test solutions together, the other notes the time.

1. **Prepare the solutions.** Into a set of three, clean 150-mm test tubes, pipet 1 mL of 0.01 M $KMnO_4$ (in 3 M H_2SO_4) and 4 mL of 3 M H_2SO_4. (**Caution:** *$KMnO_4$ is a strong oxidant and causes brown skin stains; H_2SO_4 is a severe skin irritant and is corrosive. Do not allow either chemical to make skin contact.*) Into a second set of three clean 150-mm test tubes pipet 5 mL of 0.33 M $H_2C_2O_4$.

2. **Record the time for reaction at room temperature.** Select a $KMnO_4$—$H_2C_2O_4$ pair of test tubes. Pour the $H_2C_2O_4$ solution into the $KMnO_4$ solution. START TIME. Agitate the mixture. Record the time for the purple color of the permanganate ion to disappear. Record room temperature using all certain digits *plus* one uncertain digit.⑧

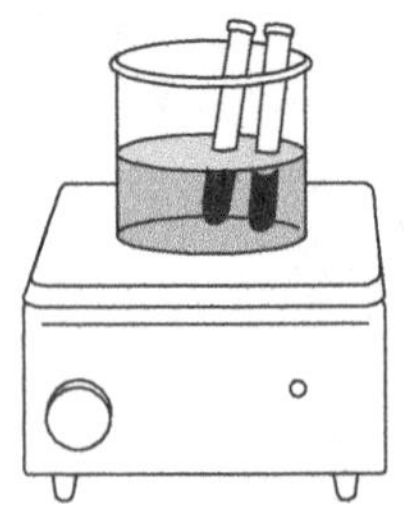

3. **Record the time for reaction at the higher temperature.** Place a second $KMnO_4$–$H_2C_2O_4$ pair of test tubes in a warm water (~40°C) bath until thermal equilibrium is established (~5 minutes). Pour the $H_2C_2O_4$ solution into the $KMnO_4$ solution. START TIME. Agitate the mixture for several seconds and return the reaction mixture to the warm water bath. Record the time for the disappearance of the purple color. Record the temperature of the bath.⑨
4. **Record the time for reaction at the highest temperature.** Repeat Part C.3 but increase the temperature of the bath to ~60°C. Record the appropriate data.⑩ Repeat any of the preceding reactions as necessary.

Data Analysis, F

5. **Plot the data.** Plot temperature (y-axis) versus time (x-axis) on one-half of a sheet of linear graph paper or by using aprropriate software for the three data points. Have the instructor approve your graph.⑪

Disposal: Dispose of the reaction solutions in the Waste Inorganic Test Solutions container.

D. Presence of a Catalyst

Hydrogen peroxide is relatively stable, but it readily decomposes in the presence of a catalyst.

1. **Add a catalyst.** Place approximately 2 mL of a 3% H_2O_2 solution in a clean, small test tube. Add 1 or 2 crystals of MnO_2 to the solution and observe. Note its instability.⑫

E. Concentration of Reactants: Magnesium–Hydrochloric Acid System

Data Analysis, A

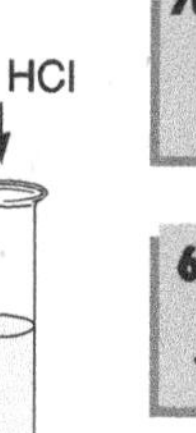

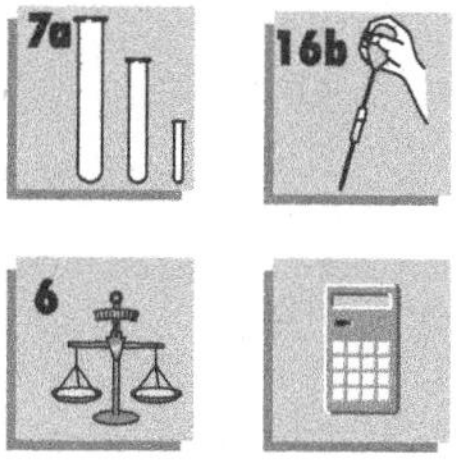

Ask your instructor for advice in completing *both* Parts E and F.

1. **Prepare the reactants.** Into a set of four clean, labeled test tubes, pipet 5 mL of 6 *M* HCl, 4 *M* HCl, 3 *M* HCl, and 1 *M* HCl, respectively (Figure 23.6).[2] Determine the mass (±0.001 g)—separately (for each solution)—of four 1-cm strips of *polished* (with steel wool or sand paper) magnesium. Calculate the number of moles of magnesium in each strip.⑬

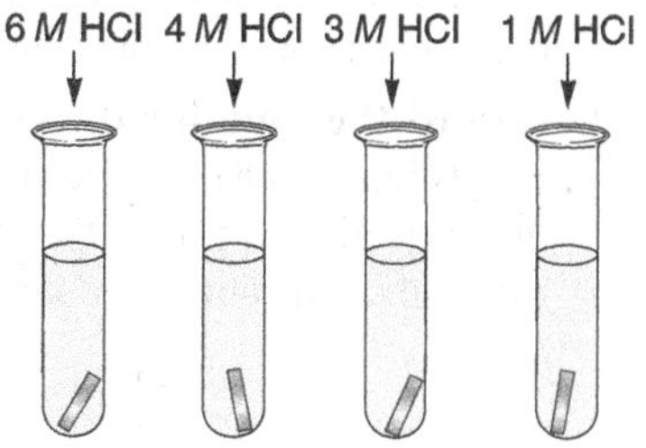

6 *M* HCl 4 *M* HCl 3 *M* HCl 1 *M* HCl

Figure 23.6 Setup for the effect of acid concentration on reaction rate

2. **Record the time for completion of the reaction.** Add the first magnesium strip to the 6 *M* HCl solution. START TIME. Record the time for all traces of the magnesium strip to disappear. Repeat the experiment with the remaining three magnesium strips and the 4 *M* HCl, 3 *M* HCl, and 1 *M* HCl, solutions.⑭
3. **Plot the data.** Plot $\frac{\text{mol HCl}}{\text{mol Mg}}$ (*y*-axis) versus time in seconds (*x*-axis) for the four tests on one-half of a sheet of linear graph paper or by using appropriate software. Have the instructor approve your graph.⑮

Data Analysis, F

Disposal: Dispose of the reaction solutions in the test tubes in the Waste Inorganic Test Solutions container.

CLEANUP: Rinse the test tubes twice with tap water and twice with deionized water. Discard each rinse in the sink; flush the sink with water.

F. Concentration of Reactants: Iodic Acid–Sulfurous Acid System

A series of interrelated oxidation–reduction reactions occur between iodic acid, HIO_3, and sulfurous acid, H_2SO_3, that ultimately lead to the formation of triiodide ion, I_3^-, and sulfuric acid, H_2SO_4, as the final products.

$$3\ HIO_3(aq) + 8\ H_2SO_3(aq) \longrightarrow H^+(aq) + I_3^-(aq) + 8\ H_2SO_4(aq) + H_2O(l) \quad (23.3)$$

The triodide ion, I_3^- ($[I_2{\cdot}I]^-$), appears *only* after all of the sulfurous acid is consumed in the reaction. Once the I_3^- forms, its presence is detected by its reaction with starch, forming a deep-blue complex.

$$I_3^-(aq) + \text{starch}(aq) \longrightarrow I_3^-{\cdot}\text{starch}(aq)\ \text{(deep blue)} \quad (23.4)$$

1. **Prepare the test solutions.** Review the preparation of the test solutions in Table 23.1, page 276. Set up five, clean and labeled test tubes (Figure 23.7) in a test tube rack. Measure the volumes of the 0.01 *M* HIO_3, starch, and water with dropping (or Beral) pipets.[3] Calibrate the HIO_3 dropping pipet to determine the volume (*mL*)

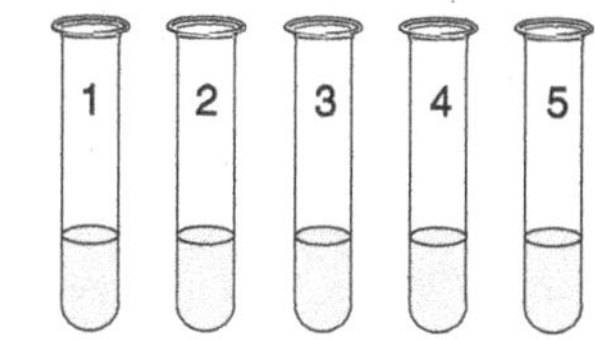

Figure 23.7 Setup for changes in HIO_3 concentration on reaction rate

[2]Remember to properly rinse the pipet with the appropriate solution before dispensing it into the test tube.
[3]Be careful! Do not intermix the dropping pipets between solutions. This error in technique causes a significant error in the data.

Table 23.1 Reactant Concentration and Reaction Rate

Test Tube	Solution in Test Tube: 0.01 *M* HIO_3	Starch	H_2O	Add to Test Tube: 0.01 *M* H_2SO_3
1	3 drops	1 drop	17 drops	1.0 mL
2	6 drops	1 drop	14 drops	1.0 mL
3	12 drops	1 drop	8 drops	1.0 mL
4	15 drops	1 drop	5 drops	1.0 mL
5	20 drops	1 drop	0 drops	1.0 mL

per drop.⑯ Calibrate a second dropping (or Beral) pipet with water to determine the number of milliliters per drop.⑰

Calibrate a third dropping (or Beral) pipet for the 0.01 *M* H_2SO_3 solution that delivers 1 mL; mark the level on the pipet so that quick delivery of 1 mL of the H_2SO_3 solution to each test tube can be made. Alternatively, use a calibrated 1-mL Beral pipet.

2. **Record the time for the reaction.** Place a sheet of white paper beside the test tube (Figure 23.8). As one student quickly transfers 1.0 mL of the 0.01 *M* H_2SO_3 to the respective test tube, the other notes the time. *Immediately* agitate the test tube; record the time lapse (seconds) for the deep-blue I_3^-•starch complex to appear.[4]

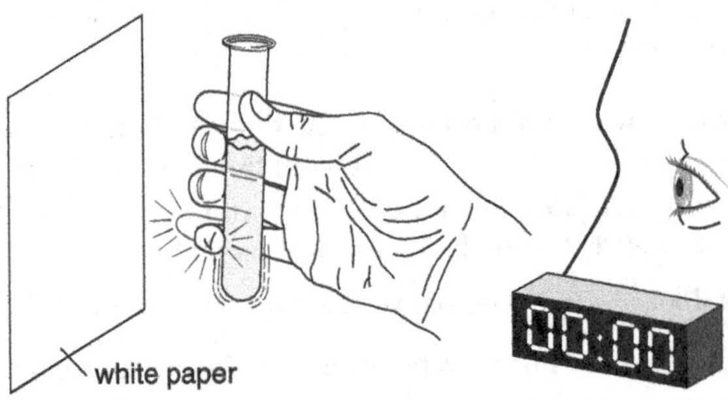

Figure 23.8 Viewing the reaction rate in a test tube

3. **Complete remaining reactions.** Repeat Part F.2. for the remaining reaction mixtures in Table 23.1. Repeat any of the trials as necessary.⑱

Data Analysis, F

4. **Plot the data.** On one-half of a sheet of linear graph paper or by using appropriate software, plot for each solution the initial concentration of iodic acid,[5] $[HIO_3]_0$ (*y*-axis), versus the time in seconds (*x*-axis) for the reaction.⑲

Disposal: Dispose of all test solutions in the Waste Inorganic Test Solutions container.

CLEANUP: Rinse the test tubes twice with tap water and discard each into the Waste Inorganic Test Solutions container. Two final rinses with deionized water can be discarded in the sink.

The Next Step

(1) The dissolution of dissolved gases such as $CO_2(aq)$ in carbonated beverages, changes significantly with temperature changes. Study the kinetics of the dissolution of dissolved gases such as $CO_2(aq)$ or $O_2(g)$ using such things as Mentos candy, salt, rust, and so on. The study may be qualitative or quantitative. For the dissolution of $O_2(g)$, refer to *Experiment 31* in this manual. (2) Corrosion of iron in deionized water, tap water, boiled deionized/tap water, salt water (varying concentrations), and so on all affect the economy.

[4]Be ready! The appearance of the deep-blue solution is sudden.
[5]Remember that in calculating $[HIO_3]_0$, the total volume of the solution is the *sum* of the volumes of the two solutions expressed in liters.

Experiment 23 *Prelaboratory Assignment*

Factors Affecting Reaction Rates

Date__________ Lab Sec. ______ Name ______________________________________ Desk No. __________

1. Identify the major factor affecting reaction rates that accounts for the following observations:
   a. Tadpoles grow more rapidly near the cooling water discharged from a power plant.

   b. Enzymes facilitate certain biochemical reactions but are not consumed.

Adam Hart-Davis/Science Source

   c. Hydrogen peroxide antiseptic rapidly decomposes when applied to an open wound.

2. Chlorofluorocarbons photodissociate to produce chlorine atoms, Cl•, which have been implicated in decreasing the concentration of ozone, O_3, in the stratosphere. The decomposition of the ozone follows a reaction sequence of

$$O_3 + Cl\cdot \rightarrow ClO\cdot + O_2$$
$$ClO\cdot + O \rightarrow Cl\cdot + O_2$$

   What role (factor affecting reaction rates) do chlorine atoms have in increasing the depletion rate of ozone?

3. Assuming that the rate of a chemical reaction doubles for every 10°C temperature increase, by what factor would a chemical reaction increase if the temperature were increased from –5°C (a cold winter morning) to 25°C (room temperature)?

4. Experimental Procedure, Part B
   a. Identify the visual evidence used for timing the reaction.

   b. A data plot is used to predict reaction rates at other conditions. What are the coordinates of the data plot?

5. Experimental Procedure, Part E.3

a. An 18-mg strip of magnesium metal reacts in 5.0 mL of 3.0 *M* HCl over a given time period. Evaluate the $\frac{\text{mol HCl}}{\text{mol Mg}}$ ratio for the reaction.

b. What are the correct labelings of the axes for the data plot?

6. Experimental Procedure, Part F. A 1.0-mL volume of 0.010 *M* H_2SO_3 is added to a mixture of 6 drops of 0.010 *M* HIO_3, 14 drops of deionized water, and 1 drop of starch solution. A color change in the reaction mixture occurred after 56 seconds.

a. Assuming 20 drops per milliliter for all solutions, determine the initial molar concentration of HIO_3 after the mixing but before any reaction occurs (at time = 0). *Hint:* Units are $\frac{\text{mol } HIO_3}{\text{total volume } (L)}$.

b. The rate of the reaction is measured by the disappearance of HIO_3. For the reaction mixture in this question, what is the reaction rate? Express the reaction rate in units of $\frac{\text{mol } HIO_3/\text{L}}{\text{sec}}$ to the correct number of significant figures.

7. The reactions in the Experimental Procedure, Parts C, E, and F, are timed. Identify the visual signal to stop timing in each reaction.

a. Part C.

b. Part E.

c. Part F.

Experiment 23 *Report Sheet*

Factors Affecting Reaction Rates

Date __________ Lab Sec. ______ Name ______________________________ Desk No. __________

A. Nature of the Reactants

1. ①List the acids in order of decreasing reaction rate with magnesium: _________, _________, __________, _________
2. ②List the metals in order of decreasing reaction rate with 6 *M* HCl: _____________, _____________, _____________
3. ③Identify the metals reacting in Figure 23.5 (from left to right). _____________, _____________, _____________

B. Temperature of the Reaction: Hydrochloric Acid–Sodium Thiosulfate Reaction System

1. Time for Sulfur to Appear — Temperature of the Reaction

Time for Sulfur to Appear	Temperature of the Reaction
④ __________ seconds	__________ °C
⑤ __________ seconds	__________ °C
⑥ __________ seconds	__________ °C

2. ⑦Plot temperature (y-axis) versus time (x-axis) for the three trials. Instructor's approval of graph: ______________
3. From the plotted data, interpret the effect of temperature on reaction rate.

4. From your graph, estimate the temperature at which the appearance of sulfur should occur in 20 seconds. Assume no changes in concentration.

C. Temperature of the Reaction: Oxalic Acid–Potassium Permanganate Reaction System

1. Time for Permanganate Ion to Disappear — Temperature of the Reaction

Time for Permanganate Ion to Disappear	Temperature of the Reaction
⑧ __________ seconds	__________ °C
⑨ __________ seconds	__________ °C
⑩ __________ seconds	__________ °C

2. ⑪Plot temperature (y-axis) versus time (x-axis) for the three trials. Instructor's approval of graph: ______________
3. From your plotted data, interpret the affect of temperature on reaction rate.

4. From your graph, estimate the time for the disappearance of the purple permanganate ion at 55°C. Assume no changes in concentration.

D. Presence of a Catalyst

1. ⑫What effect does the MnO_2 catalyst have on the rate of evolution of O_2 gas?

2. Write a balanced equation for the decomposition of H_2O_2.

E. Concentration of Reactants: Magnesium–Hydrochloric Acid System

Concentration of HCl	Volume of HCl	mol HCl	mass of Mg	⑬mol Mg	$\frac{\text{mol HCl}}{\text{mol Mg}}$	⑭Time (sec)
6 *M*						
4 *M*						
3 *M*						
1 *M*						

1. ⑮Plot $\frac{\text{mol HCl}}{\text{mol Mg}}$ (*y*-axis) versus time (*x*-axis). Instructor's approval of graph: ____________
2. From your graph, predict the time, in seconds, for 5 mg of Mg to react in 5 mL of 2.0 *M* HCl.

F. Concentration of Reactants: Iodic Acid–Sulfurous Acid System

Molar concentration of HIO_3 __________ Molar concentration of H_2SO_3 __________

⑯What is the volume (*mL*) per drop of the HIO_3 solution? _____ ⑰What is the volume (*mL*) per drop of the water? _____

Test Tube	Drops of HIO_3	mL HIO_3	Drops of H_2O	mL H_2O	mL H_2SO_3	$[HIO_3]_0$[6] (diluted)	Time (sec)
⑱1					1.0		
2					1.0		
3					1.0		
4					1.0		
5					1.0		

1. ⑲Plot $[HIO_3]_0$ (*y*-axis) versus time (*x*-axis). Instructor's approval of graph: ____________
2. How does a change in the molar concentration of HIO_3 affect the time required for the appearance of the deep-blue I_3^-•starch complex?

3. Estimate the time, in seconds, for the deep-blue I_3^-•starch complex to form when 10 drops of 0.01 *M* HIO_3 are used for the reaction. Assume all other conditions remain constant.

[6]See footnote 5.

Experiment 24

A Rate Law and Activation Energy

Ken Karp

Drops of blood catalyze the decomposition of hydrogen peroxide to water and oxygen gas.

OBJECTIVES

- To determine the rate law for a chemical reaction
- To utilize a graphical analysis of experimental data to
  —determine the order of each reactant in the reaction
  —determine the activation energy for the reaction

TECHNIQUES

The following techniques are used in the Experimental Procedure:

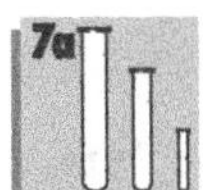

INTRODUCTION

The rate of a chemical reaction is affected by a number of factors, most of which were observed in *Experiment 23*. The rate of a reaction can be expressed in a number of ways, depending on the nature of the reactants being consumed or the products being formed. The rate may be followed as a change in concentration (*mol/L*) of one of the reactants or products per unit of time, the volume of gas produced per unit of time (Figure 24.1), or the change in color (measured as light absorbance) per unit of time, just to cite a few examples.

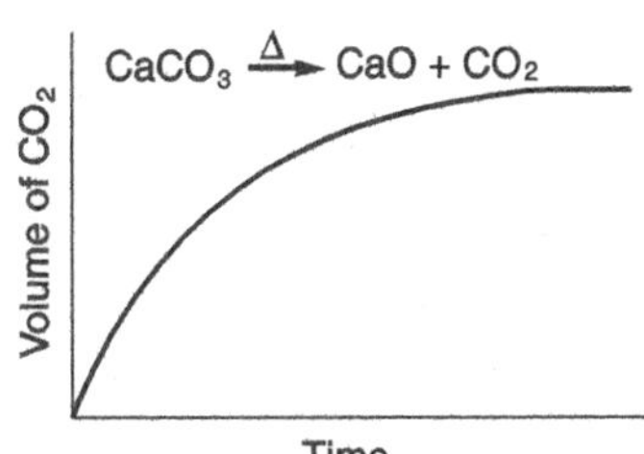

Figure 24.1 The rate of thermal decomposition of calcium carbonate is determined by measuring the volume of evolved carbon dioxide gas versus time.

In Parts A–D of this experiment, a quantitative statement is determined as to how changes in reactant concentrations affect reaction rate at room temperature, the statement being the rate law for the reaction. In Part E, the reaction rate is determined at different temperatures, allowing us to use the data to calculate the activation energy for the reaction.

To assist in understanding the relationship between reactant concentration and reaction rate, consider the general reaction, $A_2 + 2\ B_2 \rightarrow 2\ AB_2$. The rate of this reaction is related, by some exponential power, to the initial concentration of each reactant. For this reaction, we can write the relationship as

$$\text{rate} = k\,[A_2]^p[B_2]^q \tag{24.1}$$

This expression is called the **rate law** for the reaction. The value of k, the reaction **rate constant,** varies with temperature but is independent of reactant concentrations.

Rate constant: a proportionality constant relating the rate of a reaction to the initial concentrations of the reactants

The superscripts p and q designate the **order** with respect to each reactant and are *always* determined experimentally. For example, if tripling the molar concentration of A_2 while holding the B_2 concentration constant increases the reaction rate by a factor of 9, then $p = 2$. In practice, when the B_2 concentration is in large excess relative to the A_2 concentration, the B_2 concentration remains essentially constant during the course of the reaction; therefore, the change in the reaction rate results from the more significant change in the smaller amount of A_2 in the reaction. An experimental study of the kinetics of any reaction involves determining the values of k, p, and q.

Order: the exponential factor by which the concentration of a substance affects reaction rate

In Parts A–D of this experiment, the rate law for the reaction of hydrogen peroxide, H_2O_2, with potassium iodide, KI, is determined.[1] When these reactants are mixed, hydrogen peroxide slowly oxidizes iodide ion to elemental iodine, I_2. In the presence of excess iodide ion, molecular I_2 forms a water-soluble triiodide complex, I_3^- or $[I_2{\cdot}I]^-$:

$$3\,I^-(aq) + H_2O_2(aq) + 2\,H_3O^+(aq) \longrightarrow I_3^-(aq) + 4\,H_2O(l) \qquad (24.2)$$

The rate of the reaction, governed by the molar concentrations of I^-, H_2O_2, and H_3O^+, is expressed by the rate law:

$$\text{rate} = k\,[I^-]^p[H_2O_2]^q[H_3O^+]^r \qquad (24.3)$$

Buffer: a solution that resists changes in acidity or basicity in the presence of added H^+ or OH^+ (Buffer solutions are studied in Experiment 16.)

When the $[H_3O^+]$ is greater than 1×10^{-3} mol/L (pH < 3), the reaction rate is too rapid to measure in the general chemistry laboratory; however, if the $[H_3O^+]$ is *less than* 1×10^{-3} mol/L (pH > 3), the reaction proceeds at a measurable rate. An acetic acid–sodium acetate **buffer** maintains a nearly constant $[H_3O^+]$ at about 1×10^{-5} mol/L (pH = ~5) during the experiment.[2] Since the molar concentration of H_3O^+ is held constant in the buffer solution and does not affect the reaction rate at the pH of the buffer, the rate law for the reaction becomes more simply

$$\text{rate} = k'[I^-]^p[H_2O_2]^q \qquad (24.4)$$

where $k' = k\,[H_3O^+]^r$.

In this experiment, Parts B–D, the values of p, q, and k' are determined from the data analysis of Part A for the hydrogen peroxide–iodide ion system. Two sets of experiments are required: One set of experiments is designed to determine the value of p and the other to determine the value of q.

Determination of p, the Order of the Reaction with Respect to Iodide Ion

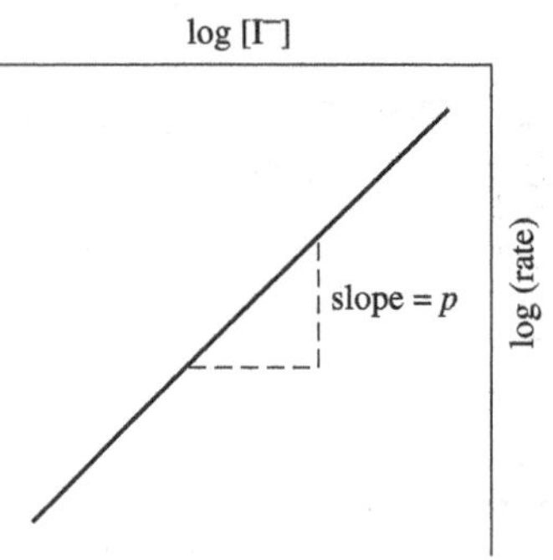

In the first set of experiments, (Table 24.1, kinetic trials 1–4, page 285), the effect that iodide ion has on the reaction rate is observed in several kinetic trials. A "large" excess of hydrogen peroxide in a buffered system maintains the H_2O_2 and H_3O^+ concentrations essentially constant during each trial. Therefore, for this set of experiments, the rate law, equation 24.4, reduces to the form

$$\text{rate} = k'[I^-]^p \bullet c \qquad (24.5)$$

c, a constant, equals $[H_2O_2]^q$.

In (common) logarithmic form, equation 24.5 becomes

$$\log(\text{rate}) = \log k' + p\log[I^-] + \log c \qquad (24.6)$$

Combining constants, we have the equation for a straight line:

$$\log(\text{rate}) = p\log[I^-] + C$$
$$y = mx + b \qquad (24.7)$$

C equals $\log k' + \log c$ or $\log k' + \log[H_2O_2]^q$.

Therefore, a plot of log (rate) versus log $[I^-]$ produces a straight line with a slope equal to p, the order of the reaction with respect to the molar concentration of iodide ion. See margin figure.

Determination of q, the Order of the Reaction with Respect to Hydrogen Peroxide

In the second set of experiments, (Table 24.1, kinetic trials 1, 5–7), the effect that hydrogen peroxide has on the reaction rate is observed in several kinetic trials. In this case, a "large" excess of iodide ion in a buffered system maintains the I^- and H_3O^+ concentrations

[1]Your laboratory instructor may substitute $K_2S_2O_8$ for H_2O_2 for this experiment. The balanced equation for the reaction is $S_2O_8^{2-}(aq) + 3\,I^-(aq) \rightarrow 2\,SO_4^{2-}(aq) + I_3^-(aq)$

[2]In general, a combined solution of H_2O_2 and I^- is only very slightly acidic, and the acidity changes little during the reaction. Therefore, the buffer solution may not be absolutely necessary for the reaction. However, to ensure that change in H_3O^+ concentrations is *not* a factor in the reaction rate, the buffer is included as a part of the experiment.

essentially constant during each trial. Under these conditions, the logarithmic form of the rate law (equation 24.4) becomes

$$\log(\text{rate}) = q \log [H_2O_2] + C'$$
$$y = mx + b \qquad (24.8)$$

C' equals $\log k' + \log [I^-]^p$.

A second plot, log (rate) versus log $[H_2O_2]$, produces a straight line with a slope equal to q, the order of the reaction with respect to the molar concentration of hydrogen peroxide.

Determination of the Specific Rate Constant, k'

Once the respective orders of I^- and H_2O_2 are determined (from the data plots) and the reaction rate for each trial has been determined, the values of p and q are substituted into equation 24.4 to calculate a specific rate constant, k', for each trial.

Determination of Activation Energy, E_a

Reaction rates are temperature dependent. Higher temperatures increase the kinetic energy of the (reactant) molecules, such that when two reacting molecules collide, they do so with a much greater force (more energy is dispersed within the collision system), causing bonds to rupture, atoms to rearrange, and new bonds (products) to form more rapidly. The energy required for a reaction to occur is called the **activation energy** for the reaction.

The relationship between the reaction rate constant, k', at a measured temperature, $T(K)$, and the activation energy, E_a, is expressed in the Arrhenius equation:

$$k' = Ae^{-E_a/RT} \qquad (24.9)$$

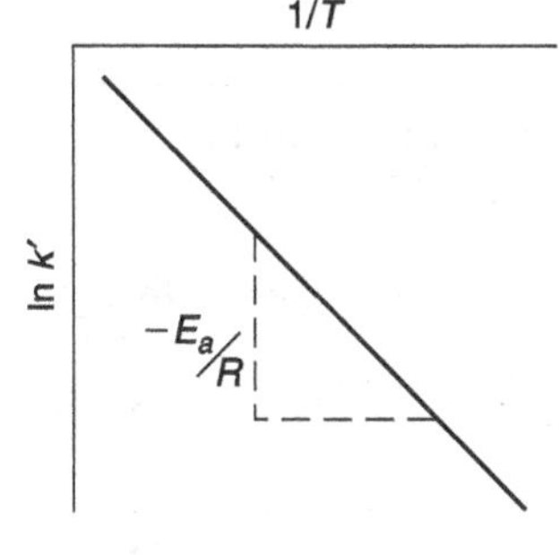

A is a collision parameter for the reaction, and R is the gas constant (=8.314 J/mol•K). The (natural) logarithmic form of equation 24.9 is

$$\ln k' = \ln A - \frac{E_a}{RT} \quad \text{or} \quad \ln k' = \ln A - \frac{E_a}{R}\left[\frac{1}{T}\right] \qquad (24.10)$$

The latter equation of 24.10 conforms to the equation for a straight line, $y = b + mx$, where a plot of $\ln k'$ versus $1/T$ yields a straight line with a slope of $-E_a/R$ and a y-intercept of $\ln A$.

As the temperature changes, the reaction rate also changes. A substitution of the "new" reaction rate at the "new" temperature into equation 24.4 (with known orders of I^- and H_2O_2) calculates a "new" specific rate constant, k'. A data plot of these new specific rate constants ($\ln k'$) at these new temperatures ($1/T$) allows for the calculation of the activation energy, E_a, for the reaction. In Part E, the temperature of the solutions for kinetic trial 4 (Table 24.1) will be increased or decreased to determine rate constants at these new temperatures.

Observing the Rate of the Reaction

To follow the progress of the rate of the reaction, two solutions are prepared (see Table 24.1):

- Solution A: a diluted solution of iodide ion, starch, thiosulfate ion ($S_2O_3^{2-}$), and the acetic acid–sodium acetate buffer
- Solution B: the hydrogen peroxide solution

When Solutions A and B are mixed, the H_2O_2 reacts with the I^-:

$$3\, I^-(aq) + H_2O_2(aq) + 2\, H_3O^+(aq) \longrightarrow I_3^-(aq) + 4\, H_2O(l) \qquad \text{(repeat of equation 24.2)}$$

To prevent an equilibrium (a back reaction) from occurring in equation 24.2, the presence of thiosulfate ion removes I_3^- as it is formed:

$$2\, S_2O_3^{2-}(aq) + I_3^-(aq) \longrightarrow 3\, I^-(aq) + S_4O_6^{2-}(aq) \qquad (24.11)$$

As a result, iodide ion is regenerated in the reaction system; this maintains a constant iodide ion concentration during the course of the reaction until the thiosulfate ion is consumed. When the thiosulfate ion has completely reacted in solution, the generated I_3^- combines with starch, forming a deep-blue I_3^-•starch complex. Its appearance signals a length of time for the reaction (equation 24.2) to occur and the length of time for the disappearance of the thiosulfate ion:

$$I_3^-(aq) + \text{starch}\ (aq) \longrightarrow I_3^- \bullet \text{starch}\ (aq, \text{deep blue}) \qquad (24.12)$$

For the reaction,

$$\text{rate} = \frac{\Delta\ \text{mol}\ I_3^-}{\Delta t}$$

The time required for a quantitative amount of thiosulfate ion to react is the time lapse for the appearance of the deep-blue solution. During that period a quantitative amount of I_3^- is generated; therefore, the rate of I_3^- production (mol I_3^- /time), and thus the rate of the reaction, is affected *only* by the initial concentrations of H_2O_2 and I^-.

Therefore, the rate of the reaction is followed by measuring the time required to generate a preset number of moles of I_3^-, *not* the time required to deplete the moles of reactants.

EXPERIMENTAL PROCEDURE

Procedure Overview: Measured volumes of several solutions having known concentrations of reactants are mixed for a series of trials at room temperature. The time required for a visible color change to appear in the solution is recorded for the trials. The data are collected and plotted (two plots). From the plotted data, the order of the reaction with respect to each reactant is calculated and the rate law for the reaction is derived. After the rate law for the reaction is established, the reaction rate is observed at nonambient temperatures. The plotted data produces a value for the activation energy of the reaction.

Read the entire procedure before beginning the experiment. Student pairs should gather the kinetic data. Be aware of the number of significant figures when recording data.

A. Determination of Reaction Times

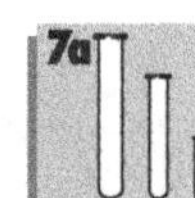

1. **Prepare solution A for the kinetic trials.** Table 24.1 summarizes the preparation of the solutions for the kinetic trials. Use previously boiled, deionized water. Measure the volumes of KI and $Na_2S_2O_3$ solutions with *clean*[3] pipets.[4] Burets or pipets can be used for the remaining solutions. At the same time, prepare, all of the solutions A for kinetic trials 1–8 in either clean and *labeled* 20-mL beakers or 150-mm test tubes. Trial 8 is to be of your design.

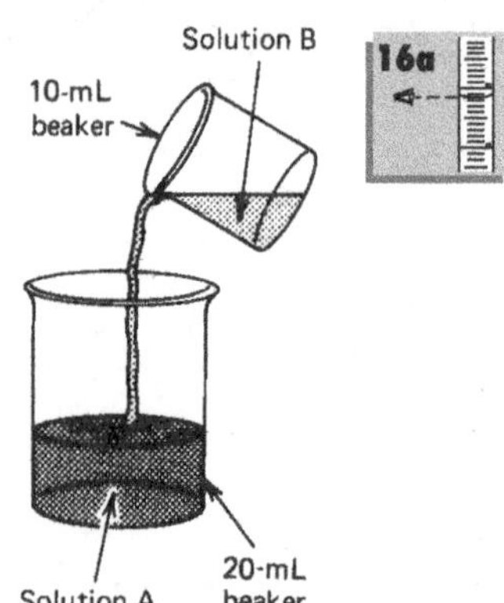

2. **Prepare solutions for kinetic trial 4.**
   Solution A. Stir the solution in a small 20-mL beaker or 150-mm test tube.
   Solution B. Pipet 3.0 mL of 0.1 *M* H_2O_2 into a clean 10-mL beaker or 150-mm test tube.
3. **Prepare for the reaction.** The reaction begins when the H_2O_2 (solution B) is added to solution A; be prepared to start timing the reaction *in seconds.* Place the beaker on a white sheet of paper so the deep-blue color change is more easily detected (Figure 24.2 or Figure 23.8). As one student mixes the solutions, the other notes the time. All of the solutions should be at ambient temperature before mixing. Record the temperature.
4. **Time the reaction.** Rapidly add solution B to solution A. START TIME and swirl (once) the contents of the mixture. Continued swirling is unnecessary. The appearance of the deep-blue color is sudden. Be ready to STOP TIME. Record the time lapse to the nearest second on the ***Report Sheet***. Repeat if necessary.

Notice! If the time for the color change of trial 4 is less than 10 seconds, STOP. Add an additional 10 mL of boiled, deionized water to each solution A for each kinetic trial (total volume of the reaction mixtures will now be 20 mL instead of 10 mL). A consequence of this dilution will result in a much longer time lapse for a color change in Trial 1—be patient! Consult with your laboratory instructor before the addition of the 10 mL of boiled, deionized water.

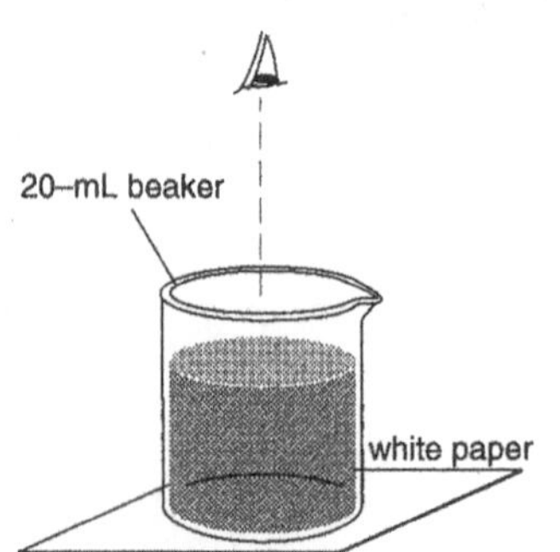

Figure 24.2 Viewing the appearance of the I_3^-•starch complex

[3]Cleanliness is important in preparing these solutions because H_2O_2 readily decomposes in the presence of foreign particles. Do *not* dry glassware with paper towels.

$$2\ H_2O_2 \xrightarrow{\text{catalyst}} 2\ H_2O + O_2$$

[4]5-mL *graduated* (±0.1 mL) pipets are suggested for measuring these volumes.

Table 24.1 Composition of Test Solutions

	Solution A					Solution B*
Kinetic Trial	Boiled, Deionized Water	Buffer**	0.3 *M* KI	0.02 *M* $Na_2S_2O_3$	Starch	0.1 *M* H_2O_2
1	4.0 mL	1.0 mL	1.0 mL	1.0 mL	5 drops	3.0 mL
2	3.0 mL	1.0 mL	2.0 mL	1.0 mL	5 drops	3.0 mL
3	2.0 mL	1.0 mL	3.0 mL	1.0 mL	5 drops	3.0 mL
4	**1.0 mL**	**1.0 mL**	**4.0 mL**	**1.0 mL**	**5 drops**	**3.0 mL**
5	2.0 mL	1.0 mL	1.0 mL	1.0 mL	5 drops	5.0 mL
6	0.0 mL	1.0 mL	1.0 mL	1.0 mL	5 drops	7.0 mL
7	5.0 mL	1.0 mL	1.0 mL	1.0 mL	5 drops	2.0 mL
8†	—	1.0 mL	—	1.0 mL	5 drops	—

*0.1 *M* $K_2S_2O_8$ may be substituted.
**0.5 *M* CH_3COOH and 0.5 *M* $NaCH_3CO_2$.
†You are to select the volumes of solutions for the trial.

5. **Repeat for the remaining kinetic trials.** Mix and time the test solutions for the remaining seven kinetic trials. If the instructor approves, conduct additional kinetic trials, either by repeating those in Table 24.1 or by preparing other combinations of KI and H_2O_2. Make sure that the total diluted volume remains constant at 10 mL.

Disposal: Dispose of the solutions from the kinetic trials in the Waste Iodide Salts container.

CLEANUP: Rinse the beakers or test tubes twice with tap water and discard in the Waste Iodide Salts container. Dispose of two final rinses with deionized water in the sink.

B. Calculations for Determining the Rate Law

Data Analysis, A

Perform the calculations, carefully *one step at a time.* Appropriate and correctly programmed software would be invaluable for completing this analysis. As you read through this section, complete the appropriate calculation and record it with the correct number of significant figure for each test solution on the ***Report Sheet.***

1. **Moles of I_3^- produced.** Calculate the moles of $S_2O_3^{2-}$ consumed in each kinetic trial. From equation 24.11, the moles of I_3^- that form in the reaction equals one-half the moles of $S_2O_3^{2-}$ that react. This also equals the change in the moles of I_3^-, starting with none at time zero up until a final amount that was produced at the time of the color change. This is designated as "$\Delta(\text{mol } I_3^-)$" produced. See ***Prelaboratory Assignment***, question 5.B.1, 2.

2. **Reaction rate.** The reaction rate for each kinetic trial is calculated as the ratio of the moles of I_3^- produced, $\Delta(\text{mol } I_3^-)$, to the time lapse, Δt, for the appearance of the deep-blue color.[5] Compute these reaction rates, $\frac{\Delta(\text{mol } I_3^-)}{\Delta t}$, and the logarithms of the reaction rates (see equations 24.7 and 24.8) for each kinetic trial and enter them on the ***Report Sheet***. See ***Prelaboratory Assignment***, question 5.B.3, 4. Because the total volume is a constant for all kinetic trials, we only need to calculate the moles of the I_3^- produced *not* the molar concentrations of the I_3^-.

3. **Initial iodide concentrations.** Calculate the initial molar concentration, $[I^-]_0$, and the logarithm of the initial molar concentration, log $[I^-]_0$, of iodide ion for each kinetic trial.[6] See ***Prelaboratory Assignment***, question 5.B.6, 7.

4. **Initial hydrogen peroxide concentrations.** Calculate the initial molar concentration, $[H_2O_2]_0$, and the logarithm of the initial molar concentration, log $[H_2O_2]_0$, of hydrogen peroxide for each kinetic trial.[7] See ***Prelaboratory Assignment***, question 5.B.9, 10.

[5]The moles of I_3^- present initially, at time zero, is zero.
[6]Remember, this is *not* 0.3 *M* I^- because the initial total volume of the solution is 10 mL after mixing.
[7]Remember, too, this is *not* 0.1 *M* H_2O_2 because the initial total volume of the solution is 10 mL after mixing.

C. Determination of the Reaction Order, *p* and *q*, for Each Reactant

Data Analysis, F, G

1. **Determination of *p* from plot of data.** Plot on the top half of a sheet of linear graph paper or preferably by using appropriate software log (Δmol $I_3^-/\Delta t$), which is log (rate) (*y*-axis), versus log $[I^-]_0$ (*x*-axis) at constant hydrogen peroxide concentration. Kinetic trials 1, 2, 3, and 4 have the same H_2O_2 concentration. Draw the best straight line through the four points. Calculate the slope of the straight line. The slope is the order of the reaction, *p*, with respect to the iodide ion.

Data Analysis, F, G

2. **Determination of *q* from plot of data.** Plot on the bottom half of the same sheet of linear graph paper or preferably by using appropriate software log (Δmol $I_3^-/\Delta t$) (*y*-axis) versus log $[H_2O_2]_0$ (*x*-axis) at constant iodide ion concentration using kinetic trials 1, 5, 6, and 7. Draw the best straight line through the four points and calculate its slope. The slope of the plot is the order of the reaction, *q*, with respect to the hydrogen peroxide.
3. **Approval of graphs.** Have your instructor approve both graphs.

D. Determination of *k*′, the Specific Rate Constant for the Reaction

Data Analysis, B, C, D

1. **Substitution of *p* and *q* into rate law.** Use the values of *p* and *q* (from Part C) and the rate law, rate $= \dfrac{\Delta(\text{mol } I_2)}{\Delta t} = k' \, [I^-]^p \, [H_2O_2]^q$, to determine k' for the seven solutions. Calculate the average value of k' with proper units. Also determine the standard deviation and relative standard deviation (*%RSD*) of k' from your data.
2. **Class data.** Obtain average k' values from other groups in the class. Calculate a standard deviation and relative standard deviation (*%RSD*) of k' for the class.

E. Determination of Activation Energy

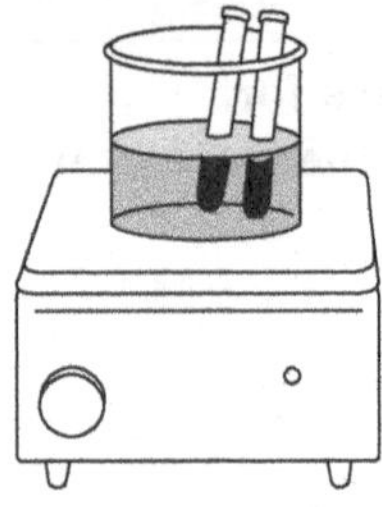

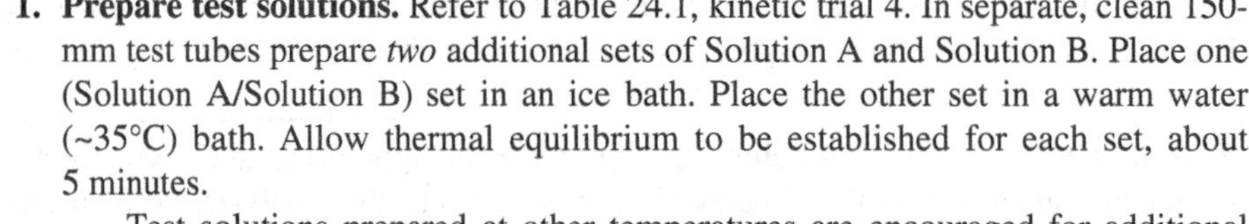

1. **Prepare test solutions.** Refer to Table 24.1, kinetic trial 4. In separate, clean 150-mm test tubes prepare *two* additional sets of Solution A and Solution B. Place one (Solution A/Solution B) set in an ice bath. Place the other set in a warm water (~35°C) bath. Allow thermal equilibrium to be established for each set, about 5 minutes.

   Test solutions prepared at other temperatures are encouraged for additional data points.

2. **Mix solutions A and B.** When thermal equilibrium has been established, quickly pour solution B into solution A, START TIME, and agitate the mixture. When the deep-blue color appears, STOP TIME. Record the time lapse as before. Record the temperature of the water bath and use this time lapse for your calculations. Repeat to check reproducibility and for the other set(s) of solutions.

Data Analysis, A

3. **The reaction rates and "new" rate constants.** The procedure for determining the reaction rates is described in Part B.2. Calculate and record the reaction rates for the (at least) two trials (two temperatures) from Part E.2 and re-record the reaction rate for the (room temperature) kinetic trial 4 in Part A.5. Carefully complete the calculations on the ***Report Sheet***.

   Use the reaction rates at the three temperatures (ice, room, and ~35°C temperatures) and the established rate law from Part C to calculate the rate constants, k', at these temperatures. Calculate the natural logarithm of these rate constants.

Data Analysis, F, G

4. **Plot the data.** Plot ln k' versus $1/T(K)$ for the (at least) three trials at which the experiment was performed. Remember to express temperature in kelvins and R = 8.314 J/mol•K.

5. **Activation energy.** From the data plot, determine the slope of the linear plot ($= -E_a/R$) and calculate the activation energy for the reaction. You may need to seek the advice of your instructor for completing the calculations on the ***Report Sheet***.

The Next Step

The rate law for any number of chemical reactions can be studied in the same manner—for example, see *Experiment 23*, Parts B, C, and F. Research the Internet for a kinetic study of interest (biochemical?) and design a systematic kinetic study of a chemical system.

Experiment 24 *Prelaboratory Assignment*

A Rate Law and Activation Energy

Date __________ Lab Sec. ______ Name ______________________________________ Desk No. __________

1. Three data plots are required for analyzing the data in this experiment, two plots from the kinetic trials outlined in Table 24.1 and one plot from Part E. From each data plot, a value is determined toward the completion of the analysis of the kinetic study for the reaction of I^- with H_2O_2. Complete the table in order to focus the analysis.

Source of Data	*y*-axis label	*x*-axis label	Data to be obtained from the data plot
Table 24.1, trials 1–4	________	________	______________________
Table 24.1, trials 1, 5–7	________	________	______________________
Part E	________	________	______________________

2. **a.** In the collection of the rate data for the experiment, when do START TIME and STOP TIME occur for each kinetic trial in Table 24.1?

   b. What is the color of the solution at STOP TIME?

   c. What is the chemical reaction that accounts for the color of the solution at STOP TIME.

3. In the kinetic analysis of this experiment for the reaction of iodide ion with hydrogen peroxide, state the purpose for each of the following solutions (see Table 24.1):

   a. deionized water

   b. buffer solution (acetic acid, sodium acetate mixture)

4. From the following data plot, calculate the activation energy, E_a, for the reaction.

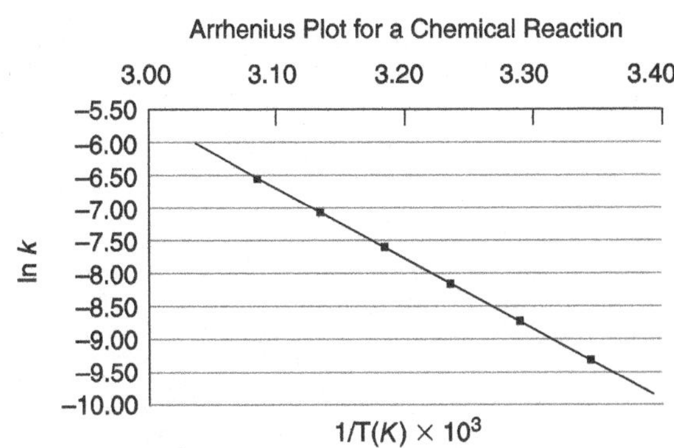

5. Data were collected to determine the rate law for the reaction of potassium iodide with hydrogen peroxide. The following data were collected for Kinetic Trial 1. See the Experimental Procedure, Part B, and the ***Report Sheet*** for completing the following table. Record the calculated values with the correct number of significant figures.

A. Determination of Reaction Times | ***Calculation Zone***

Molar concentration of $Na_2S_2O_3$ (*mol/L*)	0.02	*Part B.1*
Volume of $Na_2S_2O_3$ (*L*)	0.001	
Ambient temperature (°C)	25	
Molar concentration of KI (*mol/L*)	0.3	
Molar concentration of H_2O_2 (*mol/L*)	0.1	
Total volume of kinetic trial (*mL*)	10	*Part B.2*
Time for color change, Δt (*sec*)	25	

B. Calculations for Determining the Rate Law

1. Moles of $S_2O_3^{2-}$ consumed (*mol*) Show calculation.		
2. Δ(mol I_3^-) produced Equation 24.11 Show calculation.		*Part B.3*
3. $\frac{\Delta(\text{mol } I_3^-)}{\Delta t}$ (*mol/sec*) Show calculation.		
4. $\log \frac{\Delta(\text{mol } I_3^-)}{\Delta t}$ Show calculation.		*Part B.6*
5. Volume KI (*mL*)	3.0	
6. $[I^-]_o$ (*mol/L*)** Show calculation. *Not* 0.3 *M*. See footnote 6.		
7. $\log [I^-]_o$		*Part B.9*
8. Volume of H_2O_2 (*mL*)	3.0	
9. $[H_2O_2]$ (*mol/L*)** Show calculation. *Not* 0.1 *M*. See footnote 7.		
10. $\log [H_2O_2]$		

See the second page of the ***Report Sheet* to determine the further use of this data.

Experiment 24 *Report Sheet*

A Rate Law and Activation Energy

Date ________ Lab Sec. ______ Name ______________________________ Desk No. ________

A. Determination of Reaction Times

Molar concentration of $Na_2S_2O_3$ ____________; Volume of $Na_2S_2O_3$ (*L*) ____________; Ambient temperature ____________ °C

Molar concentration of KI ____________; Molar concentration of H_2O_2 ____________; Total volume of kinetic trials (*mL*) ____________

Kinetic Trial	*1**	*2*	*3*	*4*	*5*	*6*	*7*	*8*
1. Time for color change, Δt (*sec*)								

B. Calculations for Determining the Rate Law

1. Moles of $S_2O_3^{2-}$ consumed (*mol*)								
2. Δ(mol I_3^-) produced								
3. $\frac{\Delta(\text{mol } I_3^-)}{\Delta t}$ (*mol/s*)								
4. $\log \frac{\Delta(\text{mol } I_3^-)}{\Delta t}$								
5. Volume KI (*mL*)								
6. $[I^-]_0$ (*mol/L*)**								
7. $\log [I^-]_0$								
8. Volume H_2O_2 (*mL*)								
9. $[H_2O_2]_0$ (*mol/L*)**								
10. $\log [H_2O_2]_0$								

*Calculations for Kinetic Trial 1.

***Diluted* initial molar concentration.

C. Determination of the Reaction Order, *p* and *q*, for Each Reactant

Instructor's approval of graphs:

1. log (Δmol $I_3^-/\Delta t$) versus log $[I^-]_0$ ____________________________

2. log (Δmol $I_3^-/\Delta t$) versus log $[H_2O_2]_0$ ____________________________

3. value of *p* from graph ____________; value of *q* from graph ____________

Write the rate law for the reaction.

D. Determination of *k*′, the Specific Rate Constant for the Reaction

Kinetic Trial	*1*	*2*	*3*	*4*	*5*	*6*	*7*	*8*
1. Value of *k*′								

2. Average value of *k*′ ____________ ***Data Analysis, B***

3. Standard deviation of *k*′ ____________ ***Data Analysis, C***

4. Relative standard deviation of *k*′ (*%RSD*) ____________ ***Data Analysis, D***

Class Data/Group	**1**	**2**	**3**	**4**	**5**	**6**
Average value of *k*′						

Calculate the average value and the standard deviation of the reaction rate constant for the class.

Calculate the relative standard deviation of *k*′ (*%RSD*).

E. Determination of Activation Energy

	Time for color change	Reaction rate	Calc. k'	ln k'	Temperature	$1/T(K)$
1. Trial 4						
2. Cold						
3. Warm						

4. Instructor's Approval of Data Plot ______________

5. Value of $(-E_a/R)$ from ln k' versus $1/T$ graph ______________

6. Activation Energy, E_a, from data plot. Show calculation. ______________

Laboratory Questions

Circle the questions that have been assigned.

1. Part A.4. Describe the chemistry that was occurring in the experiment between the time when solutions A and B were mixed and STOP TIME.

2. Part A.4. For kinetic trial 2, Alicia was distracted when the color change occurred but decided to record the time lapse read from her watch. Will this distraction cause an increase or decrease in the slope of the log (rate) versus log $[I^-]_0$? Explain.

3. Part A, Table 24.1.
   a. When doing the kinetic trials, Susan forgot to include the deionized water. Will this omission hasten or delay the formation of the blue color in the trials (exclusive of Trial 6)? Explain.
   b. When doing the kinetic trials, Oscar mistakenly omitted the sodium thiosulfate solution. How will this omission change the appearance of the resultant solution (from the mixing solutions A and B) from that of a correctly completed experiment? Explain your reasoning.
   c. When doing the kinetic trials, Peyton mistakenly omitted the starch solution from the kinetic trials. How will this omission change the appearance of the resultant solution (from the mixing solutions A and B) from that of a correctly completed experiment? Explain your reasoning.
   d. Of the three chemists above, which chemist will have the most accurate results? Explain.

4. Part C.2. Review the plotted data.
   a. What is the numerical value of the *y*-intercept?
   b. What is the kinetic interpretation of the value for the *y*-intercept?
   c. What does its value equal in equation 24.8?

5. State the effect that each of the following changes has on the reaction rate in this experiment—increase, decrease, or no effect. (Assume no volume change for any of the concentration changes.)
   a. An increase in the H_2O_2 concentration. Explain.
   b. An increase in the volume of water in solution A. Explain.
   c. An increase in the $Na_2S_2O_3$ concentration. Explain.
   d. The substitution of a 0.5% starch solution for one at 0.2%. Explain.

*6. If 0.2 *M* KI replaced the 0.3 *M* KI in this experiment, how would this affect the following—increase, decrease, or no effect?
   a. The rate of the reaction. Explain.
   b. The slopes of the graphs used to determine *p* and *q*. Explain.
   c. The value of the reaction rate constant. Explain.

7. Part E.2. The temperature of the warm water bath is recorded too high. How will this technique error affect the reported activation energy for the reaction—too high or too low? Explain.

8. Part E.4. Arnie's data plot has a greater negative slope than Bill's. Which student will record the higher activation energy for the reaction? Describe your reasoning.

Experiment 26

Thermodynamics of the Dissolution of Borax

sphraner/iStockphoto

Two wagons and a water wagon pulled by a team of 20 miles transported large quantities of borax from Death Valley, California.

OBJECTIVES

- To standardize a hydrochloric acid solution
- To determine the solubility product of borax as a function of temperature
- To determine the standard free energy, standard enthalpy, and standard entropy changes for the dissolution of borax in an aqueous solution

TECHNIQUES

The following techniques are used in the Experimental Procedure:

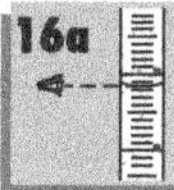

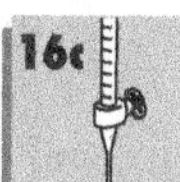

INTRODUCTION

Large deposits of borax are found in the arid regions of the southwestern United States, most notably in the Mojave Desert (east central) region of California. Borax is obtained as tincal, $Na_2B_4O_5(OH)_4{\cdot}8H_2O$, and kernite, $Na_2B_4O_7{\cdot}4H_2O$, from an open-pit mine near Boron, California, and as tincal from brines of Searles Lake near Trona, California. Borax, used as a washing powder for laundry formulations, is commonly sold as 20-Mule Team Borax. Historically, borax was mined in Death Valley, California, in the late nineteenth century. To transport the borax from this harsh environment, teams of 20 mules were used to pull heavy wagons loaded with borax and a water wagon (see opening photo) across the desert and over the mountains to railroad depots for shipment to other parts of the world. Borax is used as a cleansing agent, in the manufacture of glazing paper and varnishes, and as a flux in soldering and brazing; however, its largest current use is in the manufacture of borosilicate glass.

The free energy change of a chemical process is proportional to its equilibrium constant according to the equation

$$\Delta G^{\circ} = -RT \ln K \tag{26.1}$$

where R, the gas constant, is 8.314×10^{-3} kJ/mol•K, and T is the temperature in kelvins. The equilibrium constant, K, is expressed for the equilibrium system when the reactants and products are in their **standard states.** For a slightly soluble salt in an

Standard state: the state of a substance at one atmosphere (and generally 25°C)

aqueous system, the precipitate and the ions in solution correspond to the standard states of the reactants and products, respectively.

The standard state equilibrium for the slightly soluble silver chromate salt is

$$Ag_2CrO_4(s) \rightleftharpoons 2\,Ag^+(aq) + CrO_4^{2-}(aq) \qquad (26.2)$$

The solubility product, K_{sp}, is set equal to the product of the molar concentrations of the ions, all raised to the power of their respective coefficients in the balanced equation—this is the mass action expression for the system:

$$K_{sp} = [Ag^+]^2\,[CrO_4^{2-}] \qquad (26.3)$$

Free energy change, $\Delta G°$: negative value, spontaneous process; positive value, nonspontaneous process

and the **free energy change** for the equilibrium is

$$\Delta G^\circ = -RT \ln K_{sp} = -RT \ln [Ag^+]^2\,[CrO_4^{2-}] \qquad (26.4)$$

Enthalpy change, $\Delta H°$: negative value, exothermic process; positive value, endothermic process

Entropy change, $\Delta S°$: negative value, decrease in randomness of the process; positive value, increase in randomness of the process

Additionally, the free energy change of a chemical process is also a function of the **enthalpy change** and the **entropy change** of the process:

$$\Delta G^\circ = \Delta H^\circ - T\Delta S^\circ \qquad (26.5)$$

When the two free energy expressions are set equal for a slightly soluble salt, such as silver chromate, then

$$-RT \ln K_{sp} = \Delta H^\circ - T\Delta S^\circ \qquad (26.6)$$

Rearranging and solving for $\ln K_{sp}$,

$$\ln K_{sp} = -\frac{\Delta H^\circ}{R}\left(\frac{1}{T}\right) + \frac{\Delta S^\circ}{R} \text{ (analogous to the equation } y = mx + b) \qquad (26.7)$$

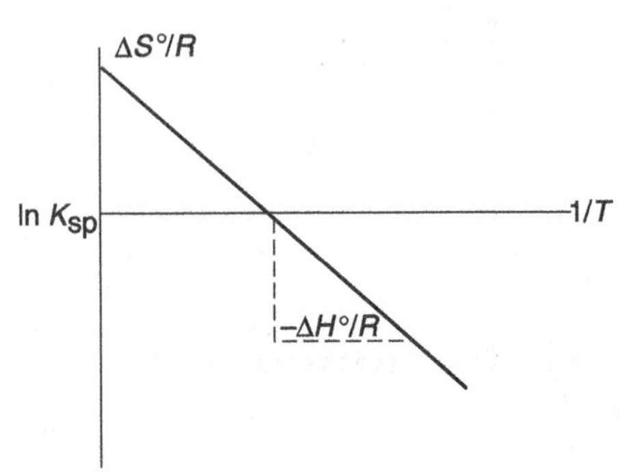

This equation can prove valuable in determining the thermodynamic properties of a chemical system such as that of a slightly soluble salt. A linear relationship exists when the values of $\ln K_{sp}$ obtained at various temperatures are plotted as a function of the reciprocal temperature. The (negative) slope of the line equals $-\Delta H°/R$, and the y-intercept (where $x = 0$) equals $\Delta S°/R$. Since R is a constant, the $\Delta H°$ and the $\Delta S°$ for the equilibrium system can easily be calculated.

Since the values of $\ln K_{sp}$ may be positive or negative for slightly soluble salts and $1/T$ values are always positive, the data plot of $\ln K_{sp}$ versus $1/T$ appears in the first and fourth quadrants of the Cartesian coordinate system.

The Borax System

Borax is often given the name *sodium tetraborate decahydrate* and the formula $Na_2B_4O_7 \cdot 10H_2O$. However, according to its chemical behavior, a more defining formula for borax is $Na_2B_4O_5(OH)_4 \cdot 8H_2O$, also called *tincal*.

In this experiment, the thermodynamic properties, $\Delta G°$, $\Delta H°$, and $\Delta S°$, are determined for the aqueous solubility of borax (tincal), $Na_2B_4O_5(OH)_4 \cdot 8H_2O$. Borax dissolves and dissociates in water according to the equation

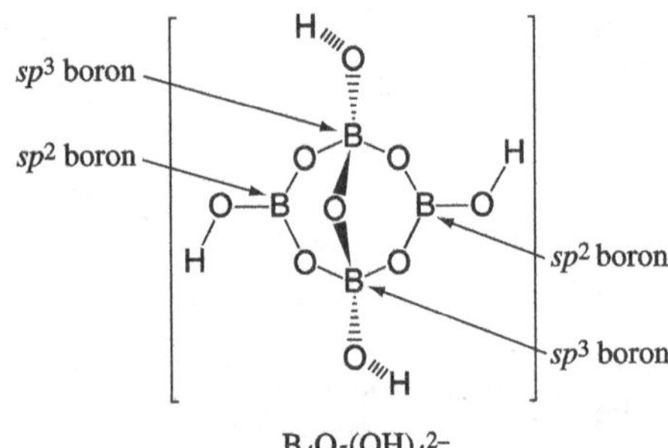

$B_4O_5(OH)_4^{2-}$

$$Na_2B_4O_5(OH)_4 \cdot 8H_2O(s) \rightleftharpoons 2\,Na^+(aq) + B_4O_5(OH)_4^{2-}(aq) + 8\,H_2O(l) \qquad (26.8)$$

The mass action expression, set equal to the solubility product at equilibrium, for the solubility of borax is

$$K_{sp} = [Na^+]^2\,[B_4O_5(OH)_4^{2-}] \qquad (26.9)$$

The $B_4O_5(OH)_4^{2-}$ anion, because it is the conjugate base of the weak acid boric acid, is capable of accepting two protons from a strong acid in an aqueous solution:

$$B_4O_5(OH)_4^{2-}(aq) + 2\,H^+(aq) + 3\,H_2O(l) \rightleftharpoons 4\,H_3BO_3(aq) \qquad (26.10)$$

H_3BO_3

Therefore, the molar concentration of the $B_4O_5(OH)_4^{2-}$ anion in a saturated borax solution can be measured with a titrimetric analysis of the saturated borax solution using a standardized hydrochloric acid solution as the titrant:

$$\text{mol } B_4O_5(OH)_4^{2-} = \text{volume } (L)\text{ HCl} \times \frac{\text{mol HCl}}{\text{volume } (L)\text{ HCl}} \times \frac{1\text{ mol } B_4O_5(OH)_4^{2-}}{2\text{ mol HCl}} \qquad (26.11)$$

$$[B_4O_5(OH)_4^{2-}] = \frac{\text{mol } B_4O_5(OH)_4^{2-}}{\text{volume } (L)\text{ sample}} \qquad (26.12)$$

[ ] = mol/L = M

This analysis is also a measure of the molar solubility of borax in water at a given temperature—according to the stoichiometry, one mole of the $B_4O_5(OH)_4^{2-}$ anion forms for every mole of borax that dissolves.

$$[B_4O_5(OH)_4^{2-}] = \text{molar solubility of borax} \qquad (26.13)$$

Temperature changes do affect the molar solubility of most salts, and borax is no exception. For example, the solubility of borax is 2.01 g/100 mL at 0°C and is 170 g/100 mL at 100°C.[1]

As a consequence of the titration and according to the stoichiometry of the dissolution of the borax (equation 26.8), the molar concentration of the sodium ion in the saturated solution is twice that of the experimentally determined $B_4O_5(OH)_4^{2-}$ anion concentration:

$$[Na^+] = 2 \times [B_4O_5(OH)_4^{2-}] \qquad (26.14)$$

The solubility product for borax at a measured temperature is, therefore,

$$K_{sp} = [Na^+]^2[B_4O_5(OH)_4^{2-}] = [2 \times [B_4O_5(OH_4^{2-}]]^2[B_4O_5(OH)_4^{2-}]$$
$$= 4[B_4O_5(OH)_4^{2-}]^3 = 4[\text{molar solubility of borax}]^3 \qquad (26.15)$$

To obtain the thermodynamic properties for the dissolution of borax, values for the molar solubility and the solubility product for borax are determined over a range of temperatures. An interpretation of a data plot for $\ln K_{sp}$ versus $1/T$ enables the chemist to determine the standard enthalpy change, $\Delta H°$; the standard entropy change, $\Delta S°$; and ultimately to calculate the standard free energy change, $\Delta G°$, for the dissolution of borax. See equations 26.7 and 26.5, respectively.

Standardized HCl Solution

A standardized HCl solution is prepared using anhydrous sodium carbonate as the primary standard. Sodium carbonate samples of known mass are transferred to Erlenmeyer flasks, dissolved in deionized water, and titrated to a methyl orange endpoint (pH range 3.1 to 4.4) with the prepared hydrochloric acid solution.

$$CO_3^{2-}(aq) + 2\,H_3O^+(aq) \longrightarrow 3\,H_2O(l) + CO_2(g) \qquad (26.16)$$

The flask is heated to near boiling close to the stoichiometric point of the analysis to remove the carbon dioxide gas produced in the reaction.[2]

[1] The solubility of borax at room temperature is about 6.3 g/100 mL.

[2] $CO_2(g)$ has a marginal solubility in water, producing carbonic acid, $H_2CO_3(aq)$. Because this acid will also react with the Na_2CO_3 primary standard, the $CO_2(g)$ is removed from the system with heat.

Analysis of Data

Data Analysis, F,G

The objectives of this experiment are fourfold: (1) determine the molar concentration of the $B_4O_5(OH)_4^{2-}$ anion and the molar solubility of borax for *at least* five different temperatures using the titration technique with a standardized hydrochloric acid solution; (2) calculate the solubility product of borax at each temperature; (3) plot the natural logarithm of the solubility product versus the reciprocal temperature of the measurements; (4) extract from the plotted data the thermodynamic properties of $\Delta H°$ and $\Delta S°$ for the dissolution of borax, from which its $\Delta G°$ is calculated.

EXPERIMENTAL PROCEDURE

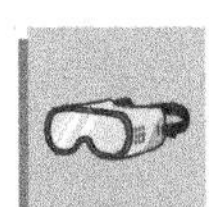

Procedure Overview: This experiment is to be completed in cooperation with other chemists/chemist groups in the laboratory. In Part A, a standardized solution of hydrochloric acid is to be prepared. In Part B, four warm water baths are to be set up (see Part B.3 and Figure 26.2) at the beginning of the laboratory, each at a different temperature, but at a maximum of 60°C. *The water baths then are to be shared.* Consult with your colleagues (and your laboratory instructor) in coordinating the setup of the apparatus. In conjunction with the four warm water baths for Part B, about 150 mL of warm (~55°C) deionized water is to be prepared for Part C.1. Begin those preparations.

Be aware of the number of significant figures when recording data.

A. Standardized HCl Solution

Data Analysis, A

Courtesy of Thermo Fisher Scientific

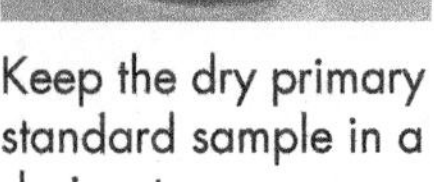

Keep the dry primary standard sample in a desiccator.

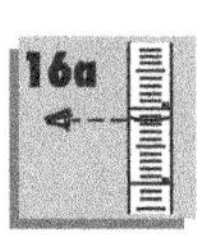

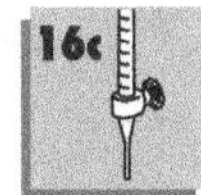

1. **Dry the primary standard.** Dry 2–3 g of anhydrous sodium carbonate, Na_2CO_3, for several hours in a drying oven set at about 110°C. Cool the sample in a desiccator. Stockroom personnel may have previously dried the sodium carbonate. Check with your laboratory instructor.

2. **Prepare the HCl solution.** Prepare 200 mL of ~0.20 *M* HCl starting with *conc* (12.1 *M*) HCl. Refer to ***Prelaboratory Assignment*** question 2a. (**Caution:** *Concentrated HCl causes severe skin burns.*) Again, stockroom personnel may have previously prepared this solution.

3. **Prepare the primary standard.** Calculate the mass of sodium carbonate that neutralizes 15–20 mL of 0.20 *M* HCl at the stoichiometric point. Refer to ***Prelaboratory Assignment*** question 2b and show the calculation on the ***Report Sheet.*** Measure this mass (±0.001 g) on a tared piece of weighing paper or dish and transfer to a 125-mL Erlenmeyer flask. Prepare *at least* three samples of sodium carbonate for the analysis of the HCl solution.

4. **Prepare the buret.** Clean a buret and rinse with several 3- to 5-mL portions of the ~0.20 *M* HCl solution. Use a clean funnel to fill the buret with the ~0.20 *M* HCl solution. After 10–15 seconds, use the proper technique to read and record the volume of HCl solution in the buret, using all certain digits *plus* one uncertain digit.

5. **Titrate the primary standard.** To each solid sodium carbonate sample, add ~50 mL of deionized water and several drops of methyl orange indicator.[3] Place a sheet of white paper beneath the Erlenmeyer flask. Dispense the HCl solution from the buret, swirling the Erlenmeyer flask during the addition.

   Very near or at the apparent endpoint of the indicator, heat the flask to near boiling (see Figures 17.2 or 20.3) to drive off the carbon dioxide gas. Carefully (dropwise) add additional HCl titrant until the endpoint is reached and the red–orange color persists for 30 seconds (a color change caused by the addition of one additional

[3]Methyl orange indicator changes color over the pH range of 3.1–4.4; its color appears yellow at a pH greater than 4.4, but red-orange at a pH less than 3.1.

drop of the HCl solution from the buret). Stop the addition of the HCl titrant. After 10–15 seconds read and record the volume of HCl in the buret.

6. **Repeat the analysis.** Refill the buret and complete the standardization procedure with the remaining sodium carbonate samples.

7. **Do the calculations.** Calculate the molar concentration of the prepared HCl solution from the sodium carbonate samples. The molar concentrations of the HCl solution from the trials should agree within ±1%; if not, complete additional trials as necessary.

Data Analysis, A

Disposal: Dispose of the analyzed samples in the Waste Salts container.

B. Preparation of Borax Solutions

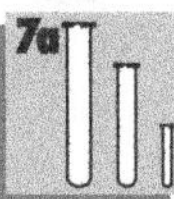

Five or six borax samples can be prepared for the experiment. The sixth sample (a saturated solution in an ice bath) will have a *very* low solubility of borax. Consult with your instructor.

1. **Calibrate test tubes.** Pipet 5 mL of deionized water into five (or six) *clean* medium-sized (~150 mm) test tubes (Figure 26.1). Mark the bottom of the meniscus (use a marking pen or tape). Discard the water and allow the test tubes to air- or oven-dry. Label the test tubes.

2. **Prepare stock solution of borax.** Using a 125- or 250-mL Erlenmeyer flask, add 30–35 g of borax to 100 mL of deionized water. Stopper the flask and agitate the mixture for several minutes to prepare the saturated solution.

3. **Prepare the test solutions of borax**
   - **a.** *Second set of test tubes.* Label a second set of clean, medium-sized test tubes for use in the setup shown in Figure 26.2.
   - **b.** *Half-fill the test tubes with stock solution.* Again, thoroughly agitate the borax stock solution and then, with the stock solution, half-fill this second set of medium-sized test tubes. Place the test tubes in the respective baths shown Figure 26.2. The temperatures of the baths need not be exactly those indicated, but the measured temperature is important (Figure 26.3, page 310). The first bath should *not* exceed 60°C.[4] Share the water baths.

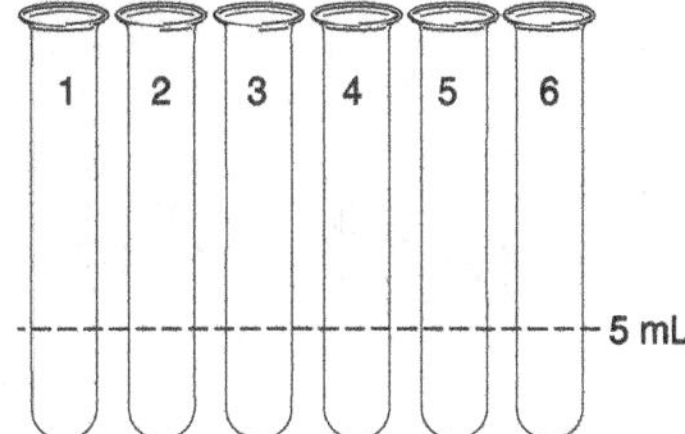

Figure 26.1 Calibrate six clean 150-mm test tubes at the 5-mL mark (Part B.1).

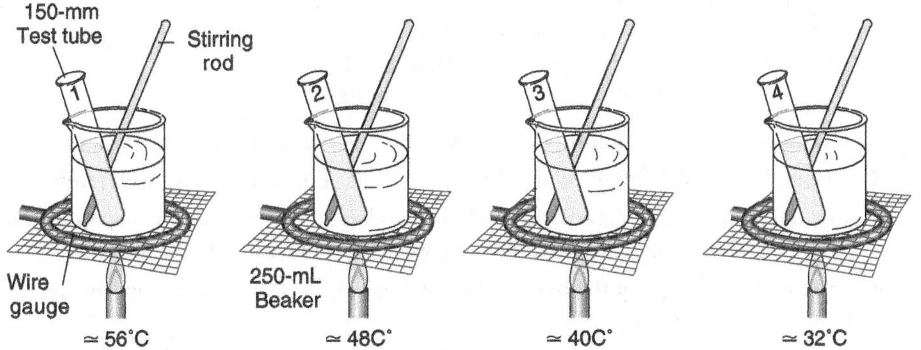

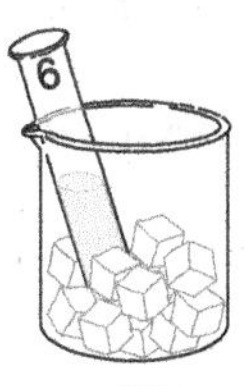

Figure 26.2 Six (different temperature) baths for preparing saturated borax solutions (Part B.3). A hot plate may be substituted for the Bunsen flame.

[4]Borax (tincal) is stable in aqueous solutions at temperatures less than 61°C; at higher temperatures, some dehydration of the $B_4O_5(OH)_4^{2-}$ anion occurs.

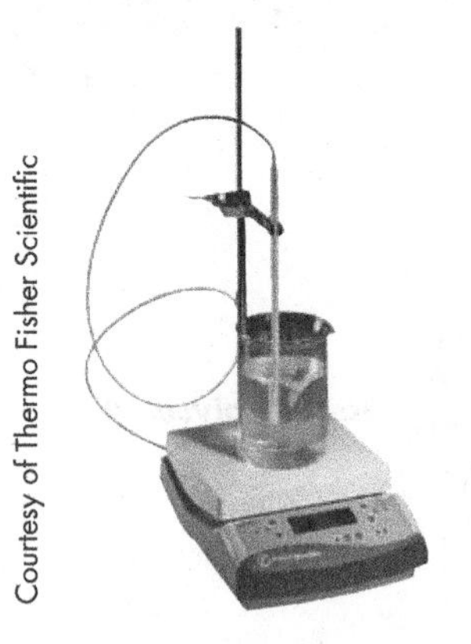

Figure 26.3 A stirring hot plate with a thermal sensor can be used to set water bath temperatures.

4. **Prepare saturated solutions of borax**
   a. *Saturate the solutions.* Occasionally agitate the test tubes in the baths (for 10–15 minutes), ensuring the formation of a saturated solution; solid borax should always be present—add more solid borax if necessary.
   b. *Allow sample to settle* (*not* change temperature). Allow the borax to settle until the solution is clear (this will require several minutes, be patient!) and has reached thermal equilibrium. Allow 10–15 minutes for thermal equilibrium to be established. Record the *exact* temperature of the respective water baths.
5. **Prepare borax samples for analysis.** Quickly but carefully transfer 5 mL of the clear solutions (the supernatant) to the correspondingly labeled, calibrated test tubes from Part B.1 and Figure 26.1 (do *not* transfer any of the solid borax!).
   Remove the heat from the water baths.

C. Analysis of Borax Test Solutions

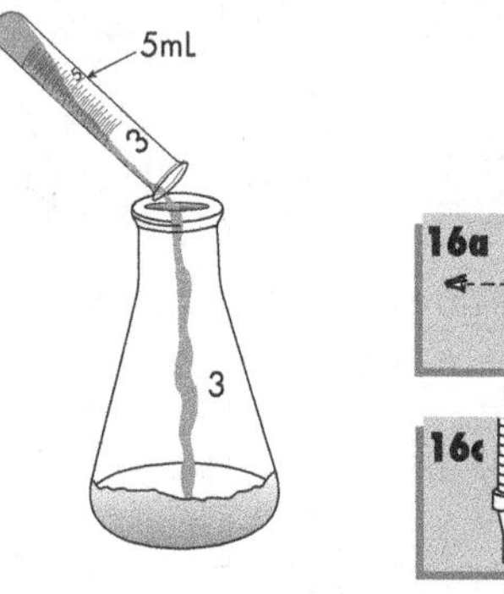

1. **Transfer the samples**
   a. *Prepare for sample transfer.* Set up and label a set of five (or six) clean labeled (1–6), 125- or 250-mL Erlenmeyer flasks. As the samples (Part B.5) cool to room temperature in the test tubes, some borax may crystallize. Return those samples to a *warm* (~55°C) water bath until all of the solid dissolves.
   b. *Transfer the samples.* After the sample is clear in the test tube, transfer the solution to the correspondingly labeled Erlenmeyer flask, rinse the test tube with two or three ~5-mL portions of *warm*, deionized water, and combine the washings with the sample.
2. **Titrate the samples.** Dilute each sample to about 25 mL with warm, deionized water. Add 2–3 drops of bromocresol green.[5] Titrate each of the five samples to a yellow endpoint with the standardized HCl solution prepared in Part A. Remember to record the buret readings before and after each analysis of a sample.

Data Analysis, A

Disposal: Dispose of the analyte in the Waste Salts container and the titrant in the Waste Acids container.

D. Data Analysis

Five (or six) repeated calculations are required to establish the data plot for the determination of $\Delta H°$ and $\Delta S°$ for the dissolution of borax. The lengthy task of completing the calculations and for minimizing errors in the calculations can be reduced with the use of an Excel (or similar) spreadsheet. The data from the calculations can then be plotted using the embedded graphing capabilities of Excel.

The following calculations and analyses are required:

Data Analysis, A

Data Analysis, F, G

1. Calculate the molar solubility of borax at each of the measured temperatures.
2. Calculate the solubility product of borax at each of the measured temperatures.
3. Plot the natural logarithm of the solubility product versus the reciprocal temperature $1/T\ (K^{-1})$ for each sample and draw the best straight line through the data points.
4. Determine the slope of the linear plot equal to $\frac{-\Delta H°}{R}$ and calculate the standard enthalpy of solution for borax.
5. Determine the y-intercept (at $x = 0$) of the linear plot equal to $\frac{\Delta S°}{R}$ and calculate the standard entropy of solution for borax.

The Next Step

An equilibrium constant is determined spectrophotometrically in *Experiment 34.* What modifications would need to be made to study the thermodynamics of that equilibrium? Design the experiment.

[5]The pH range for the color change of bromocresol green is 4.0 to 5.6. The indicator appears yellow at a pH less than 4.0 and blue at a pH greater than 5.6.

Experiment 26 *Prelaboratory Assignment*

Thermodynamics of the Dissolution of Borax

Date __________ Lab Sec. ______ Name ______________________________________ Desk No. __________

1. The standard free energy change for the decomposition of two moles of hydrogen peroxide at 25°C is –224kJ.

$$2H_2O_2(l) \longrightarrow 2H_2O(l) + O_2(g) \qquad \Delta G^\circ = -224\text{kJ}$$

a. Calculate the equilibrium constant for the reaction. See equation 26.1.

b. Explain the chemical significance of the magnitude of the calculated equilibrium constant for the neutralization reaction.

c. The standard enthalpy change, ΔH°, for the decomposition of hydrogen peroxide is +196.1kJ. Determine the standard entropy change, ΔS°, for the reaction at 25°C. See equation 26.5.

d. Explain the chemical significance of the calculated entropy change for the neutralization reaction.

2. a. Experimental Procedure, Part A.2. Describe the preparation of 200 mL of 0.20 *M* HCl starting with *conc* HCl (12.1 *M*).

b. Experimental Procedure, Part A.3. How many grams of the primary standard sodium carbonate, Na_2CO_3 (molar mass = 105.99 g/mol) is needed to react with 15 mL of 0.20 *M* HCl?

3. Experimental Procedure, Part C.

a. How many saturated solutions of borax are to be titrated?

b. Each saturated solution of borax is prepared at a different temperature. How many trials per saturated solution are to be completed?

c. What values are to be calculated from the data of the titrations?

4. Several thermodynamic values are determined from the data plot of ln K_{sp} vs. $1/T$ in Part D of the Experimental Procedure in this experiment. Complete the following table for Trial 1 (See ***Report Sheet.***) for determining ln K_{sp} and $1/T$. Record the calculated values with the correct number of significant figures.

A. Standardized HCl Solution		***Calculation Zone***
8. Average molar concentration of HCl (*mol/L*)	0.182	***Part D.3***
B. Preparation of Borax Solution		
2. Volume of sample (*mL*)	5.00	
C. Analysis of Borax Test Solutions		***Part D.4***
1. Buret reading, *initial* (*mL*)	4.75	
2. Buret reading, *final* (*mL*)	10.03	
3. Volume of HCl added (*mL*)		
C. Data Analysis		
1. Temperature, *T* (*K*)	295	***Part D.5***
2. $1/T$ (K^{-1})		
3. Moles of HCl used (*mol*) Show calculation.		
4. Moles of $B_4O_5(OH)_4^{2-}$ (*mol*) Equation 26.11 Show calculation.		***Part D.7***
5. $[B_4O_5(OH)_4^{2-}]$ (*mol/L*) Equation 26.12 Show calculation.		
6. Molar solubility of borax (*mol/L*)		
7. Solubility product, K_{sp} Equation 26.15 Show calculation.		
8. ln K_{sp}		

Experiment 26 *Report Sheet*

Thermodynamics of the Dissolution of Borax

Date ________ Lab Sec. ______ Name ______________________________ Desk No. ________

A. Standardized HCl Solution

Calculate the mass of sodium carbonate sample required in Part A.3.

	Trial 1	*Trial 2*	*Trial 3*	*Trial 4*
1. Tared mass of Na_2CO_3 (*g*)				
2. Moles of Na_2CO_3 (*mol*)				
3. Buret reading, *initial* (*mL*)				
4. Buret reading, *final* (*mL*)				
5. Volume of HCl added (*mL*)				
6. Moles of HCl added (*mol*)				
7. Molar concentration of HCl (*mol/L*)				
8. Average molar concentration of HCl (*mol/L*)				

B. Preparation of Borax Solution

Sample number	*1*	*2*	*3*	*4*	*5*	*6*
1. Volume of sample (*mL*)	5.00	5.00	5.00	5.00	5.00	5.00
2. Temperature of sample (°*C*)						

C. Analysis of Borax Test Solutions

1. Buret reading, *initial* (*mL*)						
2. Buret reading, *final* (*mL*)						
3. Volume of HCl added (*mL*)						

D. Data Analysis

Express all calculated values with the correct number of significant figures.

Sample number	*1*	*2*	*3*	*4*	*5*	*6*
1. Temperature, $T(K)$						
2. $1/T$ (K^{-1})						
3. Moles of HCl used (*mol*)						
4. Moles of $B_4O_5(OH)_4^{2-}$ (*mol*)						
5. $[B_4O_5(OH)_4^{2-}]$ (*mol/L*)						
6. Molar solubility of borax (*mol/L*)						
7. Solubility product, K_{sp}						
8. $\ln K_{sp}$						

9. Instructor's approval of plotted data __________

10. $-\Delta H°/R$ (from data plot) __________

11. $\Delta S°/R$ (from data plot) __________

12. $\Delta H°$ (*kJ/mol*) __________

13. $\Delta S°$ (*J/mol•K*) __________

14. $\Delta G°$ (*kJ*), at 298 K __________

Laboratory Questions

Circle the questions that have been assigned.

1. Part A.1. No desiccator is available. The sodium carbonate is cooled to room temperature, but the humidity in the room is high. How will this affect the reported molar concentration of the hydrochloric acid solution in Part A.7—too high, too low, or unaffected? Explain.
2. Part A.5. The endpoint in the titration is "overshot."
   a. Is the reported molar concentration of the hydrochloric acid solution too high or too low? Explain.
   b. As a result of this poor titration technique, is the reported number of moles of $B_4O_5(OH)_4^{2-}$ in each of the analyses (Part C.2) too high or too low? Explain.
3. Part B.2. The solid borax reagent is contaminated with a water-soluble substance that does not react with hydrochloric acid. As a result of this contamination, will the K_{sp} of the borax be reported as too high, too low, or unaffected. Explain.
4. Part B.4. For the borax solution at 48°C, no solid borax is present in the test tube. Five milliliters is transferred to the corresponding calibrated test tube and subsequently titrated with the standardized hydrochloric acid solution. How will this oversight in technique affect the reported K_{sp} of borax at 48°C—too high, too low, or unaffected? Explain.
5. Part B.5. A "little more" than 5 mL of a saturated solution is transferred to the corresponding calibrated test tube and subsequently titrated with the standardized hydrochloric acid solution. How will this "generosity" affect the reported molar solubility of borax for that sample—too high, too low, or unaffected? Explain.
6. Part C.2. The saturated solution of borax is diluted with "more than" 25 mL of deionized water. How does this dilution affect the reported number of moles of $B_4O_5(OH)_4^{2-}$ in the saturated solution—too high, too low, or unaffected? Explain.
7. Part D. Judy's data plot has a lesser slope than Nancy's. Which student will have the more positive $\Delta H°$ for the dissolution of borax? Explain. *Hint:* for interpretation remember that a slope of –100 is less than a slope of –150.

Michael Watson

Experiment 28

Chemistry of Copper

The reaction of copper with nitric acid is spontaneous, producing nitrogen dioxide gas and copper(II) ion.

OBJECTIVES

- To observe the chemical properties of copper through a series of chemical reactions
- To use several separation and recovery techniques to isolate the copper compounds from solution
- To determine percent recovery of copper through a cycle of reactions

TECHNIQUES

The following techniques are used in the Experimental Procedure:

INTRODUCTION

Copper is an element that is chemically combined into a variety of compounds in nature, most commonly in the form of a sulfide, as in chalcocite, Cu_2S, and chalcopyrite, $FeCuS_2$. Copper metal is an excellent conductor of heat and electricity and is an **alloying element** in bronze and brass. Copper is a soft metal with a characteristic bright orange-brown color, which we often call *copper color* (Figure 28.1). Copper is relatively inert chemically; it does not readily air oxidize (react with oxygen in air) and is not attacked by simple inorganic acids such as sulfuric and hydrochloric acids. Copper metal that does oxidize in air is called **patina.**

Alloying element: an element of low percent composition in a mixture of metals, the result of which produces an alloy with unique, desirable properties

Copper(II) ion forms a number of very colorful compounds; most often, these compounds are blue or blue-green, although other colors are found, depending on the copper(II) compound.

We will observe several chemical and physical properties of copper through a cyclical sequence of redox, precipitation, decomposition, and acid–base reactions that produce a number of colorful compounds.

Starting with metallic copper at the top of the cycle, the sequence of products formed in this experiment is shown in the diagram:

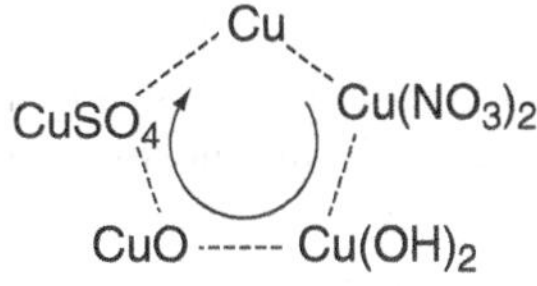

Jo A. Beran/Trey Hernandez

Figure 28.1 The penny is made of zinc (bottom) with a thin copper coating (top).

Dissolution of Copper Metal

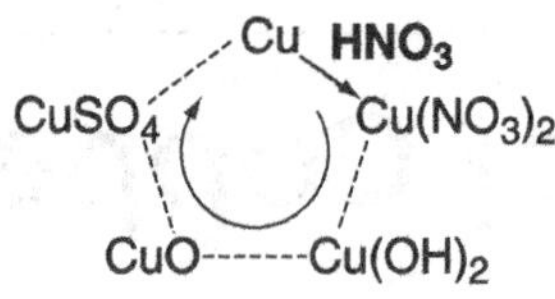

Copper reacts readily with strong oxidizing agents (substances that readily remove electrons from other substances—i.e., $Cu \rightarrow Cu^{2+} + 2e^-$). In this experiment, aqueous nitric acid, HNO_3, oxidizes copper metal to the copper(II) ion (opening photo):

$$Cu(s) + 4\ HNO_3(aq) \longrightarrow Cu(NO_3)_2(aq) + 2\ NO_2(g) + 2\ H_2O(l) \qquad (28.1)$$

The products of this reaction are copper(II) nitrate, $Cu(NO_3)_2$ (a water-soluble salt that produces a blue solution), and nitrogen dioxide, NO_2 (a dense, toxic, red-brown gas). The solution remains acidic because an excess of nitric acid is used for the reaction.

The net ionic equation for the reaction is

$$Cu(s) + 4\ H^+(aq) + 2\ NO_3^-(aq) \longrightarrow Cu^{2+}(aq) + 2\ NO_2(g) + 2\ H_2O(l) \qquad (28.2)$$

Precipitation of Copper(II) Hydroxide from Solution

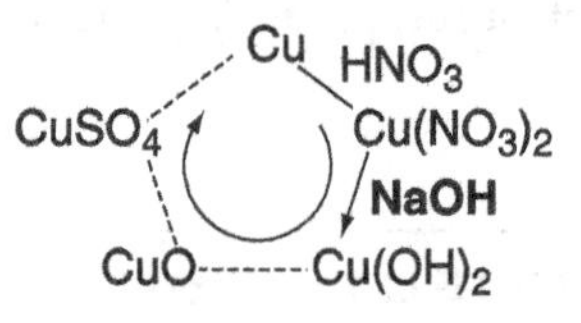

Appendix E

For Part B of the Experimental Procedure, the solution containing the soluble $Cu(NO_3)_2$ is treated with sodium hydroxide, NaOH, a base. Copper(II) hydroxide, $Cu(OH)_2$, a light-blue solid, precipitates from the solution:

$$Cu(NO_3)_2(aq) + 2\ NaOH(aq) \longrightarrow Cu(OH)_2(s) + 2\ NaNO_3(aq) \qquad (28.3)$$

Sodium nitrate, $NaNO_3$, is a colorless salt that remains dissolved in solution as $Na^+(aq)$ and $NO_3^-(aq)$—so these two species are spectator ions.

The net ionic equation for the reaction is

$$Cu^{2+}(aq) + 2\ OH^-(aq) \longrightarrow Cu(OH)_2(s) \qquad (28.4)$$

Conversion of Copper(II) Hydroxide to a Second Insoluble Salt

Heat applied to solid copper(II) hydroxide causes black, insoluble copper(II) oxide, CuO, to form and H_2O to vaporize:

$$Cu(OH)_2(s) \xrightarrow{\Delta} CuO(s) + H_2O(g) \qquad (28.5)$$

Dissolution of Copper(II) Oxide

Copper(II) oxide reacts readily with the addition of aqueous sulfuric acid, H_2SO_4, forming a sky-blue solution as a result of the formation of the water-soluble salt, copper(II) sulfate, $CuSO_4$:

$$CuO(s) + H_2SO_4(aq) \longrightarrow CuSO_4(aq) + H_2O(l) \qquad (28.6)$$

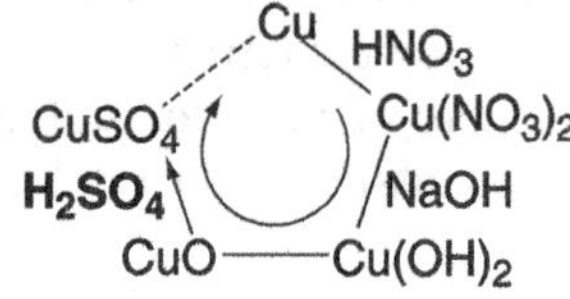

The net ionic equation for the reaction is

$$CuO(s) + 2\ H^+(aq) \longrightarrow Cu^{2+}(aq) + H_2O(l) \qquad (28.7)$$

Reformation of Copper Metal

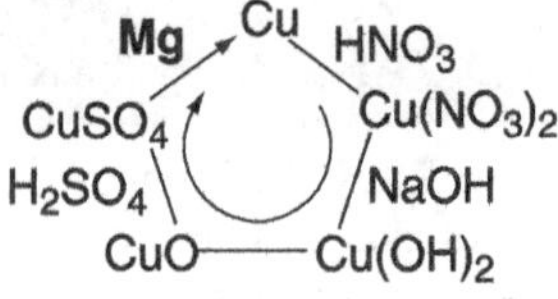

Finally, the addition of magnesium metal, Mg, to the copper(II) sulfate solution completes the copper cycle.

In this reaction, magnesium serves as a **reducing agent** (a substance that donates electrons to another substance—i.e., $Cu^{2+} + 2e^- \rightarrow Cu$). Magnesium, being a more active metal than copper, reduces copper(II) ion from the copper(II) sulfate solution to copper metal and forms water-soluble magnesium sulfate, $MgSO_4$, completing the chemistry of copper cycle.

$$CuSO_4(aq) + Mg(s) \longrightarrow Cu(s) + MgSO_4(aq) \qquad (28.8)$$

The net ionic equation for the reaction is

$$Cu^{2+}(aq) + Mg(s) \longrightarrow Cu(s) + Mg^{2+}(aq) \qquad (28.9)$$

Magnesium metal also reacts with sulfuric acid. Therefore, when magnesium metal is added to the acidic copper(II) sulfate solution, a second reaction occurs that produces hydrogen gas, H_2, and additional magnesium sulfate:

$$Mg(s) + H_2SO_4(aq) \longrightarrow H_2(g) + MgSO_4(aq) \qquad (28.10)$$

The net ionic equation for this reaction is

$$Mg(s) + 2\,H^+(aq) \longrightarrow Mg^{2+}(aq) + H_2(g) \qquad (28.11)$$

Therefore hydrogen gas bubbles are observed during this reaction step of the cycle. This reaction also removes any excess magnesium metal that remains after the copper metal has been recovered.

EXPERIMENTAL PROCEDURE

Procedure Overview: Copper metal is successively treated with nitric acid, sodium hydroxide, heat, sulfuric acid, and magnesium in a cycle of chemical reactions to regenerate the copper metal. The percent recovery is determined.

You will need to obtain instructor approval after each step in the Experimental Procedure. Perform the experiment with a partner. At each circled superscript(1–5) in the procedure, *stop* and record your observation on the ***Report Sheet***. Discuss your observations with your lab partner and your instructor.

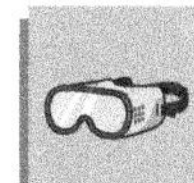

Be aware of the number of significant figures when recording data in Parts A.1 and E.3.

A. Copper Metal to Copper(II) Nitrate

Perform the series of reactions in a test tube that is compatible with your laboratory centrifuge. Three trials are suggested. Consult with your laboratory instructor.

1. **Prepare the copper metal sample.** Obtain a *less than* 0.02-g sample of Cu wool. Measure the mass (±0.001 g) of the selected test tube.[1] Roll and place the Cu wool into the test tube and then measure and record the mass of the test tube and copper sample. Repeat for Trails 2 and 3.

Data Analysis, A

2. **Reaction of the copper metal.** Hold the test tube with a test tube clamp for the remainder of the experiment—do *not* use your fingers.

   Perform this step in the fume hood because of the evolution of toxic $NO_2(g)$. (**Caution:** *Do not inhale the evolved nitrogen dioxide gas.*) Using a dropper bottle or a dropper pipet, add drops (≤10 drops) of *conc* HNO_3 to the copper sample until no further evidence of a chemical reaction is observed. Do not add an excess! (**Caution:** *Concentrated* HNO_3 *is very corrosive. Do not allow it to touch the skin.*)

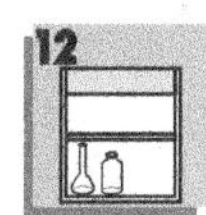

   At this point, the Cu metal has completely reacted. What is the color of the gas? Add 10 drops of deionized water. Show the resulting solution to your laboratory instructor for approval(1) and save the solution for Part B.

B. Copper(II) Nitrate to Copper(II) Hydroxide

1. **Preparation of copper(II) hydroxide.** Agitate or continuously stir with a stirring rod the solution from Part A.2 while slowly adding ~10 drops of 6 *M* NaOH. (**Caution:** *Wash with water immediately if the* NaOH *comes into contact with the skin.*) This forms the $Cu(OH)_2$ precipitate. After the first 10 drops are added, add ~10 more drops of 6 *M* NaOH. Using a wash bottle and deionized water, rinse the stirring rod, allowing the rinse water to go into the test tube. Centrifuge the solution for 30 seconds (ask your instructor for instructions in operating the centrifuge).

2. **A complete precipitation.** Test for a complete precipitation of $Cu(OH)_2$ by adding 2–3 more drops of 6 *M* NaOH to the **supernatant.** If additional precipitate forms, add 4–5 more drops and again centrifuge. Repeat the test until no further formation of the $Cu(OH)_2$ occurs. The solution should appear colorless, and the precipitate should be light blue. Obtain your laboratory instructor's approval(2) and save for Part C.

Supernatant: the clear solution in the test tube

[1]Consult with your instructor.

C. Copper(II) Hydroxide to Copper(II) Oxide

Cool flame: an adjusted Bunsen flame having a low supply of fuel

1. **Heat the sample.** Decant (pour off) and discard the supernatant from the test tube. *Carefully* (***very carefully!***) and slowly heat the test tube with a **cool flame**[2] until the $Cu(OH)_2$ precipitate changes color. **Read footnote 2!** You need *not* heat the contents to dryness. Avoid ejection (and projection) of your copper compound by *not* holding the test tube over the direct flame for a prolonged period of time. If the contents of the test tube are ejected, you will need to restart the Experimental Procedure at Part A. Obtain your instructor's approval③ and save for Part D.

D. Copper(II) Oxide to Copper(II) Sulfate

1. **Dissolution of copper(II) oxide.** To the solid CuO in the test tube from Part C, add drops of 6 *M* H_2SO_4 with agitation until the CuO dissolves (≤20 drops, 1 mL). (**Caution:** *Do not let sulfuric acid touch the skin!*) (Slight heating *may* be necessary, but be careful not to eject the contents!) The solution's sky-blue appearance is evidence of the presence of soluble $CuSO_4$. Obtain your instructor's approval④ and save for Part E.

E. Copper(II) Sulfate to Copper Metal

1. **Formation of copper metal.**
   a. Using fine steel wool (or sandpaper), polish about 5–7 cm of Mg ribbon. Cut or tear the ribbon into 1-cm lengths. Dilute the solution from Part D with deionized water until the test tube is half-full. Add a 1-cm Mg strip to the solution. When the Mg strip has reacted (disappeared), add a second Mg strip and so on until the blue has disappeared from the solution. Describe what is happening. What is the coating on the magnesium ribbon? What is the gas?⑤

   b. If a white, milky precipitate forms [from the formation of magnesium hydroxide, $Mg(OH)_2$], add several drops of 6 *M* H_2SO_4. (**Caution:** *Avoid skin contact.*) Break up the red-brown Cu coating on the Mg ribbon with a stirring rod. *After* breaking up the Cu metal *and* after adding several pieces of Mg ribbon, centrifuge the mixture.

2. **Washing.**

Dry Lab 4, Part C, page 410, describes the procedure for washing a precipitate.

   a. Add drops of 6 *M* H_2SO_4 to react any excess Mg ribbon. (**Caution:** *Avoid skin contact.*) Do this by breaking up the Cu metal with a stirring rod to expose the Mg ribbon, coated with Cu metal, to the H_2SO_4 solution. Centrifuge for 30 seconds, decant, and discard the supernatant. Be careful to keep the Cu metal in the test tube.
   b. Wash the red-brown Cu metal with three 1-mL portions of deionized water.[3] Rinse the stirring rod in the test tube. Centrifuge, decant, and discard each washing.

3. **Determination of the mass of recovered copper.** *Very gently* dry the Cu in the test tube over a *cool* flame (**see footnote 2**). Allow the tube and contents to cool and determine the mass (±0.001 g). Repeat the heating procedure until a reproducibility in mass of ±1% is obtained. Record the mass of Cu recovered in the experiment.

Disposal: All solutions used in the procedure can be disposed of in the Waste Salts container. Dispose of the copper metal in the Waste Solids container. Check with your instructor.

CLEANUP: Rinse all glassware twice with tap water and twice with deionized water. Discard all rinses in the sink.

The Next Step

Many alloys other than coinage alloys have varying amounts of copper—brass, for example. What are some other methods for determining the amount of copper in a sample—gravimetrically, spectrophotometrically (see *Experiment 35*), or volumetrically (see *Experiments 23, 24, or 29*—also copper(II) ion reacts with iodide ion to produce I_3^-)?

[2]From *Technique 13C*, "If you can feel the heat of the flame with the hand holding the test tube clamp, the flame is too hot!"

[3]Wash the Cu metal by adding water, stirring the mixture with a stirring rod, and allowing the mixture to settle.

Experiment 28 *Prelaboratory Assignment*

Chemistry of Copper

Date __________ Lab Sec. ______ Name ____ Desk No. _________

1. Review net-ionic equations 28.2, 28.4, 28.7, 28.9, and 28.11.
   a. Three of the equations represent oxidation–reduction reactions. Identify the three equations and indicate the oxidizing agent in each.

   b. One of the equations represents an acid–base reaction. Identify the equation and indicate the base.

2. Copper forms many different compounds in this experiment.
   a. Experimental Procedure, Part A. Identify the *oxidizing agent* in the conversion of copper metal to copper(II) ion.

   b. Experimental Procedure, Part E. Identify the *oxidizing agent* in the conversion of copper(II) ion to copper metal.

   c. Experimental Procedure, Part D. Classify the type of reaction for the conversion of copper(II) oxide to copper(II) sulfate.

3. A number of **Caution** chemicals and solutions are used in this experiment. Refer to the Experimental Procedure and the corresponding sections to identify the specific chemical or solution that must be handled with care.

Experimental Procedure	Precautionary Chemical/Solution
Part A.2	
Part A.2	
Part B.1	
Part D.1	
Part E.1	

4. Experimental Procedure, Part A.2. What volume, in drops, of 16 *M* (*conc*) HNO_3 is required to react with 0.0214 g of Cu metal? See equation 28.1. Assume 20 drops per milliliter.

5. Experimental Procedure, Parts C.1 and E.3. Extreme caution *must* be observed when heating a solution in a test tube. 13c

   a. What criterion indicates that you are heating the solution in the test tube with a "cool flame"?

   b. At what angle should the test tube be held while moving the test tube circularly in and out of the cool flame?

   c. What is the consequence of not using this technique properly?

6. a. Describe the technique for balancing a centrifuge when centrifuging a sample. 11f

   b. Describe the technique for washing a precipitate. See Dry Lab 4C, p. 410.

7. A 0.0194-g sample of copper metal is recycled through the series of reactions in this experiment. If 0.0169 g of copper is then recovered after the series of reactions in this experiment, what is the percent recovery of the copper metal?

Experiment 28 *Report Sheet*

Chemistry of Copper

Date _________ Lab Sec. ______ Name ______________________________ Desk No. _________

Data for Copper Cycle	*Trial 1*	*Trial 2*	*Trial 3*
1. Mass of test tube (*g*)	________	________	________
2. Mass of test tube (*g*) + copper (*g*)	________	________	________
3. Mass of copper sample (*g*)	________	________	________

Synthesis of	**Observation**	**Instructor Approval**	**Balanced Equation**
①A. $Cu(NO_3)_2$ (*aq*)	________________	______	________________
②B. $Cu(OH)_2$ (*s*)	________________	______	________________
③C. CuO (*s*)	________________	______	________________
④D. $CuSO_4$ (*aq*)	________________	______	________________

⑤E. Copper(II) sulfate to copper metal. Write a full description of the reactions that occurred. Include a balanced equation in your discussion.

4. Mass of test tube and recovered copper (*g*) 1st mass (*g*) ________ ________ ________

2nd mass (*g*) ________ ________ ________

3rd mass (*g*) ________ ________ ________

5. Final mass of Cu recovered (*g*) ________ ________ ________

6. Percent recovery, $\frac{\text{mass Cu (recovered)}}{\text{mass Cu (original)}} \times 100$ ________ ________ ________

7. Average percent recovery ________

8. Account for the percent recovery being equal to or less than 100%.

Laboratory Questions

Circle the questions that have been assigned.

1. Part A.2 What is the formula *and* the color of the gas that is evolved?
2. Part B.1. When the NaOH solution is added, $Cu(OH)_2$ does not precipitate immediately. What else present in the reaction mixture from Part A reacts with the NaOH before the copper(II) ion? Explain.
3. Part C.1. The sample in Part B was *not* centrifuged. Why? Perhaps the student chemist had to be across campus for another appointment. Because of the student's "other priorities" the percent recovery of copper in the experiment will decrease. Explain why.
4. Part D.1. All of the CuO does *not* react with the sulfuric acid. Will the reported percent recovery of copper in the experiment be too high or too low? Explain.
5. Part E. Sulfuric acid has a dual role in the chemistry of this experiment. What are its two roles in the recovery of the copper metal?
6. Part E.2. Jacob couldn't find the 6 *M* H_2SO_4, so instead substituted the 6 *M* HNO_3 that was available. What change was most likely observed as a result of this decision? Explain.
7. Part E. Errors in experimental technique can lead to the percent recovery of copper being *too high*—one such error may occur in Part E.2 and another in Part E.3. Cite those two errors and explain what should be done to ensure that those errors do not occur in the recovery.

Experiment 29

Bleach Analysis

Judith Beran

Bleach is used for stamping images on dark paper and cloth.

OBJECTIVES

- To determine the available chlorine in commercial bleaching agents
- To prepare a standardized sodium thiosulfate solution

TECHNIQUES

The following techniques are used in the Experimental Procedure:

16a
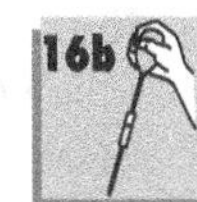

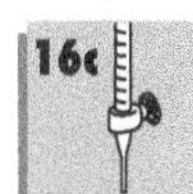

INTRODUCTION

Natural fibers, such as cotton and wool, and paper products tend to retain some of their original color during the manufacturing process. For example, brown paper is more "natural" than white paper, and original cotton fibers tend *not* to be "white."

Natural dyes and, in general, all of nature's colors exist because of the presence of molecules with multiple bonds. Likewise, stains and synthetic colors are due to molecules with one or more double and/or triple bonds. The electrons of the multiple bond readily absorb visible radiation, reflecting (or transmitting) the colors of the visible radiation that are *not* absorbed.[1] These electrons of the double/triple bonds are readily removed by **oxidizing agents**. Because the oxidized form[2] of the molecules causing the colors and stains no longer absorb visible radiation, the fabric or paper appears whiter.

Oxidizing agents remove electrons from other substances

All of the halogens and solutions of the oxyhalides are excellent oxidizing agents. Because of its low cost, chlorine, as an **oxidant**, is often used as a bactericide for use in swimming pools, drinking water, and sewage-treatment plants.

Oxidant: oxidizing agent, a substance that causes the oxidation of another substance

Most commercial **bleaching agents** contain the hypochlorite ion, ClO^-. The $\mathbf{ClO^-}$ ion removes light-absorbing electrons from the multiple bonds of molecules. Therefore, the absorption of visible radiation does not occur; all visible light is reflected (or transmitted), giving the object a white appearance.

Bleaching agent: an oxidizing agent

ClO^- is reduced when removing electrons from another substance

$$ClO^-(aq) + H_2O(l) + 2\,e^- \longrightarrow Cl^-(aq) + 2\,OH^-(aq) \qquad (29.1)$$

The textile and paper industries, as well as home and commercial laundries, use large quantities of hypochlorite solutions to oxidize the color- and stain-causing molecules. The hypochlorite ion is generally in the form of a sodium or calcium salt in the bleaching agent.

[1] In *Dry Lab 3* the explanation of light absorption in the visible region is discussed in terms of an absorption of energy (from the visible region) by electrons.

[2] The stains or impurities may be oxidized to form several products.

Strengths of Bleaching Agents

Mass ratio: mass of Cl_2/mass of sample (solution or solid)

Electrolysis and electrolytic cells are studied in Experiment 33.

Industry expresses the strength of the bleaching agents as the mass of molecular *chlorine,* Cl_2, per unit mass of solution (or mass of powder) regardless of the actual chemical form of the oxidizing agent. This **mass ratio,** expressed as a percent, is called the **percent available chlorine** in the bleach solution.

As an example, Ultra liquid laundry bleach is generally a 6.00% by mass NaClO aqueous solution. Liquid laundry bleach is manufactured by the **electrolysis** of a cold, stirred, concentrated sodium chloride solution. The chlorine gas and the hydroxide ion that are generated at the electrodes in the electrolysis cell combine to form the hypochlorite ion, ClO^-, and in the presence of Na^+, a sodium hypochlorite solution:

$$Cl_2(aq) + 2\,OH^-(aq) \longrightarrow ClO^-(aq) + Cl^-(aq) + H_2O(l) \qquad (29.2)$$

The percent available chlorine in a 6.00% NaClO solution is calculated as

$$\frac{\text{grams } Cl_2}{\text{grams soln}} \times 100 = \frac{6.00 \text{ g NaClO}}{100 \text{ g soln}} \times \frac{\text{mol NaClO}}{74.44 \text{ g NaClO}} \times \frac{1 \text{ mol } Cl_2}{1 \text{ mol NaClO}} \times \frac{70.90 \text{ g } Cl_2}{\text{mol } Cl_2} \times 100 = 5.71\% \; Cl_2$$

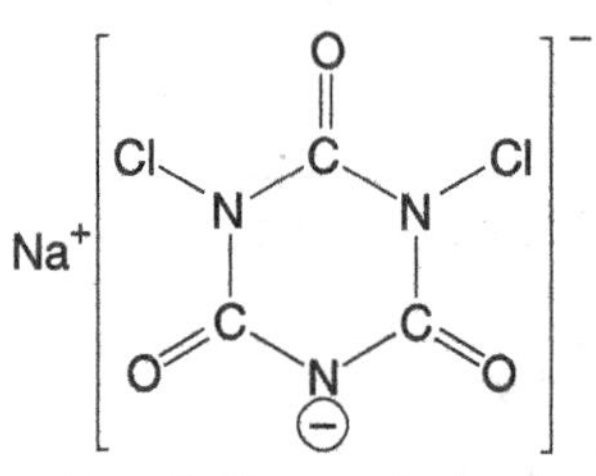

sodium dichloro-*s*-triazinetrione

Solid bleaching powders and water disinfectants (e.g., for home swimming pools or hot tubs) contain a variety of compounds that serve as oxidizing agents. Solids such as $Ca(ClO)Cl/Ca(ClO)_2$ mixtures and sodium dichloro-*s*-triazinetrione, commonly found in household cleansers and water disinfectants, are substances that release ClO^- in solution. Solid household bleaches often contain sodium perborate, $NaBO_2 \cdot H_2O_2 \cdot 3H_2O$, in which the bleaching agent is hydrogen peroxide, a compound that is also found in hair bleaches.

Analysis of Bleach with Potassium Iodide and Sodium Thiosulfate Solutions

$3\,I^-(aq) \rightarrow I_3^-(aq) + 2\,e^-$

The oxidizing property of the hypochlorite ion is used to perform an analysis for the amount of available chlorine in a bleach sample for this experiment. In the analysis, the hypochlorite ion oxidizes iodide ion to molecular iodine—the hypochlorite ion is the limiting reactant in the analysis. In the presence of an excess amount of iodide ion, the molecular iodine actually exists as a water-soluble triiodide complex, I_3^- (or $[I_2 \cdot I^-]$):

$$ClO^-(aq) + 3\,I^-(aq) + H_2O(l) \longrightarrow I_3^-(aq) + Cl^-(aq) + 2\,OH^-(aq) \qquad (29.3)$$

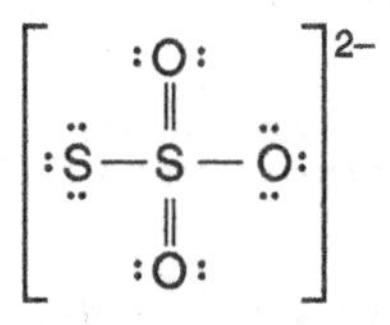

thiosulfate ion

Stoichiometric point: point at which the mole ratio of reactants in a titration is the same as the mole ratio in the balanced equation

The amount of I_3^- produced in the reaction is determined by its subsequent titration with a standardized sodium thiosulfate, $Na_2S_2O_3$, solution:

$$I_3^-(aq) + 2\,S_2O_3^{2-}(aq) \longrightarrow 3\,I^-(aq) + S_4O_6^{2-}(aq) \qquad (29.4)$$

The **stoichiometric point** for this redox titration is detected by adding a small amount of starch. Starch forms a rather strong bond to I_3^-; whereas I_3^- has a yellow-brown color, the I_3^-•starch complex is a deep, and very intense, blue. Just prior to the disappearance of the yellow-brown color of the I_3^- ion in the titration, the starch is added to intensify the presence of the I_3^- still to be titrated (Figure 29.1, p. 333).

$$I_3^-(aq) + \text{starch}(aq) \longrightarrow I_3^- \cdot \text{starch}(aq, \text{deep blue}) \qquad (29.5)$$

Titrant: the solution being added from the buret

The addition of the sodium thiosulfate **titrant** is then resumed until the deep-blue color of the I_3^-•starch complex disappears.

$$I_3^- \cdot \text{starch}(aq) + 2\,S_2O_3^{2-}(aq) \longrightarrow 3\,I^-(aq) + S_4O_6^{2-}(aq) + \text{starch}(aq, \text{colorless}) \qquad (29.6)$$

Figure 29.1 I_3^- without starch added (left); I_3^- with starch added (right)

From the stoichiometries of equations 29.4 (2 mol $S_2O_3^{2-}$ to 1 mol I_3^-), 29.3 (1 mol I_3^- from 1 mol ClO^-), and 29.2 (1 mol ClO^- from 1 mol Cl_2) in that sequence, the moles of available chlorine in the sample can be calculated. From the molar mass of chlorine and the mass of the sample used for the analysis, the percent available chlorine is calculated.

Note that the chemical analysis of a bleach solution follows the same chemistry as was applied to the chemical systems in *Experiment 23* (Part F) *and 24*, where the oxidizing agents were $HIO_3(aq)$ and $H_2O_2(aq)$, respectively and again in *Experiment 31* where the oxidizing agent is oxygen.

$S_4O_6^{2-}$, tetrathionate ion

A Standard Solution of Sodium Thiosulfate, $Na_2S_2O_3$

Primary standard: a substance that has a known high degree of purity, a relatively large molar mass, is nonhygroscopic, and reacts in a predictable way

The concentration of a standard $Na_2S_2O_3$ solution (used in equation 29.4)[3] is determined by its reaction with solid potassium iodate, KIO_3, a **primary standard** (Figure 29.2). A measured mass of potassium iodate is dissolved in an acidic solution containing an excess of potassium iodide, KI. Potassium iodate, a strong oxidizing agent, oxidizes I^- to the water-soluble, yellow-brown $I_3^-(aq)$ in solution:

$$IO_3^-(aq) + 8\,I^-(aq) + 6\,H^+(aq) \longrightarrow 3\,I_3^-(aq) + 3\,H_2O(l) \qquad (29.7)$$

The I_3^- is then titrated with a prepared sodium thiosulfate solution, where the I_3^- is reduced to I^- and the thiosulfate ion, $S_2O_3^{2-}$, is oxidized to the tetrathionate ion, $S_4O_6^{2-}$ (equation 29.4).

The stoichiometric point is detected using a starch solution. Just prior to the disappearance of the yellow-brown iodine in solution, starch is added to form a deep-blue complex with iodine (equation 29.5).

The addition of the thiosulfate solution is then continued until the remaining I_3^- is converted to I^- and the deep-blue color disappears (equation 29.6).

Note that the reaction of IO_3^- with I^- (equation 29.7) for the standardization of the sodium thiosulfate solution substitutes for the reaction of ClO^- with I^- (equation 29.3) in the analysis of the bleaching agent, as IO_3^- is also an oxidizing agent.

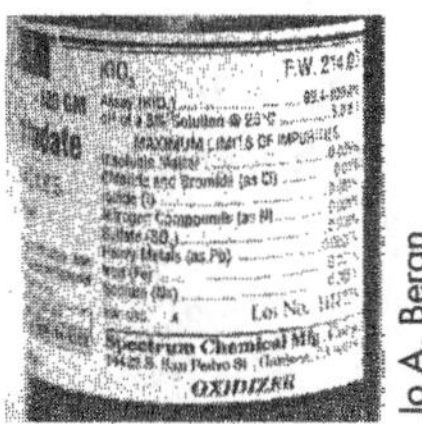

Figure 29.2 Potassium iodate has the necessary properties of a primary standard.

EXPERIMENTAL PROCEDURE

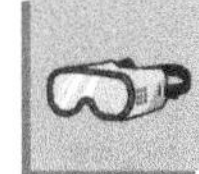

Procedure Overview: A solution of $Na_2S_2O_3$ is prepared and standardized using solid KIO_3 as a primary standard. A bleach sample is mixed with an excess of iodide ion, generating I_3^-. The amount of I_3^- generated is analyzed by titration with the standard $Na_2S_2O_3$ solution to determine the percent available chlorine in the bleach sample.

Quantitative, reproducible data are an objective of this experiment. Practice good laboratory techniques. Two trials are required for analyzing each of two bleaches to compare the ClO^- concentrations or three trials for analyzing a single bleach. Consult your instructor. Ask your instructor about the completion of both Parts C and D in this experiment.

[3] The $Na_2S_2O_3$ solution is a secondary standard solution in that its concentration can only be determined from an analysis; it cannot be prepared directly from solid $Na_2S_2O_3$.

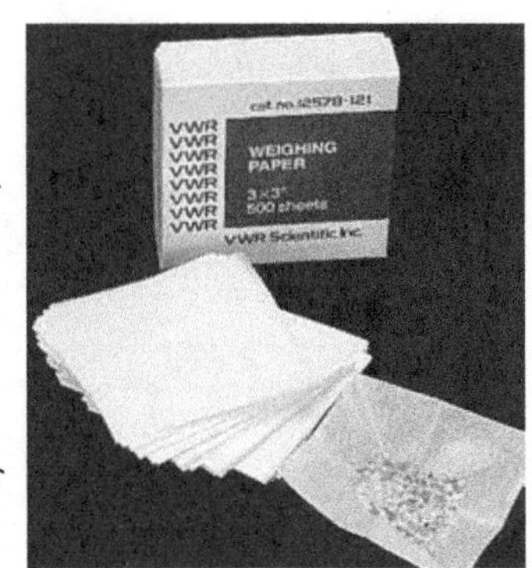

Courtesy of VWR International, LLC

Figure 29.3 Weighing paper for measuring the KIO_3 primary standard

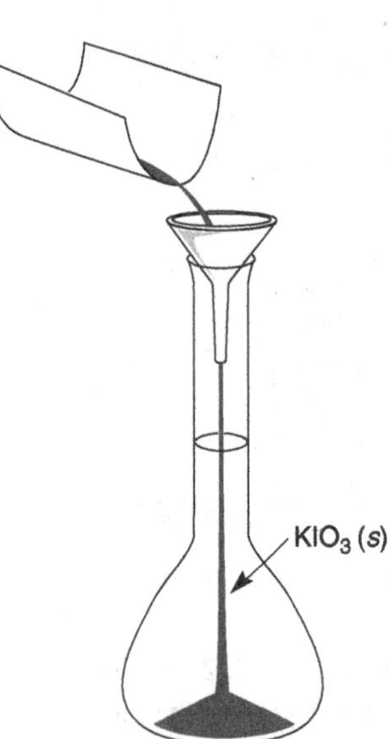

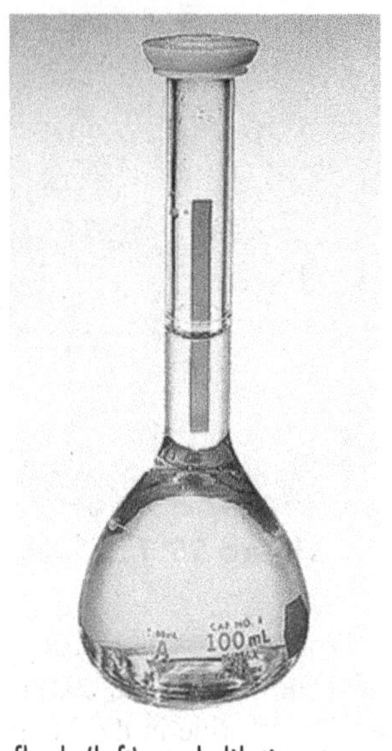

Courtesy of VWR International, LLC

Figure 29.4 Transferring a solid reagent to a volumetric flask (left) and diluting to volume (right)

Nearly 800 mL of boiled, deionized water cooled to room temperature is required for this experiment. Begin preparing this at the beginning of the laboratory period.

Be aware of the number of significant figures when recording data.

A. Preparation of the KIO_3 Primary Standard

Data Analysis, A

1. **Prepare a primary standard solution.** (Check with your instructor—this solution may have already been prepared by stockroom personnel.) Use weighing paper (Figure 29.3) to measure the mass (±0.001 g) of KIO_3 (previously dried[4] at 110°C) that is required to prepare 100 mL of 0.01 *M* KIO_3. See ***Prelaboratory Assignment*** question 3a and show this calculation on the ***Report Sheet.*** Dissolve the solid KIO_3 and dilute to volume with the freshly boiled, deionized water in a 100-mL volumetric flask (Figure 29.4). Calculate and record its *exact* molar concentration.

B. Standard 0.1 *M* $Na_2S_2O_3$ Solution

1. **Prepare a $Na_2S_2O_3$ solution.** (Check with your instructor—this solution may have already been prepared by stockroom personnel.) This solution should be prepared no more than 1 week in advance because unavoidable decomposition occurs. Measure the mass (±0.01 g) of $Na_2S_2O_3{\cdot}5H_2O$ needed to prepare 250 mL of a 0.1 *M* $Na_2S_2O_3$ solution. See ***Prelaboratory Assignment*** question 3b and show this calculation on the ***Report Sheet.*** Dissolve the solid $Na_2S_2O_3{\cdot}5H_2O$ with the freshly boiled, deionized water and dilute to 250 mL; an Erlenmeyer flask can be used to prepare and store the solution. Agitate until the salt dissolves.

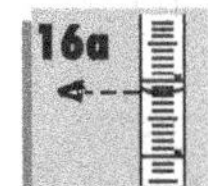

Data Analysis, A

2. **Prepare a buret.** Prepare a *clean* 50-mL buret for titration. Rinse the clean buret with two or three 5-mL portions of the $Na_2S_2O_3$ solution, draining each rinse through the buret tip. Fill the buret with the $Na_2S_2O_3$ solution, drain the tip of air bubbles, and after 10–15 seconds record the volume using all certain digits (from the labeled calibration marks on the buret) *plus* one uncertain digit (the last digit which is the best estimate between the calibration marks).

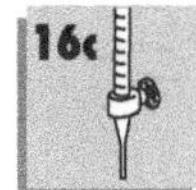

3. **Titrate the KIO_3 solution.** Pipet 25 mL of the standard KIO_3 solution (from Part A) into a 125-mL Erlenmeyer flask, add ~2 g (±0.01 g) of solid KI, and swirl to dissolve. Add ~10 mL of 0.5 *M* H_2SO_4. Begin titrating the KIO_3 solution immediately. When the yellow-brown I_3^- nearly disappears (pale yellow color appears),[5]

[4]The KIO_3 should have been dried prior to your coming to the laboratory.
[5]Consult your instructor at this point.

add 2 mL of starch solution.[6] Stirring constantly, continue titrating *slowly*[7] until the deep-blue color completely disappears.

4. **Repeat the titration with another KIO_3 sample.** Repeat twice the procedure in Part B.3 by rapidly adding the $Na_2S_2O_3$ titrant until ~1 mL before the yellow-brown color of I_3^- disappears. Add the starch solution and continue titrating until the solution is colorless. Three trials for the standardization of $Na_2S_2O_3$ should yield molar concentrations that agree to within ±1%.

Data Analysis, A

5. **Calculate concentration of $Na_2S_2O_3$.** Calculate the molar concentration of the (now) standardized $Na_2S_2O_3$ solution.

Disposal: Dispose of the test solutions as directed by your instructor.

6. **Prepare the buret for bleach analysis.** Prepare the 50-mL buret with the $Na_2S_2O_3$ solution for titration as described in Part B.2. This is to be ready for immediate use in Part E. Ten to fifteen seconds after filling the buret, read and record (***Report Sheet***, E.1) the volume of $Na_2S_2O_3$ solution.

C. Preparation of Liquid Bleach for Analysis

Jo A. Beran

1. **Obtain bleach samples.** Two trials for each bleach or three trials of a single bleach are suggested. Obtain about 12 mL of each liquid bleach from your instructor.
2. **Prepare the bleach solution for analysis.** Pipet 10 mL of bleach into a 100-mL volumetric flask and dilute to the 100-mL mark with the boiled, deionized water. Mix the solution thoroughly. Pipet 25 mL of this diluted bleach solution into a 250-mL Erlenmeyer flask; add 20 mL of deionized water, ~2 g of KI, and ~10 mL of 0.5 *M* H_2SO_4. A yellow-brown color indicates the presence of I_3^- that has been generated by the ClO^- ion. Proceed *immediately* to Part E.

D. Preparation of Solid Bleach for Analysis

1. **Obtain bleach samples.** Two trials for each bleach or three trials of a single bleach are suggested. Obtain about 5 g of each powdered bleach from your instructor.
2. **Prepare a solution from the powdered bleach.** Place about 5 g of a powdered bleach sample into a mortar and grind (Figure 29.5). Measure the mass (±0.001 g) of the finely pulverized sample on weighing paper and transfer it to a 100-mL volumetric flask fitted with a funnel. Dilute the sample to the 100 mL mark with the boiled, deionized water. Mix thoroughly. If an abrasive is present in the powder, the sample may *not* dissolve completely. Allow the insolubles to settle.
3. **Prepare the bleach solution for analysis.** Pipet 25 mL of this bleach solution (be careful to *not* draw any solids into the pipet!) into a 250-mL Erlenmeyer flask and add 20 mL of deionized water, ~2 g of KI, and ~10 mL of 0.5 *M* H_2SO_4. A yellow-brown color indicates the presence of I_3^- that has been generated by the ClO^- ion. Proceed *immediately* to Part E.

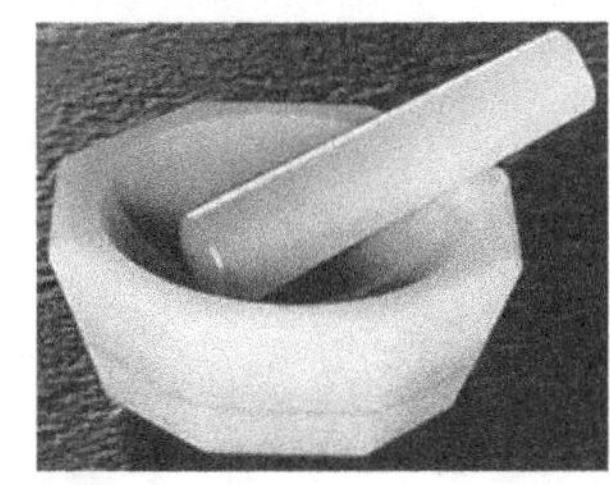

Courtesy of VWR International, LLC

Figure 29.5 A mortar and pestle is used to grind the powder.

Data Analysis, A

[6]If the deep-blue color of I_3^-•starch does *not* appear, you have passed the stoichiometric point in the titration and you will need to discard the sample and prepare another.
[7]The I_3^-•starch complex is slow to dissociate.

E. Analysis of Bleach Samples

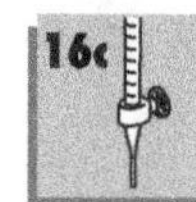

Read and record the volume in the buret to the correct number of significant figures.

1. **Titrate the bleach sample.** *Immediately* titrate the liberated I_3^- with the standardized $Na_2S_2O_3$, prepared in Part B.6, until the yellow-brown I_3^- color is almost discharged.
2. **Perform the final steps in the analysis.** Add ~2 mL of starch solution to form the deep-blue I_3^-•starch complex.[8] While swirling the flask, continue titrating *slowly* until the deep-blue color disappears. Refer to the titration procedure in Part B.3. Record the final volume of the titrant in the buret.
3. **Repeat with another sample.** Repeat the experiment with a second sample of the same bleach. If only one bleach is to be analyzed, repeat the analysis with a third sample. If a second bleach is to be analyzed, proceed to Part E.4.
4. **Repeat the analysis for another bleach.** Analyze another bleaching agent (liquid, Part C, or solid, Part D) to determine the amount of available chlorine. Compare the available chlorine content of the two bleaches.

Disposal: Dispose of the KIO_3 solution and the remaining bleach solutions in the Waste Oxidants container. Dispose of the $Na_2S_2O_3$ solution in the buret and the Erlenmeyer flask in the Waste Reducing Agent container. Dispose of the sulfuric acid in the Waste Acids container. Dispose of all test solutions as directed by your instructor.

CLEANUP: Flush the buret twice with tap water and twice with deionized water. Repeat the cleaning operation with the pipets. Discard all washings as directed by your instructor. Clean up the balance area, discarding any solids in the Waste Solids container.

The Next Step

What other oxidants are used as bleaches or as bactericides in the treatment of water? Are they more or less effective than hypochlorite bleach? For example, is this procedure applicable for the analysis for sodium perborate in powdered bleaches or the disinfectants used in home and public swimming pools? Devise a procedure for the analysis of a series of commercial or industrial oxidants.

Notes and Calculations

[8]If you are analyzing a powdered bleach, the 2 mL of starch may be added immediately after the 0.5 *M* H_2SO_4 in Part D.3.

Experiment 29 *Prelaboratory Assignment*

Bleach Analysis

Date __________ Lab Sec. ______ Name ______________________________ Desk No. __________

1. a. Potassium iodate, KIO_3, and the bleach's hypochlorite ion, ClO^-, are oxidizing agents. What do they oxidize in this experiment?

b. Sodium thiosulfate, $Na_2S_2O_3$, is a reducing agent. What does it reduce in this experiment?

2. Write the balanced net-ionic equation for the standardization of the sodium thiosulfate solution by combining equations 29.7 and 29.4.

3. a. Experimental Procedure, Part A.1. Describe the procedure for the preparation of 100 mL of a 0.010 *M* KIO_3 solution, starting with solid KIO_3 (molar mass = 214.02 g/mol).

b. Experimental Procedure, Part B.1. Describe the procedure for the preparation of 250 mL of 0.10 *M* $Na_2S_2O_3$ starting with solid $Na_2S_2O_3 \bullet 5H_2O$ (molar mass = 248.2 g/mol).

4. Experimental Procedure, Part B.3. Explain why a minimum, and *not* a maximum, mass of ~2 g of KI is critical for the standardization of the sodium thiosulfate solution.

5. Write the balanced net-ionic equation for the analysis of the "available chlorine" in a sample using sodium thiosulfate as the reducing agent by combining equations 29.2, 29.3, and 29.4.

6. a. An analysis of a commercial bleach sample provided the data in the following table. Complete the analysis for Trial 1 (See ***Report Sheet***.) of the bleach sample. Record the calculated values with the correct number of significant figures.

			Calculation Zone
B. Standard 0.01 *M* $Na_2S_2O_3$ Solution			
8.	Average molar concentration of $Na_2S_2O_3$ (*mol/L*)	0.135	*Data Analysis 1.*
C. Preparation of Liquid Bleach for Analysis			
1.	Volume of original bleach titrated (*mL*)	2.50	*Data Analysis 2.*
2.	Mass of bleach titrated (*g*) (assume the density of the liquid bleach is 1.084 g/mL)		
E. Analysis of Bleach Samples			*Data Analysis 3.*
1.	Buret reading, *initial* (*mL*)	3.85	
2.	Buret reading, *final* (*mL*)	37.60	
3.	Volume of $Na_2S_2O_3$ added (*mL*)		
Data Analysis			*Data Analysis 4.*
1.	Moles of $Na_2S_2O_3$ added (*mol*) Show calculation.		
2.	Moles of ClO^- reacted (*mol*) Equations 29.4 and 29.3. Show calculation.		
3.	Moles of available chlorine (*mol*) Equation 29.2. Show calculation.		*Data Analysis 5.*
4.	Mass of available chlorine (*g*) Show calculation.		
5.	Mass percent available chlorine (**liquid**) (%) Show calculation.		

6. b. For Trials 2 and 3, the percents available chlorine were 5.85% and 6.01% respectively.

a. What is the average percent available chlorine for the bleach sample?

b. What are the standard deviation and the relative standard deviation (%RSD) of available chlorine for the bleach sample?

Experiment 29 *Report Sheet*

Bleach Analysis

Date ________ Lab Sec. ______ Name ______________________________ Desk No. ________

A. Preparation of the KIO_3 Primary Standard

Calculate the mass of KIO_3 (molar mass = 214.02 g/mol) required for Part A.1.

1. Mass of weighing paper (*g*) ________
2. Mass of weighing paper plus KIO_3 (*g*) ________
3. Mass of KIO_3 (*g*) ________
4. Moles of KIO_3 (*mol*) ________
5. Molar concentration of KIO_3 solution (*mol/L*) ________

B. Standard 0.1 *M* $Na_2S_2O_3$ Solution

Calculate the mass of $Na_2S_2O_3{\cdot}5H_2O$ (molar mass = 248.19 g/mol) required for Part B.1.

	Trial 1	*Trial 2*	*Trial 3*
1. Volume of KIO_3 solution (*mL*)	25.0	25.0	25.0
2. Moles of KIO_3 titrated (*mol*)			
3. Buret reading, *initial* (*mL*)			
4. Buret reading, *final* (*mL*)			
5. Volume of $Na_2S_2O_3$ added (*mL*)			
6. Moles of $Na_2S_2O_3$ added (*mol*)			
7. Molar concentration of $Na_2S_2O_3$ (*mol/L*)			

8. Average molar concentration of $Na_2S_2O_3$ (*mol/L*) ________ ***Data Analysis, B***
9. Standard deviation ________ ***Data Analysis, C***
10. Relative standard deviation (*%RSD*) ________ ***Data Analysis, D***

C. Preparation of Liquid Bleach for Analysis

	Trial 1	*Trial 2*	*Trial 1*	*Trial 2*
Sample Name or Description				
1. Volume of original bleach titrated (*mL*)	2.5	2.5	2.5	2.5
2. Mass of bleach titrated (*g*) (assume the density of liquid bleach is 1.084 g/mL)				

D. Preparation of Solid Bleach for Analysis

	Trial 1	Trial 2	Trial 1	Trial 2
Sample name or description				
1. Tared mass of bleach (*g*)				

E. Analysis of Bleach Samples

	Trial 1	Trial 2	Trial 1	Trial 2
1. Buret reading, *initial* (*mL*)				
2. Buret reading, *final* (*mL*)				
3. Volume of $Na_2S_2O_3$ added (*mL*)				

Data Analysis

	Trial 1	Trial 2	Trial 1	Trial 2
1. Moles of $Na_2S_2O_3$ added (*mol*)				
2. Moles of ClO^- reacted (*mol*)				
3. Moles of available chlorine (*mol*)				
4. Mass of available chlorine (*g*)				
5. Mass percent available chlorine (**liquid**) (assume the density of liquid bleach is 1.084 g/mL) (%)				
6. Average mass percent available chlorine (**liquid**) (%)				
7. Mass percent available chlorine (**solid**) (%)				
8. Average mass percent available chlorine (**solid**) (%)				

Laboratory Questions

Circle the questions that have been assigned.

1. Part A.1. The KIO_3 sample was not sufficiently dried prior to the preparation of the solution. Will the molar concentration of the sodium thiosulfate solution (Part B.5) be reported as too high or too low? Explain.
2. Part A.1. The solid KIO_3 is diluted shy of the 100-mL mark in the volumetric flask.
   a. Does this technique error result in a reported molar concentration of KIO_3 that is too high or too low? Explain.
   b. As a result, will the reported molar concentration of the standardized $Na_2S_2O_3$ solution be too high, too low, or unaffected? Explain.
3. Part B.1. In preparing the sodium thiosulfate solution, the solid $Na_2S_2O_3{\bullet}5H_2O$ is not dried (as was the KIO_3 in Part A.1). Will this oversight cause the reported molar concentration of the standard $Na_2S_2O_3$ solution to be too high, too low, or unaffected? Explain.
4. Part B.3. Deionized water from a wash bottle was added to wash down the wall of the receiving flask during the titration. How does this affect the reported molar concentration of the sodium thiosulfate solution—too high, too low, or unaffected? Explain.
5. Part C.2. The bleach is diluted but beyond the 100-mL mark in the volumetric flask. Will the percent available chlorine calculated after the analysis in Part E be reported as being too high or too low? Explain.
6. Part E.2. The endpoint of the titration is surpassed. How will this technique error affect the reported percent available chlorine in the bleach sample—too high or too low? Explain.
7. A shower stall is laden with mildew and has accumulated lime deposits from the use of hard water. If a one-step cleaning operation is used—that is, a mixture of liquid bleach and tub and tile cleaner (which is usually acidic in order to react with the lime deposits) is used—a potentially lethal gas is generated. Explain how this occurs (refer to equation 29.2).

Ken Karp

Experiment 30

Vitamin C Analysis

Ken Karp

Vitamin C is available in tablets or from natural sources such as citrus fruits.

OBJECTIVE

- To determine the amount of vitamin C in a vitamin tablet, a fresh fruit, or a fresh vegetable sample

TECHNIQUES

The following techniques are used in the Experimental Procedure:

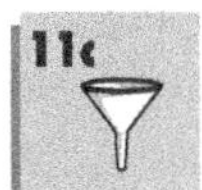

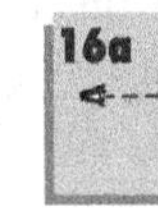

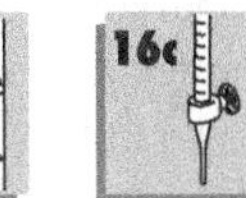

PRINCIPLES

The human body does not synthesize vitamins, so the vitamins we need for catalyzing specific biochemical reactions are gained only from the food we eat. Vitamin C can be obtained from a variety of fresh fruits (most notably, citrus fruits) and vegetables.

Vitamin C plays a vital role for the proper growth and development of teeth, bones, gums, cartilage, skin, and blood vessels. It is an important antioxidant (reducing agent) that helps protect against cancers, heart disease, and stress. Vitamin C is also critical in enabling the body to absorb iron and folic acid.

The recommended daily allowance (RDA) of vitamin C for an adult is 75–90 mg, however levels as high as 200 mg are proven to be beneficial. Table 30.1 lists the concentration ranges of vitamin C for various fruits and vegetables (Figure 30.1).

Vitamin C, also called **ascorbic acid**, is one of the more abundant and easily obtained vitamins in nature. It is a colorless, water-soluble acid that, in addition to its acidic properties, is a powerful biochemical reducing agent, meaning it readily undergoes oxidation, even by the oxygen of the air.

Even though ascorbic acid is an acid, its *reducing* properties are used in this experiment to analyze its concentration in various samples. There are many other acids present in foods (e.g., citric acid) that could interfere with an acid analysis of

© Michael Siluk/The Image Works

Figure 30.1 Vegetables are a good supply of vitamin C

Table 30.1 Vitamin C in Foods

<10 mg/100 g	Beets, carrots, eggs, milk
10–25 mg/100 g	Asparagus, cranberries, cucumbers, green peas, lettuce, pineapple
25–100 mg/100 g	Brussels sprouts, citrus fruits, tomatoes, spinach
100–350 mg/100 g	Chili peppers, sweet peppers, turnip, greens, kiwi

ascorbic acid and not permit a selective determination of the ascorbic acid content. The equation for the oxidation of ascorbic acid is

$$\text{ascorbic acid} + H_2O \rightarrow \text{dehydroascorbic acid (hydrated)} + 2\,H^+ + 2\,e^- \qquad (30.1)$$

or $C_6H_8O_6(aq) + H_2O(l) \rightarrow C_6H_8O_7(aq) + 2\,H^+(aq) + 2\,e^-$.

Analysis of Vitamin C

A sample containing ascorbic acid is prepared as the analyte, dissolved in an acidic solution to which is added solid KI. The titrant is a standard potassium iodate, KIO_3, solution.

The analysis of Vitamin C in a sample is completed in three steps:

1. As the KIO_3 solution is added to the analyte, the iodide ion, I^-, is oxidized to the water-soluble triiodide complex, I_3^- (or $[I_2 \bullet I]^-$):

$$IO_3^-(aq) + 8\,I^-(aq) + 6\,H^+(aq) \longrightarrow 3\,I_3^-(aq) + 3\,H_2O(l) \qquad (30.2)$$

2. Ascorbic acid, $C_6H_8O_6$, being a reducing agent, immediately reduces the triiodide ion, I_3^-, as it forms the colorless iodide ion, I^-, according to equation 30.3:

$$C_6H_8O_6(aq) + I_3^-(aq) + H_2O(l) \longrightarrow C_6H_8O_7(aq) + 3\,I^-(aq) + 2\,H^+(aq) \qquad (30.3)$$

3. Finally, when the ascorbic acid in the analyte is consumed (at the stoichiometric point) by the I_3^-, the KIO_3 titrant generates an excess of I_3^- (again according to equation 30.2) producing the yellow-brown color of I_3^- in solution.

The sudden appearance of the excess I_3^- is enhanced by the presence of an added starch solution to the analyte. Starch forms a deep-blue $I_3^- \bullet$starch complex that is easier to view than the yellow-brown color of I_3^-:

$$I_3^-(aq,\ \text{yellow-brown}) + \text{starch}(aq) \text{ — } I_3^- \cdot \text{starch}(aq,\ \text{deep blue}) \qquad (30.4)$$

To summarize, (1) IO_3^-, the titrant, generates I_3^- (equation 30.2) in the analyte; (2) $C_6H_8O_6$ immediately reacts with the I_3^- (equation 30.3) until it is depleted from the analyte; and (3) the excess I_3^- forms a deep-blue complex to signal the depletion of the ascorbic acid in the sample (equation 30.4).

Therefore, to calculate the mass of vitamin C in a sample using, equations 30.2 and 30.3, gives,

$$\text{mass } (mg)\, C_6H_8O_6 = \text{volume } (L)\, KIO_3 \times \frac{\text{mol } KIO_3}{\text{L } KIO_3} \times \frac{3 \text{ mol } I_3^-}{\text{mol } KIO_3} \times \frac{1 \text{ mol } C_6H_8O_6}{1 \text{ mol } I_3^-}$$

$$\times \frac{176.1 \text{ g } C_6H_8O_6}{\text{mol } C_6H_8O_6} \times \frac{\text{mg } C_6H_8O_6}{10^{-3} \text{ g } C_6H_8O_6} \qquad (30.5)$$

Standard Solution of Potassium Iodate, KIO_3

Primary standard: a substance that has a known high degree of purity, a relatively large molar mass, is nonhygroscopic, and reacts in a predictable way

Potassium iodate, KIO_3, is a **primary standard** (Figure 30.2). A dried, accurately measured mass of previously dried KIO_3 is diluted to volume in a volumetric flask. This solution becomes the standard solution (as the titrant) for the analysis of ascorbic acid in a sample.

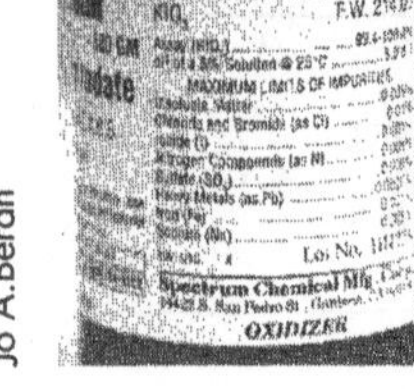

Jo A.Beran

Figure 30.2 Potassium iodate has the necessary properties of a primary standard

EXPERIMENTAL PROCEDURE

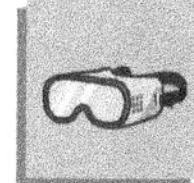

A standard solution of potassium iodate is prepared from solid KIO_3, a primary standard. The standard KIO_3 solution in conjunction with KI is used to analyze an ascorbic acid sample. Excess I_3^- generated at the stoichiometric point is detected using starch as an indicator.

In Part B, which source of Vitamin C are you to analyze? Consult with your instructor. Quantitative, reproducible data are objectives of this experiment; practice good laboratory techniques. Nearly 300 mL of boiled and cooled deionized water is required for this experiment. Begin preparing this at the beginning of the laboratory period.

Be aware of the number of significant figures when recording data.

A. Preparation of the KIO_3 Primary Standard

Data Analysis, A

1. **Prepare the primary standard solution.** (Check with your instructor—this solution may have already been prepared by stockroom personnel.) Use weighing paper to measure the mass (±0.001 g) of KIO_3 (previously dried[1] at 110°C) that is required to prepare 250 mL of 0.01 *M* KIO_3. See ***Prelaboratory Assignment*** question 2 and show *this calculation on the **Report Sheet**.* Dissolve the solid KIO_3 and dilute to volume with the freshly boiled, deionized water in a 250-mL volumetric flask. Calculate and record its *exact* molar concentration.
2. **Prepare the buret for the ascorbic acid analysis.** Prepare a *clean* 50-mL buret for the standard KIO_3 solution. Add 2–3 mL of the KIO_3 solution to the buret, wet the wall of the buret, and drain through the buret tip. Repeat once. Fill the buret and eliminate all air bubbles in the buret tip. After 10–15 seconds, read and record the volume of titrant.

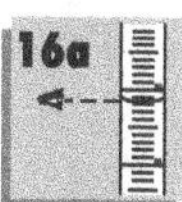

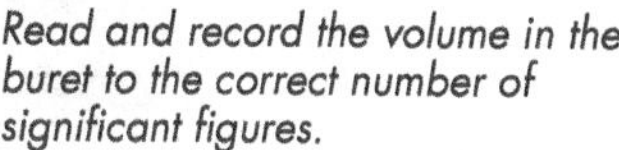
Read and record the volume in the buret to the correct number of significant figures.

B. Sample Preparation

Data Analysis, A

1. **Vitamin C tablet.**
   a. Read the label on the bottle to determine the approximate mass of vitamin C in each tablet. Measure (±0.001 g) the fraction of the total mass of a tablet that corresponds to ~100 mg of ascorbic acid.
   b. Dissolve the sample[2] in a 250-mL Erlenmeyer flask with ~40 mL of 0.5 *M* H_2SO_4 and then ~0.5 g $NaHCO_3$.[3] *Proceed immediately to Part C.*
   c. Kool-Aid, Tang, or Gatorade may be substituted as dry samples, even though their ascorbic acid concentrations are much lower. Fresh Fruit has a very high concentration of ascorbic acid.
   d. Repeat the sample preparation for Trials 2 and 3.
2. **Fresh fruit sample.**
   a. Filter 125–130 mL of freshly squeezed juice through several layers of cheesecloth (or vacuum filter).
   b. Measure the mass (±0.01 g) of a clean, dry 250-mL Erlenmeyer flask.
   c. Add about 100 mL of filtered juice and again determine the mass. Add ~40 mL of 0.5 *M* H_2SO_4 and ~0.5 g $NaHCO_3$. Concentrated fruit juices may also be used as samples. *Proceed immediately to Part C.*
   d. Repeat the sample preparation for Trials 2 and 3.

3. **Fresh vegetable sample.**
   a. Measure about 100 g (±0.01 g) of a fresh vegetable. Transfer the sample to a mortar[4] (Figure 30.3, page 344) and grind.

---

[1]The KIO_3 should have been previously dried.

[2]Remember that vitamin tablets contain binders and other material that may be insoluble in water—*do not heat* in an attempt to dissolve the tablet!

[3]The $NaHCO_3$ reacts in the acidic solution to produce $CO_2(g)$, providing an inert atmosphere above the analyte solution, minimizing the possibility of the air oxidation of the ascorbic acid.

[4]A blender may be substituted for the mortar and pestle.

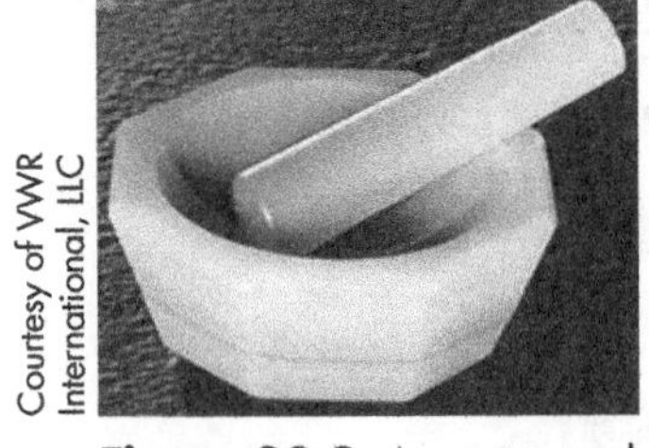
Courtesy of VWR International, LLC

Figure 30.3 A mortar and pestle is used to grind the sample

b. Add ~5 mL of 0.5 *M* H_2SO_4 and continue to pulverize the sample. Add another ~15 mL of 0.5 *M* H_2SO_4, stir, and filter through several layers of cheesecloth (or vacuum filter). Add ~20 mL of 0.5 *M* H_2SO_4 to the mortar, stir, and pour through the same filter.

c. Repeat the washing of the mortar with ~20 mL of the freshly boiled, deionized water. Combine all of the washings in a 250-mL Erlenmeyer flask and add ~0.5 g $NaHCO_3$. *Proceed immediately to Part C.*

d. Repeat the sample preparation for Trials 2 and 3.

C. Vitamin C Analysis

1. **Prepare the vitamin C sample for analysis.** To the sample from Part B add ~1 g of KI and ~2 mL of the starch solution.

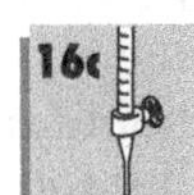

2. **Immediately titrate the sample.** While swirling the flask, *slowly* dispense the standard KIO_3 solution—you will note that the deep-blue color appears but then disappears near the endpoint. Continue swirling the flask while adding the KIO_3 titrant until the deep-blue color persists for at least 20 seconds. Read and record the final volume in the buret to the correct number of significant figures.

3. **Repeat the analysis.** Repeat the sample preparation (Part B) and the analysis twice in order to complete the three trials. Repeated analyses of the ascorbic acid content of the sample should be ±1%.

> *Disposal:* Dispose of the remaining KIO_3 solution in the Waste Oxidants container. Dispose of the excess $Na_2S_2O_3$ solution in the Waste Reducing Agent container.

CLEANUP: Flush the buret twice with tap water and twice with deionized water. Repeat the cleaning operation with the pipets. Discard all washings as advised by your instructor. Clean up the balance area, discarding any solids in the Waste Solids container.

The Next Step

Vitamin C is present in many foods (Table 30.1) at various concentrations and in vitamin supplements. What are those concentrations? What effects do weather conditions, soils, geographic regions, and seasonal variations have on vitamin C levels in fruits and vegetables? Is the concentration in vitamin supplements what the manufacturer claims? What other experimental procedures are used for vitamin C analysis? Design a study to further investigate vitamin C levels.

NOTES AND CALCULATIONS

Experiment 30 *Prelaboratory Assignment*

Vitamin C Analysis

Date __________ Lab Sec. ______ Name ______________________________________ Desk No. __________

1. Vitamin C is a reducing agent and antioxidant. What ion does it reduce in this experiment? Explain.

2. Experimental Procedure, Part A.1. Determine the mass of solid KIO_3 required for the preparation of 250 mL of a 0.01 *M* KIO_3 solution. Repeat and record this calculatoin on the ***Report Sheet***.

3. Experimental Procedure, Part B.1. What is the purpose of adding $NaHCO_3$ to the reaction mixture? Explain. Write a balanced equation for its reaction.

4. **a.** Experimental Procedure, Part C. What is the oxidizing agent in the titration?

   b. What is the color change of the starch indicator that signals the stoichiometric point in Part C?

5. **a.** Eight ounces (1 fl. oz = 29.57 mL) of orange juice contains 160% of the recommended daily allowance of vitamin C (RDA = 75–90 mg for adults). How many milliliters of the orange juice will provide 100% of the recommended daily allowance?

   b. Assuming 80 mg of vitamin C present in 29.57 mL of the orange juice, how many milliliters of 0.0102 *M* KIO_3 would be required to reach the stoichiometric point?

6. **a.** An analysis of a fresh fruit sample for vitamin C provided the data in the following table. Complete the analysis for Trial 1 (See ***Report Sheet***.) of the fresh fruit sample. Record the calculated values with the correct number of significant figures.

			Calculation Zone
A. Preparation of the KIO_3 Primary Standard			
3. Molar concentration of KIO_3 solution *(mol/L)*	0.0111	*Part C.4*	
B. Sample Preparation			
2. Mass of sample (g)	64.11	*Part C.5*	
C. Vitamin C Analysis			
1. Buret reading, initial *(mL)*	5.85		
2. Buret reading, final *(mL)*	14.80	*Part C.6*	
3. Volume of KIO_3 added *(mL)*			
4. Moles of IO_3^- dispensed *(mol)* Show calculation.			
5. Moles of I_3^- produced *(mol)* Equation 30.2. Show calculation.		*Part C.7*	
6. Moles of $C_6H_8O_6$ in sample *(mol)* Equation 30.3. Show calculation.		*Part C.8*	
7. Mass of $C_6H_8O_6$ in sample *(g)* Show calculation.			
8. Mass ratio *(mg $C_6H_8O_6$/100 g sample)* Show calculation.			

6.b. For Trials 2 and 3, the number of milligrams of ascorbic acid per 100 g of citrus juice was 79.8 mg $C_6H_8O_6$/100 g sample and 78.6 mg $C_6H_8O_6$/100 g sample respectively.

a. What is the average mg $C_6H_8O_6$/100 g sample?

b. What are the standard deviation and the relative standard deviation (%RSD) of mg $C_6H_8O_6$/100 g sample?

Experiment 30 *Report Sheet*

Vitamin C Analysis

Date __________ Lab Sec. ______ Name ____ Desk No. _________

A. Preparation of the KIO_3 Primary Standard

Calculate the mass of KIO_3 (molar mass = 214.02 g/mol) required for Part A.1. See ***Prelaboratory Assignment***, question 2.

1. Mass of weighing paper (*g*)	
2. Mass of weighing paper plane KIO_3 (*g*)	
3. Mass of KIO_3 (*g*)	
4. Moles of KIO_3 (*mol*)	
5. Molar concentration of KIO_3 solution (*mol/L*)	

B. Sample Preparation

Sample name: ________________	***Trial 1***	***Trial 2***	***Trial 3***
1. Vitamin C tablet			
Mass of tablet (*g*) ________________			
Mass of sample analyzed (*g*)			
2. Fresh fruit sample			
Mass of flask (*g*)			
Mass of flask plus sample (*g*)			
Mass of sample (*g*)			
3. Fresh vegetable sample			
Mass of sample (*g*)			

C. Vitamin C Analysis

	Trial 1	***Trial 2***	***Trial 3***
1. Buret reading, *initial* (*mL*)			
2. Buret reading, *final* (*mL*)			
3. Volume of KIO_3 added (*mL*)			
4. Moles of IO_3^- dispensed (*mol*)			

5. Moles of I_3^- produced (*mol*) ______ ______ ______

6. Moles of $C_6H_8O_6$ in sample (*mol*) ______ ______ ______

7. Mass of $C_6H_8O_6$ in sample (*g*) ______* ______ ______

8. Mass ratio (*mg* $C_6H_8O_6$*/100* g *sample)* ______ ______ ______

9. Average mass ratio of $C_6H_8O_6$ in sample (*mg/100 g*). See Table 30.1. ______ ***Data Analysis, B***

10. Standard deviation of mass ratio ______ ***Data Analysis, C***

11. Relative standard deviation of mass ratio ______ ***Data Analysis, D***

*Show calculations for Trial 1.

Laboratory Questions

Circle the questions that have been assigned.

1. Part A.1. The KIO_3 sample was not sufficiently dried. Will the reported molar concentration of the KIO_3 solution (Part B.3) be too high, too low, or unaffected? Explain.
2. Part A.1. The mass of KIO_3 used to prepare the solution was measured to be 0.585 g instead of the calculated 0.535 g.
   a. Will the molar concentration of the KIO_3 solution be greater or less than 0.01 *M* KIO_3? Explain.
   b. As a result of this (now) prepared KIO_3 solution, will more or less volume of KIO_3 solution be used for the vitamin C analysis? Explain.
3. Part B.1. The $NaHCO_3$ solution is omitted in an analysis of the sample. Will the reported amount of ascorbic acid in the sample be too high, too low, or unaffected? Explain.
4. Part C.1. Explain why the mass of KI (~1 g), and the volume of starch (~2 mL) are only approximate even though the analysis is quantitative.
5. Part C.2. After adding the standard solution of KIO_3 to the prepared analyte, the sample solution *never* forms the deep-blue color. What modification of the Experimental Procedure or error corrected can be made in order to complete the analysis?
6. Part C.2. The deep-blue color of the I_3^-•starch complex does not appear but a yellow-brown does appear! What next? Should you continue titrating with the standard KIO_3 solution or discard the sample? Explain.
7. Part C.2. The final buret reading is read and recorded as 27.43 mL instead of the correct 28.43 mL. Will the reported amount of ascorbic acid in the sample be too high or too low? Explain.

Jo A. Beran

Experiment 31

Dissolved Oxygen Levels in Natural Waters

The dissolved oxygen levels in natural waters are dependent on temperature and water flow.

OBJECTIVES

- To develop a proper technique for obtaining a natural water sample
- To determine the dissolved oxygen concentration of a natural water sample
- To learn the chemical reactions involved in fixing and analyzing a water sample for dissolved oxygen using the Winkler method

TECHNIQUES

The following techniques are used in the Experimental Procedure:

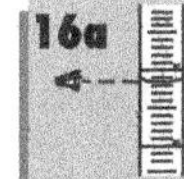

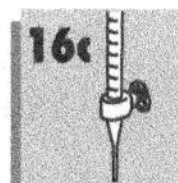

INTRODUCTION

Streams, rivers, lakes, and oceans play vital roles in our quality of life. They not only are a source of food supplies with the likes of shrimp and salmon but also provide recreational opportunities in the forms of boating and swimming. Additionally, the larger bodies of water such as lakes and oceans affect seasonal weather patterns, producing changes in rainfall and snowfall and generating conditions for hurricanes and typhoons.

The aesthetic appearance of smaller bodies of water such as rivers and lakes indicates an immediate perception of the quality of the water. Color, surface growth, and odor are early indicators of the quality of the water and the nature of its marine life. As the public water supplies of most larger cities rely on the presence of surface water, water chemists must be keenly aware of the makeup of that water. "How must the water be treated to provide safe and clean water to the consumers?"

A number of water-quality parameters are of primary interest in analyzing a "natural" water sample: pH, dissolved oxygen, alkalinity, and hardness are but a few. A quick test, pH, is generally determined with a previously calibrated pH meter; dissolved oxygen concentrations can be completed with a dissolved oxygen meter (Figure 31.1) although its availability is less likely than that of a pH meter. Alkalinity and hardness levels are determined using the titrimetric technique (see *Experiments 20* and *21*).

The concentration of dissolved oxygen in a water sample is an important indicator of water quality. Waters with high oxygen concentrations indicate aerobic conditions: clean, clear, and unpolluted. Low oxygen concentrations indicate anaerobic conditions: high turbidity, foul odors, extensive plant growth on the surface. Dissolved oxygen levels that drop to less than 5 ppm can stress the existing aquatic life.

The solubilities of oxygen in fresh water (saturated solution) at various temperatures are listed in Table 31.1.

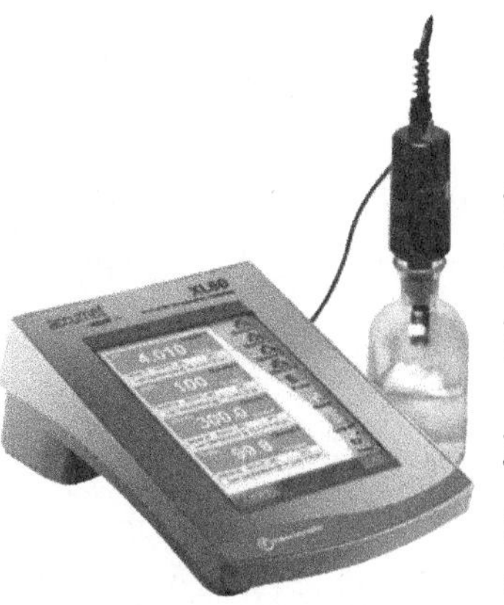

Courtesy of Thermo Fisher Scientific

Figure 31.1 Dissolved oxygen meters can be used for determining $O_2(aq)$ levels in water samples

Table 31.1 Solubility of Oxygen in Freshwater at Various Temperatures

Temperature (°C)	ppm O_2	Temperature (°C)	ppm O_2
0	14.6	24	8.5
5	12.8	27	8.1
10	11.3	30	7.6
15	10.2	35	7.1
18	9.5	40	6.5
21	9.0	45	6.0

Winkler Method of Analysis

The Winkler method of analysis for dissolved oxygen, developed by Lajos Winkler in 1888, is the standard experimental procedure for determining the dissolved oxygen concentration in water and for the calibration of dissolved oxygen meters.

The Winker test is performed in two parts: (1) the water sample is gathered in the field, where the dissolved oxygen is "fixed" with two reagents, and (2) the sample is titrated for final analysis in the laboratory within a 48-hour period.

Field Sampling. The natural water sample is carefully collected on-site such that no air bubbles remain trapped in the flask after collection. The oxygen is fixed by an immediate oxidation of manganese(II) sulfate to manganese (III) hydroxide in a basic solution:

$$O_2(aq) + 4\,MnSO_4(aq) + 8\,NaOH(aq) + 2\,H_2O(l) \longrightarrow 4\,Mn(OH)_3(s) + 4\,Na_2SO_4(aq) \quad (31.1)$$

The oxygen is fixed as the manganese(III) hydroxide,[1] an orange-brown color precipitate—the more precipitate, the greater is the dissolved oxygen concentration.

While on-site, a basic solution of KI-NaN_3 is also added to the sample.[2] The manganese(III) hydroxide oxidizes the iodide ion to the triiodide ion, I_3^-, while the manganese(III) reduces to the manganese(II) ion:

$$2\,Mn(OH)_3(s) + 3\,I^-(aq) + 6\,H^+(aq) \longrightarrow I_3^-(aq) + 6\,H_2O(l) + 2\,Mn^{2+}(aq) \quad (31.2)$$

The resulting solution now has a slight yellow-brown color due to the presence of I_3^- ($[I_2{\bullet}I]^-$).

Laboratory Analysis. The remainder of the dissolved oxygen analysis is completed in the laboratory (but within 48 hours). The sample is acidified with sulfuric acid to dissolve any precipitate. A titration of the sample with a standardized sodium thiosulfate solution in the presence of a starch indicator determines the amount of I_3^- generated in the reactions conducted on-site and provides a direct determination of the dissolved oxygen concentration in the water sample:

$$I_3^-(aq) + 2\,S_2O_3^{2-}(aq) \longrightarrow 3\,I^-(aq) + S_4O_6^{2-}(aq) \quad (31.3)$$

The starch indicator forms a deep-blue complex with I_3^- but is colorless in the presence of I^-:

$$I_3^-{\bullet}\text{starch (deep blue)} \rightarrow 3\,I^- + \text{starch (colorless)} \quad (31.4)$$

From equations 31.1–31.3, 1 mole O_2 reacts to produce 4 moles of $Mn(OH)_3$, of which 2 moles of $Mn(OH)_3$ react to produce 1 mole of I_3^-. The I_3^-, which is the result of the fixing of the dissolved oxygen, reacts with 2 moles of $S_2O_3^{2-}$ in the titration.

$$\text{mol } O_2 = \text{volume } (L)\ S_2O_3^{2-} \times \frac{\text{mol } S_2O_3^{2-}}{\text{L } S_2O_3^{2-}} \times \frac{1 \text{ mol } I_3^-}{2 \text{ mol } S_2O_3^{2-}} \times \frac{2 \text{ mol Mn } (OH)_2}{1 \text{ mol } I_3^-} \times \frac{1 \text{ mol } O_2}{4 \text{ mol } Mn(OH)_3} \quad (31.5)$$

[1]There is uncertainty among chemists as to the oxidation number of manganese in the precipitate—$MnO(OH)_2$, the hydrated form of MnO_2, often represents the form of the precipitate.
[2]Sodium azide, NaN_3, is added to eliminate interference in the dissolved oxygen analysis caused by the presence of nitrite ion, NO_2^-, common in wastewater samples.

From the data collected and analyzed, the moles of O_2 converted to milligrams divided by the volume of the water sample (in liters) that is titrated results in the dissolved oxygen concentration expressed in mg/L or ppm (parts per million) O_2:

$$\frac{\text{mg } O_2}{\text{L sample}} = \text{ppm } O_2 \tag{31.6}$$

Standard Solution of Sodium Thiosulfate

A sodium thiosulfate solution is standardized for the experiment with potassium iodate, KIO_3, a primary standard. In the presence of iodide ion, KIO_3 generates a quantified concentration of triiodide ion, I_3^-.

See *Experiment 29* for further explanation and Experimental Procedure.

$$IO_3^-(aq) + 8\ I^-(aq) + 6\ H^+(aq) \longrightarrow 3\ I_3^-(aq) + 3\ H_2O(l) \tag{31.7}$$

This solution is then titrated to the starch endpoint with the prepared sodium thiosulfate solution.

$$I_3^-(aq) + 2\ S_2O_3^{2-}(aq) \longrightarrow 3\ I^-(aq) + S_4O_6^{2-}(aq) \tag{31.8}$$

For the analysis of the dissolved oxygen concentration in a water sample, the standard $Na_2S_2O_3$ solution should have a molar concentration of 0.025 *M* or less.

Experimental Procedure

Procedure Overview. Three water samples are collected from a source that is selected either by the student chemist or the instructor. The samples are immediately "fixed" with the addition of a basic solution of manganese(II) sulfate and a basic solution of KI-NaN_3. The samples are stored in the dark on ice and analyzed in the laboratory within *ideally* 6 hours of sampling. The dissolved oxygen concentrations are reported in units of parts per million (ppm) O_2.

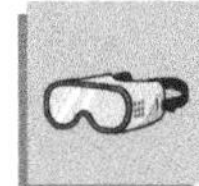

Ask your instructor if a standard solution of $Na_2S_2O_3$ is available. If so, proceed to Part B of the Experimental Procedure.

Be aware of the number of significant figures when recording data.

A. A Standard 0.025 *M* $Na_2S_2O_3$ Solution

Create and design your own ***Report Sheet*** for this part of the experiment.

1. **Preparation and standardization of 0.1 *M* $Na_2S_2O_3$ solution.** Refer to *Experiment 29*, Parts A and B of the Experimental Procedure for the preparation and standardization of a 0.1 *M* $Na_2S_2O_3$ solution. Prepare only 100 mL of the $Na_2S_2O_3$ of the solution described in *Experiment 29*, Part B.1 and standardize the solution using KIO_3 as the primary standard solution (Part B.3–4). Calculate the average concentration of the $Na_2S_2O_3$ solution for three trials.
2. **Preparation of a standard 0.025 *M* $Na_2S_2O_3$ solution.** Using a pipet and 100-mL volumetric flask, prepare a 0.025 *M* $Na_2S_2O_3$ solution from the standardized 0.1 *M* $Na_2S_2O_3$. See ***Prelaboratory Assignment***, question 4a.

Disposal: Dispose of the test solutions as directed by your instructor.

B. Collection of Water Sample

1. **Prepare the flask for sampling.** Thoroughly clean and rinse at *least* three 250-mL Erlenmeyer flasks and rubber stoppers to fit. Allow to air dry.
2. **Collect the water sample.** Gently lay the flask along the horizontal surface of the water. See Figure 31.2, page 352. Slowly and gradually turn the flask upright as the flask fills being careful not to allow any air bubbles to form in the flask. Fill the flask to overflowing.
3. **"Fix" the dissolved oxygen.** *Below the surface* of the water sample, pipet ~1 mL of the basic 2.1 *M* $MnSO_4$ solution into the sample (some overflowing will occur). Similarly pipet ~1 mL of the basic KI-NaN_3 solution. A precipitate should form (equation 31.1).

4. **Secure the sample.**
   a. Carefully stopper the sample to ensure that no air bubbles become entrapped beneath the stopper in the water sample. Again, some overflowing will occur.

Figure 31.2 Allow a gentle flow of water into the flask. Slowly turn the flask upright as it fills to overflowing

b. Invert and roll the flask to thoroughly mix the reagents. Once the precipitate settles, repeat the mixing process.

c. Label the sample number for each of the flasks. Store the sample in the dark and, preferably, in a cool or cold location or on ice.

5. **Temperature.** Read and record the temperature of the water at the sample site. Also, write a brief description of the sample site.

6. Analysis should begin within 6 hours of sampling.

C. Sample Analysis

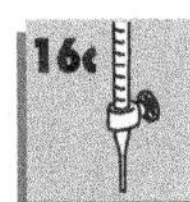

Read and record the buret to the correct number of significant figures.

1. **Prepare the titrant.** Prepare a clean buret. Add 3 to 5 mL of the standard $Na_2S_2O_3$ solution to the buret, roll the solution to wet the wall of the buret, and dispense through the buret tip and discard. Use a clean funnel to fill the buret—dispense a small portion through the buret tip. Read and record the volume of $Na_2S_2O_3$ solution in the buret (*Technique 16A.2*), using all certain digits *plus* one uncertain digit.

   Place a white sheet of paper beneath the receiving flask.

2. **Prepare sample 1**

   a. Remove the stopper from the 250-mL Erlenmeyer flask. To the collected water sample, add ~1 mL of *conc* H_2SO_4 (**Caution**!) and stir or swirl to dissolve any precipitate. The sample can now be handled in open vessels.

Data Analysis, A

   b. Transfer a known, measured but exact volume (~200 mL, ±0.1 mL) to a receiving flask (either a beaker or Erlenmeyer flask) for the titrimetric analysis (Part C.3).

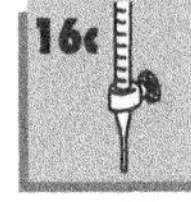

3. **Titrate water sample 1.** Slowly dispense the $Na_2S_2O_3$ titrant into the water sample. Swirl the flask as titrant is added (*Technique 16C.4*). When the color of the analyte fades to a light yellow-brown, add ~1 mL of the starch solution. Continue slowly adding titrant—when one drop (ideally, half-drop) results in the disappearance of the deep-blue color of the I_3^-•starch complex, stop the titration and again (after ~15 seconds) read and record the volume of titrant in the buret.

4. **Additional trials.** Repeat the analysis for the two remaining samples.

Data Analysis, A

5. **Calculations.** Calculate the dissolved oxygen concentration for each sample expressed in ppm O_2 (mg O_2/L sample).

Disposal: Dispose of the test solutions as directed by your instructor.

The Next Step

The biological oxygen demand (BOD) of a water sample is a measure of the organic material in a water sample that is consumable by aerobic bacteria. The $O_2(aq)$ concentration is measured when a sample is taken and then again five days later, that period being the incubation period for the aerobic bacteria to consume a portion of the $O_2(aq)$ to biodegrade the organic material. Research the importance and significance of BOD levels in natural waters and develop an experiment to determine the BOD for a water analysis.

Experiment 31 *Prelaboratory Assignment*

Dissolved Oxygen Levels in Natural Waters

Date __________ Lab Sec. ______ Name ______________________________________ Desk No. __________

1. For a natural water sample, what range of dissolved oxygen concentrations may you expect? Explain your reasoning.

2. How does the dissolved oxygen concentration in a water sample change (if at all) with
   a. ambient temperature changes?

   b. atmospheric pressure changes?

   c. the volume of the flask collecting the water sample?

   d. the amount of organic matter in the water sample?

   e. the depth of the body of water (e.g., lake, river, or ocean)?

3. Experimental Procedure, Part A.1. A 100-mL volume of a primary standard 0.0110 *M* KIO_3 solution is prepared. A 25.0-mL aliquot of this solution is used to standardize a prepared $Na_2S_2O_3$ solution. A 15.6-mL volume of the $Na_2S_2O_3$ solution titrated the KIO_3 solution to the starch endpoint. What is the molar concentration of the $Na_2S_2O_3$ solution?

$$IO_3^-(aq) + 8\,I^-(aq) + 6\,H^+(aq) \longrightarrow 3\,I_3^-(aq) + 3\,H_2O(l)$$

$$I_3^-(aq) + 2\,S_2O_3^{2-}(aq) \longrightarrow 3\,I^-(aq) + S_4O_6^{2-}(aq)$$

4. Experimental Procedure, Part A.2. What is the procedure for preparing 250 mL of 0.0210 M $Na_2S_2O_3$ for this experiment from a 100-mL volume of standard 0.106 M $Na_2S_2O_3$?

5. a. An analysis of a water sample for dissolved oxygen levels provided the data in the following table. Complete the analysis for Trial 1 (See ***Report Sheet.***) of the water sample. Record the calculated values with the correct number of significant figures.

B. Standard 0.025 *M* $Na_2S_2O_3$ Solution — ***Calculation Zone***

1. Sample volume (*mL*)	200.0	*Part B.6*
2. Buret reading, *initial* (*mL*)	3.85	
3. Buret reading, *final* (*mL*)	18.25	
4. Volume of $Na_2S_2O_3$ dispensed (*mL*)		*Part B.7*
5. Average molar concentration of $Na_2S_2O_3$ (*mol/L*)	0.0213	
6. Moles of $Na_2S_2O_3$ dispensed (*mol*) Show calculation.		*Part B.8*
7. Moles of I_3^- reduced by $S_2O_3^{2-}$ (*mol*), Equation 31.3. Show calculation.		*Part B.9*
8. Moles of O_2 (*mol*) Equations 31.2 and 31.1. Show calculation.		*Part B.10*
9. Mass of O_2 (*mg*) Show calculation.		
10. Dissolved oxygen, ppm O_2 (*mg/L*) Show calculation.		

5.b. For Trials 2 and 3, the dissolved oxygen levels were 10.9 ppm and 11.1 ppm respectively.

a. What is the average dissolved oxygen level in the water sample?

b. What are the standard deviation and the relative standard deviation (%RSD) of the dissolved oxygen level in the water sample?

Experiment 31 *Report Sheet*

Dissolved Oxygen Levels in Natural Waters

Date _________ Lab Sec. _____ Name ____________________________________ Desk No. _________

A. A Standard 0.025 *M* $Na_2S_2O_3$ Solution

Prepare a self-designed ***Report Sheet*** for this part of the experiment. Review the ***Report Sheet*** of *Experiment 29* for guidance. Submit this with the completed ***Report Sheet***.

B. Collection of Water Sample

Sampling site: Temperature: __________°C

Characterize/describe the sampling site.

C. Sample Analysis	***Sample 1***	***Sample 2***	***Sample 3***
1. Sample volume (*mL*)			
2. Buret reading, *initial* (*mL*)			
3. Buret reading, *final* (*mL*)			
4. Volume $Na_2S_2O_3$ dispensed (*mL*)			
5. Molar concentration of $Na_2S_2O_3$ (*mol/L*), Part A			
6. Moles of $Na_2S_2O_3$ dispensed (*mol*)			
7. Moles of I_3^- reduced by $S_2O_3^{2-}$ (*mol*)			
8. Moles of O_2 (*mol*)			
9. Mass of O_2 (*mg*)			
10. Dissolved oxygen, ppm O_2 (*mg/L*)			
11. Average dissolved oxygen, ppm O_2			***Data Analysis, B***
12. Standard deviation			***Data Analysis, C***
13. Relative standard deviation (*%RSD*)			***Data Analysis, D***

Write a short summary based on an interpretation of your analytical data.

Laboratory Questions

Circle the questions that have been assigned.

1. Part B. The water chemist waits until returning to the laboratory to fix the water sample for the dissolved oxygen analysis. Will the reported dissolved oxygen concentration be reported as too high, too low, or remain unchanged? Explain.
2. Part B.3. A solution of $MnSO_4$ is added to fix the dissolved oxygen in the collected sample.
   a. What is the meaning of the expression, "fix the dissolved oxygen," and why is it so important for the analysis of dissolved oxygen in a water sample?
   b. Only an approximate volume (~1 mL) of $MnSO_4$ is required for fixing the dissolved oxygen in the sample. Explain why an exact volume is not critical.
3. Part B.4. No precipitate forms! Assuming the reagents were properly prepared and dispensed into the sample, what might be predicted about its dissolved oxygen concentration? Explain.
4. Part B.5. A water chemist measured and recorded the air temperature at 27°C when he should have measured the water temperature, which was only 21°C. As a result of this error, will the dissolved oxygen concentration be reported as being higher or lower than it should be? Explain.
5. Part C.3. The color of the analyte did not fade to form the light yellow-brown color but remained intense even after the addition of a full buret of the $S_2O_3^{2-}$ titrant, even though a precipitate formed in Part B.4. What can be stated about the dissolved oxygen concentration of the sample? Explain.
6. Assuming a dissolved oxygen concentration of 7.0 ppm (*mg/L*) in a 200-mL water sample,
   a. how many moles of $Mn(OH)_3$ will be produced with the addition of the $MnSO_4$ solution?
   b. how many moles of I_3^- will be produced when the KI-NaN_3 solution is added to the above solution?
   c. how many moles of $S_2O_3^{2-}$ will be needed to react with the I_3^- that is generated?
   d. and also assuming the concentration of the $S_2O_3^{2-}$ titrant to be 0.025 *M*, how many milliliters of titrant will be predictably used for the analysis.
7. A nonscientist brings a water sample to your laboratory and asks you to determine why there was a fish kill in the nearby lake. Having recently finished this experiment, what might you tell that person about the legitimacy of a test for dissolved oxygen? What reasoning would you use to maintain the integrity of your laboratory?
8. **a.** Fish kills are often found near the discharge point of water from cooling waters at electrical generating power plants. Explain why this occurrence may occur.
   b. Fish kills are often found in streams following heavy rainfall in a watershed dominated by farmland or denuded forestland. Explain why this occurrence may occur.
9. Explain how the dissolved oxygen concentrations may change starting at the headwaters of a river and ending at the ocean. Account for the changes.

***10.** Salt (ocean) water generally has a lower dissolved oxygen concentration than freshwater at a given temperature. Explain why this is generally observed.

Experiment 32

Galvanic Cells, the Nernst Equation

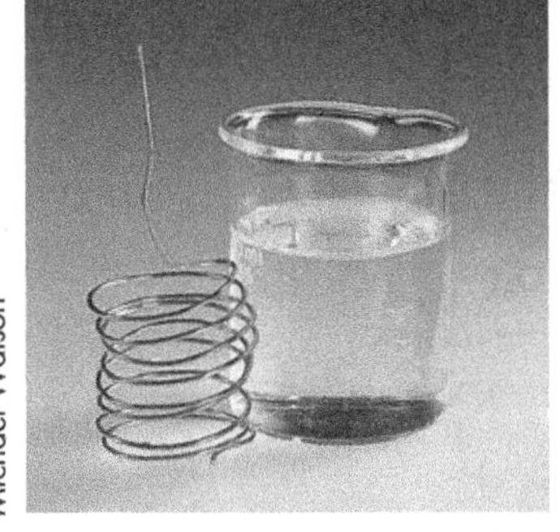

Michael Watson

Copper metal spontaneously oxidizes to copper(II) ion in a solution containing silver ion. Silver metal crystals form on the surface of the copper metal.

OBJECTIVES

- To measure the relative reduction potentials for a number of redox couples
- To develop an understanding of the movement of electrons, anions, and cations in a galvanic cell
- To study factors affecting cell potentials
- To estimate the concentration of ions in solution using the Nernst equation

TECHNIQUES

The following techniques are used in the Experimental Procedure:

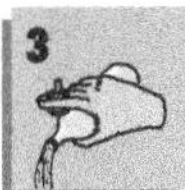

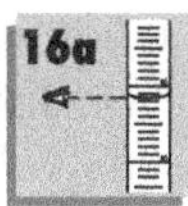

INTRODUCTION

Electrochemical cells are of two types, galvanic and electrolytic, both employing the principle of oxidation–reduction (redox) reactions. In galvanic (or voltaic) cells (this experiment), redox reactions occur spontaneously as is common with all portable batteries of which we are very familiar. Electric cars, flashlights, watches, and power tools operate because of a specific spontaneous redox reaction. Electrolytic cells (*Experiment 33*) are driven by nonspontaneous redox reactions, reactions that require energy to occur. The recharging of batteries, electroplating and refining of metals, and generation of various gases all require the use of energy to cause the redox reaction to proceed.

Experimentally, when copper wire is placed into a silver ion solution (see opening photo), copper atoms *spontaneously* donate electrons (copper atoms are oxidized) to the silver ions (which are reduced). Silver ions migrate to the copper atoms to pick up electrons and form silver atoms at the copper metal–solution **interface;** the copper ions that form then move into the solution away from the interface. The overall reaction that occurs at the interface is:

Interface: the boundary between two phases; in this case, the boundary that separates the solid metal from the aqueous solution

$$Cu(s) + 2\,Ag^{+}(aq) \longrightarrow 2\,Ag(s) + Cu^{2+}(aq) \qquad (32.1)$$

This redox reaction can be divided into an oxidation and a reduction half-reaction. Each half-reaction, called a **redox couple,** consists of the reduced state and the oxidized state of the substance:

Redox couple: an oxidized and reduced form of an ion/substance appearing in a reduction or oxidation half-reaction, generally associated with galvanic cells

$$Cu(s) \longrightarrow Cu^{2+}(aq) + 2\,e^{-} \quad \text{oxidation half-reaction (redox couple)} \qquad (32.2)$$

$$2\,Ag^{+}(aq) + 2\,e^{-} \longrightarrow 2\,Ag(s) \quad \text{reduction half-reaction (redox couple)} \qquad (32.3)$$

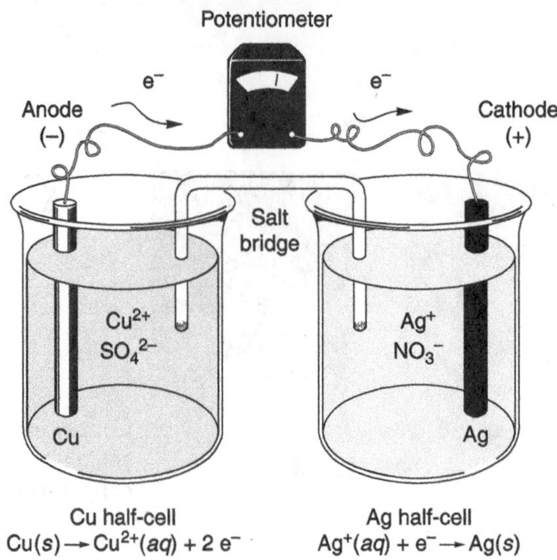

Figure 32.1 Schematic diagram of a galvanic cell

A **galvanic cell** is designed to take advantage of this *spontaneous transfer of electrons.* Instead of electrons being transferred at the interface of the copper metal and the silver ions in solution, a galvanic cell separates the copper metal from the silver ions to force the electrons to pass externally through a wire, an external circuit, for the reduction of the silver ions. Figure 32.1 is a schematic diagram of a galvanic cell setup for these two redox couples.

Half-cell: a part of the galvanic cell that hosts a redox couple

The two redox couples are placed in separate compartments called **half-cells.** Each half-cell consists of an electrode, usually the metal (reduced state) of the redox couple, and a solution containing the corresponding cation (oxidized state) of the redox couple. The electrodes of the half-cells are connected by a wire through which the electrons flow, providing current for the **external circuit.**

External circuit: the movement of charge as electrons through a wire connecting the two half-cells, forming one-half of the electrical circuit in a galvanic cell

Salt bridge: paper moistened with a salt solution, or an inverted tube containing a salt solution, that bridges two half-cells to complete the solution part of an electrical circuit

Internal circuit: the movement of charge as ions through solution from one half-cell to the other, forming one-half of the electrical circuit in a galvanic cell

A **salt bridge** that connects the two half-cells completes the construction of the galvanic cell (and the circuit). The salt bridge permits limited movement of ions from one half-cell to the other, the **internal circuit,** so that when the cell operates, electrical neutrality is maintained in each half-cell. For example, when copper metal is oxidized to copper(II) ions in the Cu^{2+}/Cu half-cell, either NO_3^- anions must enter or copper(II) ions must leave the half-cell to maintain neutrality. Similarly, when silver ions are reduced to form silver metal in its half-cell, either NO_3^- anions must leave or cations must enter its half-cell to maintain neutrality.

The silver electrode at which reduction occurs is called the **cathode;** the copper electrode at which oxidation occurs is called the **anode.** Because an oxidation process donates electrons to the copper electrode to provide a current in the external circuit, the anode is designated the *negative* electrode in a galvanic cell. A reduction process accepts electrons from the circuit and supplies them to the silver ions in solution; the silver cathode is the *positive* electrode. This sign designation allows us to distinguish the anode from the cathode in a galvanic cell.

Cell Potentials

Different metals, such as copper and silver, have different tendencies to oxidize; similarly, their ions have different tendencies to undergo reduction. The **cell potential** of a galvanic cell is due to the difference in tendencies of the two metals to oxidize (donate electrons) or of their ions to reduce (accept electrons). Commonly, a measured **reduction potential,** the tendency for an ion (or molecule) to accept electrons, is the value used to identify the relative ease of reduction for a half-reaction.

A **potentiometer** or **multimeter,** placed in the external circuit between the two electrodes, measures the cell potential, E_{cell}, a value that represents the *difference* between the tendencies of the metal ions in their respective half-cells to undergo reduction (i.e., the difference between the reduction potentials of the two redox couples).

For the copper and silver redox couples, we can represent their reduction potentials as $E_{Cu^{2+},Cu}$ and $E_{Ag^+,Ag}$, respectively. The cell potential being the difference of the two reduction potentials is therefore

$$E_{cell} = E_{Ag^+,Ag} - E_{Cu^{2+},Cu} \tag{32.4}$$

Experimentally, silver ion has a greater tendency than copper ion does to be in the reduced (metallic) state; therefore, Ag^+ has a greater (more positive) reduction potential. Since the cell potential, E_{cell}, is measured as a positive value, $E_{Ag^+,Ag}$ is placed before $E_{Cu^{2+},Cu}$ in equation 32.4.

Silver jewelry is longer lasting than copper jewelry; therefore silver has a higher tendency to be in the reduced state, a higher reduction potential

The measured cell potential corresponds to the **standard cell potential** when the concentrations of all ions are 1 mol/L and the temperature of the solutions is 25°C.

The *standard* reduction potential for the Ag^+(1 *M*)/Ag redox couple, $E°_{Ag^+,Ag}$, is +0.80 V, and the *standard* reduction potential for the Cu^{2+}(1 *M*)/Cu redox couple, $E°_{Cu^{2+},Cu}$, is +0.34 *V*. Theoretically, a potentiometer (or multimeter) would show the difference between these two potentials, or, at standard conditions,

$$E°_{cell} = E°_{Ag^+,Ag} - E°_{Cu^{2+},Cu} = +0.80 \text{ V} - (+0.34 \text{ V}) = +0.46\text{V} \tag{32.5}$$

Deviation from the theoretical value may be the result of surface activity at the electrodes or activity of the ions in solution.

Measure Cell Potentials

In Part A of this experiment, several cells are "built" from a selection of redox couples and data are collected. From an analysis of the data, the relative reduction potentials for the redox couples are determined and placed in an order of decreasing reduction potentials.

In Part B, the formations of the complex $[Cu(NH_3)_4]^{2+}$ and the precipitate CuS are used to change the concentration of $Cu^{2+}(aq)$ in the Cu^{2+}/Cu redox couple. The observed changes in the cell potentials are interpreted.

Measure Nonstandard Cell Potentials

The Nernst equation is applicable to redox systems that are *not* at standard conditions, most often when the concentrations of the ions in solution are *not* 1 mol/L. At 25°C, the measured cell potential, E_{cell}, is related to $E°_{cell}$ and ionic concentrations by

$$\textbf{Nernst equation: } E_{cell} = E°_{cell} - \frac{0.0592}{n} \log Q \tag{32.6}$$

where *n* represents the moles of electrons exchanged according to the cell reaction. For the copper–silver cell, $n = 2$; two electrons are lost per copper atom and two electrons are gained per two silver ions (see equations 32.1–32.3). For dilute ionic concentrations, the *reaction quotient, Q*, equals the **mass action expression** for the cell reaction. For the copper–silver cell (see equation 32.1):

Mass action expression: the product of the molar concentrations of the products divided by the product of the molar concentrations of the reactants, each concentration raised to the power of its coefficient in the balanced cell equation

$$Q = \frac{[Cu^{2+}]}{[Ag^+]^2}$$

The concentrations (i.e., density) of solids are constant and therefore do not appear in mass action expressions.

In Part C of this experiment, we study in depth the effect that changes in concentration of an ion have on the potential of the cell. The cell potentials for a number of zinc–copper redox couples are measured in which the copper ion concentrations are varied but the zinc ion concentration is maintained constant.

$$Zn(s) + Cu^{2+}(aq) \longrightarrow Cu(s) + Zn^{2+}(aq)$$

The Nernst equation for this reaction is

$$E_{cell} = E°_{cell} - \frac{0.0592}{2} \log \frac{[Zn^{2+}]}{[Cu^{2+}]} \tag{32.7}$$

Rearrangement of this equation (where $E°_{cell}$ and $[Zn^{2+}]$ are constants in the experiment) yields an equation for a straight line:

$$\underset{y\ =}{E_{cell}} = \underbrace{E°_{cell} - \frac{0.0592}{2} \log [Zn^{2+}]}_{b} + \underset{m}{\frac{0.0592}{2}} \underset{x}{\log [Cu^{2+}]} \tag{32.8}$$

$pCu = -log [Cu^{2+}]$

To simplify,

$$E_{cell} = \text{constant} - \frac{0.0592}{2}\,\text{pCu} \qquad (32.9)$$

A plot of E_{cell} versus pCu for solutions of known copper ion concentrations has a negative slope of 0.0592/2 and an intercept b that includes not only the constants in equation 32.8 but also the inherent characteristics of the cell and potentiometer (Figure 32.2).

The E_{cell} of a solution with an *unknown* copper ion concentration is then measured; from the linear plot, its concentration is determined.

EXPERIMENTAL PROCEDURE

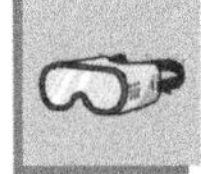

Procedure Overview: The cell potentials for a number of galvanic cells are measured and the redox couples are placed in order of decreasing reduction potentials. The effects of changes in ion concentrations on cell potentials are observed and analyzed.

Perform the experiment with a partner. At each circled superscript (1–12) in the procedure, *stop* and record your observation on the ***Report Sheet***. Discuss your observations with your lab partner and your instructor.

A. Reduction Potentials of Several Redox Couples

The apparatus for the voltaic cell described in the Experimental Procedure may be different in your laboratory. Consult with your instructor.

1. **Collect the electrodes, solutions, and equipment.** Obtain four small (~50 mL) beakers and fill them three-fourths full of the 0.1 *M* solutions as shown in Figure 32.3. Share these solutions with other chemists/groups of chemists in the laboratory.

   Polish strips of copper, zinc, magnesium, and iron metal with steel wool or sandpaper, rinse briefly with dilute (~0.1 *M*) HNO_3 **(Caution!)**, and rinse with deionized water. These polished metals, used as electrodes, should be bent to extend over the lip of their respective beakers. Check out a multimeter (Figure 32.4) (or a voltmeter) with two electrical wires (preferably a red and black wire) attached to alligator clips.
2. **Set up the copper–zinc cell.** Place a Cu strip (electrode) in the $CuSO_4$ solution and a Zn strip (electrode) in the $Zn(NO_3)_2$ solution. Roll and flatten a piece of filter paper; wet the filter paper with a 0.1 *M* KNO_3 solution. Fold and insert the ends of the filter paper into the solutions in the two beakers; this is the *salt bridge* shown in Figures 32.1 and 32.3. Set the multimeter to the 2000-mV range or as appropriate. Connect one electrode to the negative terminal of the multimeter and the other to the positive terminal.[1]

Chemists often use the "red, right, plus" rule in connecting the red wire of the multimeter to the right-side positive electrode (cathode) of the galvanic cell

3. **Determine the copper–zinc cell potential.** If the multimeter reads a negative potential, reverse the connections to the electrodes. Read and record the (positive) cell potential. Identify the metal strips that serve as the cathode (positive terminal)

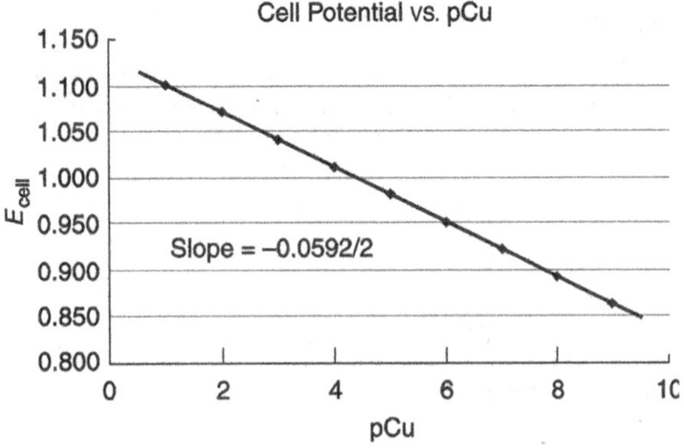

Figure 32.2 The variation of E_{cell} versus the pCu

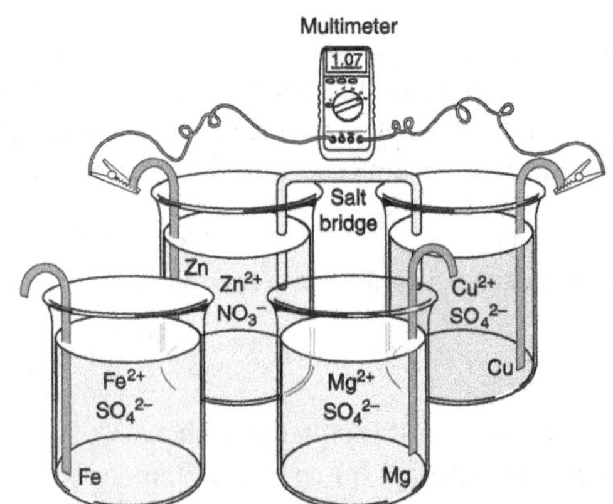

Figure 32.3 Setup for measuring the cell potentials of six galvanic cells

[1]You have now combined two half-cells to form a galvanic cell.

and the anode. Write an equation for the half-reaction occurring at each electrode. Combine the two half-reactions to write the equation for the cell reaction.①

4. **Repeat for the remaining cells.** Determine the cell potentials for all possible galvanic cells that can be constructed from the four redox couples. Refer to the ***Report Sheet*** for the various galvanic cells. Prepare a new salt bridge for each galvanic cell.②
5. **Determine the relative reduction potentials.** Assuming the reduction potential of the Zn^{2+}(0.1 *M*)/Zn redox couple is –0.79 V, calculate the reduction potentials of all other redox couples.[2]③
6. **Determine the reduction potential of the unknown redox couple.** Place a 0.1 *M* solution and electrode obtained from your instructor in a small beaker. Determine the reduction potential, relative to the Zn^{2+}(0.1 *M*)/Zn redox couple, for your unknown redox couple.④

B. Effect of Concentration Changes on Cell Potential

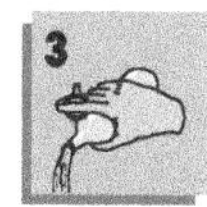

1. **Effect of different molar concentrations.** Set up the galvanic cell shown in Figure 32.5, using 1 *M* $CuSO_4$ and 0.001 *M* $CuSO_4$ solutions. Immerse a polished copper electrode in each solution. Prepare a salt bridge (Part A.2) to connect the two half-cells. Measure the cell potential. Determine the anode and the cathode. Write an equation for the reaction occurring at each electrode.⑤
2. **Effect of complex formation.** Add 2–5 mL of 6 *M* NH_3 to the 0.001 *M* $CuSO_4$ solution until any precipitate redissolves.[3] (**Caution:** *Do not inhale* NH_3.) Observe and record any changes in the half-cell and the cell potential.⑥
3. **Effect of precipitate formation.** Add 2–5 mL of 0.2 *M* Na_2S to the 0.001 *M* $CuSO_4$ solution now containing the added NH_3. What is observed in the half-cell and what happens to the cell potential? Record your observations.⑦

C. The Nernst Equation and an Unknown Concentration

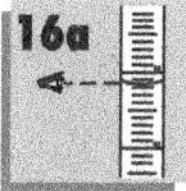

Data Analysis, A

1. **Prepare the diluted solutions.** Prepare solutions 1 through 4 as shown in Figure 32.6 using a 1-mL pipet and 100-mL volumetric flasks.[4] See ***Prelaboratory Assignment***, *question 3*. Be sure to rinse the pipet with the more concentrated solution before making the transfer. Use deionized water for dilution to the mark in the volumetric flasks. Calculate the molar concentration of the Cu^{2+} ion for each solution and record.⑧
2. **Measure and calculate the cell potential for *solution 4*.** Set up the experiment as shown in Figure 32.7, page 362, using small (~50 mL) beakers.

Figure 32.4 A modern multimeter

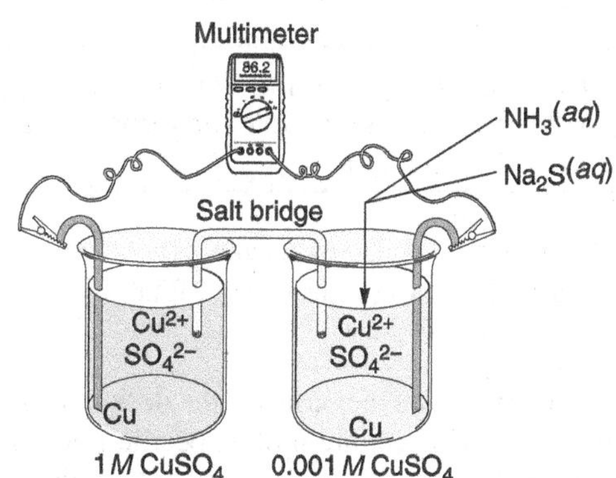

Figure 32.5 Setup for measuring the cell potential of a Cu^{2+} concentration cell

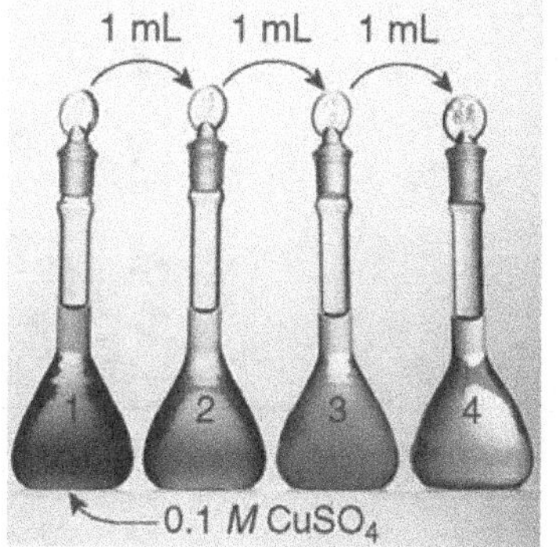

Figure 32.6 Successive quantitative dilution, starting with 0.1 *M* $CuSO_4$

[2]*Note:* These are *not* standard reduction potentials because 1 *M* concentrations of cations at 25°C are not used.

[3]Copper ion forms a complex with ammonia: $Cu^{2+}(aq) + 4\ NH_3(aq) \rightarrow [Cu(NH_3)_4]^{2+}(aq)$

[4]Share these prepared solutions with other chemists/groups of chemists in the laboratory.

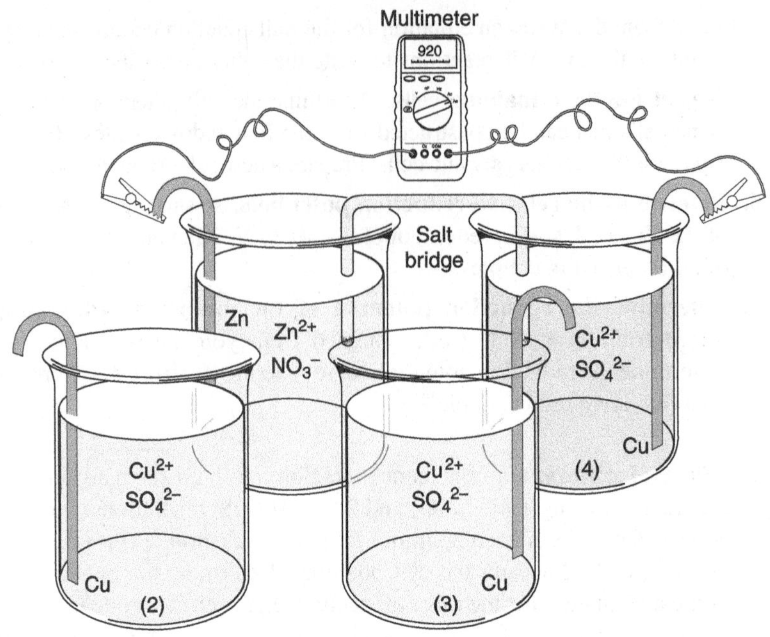

Figure 32.7 Setup to measure the effect that diluted solutions have on cell potentials

The Zn^{2+}/Zn redox couple is the reference half-cell for this part of the experiment. Connect the two half-cells with a new salt bridge. Reset the multimeter to the lowest range (~200 mV). Connect the electrodes to the multimeter and record the potential difference, $E_{cell, expt}$. (9) Calculate the *theoretical* cell potential $E_{cell, calc}$. (Use a table of standard reduction potentials and the Nernst equation.) (10)

3. **Measure and calculate the cell potentials for solutions 3 and 2.** Repeat Part C.2 with solutions 3 and 2, respectively. A freshly prepared salt bridge is required for each cell. See data from Part A.3 for the potential of Solution 1.

Data Analysis, F, G

4. **Plot the data.** Plot $E_{cell, expt}$ *and* $E_{cell, calc}$ (ordinate) versus pCu (abscissa) on the *same* piece of linear graph paper (page 368) or by using appropriate software for the *four* concentrations of $CuSO_4$. Have your instructor approve your graph. (11)
5. **Determine the concentration of the unknown.** Obtain a $CuSO_4$ solution with an unknown copper ion concentration from your instructor and set up a like galvanic cell. Determine E_{cell} as in Part C.2. Using the graph, determine the unknown copper(II) ion concentration in the solution. (12)

Disposal: Dispose of the waste zinc, copper, magnesium, and iron solutions in the Waste Metal Solutions container. Return the metals to appropriately marked containers.

CLEANUP: Rinse the beakers twice with tap water and twice with deionized water. Discard the rinses in the Waste Metal Solutions container.

The Next Step

Galvanic cells are the basis for the design of specific ion electrodes, electrodes that sense the relative concentration of a specific ion (e.g., hydrogen ion) relative to the electrode that has a fixed concentration. Part C of this experiment could be the apparatus for measuring concentrations of Cu^{2+} in other samples. According to equation 32.8, the pCu (negative log of $[Cu^{2+}]$) is proportional to the E_{cell}! Research specific ion electrodes, their design, and their application. Design an experiment in which a specific ion electrode, other than the pH electrode, can be used to systematically study an ion of interest.

Experiment 32 *Prelaboratory Assignment*

Galvanic Cells, the Nernst Equation

Date ________ Lab Sec. ______ Name ______________________________ Desk No. ________

1. In a galvanic cell,
   a. oxidation occurs at the (name of electrode) ____________
   b. the cathode is the (sign) electrode ____________
   c. cations flow in solution toward the (name of electrode) ____________
   d. electrons flow from the (name of electrode) to (name of electrode) ________ ________

2. a. What is the purpose of a salt bridge? Explain.

   b. How is the salt bridge prepared in this experiment?

3. Experimental Procedure, Part C.1. A 1-mL pipet is used to transfer 1.0 mL of a 0.10 *M* $CuSO_4$ solution to a 100-mL volumetric flask. The volumetric flask is then filled to the mark with deionized water. See Figure 32.6. What is the molar concentration of the diluted solution? Show calculations expressing the concentration with the correct number of significant figures.

4. Refer to Figure 32.2 and equations 32.8 and 32.9.
   a. What is the value of the cell constant (y-intercept)?

   b. What is the $[Cu^{2+}]$ if the measured cell potential is 1.05 V?

   c. What should be the cell potential if the $[Cu^{2+}]$ is 1.0×10^{-6} mol/L?

5. Consider a galvanic cell consisting of the following two redox couples:

$$Ag^{+}(0.010\ M) + e^{-} \longrightarrow Ag(s) \qquad E^{\circ} = +0.80\ V$$

$$Cr^{3+}(0.010\ M) + 3\ e^{-} \longrightarrow Cr(s) \qquad E^{\circ} = -0.74\ V$$

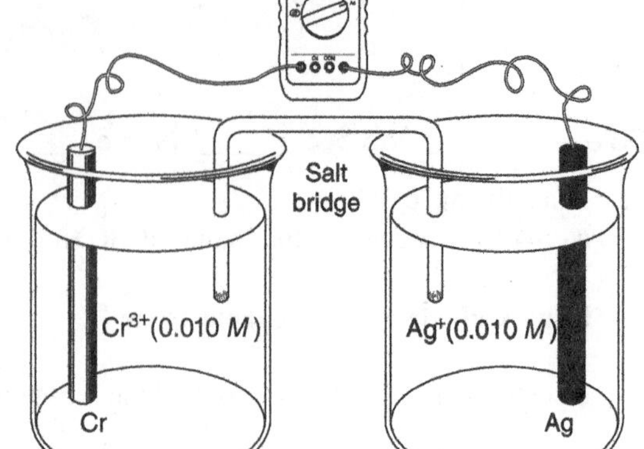

a. Write the equation for the half-reaction occurring at the cathode.

b. Write the equation for the half-reaction occurring at the anode.

c. Write the equation for the cell reaction.

d. What is the *standard* cell potential, E°_{cell}, for the cell?

e. Realizing the nonstandard concentrations, what is the *actual* cell potential, E_{cell}, for the cell? See equation 32.6. *Hint:* What is the value of n in the Nernst equation?

*6. The extent of corrosion in the steel reinforcing rods (rebar) of concrete is measured by the galvanic cell shown in the diagram of the instrument. The half-cell of the probe is usually a AgCl/Ag redox couple:

$$AgCl + e^{-} \rightarrow Ag + Cl^{-}\ (1.0\ M) \qquad E^{\circ} = +0.23\ V$$

Corrosion is said to be severe if the cell potential is measured at greater than 0.41 V. Under these conditions, what is the iron(II) concentration on the rebar? See equation 32.6.

$$Fe^{2+} + 2\ e^{-} \rightarrow Fe \qquad E^{\circ} = -0.44\ V$$

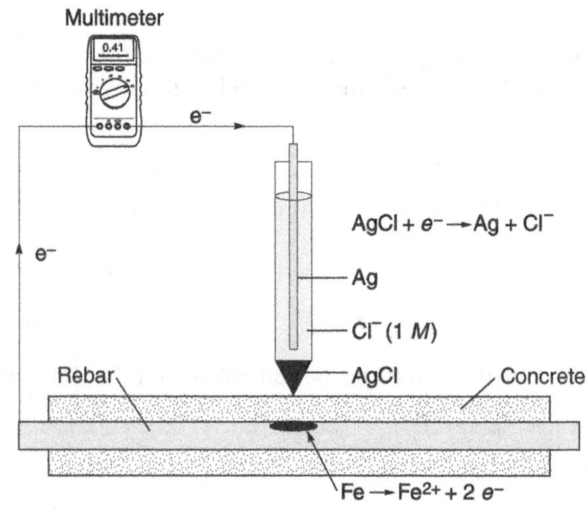

Experiment 32 *Report Sheet*

Galvanic Cells, the Nernst Equation

Date ________ Lab Sec. _____ Name ______________________________ Desk No. ________

A. Reduction Potentials of Several Redox Couples

Fill in the following table with your observations and interpretations from the galvanic cells.

Galvanic Cell	E_{cell} Measured	Anode	Equation for Anode Half-Reaction	Cathode	Equation for Cathode Half-Reaction
①Cu–Zn					
②Cu–Mg					
Cu–Fe					
Zn–Mg					
Fe–Mg					
Zn–Fe					

1. Write *balanced* equations for the six cell reactions.

2. What is the oxidizing agent in the Zn–Mg cell?

3. Compare the *sum* of the Cu–Zn and Zn–Mg cell potentials with the Cu–Mg cell potential. Explain.

4. Compare the *sum* of the Zn–Fe and Zn–Mg cell potentials with the Fe–Mg cell potential. Explain.

5. Complete the table as follows:
   - **E_{cell} Measured:** Re-enter the values from Part A, Column 2 of the ***Report sheet***.
   - **Reduction potential (experimental):** Enter the reduction potential for each redox couple relative to –0.79V for the Zn^{2+} (0.1 *M*)/Zn redox couple. Use $E_{M^{2+}/M} = E_{cell,\ measured} + (-0.79V)$, assuming Zn as the anode.
   - **Reduction potential (theoretical):** The reduction potential for each redox couple (M^{2+}/M) is calculated from a table of standard reduction potentials and the Nernst equation (equation 32.7) for $[M^{2+}] = 0.10\ M$.
   - **% Error:** See Data Analysis, E.

③

Galvanic Cell	E_{cell} Measured	For the Redox Couple	Reduction Potential (experimental)	Reduction Potential (theoretical)	% Error
Cu–Zn		Cu^{2+}/Cu		0.31	
Zn–Fe		Fe^{2+}/Fe		–0.47	
Zn–Zn	0	Zn^{2+}/Zn	–0.79 V	–0.79	0.00
Zn–Mg		Mg^{2+}/Mg		–2.40	
Zn–unknown, X		X^{2+}, X			

6. ④Reduction potential of the unknown redox couple: ____________________

B. Effect of Concentration Changes on Cell Potential

1. ⑤Cell potential of concentration cell: ____________________

   Anode half-reaction: ____________________

   Cathode half-reaction: ____________________

   Explain *why* a potential is recorded.

2. ⑥Cell potential from complex formation: ____________________

   Observation of solution in half-cell.

   Explain *why* the potential changes as it does with the addition of $NH_3(aq)$.

3. ⑦Cell potential from precipitate formation: ____________________

   Observation of solution in half-cell.

   Explain *why* the potential changes as it does with the addition of Na_2S.

C. The Nernst Equation and an Unknown Concentration

1. Complete the following table with the concentrations of the $Cu(NO_3)_2$ solutions and the measured cell potentials, $E_{cell, expt}$. Use equation 32.9 to determine $E_{cell, calc}$.

Solution Number	⑧Concentration of $Cu(NO_3)_2$	⑨E_{cell}, experimental	$-\log [Cu^{2+}]$, pCu	⑩E_{cell}, calculated
1	0.1 mol/L	______	1	
2	______	______		
3	______	______		
4	______	______		

2. ⑪Instructor's approval of graph: ______

Account for any significant difference between the measured and calculated E_{cell} values.

3. ⑫E_{cell} for the solution of unknown concentration: ______

From the graph, determine the pCu and calculate the molar concentration of Cu^{2+} in the unknown: ______

Laboratory Questions

Circle the questions that have been assigned.

1. Part A.3. The filter paper salt bridge is *not* wetted with the 0.1 *M* KNO_3 solution. As a result, will the measured potential of the cell be too high, too low, or unaffected? Explain.
2. Part A.3. A positive potential is recorded when the copper electrode is the positive electrode. Is the copper electrode the cathode or the anode of the cell? Explain.
3. Part A.5. The measured reduction potentials are not equal to the calculated reduction potentials. Give two reasons why this might be observed.
4. Part B.2. Would the cell potential be higher or lower if the $NH_3(aq)$ had been added to the 1 *M* $CuSO_4$ solution instead of the 0.001 *M* $CuSO_4$ solution of the cell? Explain.
5. Part B.3. The cell potential increased (compared to Part B.2) with the addition of the Na_2S solution to the 0.001 *M* $CuSO_4$ solution. Explain.
6. Part C. As the concentration of the copper(II) ion increased from solution 4 to solution 1, did the measured cell potentials increase or decrease? Explain why the change occurred.
7. Part C. Suppose the 0.1 *M* Zn^{2+} solution had been diluted (instead of the Cu^{2+} solution), Would the measured cell potentials have increased or decreased? Explain why the change occurred.
8. Part C. How would you increase or decrease the Cu^{2+} concentration and/or increase or decrease the Zn^{2+} concentration to maximize the cell potential? Explain how the change for each ion would maximize the cell potential.

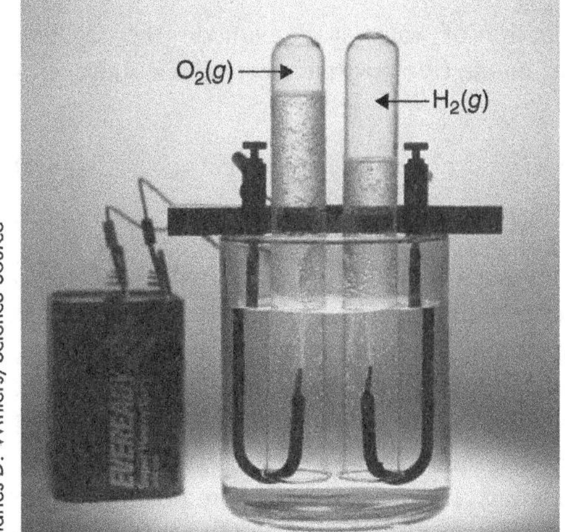

Charles D. Winters/Science Source

A 1:2 mole (and volume) ratio of oxygen (left) to hydrogen (right) is produced from the electrolysis of water.

Experiment 33

Electrolytic Cells, Avogadro's Number

OBJECTIVES

- To identify the reactions occurring at the anode and cathode during the electrolysis of various aqueous salt solutions
- To determine Avogadro's number and the Faraday constant

TECHNIQUES

The following techniques are used in the Experimental Procedure:

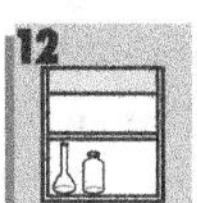

INTRODUCTION

Electrolysis: Use of electrical energy to cause a chemical reaction to occur

Electroplating: the use of electrical current to deposit a metal onto an electrode

Electrolytic cell: an apparatus used for an electrolysis reaction

Electrolysis processes are very important in achieving high standards of living. The industrial production of metals such as aluminum and magnesium and nonmetals such as chlorine and fluorine occurs in electrolytic cells. The highly refined copper metal required for electrical wiring is obtained through an **electroplating** process.

In an **electrolytic cell,** the input of an electric current causes an otherwise nonspontaneous oxidation–reduction reaction, a nonspontaneous transfer of electrons, to occur. For example, sodium metal, a very active metal, and chlorine gas, a very toxic gas, both very reactive elements, are prepared industrially by the electrolysis of molten sodium chloride. Electrical energy is supplied to a molten NaCl system (Figure 33.1) by a direct current (dc) power source (set at an appropriate voltage) across the electrodes of an electrolytic cell.

The electrical energy causes the reduction of the sodium ion, Na^+, at the cathode and oxidation of the chloride ion, Cl^-, at the anode. Because cations migrate to the cathode and anions migrate to the anode, the cathode is the negative electrode (opposite charges attract), and the anode is designated the positive electrode.[1]

cathode (–) reaction: $Na^+(l) + e^- \longrightarrow Na(l)$

anode (+) reaction: $2\ Cl^-(l) \longrightarrow Cl_2(g) + 2\ e^-$

Electrolysis reactions also occur in aqueous solutions. For example, in the electrolysis of an aqueous copper(II) bromide, $CuBr_2$, solution, copper(II) ions, Cu^{2+}, are reduced at the cathode and bromide ions, Br^-, are oxidized at the anode (Figure 33.2, page 370).

cathode (–) reaction: $Cu^{2+}(aq) + 2\ e^- \longrightarrow Cu(s)$

anode (+) reaction: $2\ Br^-(aq) \longrightarrow Br_2(l) + 2\ e^-$

cell reaction: $Cu^{2+}(aq) + 2\ Br^-(aq) \longrightarrow Cu(s) + Br_2(l)$

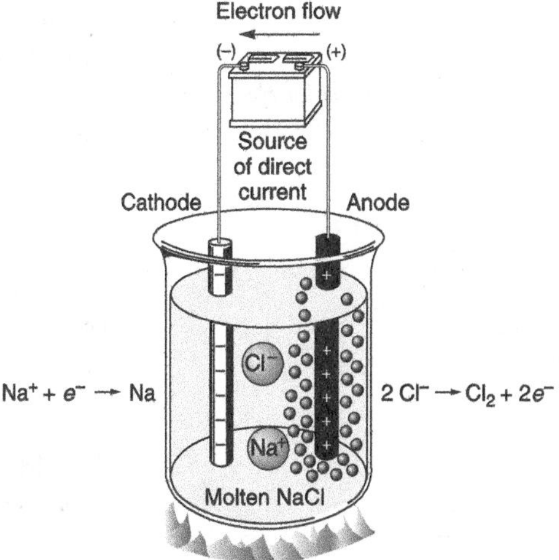

Figure 33.1 Schematic diagram of the electrolysis of molten sodium chloride

[1]Note that the cathode is "–" in an electrolytic cell but "+" in a galvanic cell; the anode is "+" in an electrolytic cell but "–" in a galvanic cell. See *Experiment 32.*

Electrolysis of Aqueous Solution

In an aqueous solution, however, the reduction of water at the cathode (the negative electrode) and the oxidation of water at the anode (the positive electrode) are also possible reactions.

$$\text{cathode (–) reaction for water:} \quad 2\,H_2O(l) + 2\,e^- \longrightarrow H_2(g) + 2\,OH^-(aq) \qquad (33.1)$$

$$\text{anode (+) reaction for water:} \quad 2\,H_2O(l) \longrightarrow O_2(g) + 4\,H^+(aq) + 4\,e^- \qquad (33.2)$$

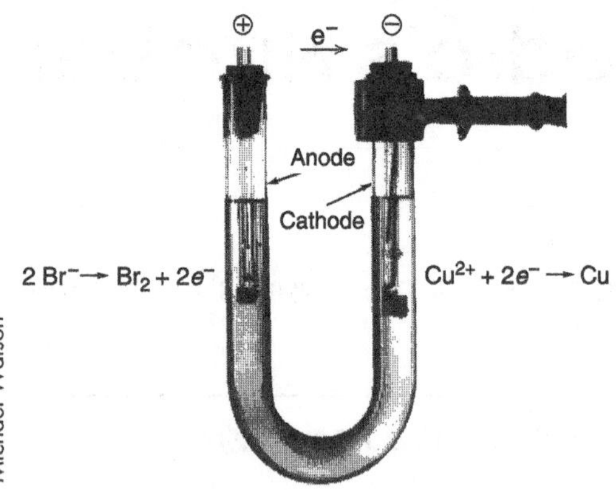

Michael Watson

Figure 33.2 Electrolysis of a copper(II) bromide solution; the anode is on the left and the cathode is on the right

If the reduction of water occurs at the cathode, hydrogen gas is evolved and the solution near the cathode becomes basic as a result of the production of hydroxide ion. If oxidation of water occurs at the anode, oxygen gas is evolved and the solution near the anode becomes acidic. The acidity (or basicity) near the respective electrodes can be detected with pH paper or another acid–base indicator.

When two or more competing reduction reactions are possible at the cathode, the reaction that occurs most easily (the one with the *higher* reduction potential) is the one that usually occurs. Conversely, for two or more competing oxidation reactions at the anode, the reaction that takes place most easily (the one with the *higher* oxidation potential or the *lower* reduction potential) is the one that usually occurs.

In the electrolysis of the aqueous copper(II) bromide solution, Cu^{2+} has a higher reduction potential than H_2O and is therefore preferentially reduced at the cathode; Br^- has a greater tendency to be oxidized than water, and so Br^- is oxidized at the anode.

In Part A of this experiment, a number of aqueous salt solutions using different electrodes are electrolyzed. The anode and cathode are identified, and the products that are formed at each electrode are also identified.

Avogadro's Number and the Faraday Constant

In Part B, a quantitative investigation of the electrolytic oxidation of copper metal is used to determine Avogadro's number and the Faraday constant:

$$Cu(s) \longrightarrow Cu^{2+}(aq) + 2\,e^- \qquad (33.3)$$

1 faraday = 1 mol e⁻ = 96,485 coulombs

Two moles of electrons (or 2 **faradays**) are released for each mole of Cu(*s*) oxidized; therefore, a mass measurement of the copper anode before and after the electrolysis determines the moles of copper that are oxidized. This in turn is used to calculate the moles of electrons that pass through the cell:

$$\text{moles of electrons} = \text{mass Cu} \times \frac{\text{mol Cu}}{63.54\ \text{g}} \times \frac{2\ \text{mol}\ e^-}{\text{mol Cu}} \qquad (33.4)$$

The actual *number* of electrons that pass through the cell is calculated from the electrical current, measured in amperes (= coulombs/second), that passes through the cell for a recorded time period (seconds). The total charge (**coulombs,** C) that passes through the cell is

Coulomb: SI base unit for electrical charge

$$\text{number of coulombs} = \frac{\text{coulombs}}{\text{second}} \times \text{seconds} \qquad (33.5)$$

As the charge of one electron equals 1.60×10^{-19} C, the number of electrons that pass through the cell can be calculated:

$$\text{number of electrons} = \text{number of coulombs} \times \frac{\text{electron}}{1.60 \times 10^{-19}\ \text{C}} \qquad (33.6)$$

Therefore, since the number of electrons (equation 33.6) and the moles of electrons (equation 33.4) can be separately determined, Avogadro's number is calculated as

$$\text{Avogadro's number} = \frac{\text{number of electrons}}{\text{mole of electrons}} \qquad (33.7)$$

In addition, the number of coulombs (equation 33.5) per mole of electrons (equation 33.4) equals the Faraday constant. With the available data, the Faraday constant can also be calculated:

$$\text{Faraday constant} = \frac{\text{number of coulombs}}{\text{mole of electrons}} \quad (33.8)$$

EXPERIMENTAL PROCEDURE

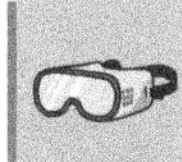

Procedure Overview: The products that result from the electrolysis of various salt solutions are observed and identified; these are qualitative measurements. An experimental setup is designed to measure quantitatively the flow of current and consequent changes in mass of the electrodes in an electrolytic cell; from these data, experimental constants are calculated.

The electrolysis apparatus may be designed differently than the one described in this experiment. Ask your instructor.

In Part B, be aware of the number of significant figures when recording data.

A. Electrolysis of Aqueous Salt Solutions

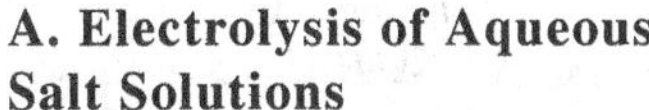

1. **Set up the electrolysis apparatus.** Connect two wire leads (different colors) attached to alligator clips to a direct current (dc) power supply.[2] Clean and mount the glass U-tube on a ring stand (see Figure 33.3). Connect the alligator clips to the corresponding electrodes, listed in Table 33.1.

Table 33.1 Electrolytic Cells for Study

Solution No.	Solution*	Electrodes (Cathode and Anode)
1	2 g NaCl/100 mL	Carbon (graphite)
2	2 g NaBr/100 mL	Carbon (graphite)
3	2 g KI/100 mL	Carbon (graphite)
4	0.1 *M* $CuSO_4$	Carbon (graphite)
5	0.1 *M* $CuSO_4$	Polished copper metal strips

*Try other solutions and electrodes as suggested by your laboratory instructor.

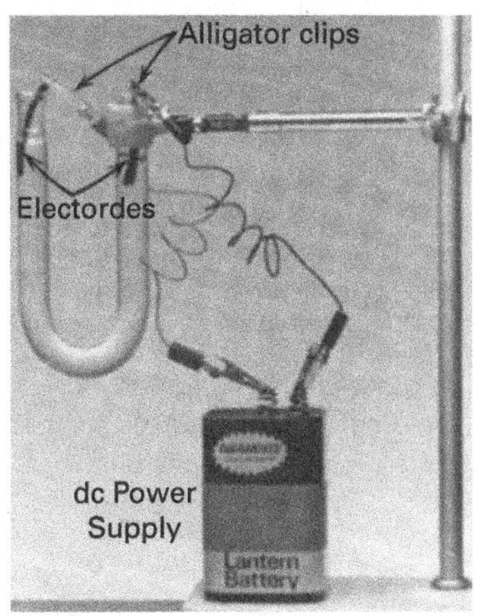

Figure 33.3 Electrolysis apparatus

2. **Electrolyze the solutions.** Fill the U-tube three-fourths full with Solution 1 from Table 33.1. Insert the corresponding electrodes into the solution and electrolyze for ~5 minutes. During the electrolysis, watch for any evidence of a reaction in the anode and cathode chambers.
   - Does the pH of the solution change at each electrode? Test each chamber with litmus or pH paper.[3] Compare the color with a pH test on the original solution.
   - Is a gas evolved at either or both electrodes? Look closely.
   - Look closely at each electrode. Is a metal depositing on the electrode or is the metal electrode slowly disappearing?

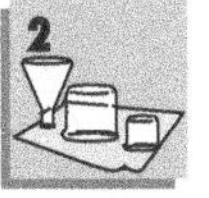

3. **Account for your observations.** Write the equations for the reactions occurring at the anode and cathode and for the cell reaction. Repeat for solutions 2–5.

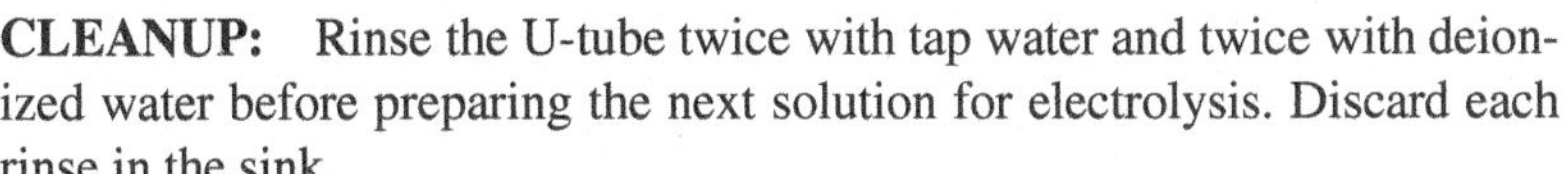
Disposal: Discard the salt solutions into the Waste Salts container.

CLEANUP: Rinse the U-tube twice with tap water and twice with deionized water before preparing the next solution for electrolysis. Discard each rinse in the sink.

[2]The dc power supply can be a 9-V transistor battery.
[3]Several drops of universal indicator can be added to the solution in both chambers to detect pH changes.

B. Determination of Avogadro's Number and the Faraday Constant

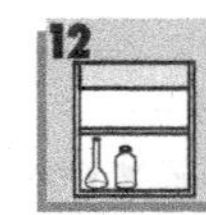

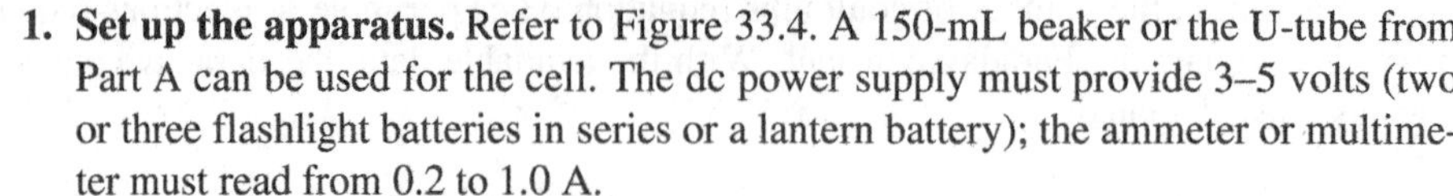

1. **Set up the apparatus.** Refer to Figure 33.4. A 150-mL beaker or the U-tube from Part A can be used for the cell. The dc power supply must provide 3–5 volts (two or three flashlight batteries in series or a lantern battery); the ammeter or multimeter must read from 0.2 to 1.0 A.

   Polish two copper metal strips (to be used as the electrodes) with steel wool or sandpaper. Briefly dip each electrode (use the fume hood) into 6 *M* HNO_3 (**Caution:** *do not allow skin contact*) for further cleaning, and then rinse with deionized water.

   Add 100 mL of 1.0 *M* $CuSO_4$ (in 0.1 *M* H_2SO_4) to the 150-mL beaker (or fill the U-tube).

Data Analysis, A

2. **Set the electrodes.** Rinse the electrodes with ethanol if available. When dry, label the two electrodes because the mass of each will be determined before and after the electrolysis. Measure the mass (±0.001 g, preferably ±0.0001 g) of each labeled electrode. The copper electrode with the lesser mass is to serve as the anode (+ terminal), and the other is to serve as the cathode (− terminal) for the electrolytic cell.

   Connect the cathode (through the variable resistor and ammeter/multimeter) to the negative terminal of the dc power supply.

   Before electrolysis begins, obtain your instructor's approval of the complete apparatus.

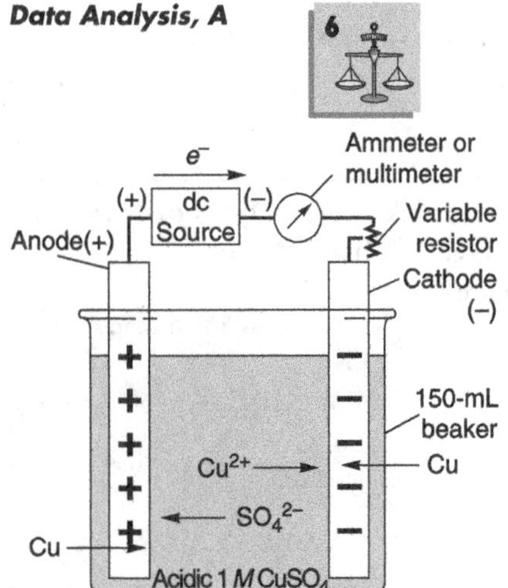

Figure 33.4 Setup for determining Avogadro's number and the Faraday constant

3. **Electrolyze the $CuSO_4$ solution.** Adjust the variable resistance to its maximum value.[4] Be ready to start timing (a stopwatch is ideal). Attach the anode to the positive terminal of the dc power supply and START TIME. During the electrolysis, do *not* move the electrodes; this changes current flow. Adjust the current with the variable resistor to about 0.5 A and, periodically during the course of the electrolysis, readjust the current to 0.5 A.[5]

   Discontinue the electrolysis after 20–30 minutes. Record the exact time (minutes and seconds) of the electrolysis process.

4. **Dry and measure the mass.** Carefully remove the electrodes (be careful not to loosen the electroplated copper metal from the cathode); carefully dip each electrode into a 400-mL beaker of deionized water to rinse the electrodes (followed by ethanol if available). Air-dry, measure the mass (±0.001 g, preferably ±0.0001 g) of each electrode, and record.

5. **Repeat the electrolysis.** If time allows, repeat Part B using the same copper electrodes (with new mass measurements!) and 1.0 *M* $CuSO_4$ solution.

Disposal: Discard the copper(II) sulfate solution into the Waste Salts container.

CLEANUP: Rinse the beaker or U-tube twice with tap water and twice with deionized water. Discard each rinse as directed by your instructor.

The Next Step

Electroplating of metals such as nickel, chromium, silver, and copper is a common industrial process. Research a specific process and design an apparatus and procedure for depositing quantitative amounts of metal to a cathode.

[4] If a variable resistor is unavailable, record the current at 1-minute intervals and then calculate an *average* current over the entire electrolysis time period.

[5] If the current is greater or less than 0.5 A, vary the time of electrolysis proportionally.

Experiment 33 *Prelaboratory Assignment*

Electrolytic Cells, Avogadro's Number

Date __________ Lab Sec. ______ Name ____ Desk No. __________

1. The standard reduction potential for the Cu^{2+}/Cu redox couple is +0.34 V; that for H_2O/H_2, OH^- at a pH of 7 is −0.41 V. For the electrolysis of a neutral 1.0 *M* $CuSO_4$ solution, write the equation for the half-reaction occurring at the cathode at standard conditions.

2. In an electrolytic cell,
   a. reduction occurs at the (name of electrode) ____________________
   b. the anode is the (sign) electrode ____________________
   c. anions flow toward the (name of electrode) ____________________
   d. electrons flow from the (name of electrode) to (name of electrode) __________ __________
   e. the cathode should be connected to the (positive/negative) terminal of the dc power supply ____________________

3. a. Identify a chemical test(s) to determine if water is oxidized at the anode of an electrolytic cell.

   17b

   b. Similarly, identify a chemical test(s) to determine if water is reduced at the cathode of an electrolytic cell.

4. Very pure copper metal is produced by the electrolytic refining of blister (impure) copper. In the cell at right, label the anode, the cathode, and the polarity (+, −) of each.

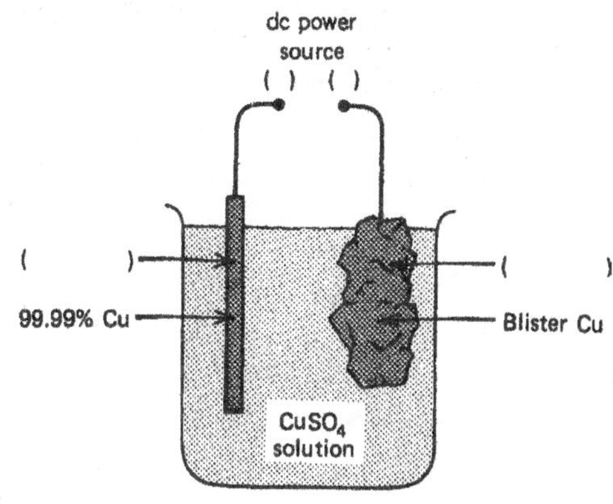

5. When a solution of nickel(II) sulfate adjusted to a pH of 7 is electrolyzed, the green color of the solution becomes less intense in the cathodic chamber and gas bubbles are detected in the anodic chamber.

(i) Write a balanced equation for the half-reaction occurring at the anode.

(ii) Write a balanced equation for the half-reaction occurring at the cathode.

6. Data for the experimental determination of Avogadro's Number and the Faraday Constant are recorded for Trial 1 (See ***Report Sheet.***) in the table. Complete the analysis for those determinations. Record the calculated values with the correct number of significant figures.

B. Determination of Avogadro's Number and the Faraday Constant

<u>*Calculation Zone*</u>

1. *Initial* mass of copper anode (*mL*) ___2.4852___
4. Time of electrolysis (*s*) ___1702___
5. Current (or average current) (*A, C/s*) ___0.622___
6. *Final* mass of copper anode (*g*) ___2.1335___

Data Analysis

1. Mass of copper oxidized at anode (*g*) ________
2. Moles of copper oxidized (*mol*)
   Show calculation. ________
3. Moles of electrons transferred (*mol* e^-)
   Equation 33.4.
   Show calculation. ________
4. Coulombs passed through cell (*C*)
   Equation 33.5.
   Show calculation. ________
5. Electrons passed through cell (e^-)
   Equation 33.6.
   Show calculation. ________
6. Avogadro's number (e^-/*mol* e^-)
   Equation 33.7.
   Show calculation. ________
9. Percent error ________
10. Faraday constant (*C/mol* e^-)
    Equation 33.8.
    Show calculation. ________

Data Analysis 2.

Data Analysis 3.

Data Analysis 4.

Data Analysis 5.

Data Analysis 6.

Data Analysis 10.

Experiment 33 *Report Sheet*

Electrolytic Cells, Avogadro's Number

Date ________ Lab Sec. ______ Name ______________________________ Desk No. ________

A. Electrolysis of Aqueous Salt Solutions

Solution	Electrodes	Litmus Test	Gas Evolved?	Balanced Equations for Reactions
NaCl	C(*gr*)			Anode ______________________ Cathode ______________________ Cell ______________________
NaBr	C(*gr*)			Anode ______________________ Cathode ______________________ Cell ______________________
KI	C(*gr*)			Anode ______________________ Cathode ______________________ Cell ______________________
$CuSO_4$	C(*gr*)			Anode ______________________ Cathode ______________________ Cell ______________________
$CuSO_4$	Cu(*s*)			Anode ______________________ Cathode ______________________ Cell ______________________

B. Determination of Avogadro's Number and the Faraday Constant

Data	Trial 1	Trial 2
1. *Initial* mass of copper anode (*g*)		
2. *Initial* mass of copper cathode (*g*)		
3. Instructor's approval of apparatus		
4. Time of electrolysis (*s*)		
5. Current (or average current) (*A*)		
6. *Final* mass of copper anode (*g*)		
7. *Final* mass of copper cathode (*g*)		

Data Analysis	Trial 1	Trial 2	
1. Mass of copper oxidized at anode (*g*)			
2. Moles of copper oxidized (*mol*)			
3. Moles of electrons transferred ($mol\ e^-$)			
4. Coulombs passed through cell (*C*)			
5. Electrons passed through cell (e^-)			
6. Avogadro's number ($e^-/mol\ e^-$)			
7. Average value of Avogadro's number			
8. Literature value of Avogadro's number			
9. Percent error			***Data Analysis, E***
10. Faraday constant ($C/mol\ e^-$)			
11. Average Faraday constant ($C/mol\ e^-$)			
12. Literature value of Faraday constant			
13. Percent error			***Data Analysis, E***

Laboratory Questions

Circle the questions that have been assigned.

1. Part A.2. If zinc electrodes are used instead of the graphite electrodes, the reaction occurring at the anode may be different, but the reaction occurring at the cathode would remain unchanged. Explain.
2. Part A.2. Nitrate ions, NO_3^-, being anions, migrate to the anode in an electrolytic cell. Explain why you would expect water rather than nitrate ions to be oxidized at the anode. *Hint:* Consider the oxidation state of nitrogen in the nitrate ion.
3. Part B. Repeat the calculation of Avogadro's number, using the mass gain of the cathode *instead* of the mass loss of the anode. Account for any difference in the calculated values.
4. Part B.2. If the current is recorded as being less than it actually is, would Avogadro's number be calculated as too high or too low, or would it be unaffected? Explain.
5. Part B.4. Because of an impure copper anode (see ***Prelaboratory Assignment*** question 4), the measured mass loss is greater than the actual mass of copper oxidized. As a result, will Avogadro's number be calculated as too high or too low? Explain.
6. Electrolysis of molten KCl produces molecular chlorine at the anode; however, in the electrolysis of an aqueous KCl solution, a gas is evolved. What is the gas and why is it produced? Explain.

*7. The electrolytic refining of copper involves the oxidaton of impure copper containing such metals as iron and nickel (oxidized to copper(II), iron(II), and nickel(II) ions) at the anode and then reduction of the copper(II) ion to copper metal at the cathode. Explain why the iron(II) and nickel(II) ions are not deposited on the cathode.

Ken Karp

Experiment 34

An Equilibrium Constant

The nearly colorless iron(III) ion (left) forms an intensely colored complex (right) in the presence of the thiocyanate ion.

OBJECTIVES

- To use a **spectrophotometer** to determine the equilibrium constant of a chemical system
- To use graphing techniques and data analysis to evaluate data
- To determine the equilibrium constant for a soluble equilibrium

Spectrophotometer: a laboratory instrument that measures the amount of light transmitted through a sample

TECHNIQUES

The following techniques are used in the Experimental Procedure:

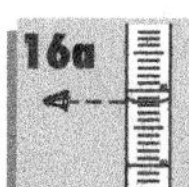

INTRODUCTION

A spectrophotometric method of analysis involves the interaction of electromagnetic (EM) radiation with matter. The most common regions of the EM spectrum used for analyses are the ultraviolet, visible, and the infrared regions. We are most familiar with the visible region of the spectrum, in which wavelengths range from 400 to 700 nm.

The visible spectra of ions and molecules in solution arise from *electron* transitions within their respective structures. The greater the concentration of the absorbing ions/molecules in solution, the greater is the absorption of the visible EM radiation (and the greater the transmittance of the *complementary* radiation). The degree of absorbed radiation (or the intensity of the transmitted radiation) is measured using an instrument called a **spectrophotometer**, which measures transmitted light intensities with a photosensitive detector at specific (but variable) visible wavelengths (Figure 34.1, page 378). The wavelength where the absorbing ions or molecules has a maximum absorption of visible radiation is determined and set on the spectrophotometer for the analysis.

The Introduction to Dry Lab 3 discusses in more detail the interaction of electromagnetic radiation with atoms, ions, and molecules in terms of energy states, excited states, wavelengths, and spectra.

The visible light path through the spectrophotometer from the light source through the sample to the photosensitive detector is shown in Figure 34.2, page 378.

Several factors control the amount of EM radiation (light energy) that a sample absorbs:

- Concentration of the absorbing substance
- Thickness of the sample containing the absorbing substance (determined by the width of the **cuvet**)
- Probability of light absorption by the absorbing substance (called the **molar absorptivity coefficient** or **extinction coefficient**)

Cuvet: a special piece of glassware to hold solutions for measurement in the spectrophotometer

Figure 34.1 Common laboratory visible spectrophotometer

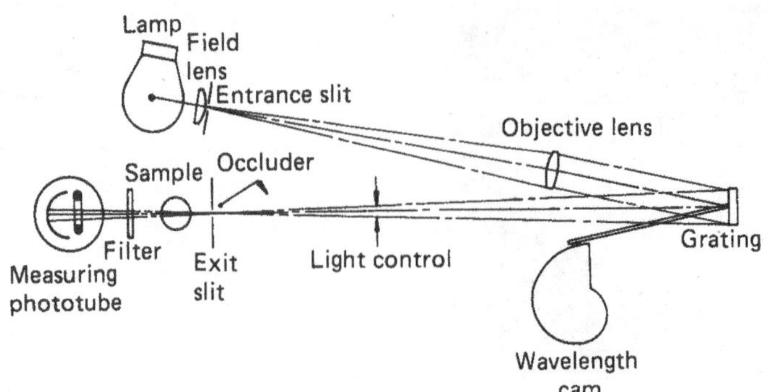

Figure 34.2 The light path through a visible spectrophotometer

The ratio of the intensity of the transmitted light, I_t, to that of the incident light, I_0 (Figure 34.3), is called the **transmittance**, T, of the EM radiation by the sample. This ratio, expressed as percent, is

$$\frac{I_t}{I_0} \times 100 = \%T \tag{34.1}$$

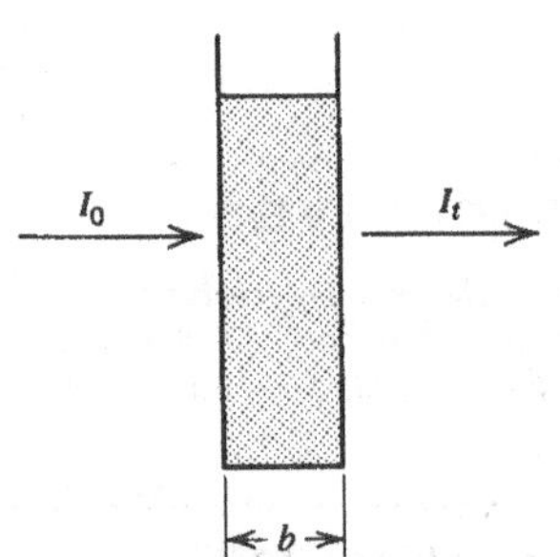

Figure 34.3 Incident light, I_0, and transmitted light, I_t, for a sample of thickness b

Most spectrophotometers have a $\%T$ (percent transmittance of light) scale. Because it is linear, the $\%T$ scale is easy to read and interpolate. However, chemists often perform calculations based on the amount of light *absorbed* by the sample rather than the amount of light transmitted because absorption is directly proportional to the concentration of the absorbing substance. The **absorbance**, A, of the substance is related to the intensity of the incident and transmitted light (and the percent transmittance) by the equations

$$A = \log \frac{I_0}{I_t} = \log \frac{1}{T} = \log \frac{100}{\%T} = a \cdot b \cdot c \tag{34.2}$$

The molar absorptivity coefficient, a, is a constant at any given wavelength for a particular absorbing substance, b is the thickness of the absorbing substance in centimeters, and c is the molar concentration of the absorbing substance.[1]

The absorbance value is directly proportional to the molar concentration of the absorbing substance *if* the same (or a matched) cuvet and a *set* wavelength are used for all measurements. A plot of absorbance versus concentration data is linear; a calculated slope and absorbance data can be used to determine the molar concentration of the same absorbing species in a solution of unknown concentration (Figure 34.4) from the linear relationship.

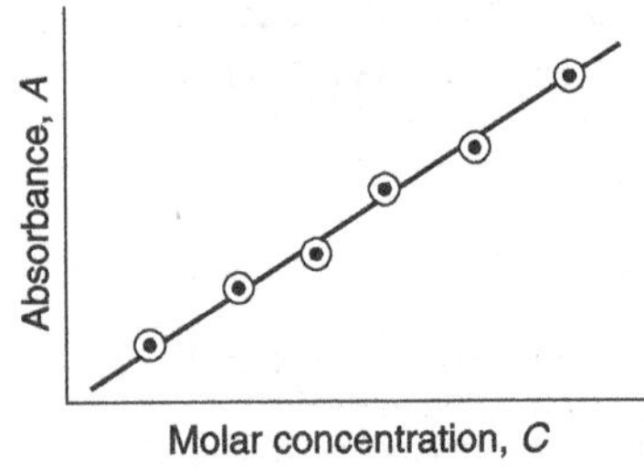

Figure 34.4 A data plot of absorbance versus concentration

Measuring an Equilibrium Constant

The magnitude of an equilibrium constant, K_c, expresses the equilibrium position for a chemical system. For the reaction, $a\text{A} + b\text{B} \rightleftharpoons x\text{X} + y\text{Y}$, the mass action expression, $\frac{[\text{X}]^x[\text{Y}]^y}{[\text{A}]^a[\text{B}]^b}$, equals the equilibrium constant, K_c, when a dynamic equilibrium has been established between reactants and products. The brackets in the mass action expression denote the equilibrium *molar concentration* of the respective substance.

The magnitude of the equilibrium constant indicates the principal species, products or reactants, that exist in the chemical system at equilibrium. For example, a large equilibrium constant indicates that the equilibrium lies to the right with a high concentration of products and correspondingly low concentration of reactants. The value of K_c is constant for a chemical system at a given temperature.

[1]Because the quantity log (I_0/I_t) is generally referred to as *absorbance*, equation 34.2 becomes $A = abc$. This equation is commonly referred to as **Beer's law.**

This experiment determines K_c for a chemical system in which all species are soluble. The chemical system involves the equilibrium between iron(III) ion, Fe^{3+}, thiocyanate ion, SCN^-, and thiocyanatoiron(III) ion, $FeNCS^{2+}$:

$$[Fe(H_2O)_6]^{3+}(aq) + SCN^-(aq) \rightleftharpoons Fe(H_2O)_5NCS]^{2+}(aq) + H_2O(l) \quad (34.3)$$

The "free" thiocyanate ion is commonly written as SCN^-; however, its bond to the ferric ion is through the nitrogen atom, thus the formula of the complex is written $FeNCS^{2+}$.

Because the concentration of water is essentially constant in dilute aqueous solutions, we omit the waters of hydration and simplify the equation to read

$$Fe^{3+}(aq) + SCN^-(aq) \rightleftharpoons FeNCS^{2+}(aq) \quad (34.4)$$

The mass action expression for the equilibrium system, equal to the equilibrium constant, is

$$K_c = \frac{[FeNCS^{2+}]}{[Fe^{3+}][SCN^-]} \quad (34.5)$$

In Part A you will prepare a set of five **standard solutions** of the $FeNCS^{2+}$ ion. As $FeNCS^{2+}$ is a deep, blood-red complex, its absorption maximum occurs at about 447 nm. The absorbance at 447 nm for each solution is plotted versus the molar concentration of $FeNCS^{2+}$; this establishes a **calibration curve** from which the concentrations of $FeNCS^{2+}$ are determined for the chemical systems in Part B.

Standard solution: a solution with a very well known concentration of solute

Calibration curve: a plot of known data from which further interpretations can be made

In preparing the standard solutions of $FeNCS^{2+}$, the Fe^{3+} concentration is set to *far* exceed the SCN^- concentration. This huge excess of Fe^{3+} pushes the equilibrium (equation 34.4) *far* to the right, consuming nearly all of the SCN^- placed in the system. As a result, the $FeNCS^{2+}$ concentration at equilibrium approximates the original SCN^- concentration. In other words, we assume that the position of the equilibrium is driven so far to the right by the excess Fe^{3+} that all of the SCN^- is **complexed,** forming $FeNCS^{2+}$ (Figure 34.5).

Complexed: the formation of a bond between the Lewis base, SCN^-, and the Lewis acid, Fe^{3+}

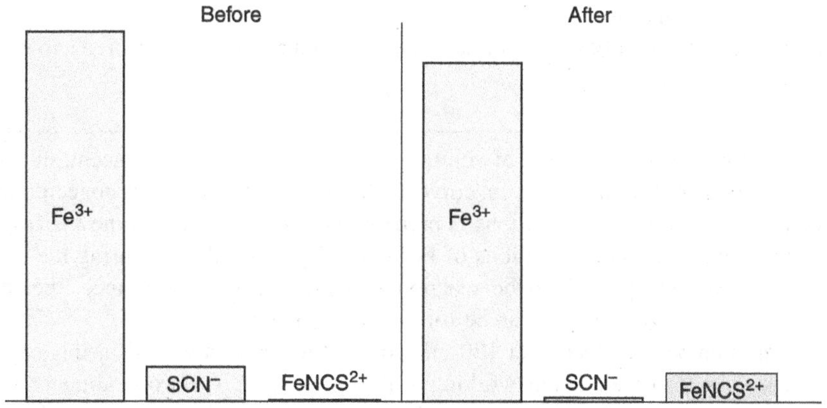

Figure 34.5 A large excess of Fe^{3+} consumes nearly all of the SCN^- to form $FeNCS^{2+}$. The amount of Fe^{3+} remains essentially unchanged in solution.

In Part B, the concentrations of the Fe^{3+} and SCN^- ions in the various test solutions are nearly the same, thus creating equilibrium systems in which there is an appreciable amount of each of the species after equilibrium is established (Figure 34.6).

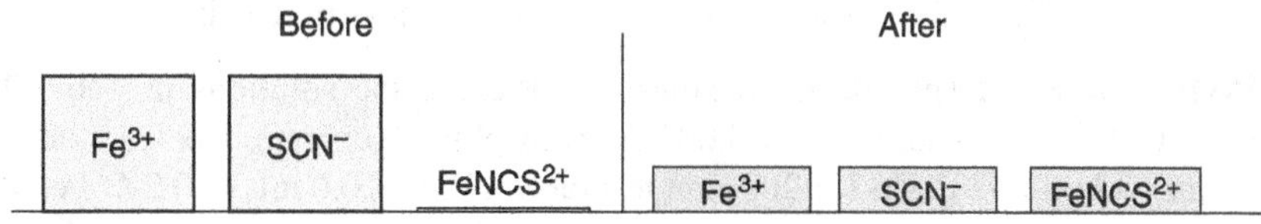

Figure 34.6 Amounts of Fe^{3+} and SCN^- are equally reduced in the formation of $FeNCS^{2+}$.

Measurements for K_c

In Part B, precise volumes of known molar concentrations of Fe^{3+} and SCN^- are mixed. The equilibrium molar concentration of $FeNCS^{2+}$ of the system is determined by measuring its absorbance and then using the calibration curve from Part A. Since the total volume of the mixed solution is measured precisely, the *initial* moles of Fe^{3+} and SCN^- and the *equilibrium* moles of $FeNCS^{2+}$ are easily calculated from known molar concentrations.

From equation 34.4, for every mole of $FeNCS^{2+}$ that exists at equilibrium, an equal number of moles of Fe^{3+} and SCN^- have reacted to reach equilibrium:

$$\text{mol } FeNCS^{2+}{}_{\text{equilibrium}} = \text{mol } Fe^{3+}{}_{\text{reacted}} = \text{mol } SCN^-{}_{\text{reacted}} \tag{34.6}$$

Therefore, the moles of Fe^{3+} at equilibrium (unreacted) is

$$\text{mol } Fe^{3+}{}_{\text{equilibrium}} = \text{mol } Fe^{3+}{}_{\text{initial}} - \text{mol } Fe^{3+}{}_{\text{reacted}} \tag{34.7}$$

Similarly, the moles of SCN^- at equilibrium (unreacted) is

$$\text{mol } SCN^-{}_{\text{equilibrium}} = \text{mol } SCN^-{}_{\text{initial}} - \text{mol } SCN^-{}_{\text{reacted}} \tag{34.8}$$

Again, since the total volume of the reaction mixture is known precisely, the equilibrium molar concentrations of Fe^{3+} and SCN^- (their *equilibrium* concentrations) can be calculated. Knowing the measured equilibrium molar concentration of $FeNCS^{2+}$ from the calibration curve, substitution of the three equilibrium molar concentrations into the mass action expression provides the value of the equilibrium constant, K_c.

Calculations for K_c

The calculations for K_c are involved, but completion of the ***Prelaboratory Assignment*** should clarify most of the steps. The ***Report Sheet*** is also outlined in such detail as to assist with the calculations.

Be aware of the number of significant figures when recording measured and calculated data.

EXPERIMENTAL PROCEDURE

Procedure Overview: One set of solutions having known molar concentrations of $FeNCS^{2+}$ is prepared for a calibration curve, a plot of absorbance versus concentration. A second set of equilibrium solutions is prepared and mixed to determine the respective equilibrium molar concentrations of $FeNCS^{2+}$. By carefully measuring the initial amounts of reactants placed in the reaction systems and the absorbance, the mass action expression at equilibrium can be solved; this equals K_c.

A large number of pipets and 100-mL volumetric flasks are used in this experiment. Ask your instructor about working with a partner. A spectrophotometer is an expensive, delicate analytical instrument. Operate it with care, following the advice of your instructor, and it will give you good data.

A. A Set of Standard Solutions to Establish a Calibration Curve

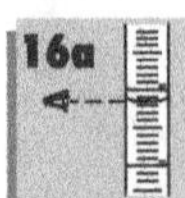

The set of standard solutions is used to determine the absorbance of known molar concentrations of $FeNCS^{2+}$. A plot of the data, known as a **calibration curve**, is used to determine the equilibrium molar concentrations of $FeNCS^{2+}$ in Part B.

Once the standard solutions are prepared, proceed smoothly and methodically through Part A.4. Therefore, read through all of Part A before proceeding.

1. **Prepare a set of the standard solutions.** Prepare the solutions in Table 34.1. Pipet 0, 1, 2, 3, 4 and 5 mL of 0.001 M NaSCN into separate, labeled, and clean 25-mL volumetric flasks (or 200-mm test tubes). Pipet 10.0 mL of 0.2 M $Fe(NO_3)_3$ into each flask (or test tube) and *quantitatively* dilute to 25 mL (the mark on the volumetric flask) with 0.1 M HNO_3. Stir or agitate each solution thoroughly to ensure that equilibrium is established.

Table 34.1 Composition of the Set of Standard $FeNCS^{2+}$ Solutions for Preparing the Calibration Curve

Standard Solution	0.2 *M* $Fe(NO_3)_3$ (in 0.1 *M* HNO_3)	0.001 *M* NaSCN (in 0.1 *M* HNO_3)	0.1 *M* HNO_3
Blank	10.0 mL	0 mL	Dilute to 25 mL
1	10.0 mL	1 mL	Dilute to 25 mL
2	10.0 mL	2 mL	Dilute to 25 mL
3	10.0 mL	3 mL	Dilute to 25 mL
4	10.0 mL	4 mL	Dilute to 25 mL
5	10.0 mL	5 mL	Dilute to 25 mL

Record on the ***Report Sheet*** the *exact* molar concentrations of the $Fe(NO_3)_3$ and NaSCN reagent solutions, i.e, the correct number of significant figures.

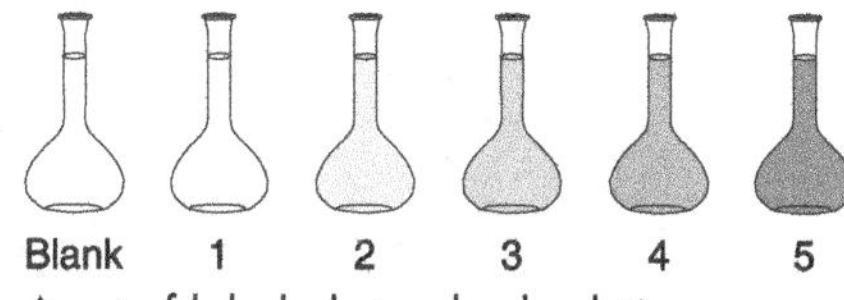

A set of labeled standard solutions.

2. **Prepare the blank solution.** After the spectrophotometer has been turned on for 10 minutes and the wavelength scale has been set at 447 nm, rinse a cuvet with several portions of the **blank solution.** Dry the outside of the cuvet with a clean Kimwipe, removing water and fingerprints.[2] Handle the lip of the cuvet thereafter. If a cuvet has two clear and two cloudy sides, be sure light passes through the clear sides and handle the cuvet on the cloudy sides.

Blank solution: a solution that contains all light-absorbing species except the one being investigated in the experiment

3. **Calibrate the spectrophotometer.** Place the cuvet, three-fourths filled with the blank solution, into the sample compartment, align the mark on the cuvet with that on the sample holder, and close the cover. Set the meter on the spectrophotometer to read zero absorbance (or 100%*T*).[3] Remove the cuvet. Consult with your instructor for any further calibration procedures. Once the instrument is set, *do not* perform any additional adjustments for the remainder of the experiment. If you accidentally do, merely repeat the calibration procedure.

4. **Record the absorbance of the standard solutions.** Empty the cuvet and rinse it *thoroughly* with several small portions of Solution 1.[4] Fill it approximately three-fourths full. Again, carefully dry the outside of the cuvet with a clean Kimwipe. Remember, handle only the lip of the cuvet. Place the cuvet into the sample compartment and align the cuvet and sample holder marks; read the absorbance (or percent transmittance if the spectrophotometer has a meter readout) and record. Repeat for Solutions 2, 3, 4, and 5.

   Share the set of standard solutions with other chemists in the laboratory.

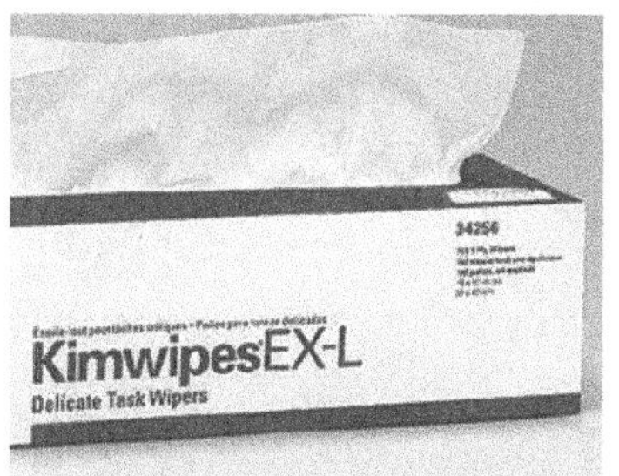

A box of lint-free tissue

Courtesy of Thermo Fisher Scientific

Data Analysis, F, G

5. **Graph the data.** Plot absorbance, *A* (ordinate), versus $[FeNCS^{2+}]$ (abscissa) for the six solutions on linear graph paper or by using appropriate software. Draw the *best straight line* through the six points (see Figure 34.4) to establish the calibration curve. Ask your instructor to approve your graph.

B. Absorbance for the Set of Test Solutions

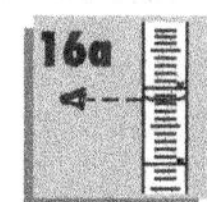

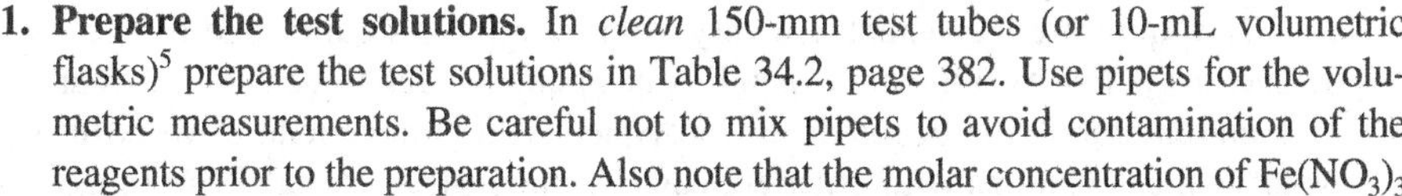

1. **Prepare the test solutions.** In *clean* 150-mm test tubes (or 10-mL volumetric flasks)[5] prepare the test solutions in Table 34.2, page 382. Use pipets for the volumetric measurements. Be careful not to mix pipets to avoid contamination of the reagents prior to the preparation. Also note that the molar concentration of $Fe(NO_3)_3$

[2]Water and fingerprints (or any foreign material) on the outside of the cuvet reduce the intensity of the light transmitted to the detector.

[3]For spectrophotometers with a meter readout (as opposed to digital), record the percent transmittance and then calculate the absorbance (equation 34.2). This procedure is more accurate because %*T* is a linear scale (whereas absorbance is logarithmic) and because it is easier to estimate the linear %*T* values more accurately and consistently. Consult with your instructor.

[4]If possible, prepare six matched cuvets, one for each standard solution, and successively measure the absorbance of each, remembering that the first solution is the blank solution.

[5]If 10-mL volumetric flasks are used, use pipets to dispense the volumes of the NaSCN and $Fe(NO_3)_3$ solutions and then dilute to the mark with 0.1 *M* HNO_3.

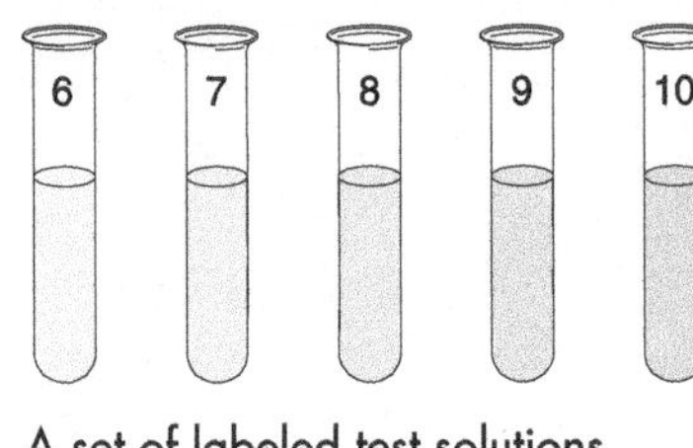

A set of labeled test solutions

Table 34.2 Composition of the Set of Equilibrium Test Solutions for the Determination of K_c

Test Solution	0.002 *M* $Fe(NO_3)_3$* (in 0.1 *M* HNO_3)	0.002 *M* NaSCN (in 0.1 *M* HNO_3)	0.1 *M* HNO_3
6	5 mL	1 mL	4 mL
7	5 mL	2 mL	3 mL
8	5 mL	3 mL	2 mL
9	5 mL	4 mL	1 mL
10	5 mL	5 mL	—

*If 0.002 *M* $Fe(NO_3)_3$ is not available, dilute 1.0 mL (measure with a 1.0-mL pipet) of the 0.2 *M* $Fe(NO_3)_3$ used in Part A with 0.1 *M* HNO_3 in a 100-mL volumetric flask and then share the remaining solution with other students.

for this set of solutions is 0.002 *M*, *not* the 0.2 *M* solution used in Part A and the molar concentration of NaSCN in 0.002 *M*, not 0.001 *M*.

Record the *exact* molar concentrations of the $Fe(NO_3)_3$ and NaSCN reagent solutions on the ***Report Sheet***, Part B, i.e, the correct number of significant figures.

Once the test solutions are prepared, proceed smoothly and methodically (you need not hurry!) through Part B.3.

2. **Recalibrate the spectrophotometer.** Use the blank solution from Part A to check the calibration of the spectrophotometer. See Part A.3.
3. **Determine the absorbance of the test solutions.** Stir or agitate each test solution until equilibrium is reached (approximately 30 seconds). Rinse the cuvet thoroughly with several portions of the test solution and fill it three-fourths full. Clean and dry the outside of the cuvet. Be cautious in handling the cuvets. Record the absorbance of each test solution as was done in Part A.4.

Disposal: Dispose of all waste thiocyanatoiron(III) ion solutions from Parts A and B in the Waste Salts container.

CLEANUP: Rinse the volumetric flasks, the pipets, and the cuvets twice with tap water and twice with deionized water. Discard each rinse in the sink.

Data Analysis, F, G

4. **Use data to determine equilibrium concentrations.** From the calibration curve prepared in Part A.5, use the recorded absorbance value for each test solution to determine the equilibrium molar concentration of $FeNCS^{2+}$ and record on the ***Report Sheet***, lines C.1.

C. Calculation of K_c

1. **Data analysis.** Complete the calculations as outlined on the ***Prelaboratory Assignment***, question 6, the ***Report Sheet*** and described in the Introduction. Complete an entire K_c calculation for Test Solution 6 before attempting the calculations for the remaining solutions.

Data Analysis, A, C, D

The equilibrium constant will vary from solution to solution and from chemist to chemist in this experiment, depending on chemical technique and the accumulation and interpretation of the data. Consequently, it is beneficial to work through your own calculations with other colleagues. The instructor may offer to assist in the calculations for K_c.

The Next Step

Spectrophotometry is a powerful tool for analyzing substances that have color such as aspirin (*Experiment 19*), transition metal ion complexes (*Experiments 34, 35, 36*), and anions (*Experiments 3* and *37*) to mention only a few. Research the spectrophotometric analysis of a specific substance and design a systematic study for its presence.

Experiment 34 *Prelaboratory Assignment*

An Equilibrium Constant

Date __________ Lab Sec. ______ Name ______________________________ Desk No. __________

1. Three parameters affect the absorbance of a sample. Which one is the focus of this experiment?

2. Experimental Procedure, Part A.1, Table 34.1. A 3.00-mL aliquot of 0.001 *M* NaSCN is diluted to 25.0 mL with 0.2 *M* $Fe(NO_3)_3$ and 0.1 *M* HNO_3.
   a. How many moles of SCN^- are present?

   b. If all of the SCN^- is complexed with Fe^{3+} to form $FeNCS^{2+}$, what is the molar concentration of $FeNCS^{2+}$?

3. Experimental Procedure, Part A.1. For preparing a set of standard solutions of $FeNCS^{2+}$, the equilibrium molar concentration of $FeNCS^{2+}$ is assumed to equal the initial molar concentration of the SCN^- in the reaction mixture. Why is this assumption valid?

4. Experimental Procedure, Part A.3. The blank solution used to calibrate the spectrophotometer is 10.0 mL of 0.2 *M* $Fe(NO_3)_3$ diluted to 25.0 mL with 0.1 *M* HNO_3. Why is this solution preferred to simply using de-ionized water for the calibration?

5. Plot the following data as absorbance versus $[M^{n+}]$ as a calibration curve:

Absorbance, *A*	Molar Concentration of M^{n+}
0.045	3.0×10^{-4} mol/L
0.097	6.2×10^{-4} mol/L
0.14	9.0×10^{-4} mol/L
0.35	2.2×10^{-3} mol/L
0.51	3.2×10^{-3} mol/L

A test solution showed a percent transmittance (%*T*) reading of 38.4%*T*. Interpret the calibration curve to determine the molar concentration of M^{n+} in the test solution.

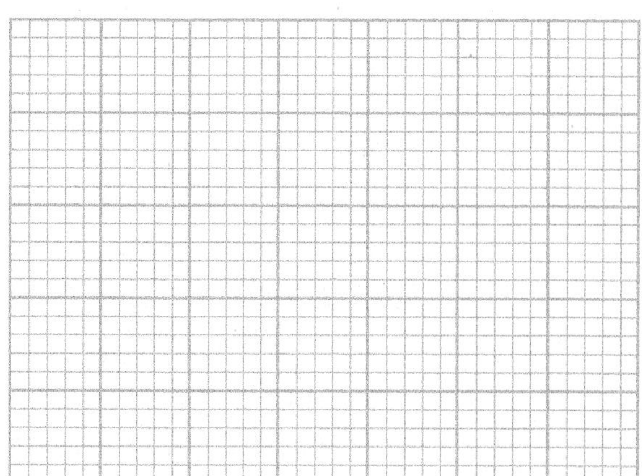

6. a. The equilibrium constant, K_c, is to be determined from the following set of data. Based upon the data, equations 34.4-8, complete the calculations (See ***Report Sheet***). Record the calculated values with the correct number of significant figures.

B. Absorbance for the set of Test Solutions — ***Calculation Zone***

Molar concentration of $Fe(NO_3)_3$	2.00×10^{-3} mol/L	***Part B.2***
Molar concentration of NaSCN	2.00×10^{-3} mol/L	
B.1 Volume of $Fe(NO_3)_3$ (*mL*)	5.00	
B.2 Moles of Fe^{3+}, initial (*mol*)		
B.3 Volume of NaSCN (*mL*)	4.00	***Part B.4***
B.4 Moles of SCN^-, initial (*mol*)		

C. Calculation of K_c

(Note: *all of the test solutions are diluted to 10 mL with 0.1 M HNO_3*)

Show calculations in the spacing provided.

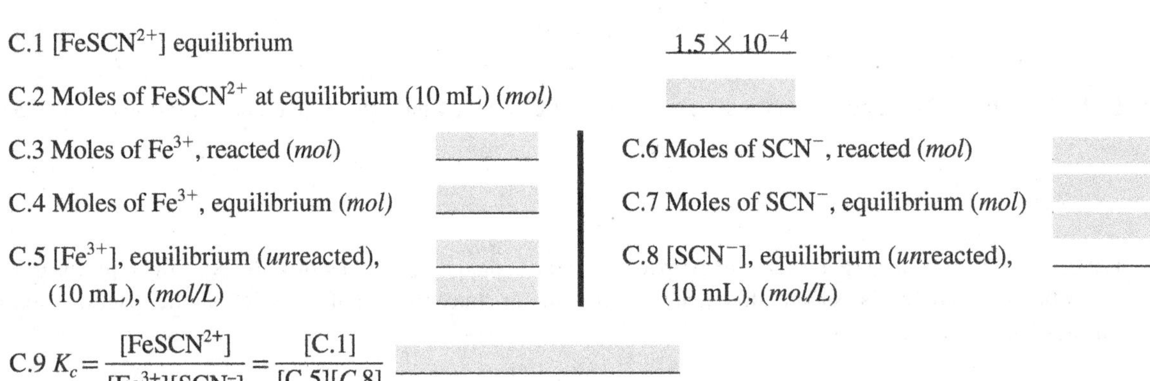

C.1 $[FeSCN^{2+}]$ equilibrium — 1.5×10^{-4}

C.2 Moles of $FeSCN^{2+}$ at equilibrium (10 mL) (*mol*) ________

C.3 Moles of Fe^{3+}, reacted (*mol*) ________

C.4 Moles of Fe^{3+}, equilibrium (*mol*) ________

C.5 $[Fe^{3+}]$, equilibrium (*un*reacted), (10 mL), (*mol/L*) ________

C.6 Moles of SCN^-, reacted (*mol*) ________

C.7 Moles of SCN^-, equilibrium (*mol*) ________

C.8 $[SCN^-]$, equilibrium (*un*reacted), (10 mL), (*mol/L*) ________

C.9 $K_c = \dfrac{[FeSCN^{2+}]}{[Fe^{3+}][SCN^-]} = \dfrac{[C.1]}{[C.5][C.8]}$ ________

6. b. For Trials 2-5, the K_c values were 255, 229, 281, and 244 respectively.

a. What is the average value for the equilibrium constant?

b. What are the standard deviation and the relative standard deviation (%RSD) for the equilibrium constant?

Experiment 34 *Report Sheet*

An Equilibrium Constant

Date ________ Lab Sec. ______ Name ______________________________ Desk No. ________

A. A Set of Standard Solutions to Establish a Standardization Curve

Molar concentration of $Fe(NO_3)_3$ ______________; Molar concentration of NaSCN ______________

Standard Solutions	*Blank*	*1**	*2*	*3*	*4*	*5*
A.1. Volume of NaSCN (*mL*)						
A.2. Moles of SCN^- (*mol*)						
A.3. $[SCN^-]$ (25.0 *mL*)						
A.4. $[FeNCS^{2+}]$ (*mol/L*)						
A.5. Percent transmittance, %*T* (for meter readings only)						
A.6. Absorbance, *A*						

*Calculation for Standard Solution 1.

A.7. Plot data of *A* versus $[FeNCS^{2+}]$. Instructor's approval ______________________________

B. Absorbance for the Set of Test Solutions

Molar concentration of $Fe(NO_3)_3$ __________; Molar concentration of NaSCN __________

Test Solutions	*6*	*7*	*8*	*9*	*10*
B.1. Volume of $Fe(NO_3)_3$ (*mL*)					
B.2. Moles of Fe^{3+}, initial (*mol*)	*				
B.3. Volume of NaSCN (*mL*)					
B.4. Moles of SCN^-, initial (*mol*)	*				
B.5. Percent transmittance, %*T* (for meter readings only)					
B.6. Absorbance, *A*					

*Calculation for Test Solution 6.

C. Calculation of K_c

	6	*7*	*8*	*9*	*10*
C.1. $[FeNCS^{2+}]$, equilibrium, from calibration curve (*mol/L*)					
C.2. Moles $FeNCS^{2+}$ at equilibrium (10 mL) (*mol*)					

$[Fe^{3+}]$, equilibrium	6	7	8	9	10
C.3. Moles Fe^{3+}, reacted (*mol*)					
C.4. Moles Fe^{3+}, equilibrium (*mol*)					
C.5. $[Fe^{3+}]$, equilibrium (*un*reacted). (10 mL) (*mol/L*)	*				

*Calculation for Test Solution 6. Express all $[Fe^{3+}]$ values with the correct number of significant figures.

$[SCN^-]$, equilibrium	6	7	8	9	10
C.6. Moles SCN^-, reacted (*mol*)					
C.7. Moles SCN^-, equilibrium (*mol*)					
C.8. $[SCN^-]$, equilibrium (*un*reacted). (10 mL) (*mol/L*)	*				

*Calculation for Test Solution 6. Express all $[SCN^-]$ values with the correct number of significant figures.

	6	7	8	9	10
C.9. $K_c = \frac{[FeNCS^{2+}]}{[Fe^{3+}][SCN^-]} = \frac{[C.1]}{[C.5][C.8]}$	*				

*Calculation for Test Solution 6. Express all K_c values with the correct number of significant figures.

C.10 Average K_c ______________ *Data Analysis, B*

C.11 Standard deviation of K_c ______________ *Data Analysis, C*

C.12 Relative standard deviation of K_c (%*RSD*) ______________ *Data Analysis, D*

Calculation for standard deviation.

Laboratory Questions

Circle the questions that have been assigned.

1. Part A.2. All spectrophotometers are different. The spectrophotometer is to be set at 447 nm. What experiment could you do, what data would you collect, and how would you analyze the data to ensure that 447 nm is the best setting for measuring the absorbance of $FeNCS^{2+}$ in this experiment?

2. Part A.3. In a hurry to complete the experiment, Joseph failed to calibrate the spectrophotometer. As a result, all absorbance values for the standard solutions that are measured and recorded are too high. How will this affect the following for the Test Solutions in Parts B and C?
   a. Will the equilibrium concentrations of $FeNCS^{2+}$ be too high, too low, or unaffected? Explain.
   b. Will the equilibrium concentrations of Fe^{3+} be too high, too low, or unaffected? Explain.
   c. Will the calculated equilibrium constants be too high, too low, or unaffected? Explain.

3. Part A.5. One of the standard solutions had an abnormally low absorbance reading, causing a less positive slope for the data plot.
   a. Will the equilibrium concentrations of $FeNCS^{2+}$ in the Test Solutions (Part B) be too high or too low? Explain.
   b. Will the calculated K_c for the equilibrium be too high, too low, or unaffected by the erred data plot? Explain.

4. Part B.3. Fingerprint smudges are present on the cuvet containing the solution placed into the spectrophotometer for analysis.
   a. How does this technique error affect the absorbance reading for $FeNCS^{2+}$ in the analysis? Explain.
   b. Will the equilibrium concentration of $FeNCS^{2+}$ be recorded as being too high or too low? Explain.
   c. Will the equilibrium concentration of SCN^- be too high, too low, or unaffected by the technique error? Explain.
   d. Will the K_c for the equilibrium be too high, too low, or unaffected by the technique error? Explain.

5. Part B.3. For the preparation of Test Solution 8 (Table 34.2), the 2.0 mL of 0.1 *M* HNO_3 is omitted.
   a. Will this technique error cause the absorbance reading for $FeNCS^{2+}$ to be too high or too low? Explain.
   b. Will the K_c for the equilibrium be too high, too low, or unaffected by the technique error? Explain.

*6. The equation, $A = a \cdot b \cdot c$ (see **footnote** 1), becomes nonlinear at high concentrations of the absorbing substance. Suppose you prepare a solution with a very high absorbance that is suspect in *not* following the linear relationship. How might you still use the sample for your analysis rather than discarding the sample and the data?

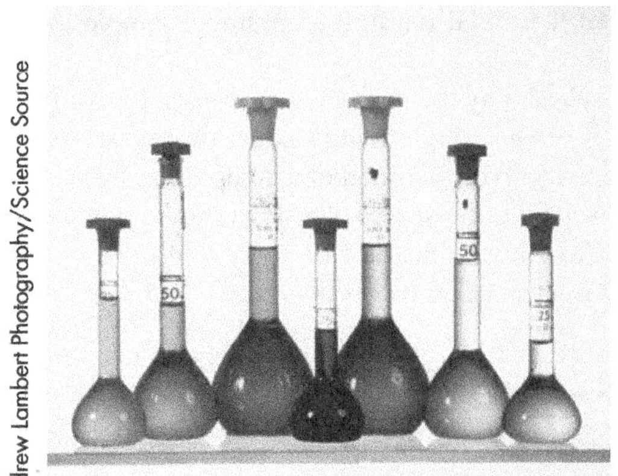

Andrew Lambert Photography/Science Source

Experiment 35

Spectrophotometric Metal Ion Analysis

The absorbance of light indicates the relative concentrations of a substance in solution.

Objectives

- To use a spectrophotometer to measure the concentration of a metal ion
- To use graphing techniques for data analysis
- To learn of the adaptability of spectrophotometric analyses

Techniques

The following techniques are used in the Experimental Procedure:

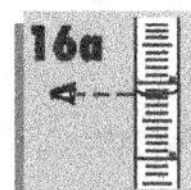

Introduction

Many transition metal cations have color but in certain concentration ranges may also be considered hazardous wastes. Disposal of electroplating baths containing copper, nickel, or chromium ions, among others, cannot be simply discarded without some type of treatment. Often the treatment is precipitation but changes in oxidation states, acidification, complexation, or simple dilution procedures also are used prior to disposal.

Because many transition metal ions do have color, their concentrations can be determined by a spectrophotometric analysis of the ion in the visible region of the electromagnetic spectrum. Those metal ions that do not have color may be analyzed by using ultraviolet radiation; however, a flame atomic absorption spectrophotometric (FAAS) analysis is by far the more common technique. The basic principles for either of the analyses are the same—standard solutions of the metal ion of interest are prepared, and the absorption of each is determined to prepare a calibration curve. The absorption of the unknown is then determined, and its concentration is determined by referring to the calibration curve.

Before beginning this experiment, read closely the Introduction to *Experiment 34*. An understanding of the absorbance and transmission of electromagnetic radiation through samples of varying concentrations in a spectrophotometer is imperative for an appreciation of the underlying chemical principles of this experiment.

Mixtures of ions can be problematic. The absorption spectrum for one ion may overlap and interfere with that of another ion. For that reason, FAAS or an induced couple plasma-atomic emission spectroscopy (ICP-AES) technique minimizes *some* of the interferences.

Experimental Procedure

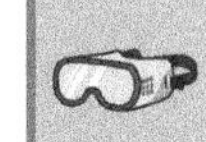

Procedure Overview: A set of standard solutions is prepared. First, the wavelength for maximum absorption, λ_{max}, of the metal ion in the visible region is determined from an absorbance, A, versus λ data plot. Next, the absorbances, A, of the standard solutions are determined at λ_{max} in order to construct a calibration curve of A versus [*conc*]. The two data plots can be constructed with the use of suitable software (e.g., Excel). The concentration of the metal ion in the unknown sample is then determined from the calibration curve.

The metal ion for your analysis will be selected by the instructor (or chosen by you) from one of the following cations: Cu^{2+}, Ni^{2+}, or Fe^{3+}. You should also be aware that the color of some of these cations may be enhanced with the addition of a complexing agent. A complexing agent used in the analysis is added to the stock solution in Part A and to the unknown in Part D. See *Experiment 36*. Consult your instructor.

Be aware of the number of significant figures when recording data.

A. A Set of Standard Solutions

Identify the metal ion for analysis on the ***Report Sheet***.

1. **Prepare a stock solution.**

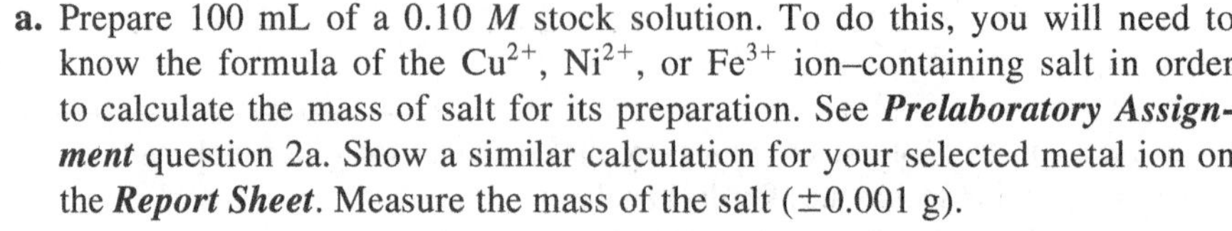

   a. Prepare 100 mL of a 0.10 *M* stock solution. To do this, you will need to know the formula of the Cu^{2+}, Ni^{2+}, or Fe^{3+} ion–containing salt in order to calculate the mass of salt for its preparation. See ***Prelaboratory Assignment*** question 2a. Show a similar calculation for your selected metal ion on the ***Report Sheet***. Measure the mass of the salt (± 0.001 g).

Data Analysis, A

   b. Transfer the salt to a 100-mL volumetric flask, half-filled with 0.01 *M* HNO_3, add the appropriate complexing agent (see Table 35.1), and then dilute to the mark with 0.01 *M* HNO_3. Record on the ***Report Sheet*** the exact molar concentration of the stock solution.

Table 35.1 Volume of Complexing Agent for Stock Solution Preparation

Metal Ion	Volume of Complexing Agent
Cu^{2+}	10 mL of *conc* NH_3
Ni^{2+}	10 mL of *conc* NH_3
Fe^{3+}	20 mL of 0.1 *M* NaSCN

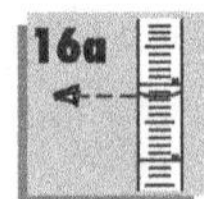

2. **Prepare the standard solutions.** Prepare the solutions in Table 35.2 using clean, labeled 25-mL volumetric flasks (or 200-mm test tubes). Use pipets to dispense the volumes of stock solution prepared in Part A.

   Additional standard solutions may need to be prepared—the absorbance values for the set of standard solutions should range from 0 to ~1.1. See Part C.1. Calculate the molar concentrations of the standard solutions and record them in Part C of the ***Report Sheet***.

B. Determination of λ_{max}

1. **Calibrate the spectrophotometer.** After the spectrophotometer has been turned on for at least 10 minutes, set the wavelength scale to its minimum (~350 nm), and set the zero (0%*T*) on the spectrophotometer. Rinse twice a cuvet with the blank solution (see Table 35.2). Fill the cuvet at least three-fourths full with the *blank solution* and dry the outside of the cuvet with a clean Kimwipe, removing fingerprints and water. Place the cuvet into the sample compartment,

Table 35.2 A Set of Standard Solutions for Metal Ion Analysis

Standard Solution	0.10 *M* Metal Ion	0.01 *M* HNO_3
Blank	0 mL	Dilute to 25 mL
1	1 mL	Dilute to 25 mL
2	5 mL	Dilute to 25 mL
3	10 mL	Dilute to 25 mL
4	15 mL	Dilute to 25 mL
5	20 mL	Dilute to 25 mL

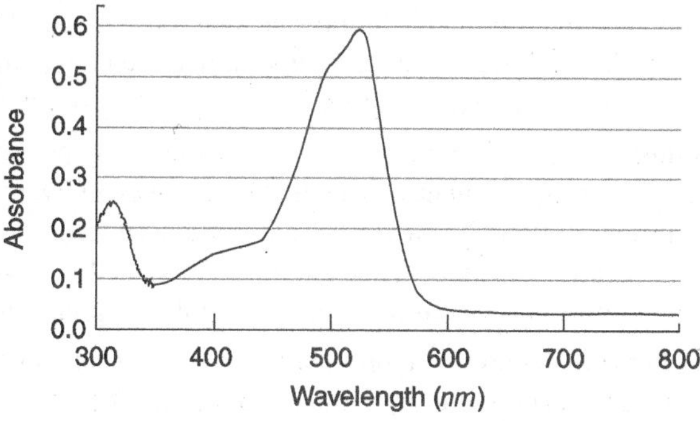

Figure 35.1 A representative absorption spectrum of a laboratory solution. Provided by Mike Schuder, Carroll College, Minnesota.

aligning the mark on the cuvet with that on the sample holder (or the clear sides of the cuvet in the path of EM radiation). The meter on the spectrophotometer should now read zero absorbance or 100%*T*. If not, consult with your instructor.

2. **Wavelength scan.** Set the wavelength of the spectrophotometer to the shortest wavelength setting (~350 nm). Place Solution 5 in Table 35.2 in a cuvet following the blank solution procedure in Part B.1. Measure and record the wavelength and absorbance.

   Scan the wavelength range of the spectrophotometer (~350 nm – ~700 nm) while recording absorbance values. The spectrophotometer may do this continuously and automatically, or you may need to manually scan every ~10 nm. If you scan manually, it is suggested that you set the absorbance at zero (100%*T*) with the blank solution (0.01 *M* HNO_3) at *each* chosen wavelength before recording the absorbance for Solution 5.

   Plot the data, absorption, *A* (ordinate) versus wavelength, λ (abscissa), manually or with the appropriate software to determine the λ_{max}, the wavelength where maximum absorption occurs for your metal ion (see Figure 35.1). Ask your instructor to approve your graph.

Data Analysis, F

C. Plot the Calibration Curve

1. **Absorbance of standard solutions.** Set the spectrophotometer at λ_{max}. Record the absorbance of Solution 5 at λ_{max}. Measure the absorbance for the other standard solutions in Table 35.2, at λ_{max} starting with the most dilute (the blank).

   If *at least four* of the standard solutions are not in the absorbance range of 0 to ~1.1, prepare additional standard solutions.

2. **Plot the data for the calibration curve.** Plot absorbance, *A* (ordinate), versus molar concentration (abscissa) for the six solutions in Table 35.2. Draw the best straight line through the data points to establish the calibration curve. Use Excel or similar graphing software to obtain values of the slope and *y*-intercept for the data plot. Ask your instructor to approve your graph.

Data Analysis, F, G

D. Unknown Metal Ion Concentration

1. **Prepare the unknown sample.** Collect a ~30-mL sample of your unknown. Filter the sample if it is cloudy (for example, if it is a sample from an unknown source or a sample from an electroplating bath).[1] Pipet 20 mL of the (filtered) sample into a 25-mL volumetric flask. Add 1–2 mL of the appropriate complexing agent (Table 35.1) and dilute to volume with 0.01 *M* HNO_3. Agitate the solution. The sample should be clear.

[1]Turbidity in the sample can dramatically affect the absorbance reading of a sample and therefore affect the presumed concentration of the metal ion in solution.

The absorbance measurement should fall within the range of the standard solutions (<1.1) on the calibration curve. If not, adjust the concentrations of the standard solutions or the sample preparation accordingly. Consult with your instructor.

2. **Concentration of metal ion.** Once the sample is prepared, measure its absorbance in the same manner as the absorbance values were measured for the standard solutions in Part C.1. Read the calibration curve to determine the molar concentration of the metal ion in the sample. Account for any dilution to determine the molar concentration of the metal ion in the original sample.
3. **Expressing concentration.** Conventionally, in real-world samples, the metal ion concentrations are expressed in units of ppm (*mg/L*) or even smaller units, depending on the concentration of the metal ion. Express the concentration of your metal ion "appropriately" in units of mass/volume. Mass per volume units may be parts per hundred (pph or percent), parts per million (ppm), parts per billion (ppb), and so on.

Dispose of all prepared solutions in the Waste Metal Salts container.

The Next Step

(1) Research the spectrophotometric analysis of a metal ion of interest. Design a procedure(s) for its analysis as a function of a few select parameters. (2) Read to determine the advantages (or disadvantages) of using FAAS or ICP-AES for the analysis of metal ions. What are the similarities in the procedure for FAAS and visible spectrophotometric analyses? (3) Other metal ion analysis methods include the use of graphite furnace atomic absorption (GFAA), microwave-induced plasma (MIP), and DC arc plasma. Where are these methods of analysis most applicable?

Notes and Calculations

Experiment 35 *Prelaboratory Assignment*

Spectrophotometric Metal Ion Analysis

Date__________ Lab Sec. ______ Name ______________________________ Desk No. __________

1. Of the 100 mL of stock solution that is to be prepared for Part A.1, how many milliliters (total volume) will be used for preparing the standard solutions in Part A.2?

2. Experimental Procedure, Part A.1. A 100.0-mL volume of a 0.10 *M* stock solution of Cu^{2+} is to be prepared using $CuSO_4 \cdot 5H_2O$ (molar mass = 249.68 g/mol).[2]

   a. How many grams of $CuSO_4 \cdot 5H_2O$ must be measured for the preparation?

   b. Describe the procedure for the preparation of 0.01 *M* HNO_3, the solution used as a diluent, starting with *conc* (16 *M*) HNO_3.

   c. A 2.0-mL pipet transfers the 0.10 *M* Cu^{2+} stock solution to a 25.0-mL volumetric flask, which is then diluted to the mark of the volumetric flask with 0.01 *M* HNO_3. What is the molar concentration of the diluted Cu^{2+} solution?

3. Experimental Procedure, Part B. Briefly describe the procedure of setting λ_{max} for a metal ion solution on the spectrophotometer.

4. Experimental Procedure, Part C. A calibration curve for a common metal(II) ion is as shown:

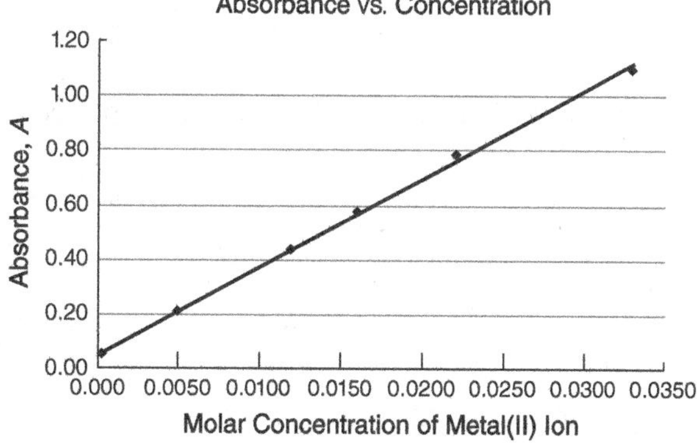

[2] $CuSO_4 \cdot 5H_2O$ is used as an agricultural fungicide, bactericide, and herbicide.

a. A metal(II) ion solution of unknown concentration shows an absorbance of 0.55. What is the molar concentration of the metal(II) ion in the sample?

b. Assuming a molar mass of the metal(II) ion is 58.93 g/mol, what is the concentration of metal(II) ion in units of mg/L (ppm)?

c. For a metal(II) ion solution having a 0.0080 *M* concentration, what would be its predicted absorbance?

5. Experimental Procedure, Part D. The unknown metal ion concentration in your sample has an absorbance that is outside the range of the absorbance values for the standard solutions. What procedure(s) should be taken to rectify the discrepancy? Explain.

6. Refer to Figure 35.1.

a. Identify the color of the visible spectrum where maximum absorption occurs (see *Dry Lab 3*).

b. What is the predicted color of the solution?

c. The Co^{2+} ion has a λ_{max} for absorption at 510 nm. Will a Co^{2+} solution have the same exact color as the solution of Figure 35.1? Explain.

Experiment 35 *Report Sheet*

Spectrophotometric Metal Ion Analysis

Date ________ Lab Sec. ______ Name ______________________________ Desk No. ________

Metal Ion for Analysis ____________________

A. A Set of Standard Solutions

1. **Prepare a stock solution.** Show the calculation for the mass of metal ion salt in the preparation of the stock solution. See ***Prelaboratory Assignment***, question 2a.

Measured tared mass of metal ion salt (*g*) __________
Describe the preparation of the 0.10 *M* stock solution.

Concentration of stock solution (*mol/L*) __________

B. Determination of λ_{max}

2. **Wavelength scan.** Use the following table to record wavelength and absorbance data.

λ	Abs	λ	Abs	λ	Abs	λ	Abs	λ	Abs	λ	Abs	λ	Abs

Plot the data of absorbance versus wavelength to set λ_{max}. From the data plot, λ_{max} = ______________ nm

Have the instructor approve your graph. ______________________________

C. Plot the Calibration Curve

1. **Absorbance of standard solutions.** Read and record the absorbance values for the standard solutions.

Standard Solution	Volume of Standard Solution (*mL*)	Absorbance	Calculated Molar Concentration
Blank	0		
1	1		
2	5		
3	10		
4	15		
5	20		
others as needed			

Plot the calibration curve of absorbance versus molar concentration for the standard solutions. ***Data Analysis, F, G***

Calculate the absorptivity coefficient for the metal ion.

Have the instructor approve your graph. ________________________________

D. Unknown Metal Ion Concentration

1. **Prepare the unknown.** Describe the preparation for the solution containing the unknown concentration of the metal ion.

   Volume of unknown sample solution (*mL*) ____________

   Volume of diluted sample (*mL*) ____________

2. **Concentration of metal ion.** Absorbance of metal ion in solution ____________

   Concentration of metal ion from the calibration curve (*mol/L*) ____________

   Concentration of metal ion in the original sample corrected for dilution (*mol/L*) ____________

   Show your calculations to account for the dilution of the original sample.

3. **Expressing Concentration.** Express the concentration of the metal ion in the sample in appropriate units of mass/volume [i.e., pph (percent), ppm, ppb, etc.].

   Concentration of metal ion in the original sample (*mass/volume*) ____________

   Show calculations.

Laboratory Questions

Circle the questions that have been assigned.

1. Part A.1. For the preparation of the stock solution, 0.01 *M* HNO_3 is used as a diluent rather than deionized water. Explain why. *Hint:* Review the solubility rules of transition metal ions in Appendix E.
2. Part A.2. In diluting the standard solutions, 0.01 *M* HNO_3 is used. In the dilution, is it more important to use the correct volume or the correct concentration of the HNO_3 solution for the dilution? Explain.
3. Part B.1. Calibration of the spectrophotometer to set the λ_{max} is important for a spectrophotometric analysis. Referring to Figure 35.1, suppose the wavelength for all subsequent absorbance measurements had been set at 450 nm instead of the λ_{max}. Explain how this would affect the recorded absorbance values for subsequent test solutions. *Note:* It is not because the absorbance values would be *wrong*!
4. Part B.2. Will $Fe^{3+}(aq)$ or $Cu^{2+}(aq)$ have the shorter λ_{max} for absorption in the visible spectrum? Explain. *Hint:* $Fe^{3+}(aq)$ has an orange–brown color, and $Cu^{2+}(aq)$ has a blue color. See *Dry Lab 3*.
5. Part D.1. An electrolytic-bath sample containing the metal ion of unknown concentration contains suspended matter. Because of a lack of time, the absorbance of the sample was measured and recorded as is. As a result, will the concentration of the metal ion in the unknown be reported as too high, too low, or remain unchanged as a result of chemist's hasty decision? Explain.
6. Part D.2. The cuvet used for the absorbance measurements is not wiped clean with a Kimwipe before the absorbance measurement. As a result, will the concentration of the metal ion in the unknown be reported as too high, too low, or remain unchanged as a result of this poor technique? Explain.

Experiment 36

Transition Metal Complexes

Jo A. Beran/Trey Hernandez

The appearance of a nickel(II) ion complex depends on the ligands; at left is $[Ni(H_2O)_6]^{2+}$ and at right is $[Ni(NH_3)_6]^{2+}$.

Objectives

- To observe the various colors associated with transition metal ions
- To determine the relative strengths of ligands
- To compare the stability of complexes
- To synthesize a coordination compound

Techniques

The following techniques are used in the Experimental Procedure:

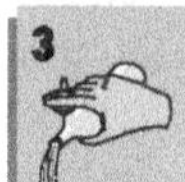

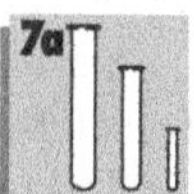

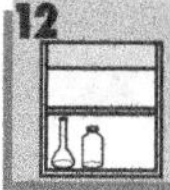

Introduction

One of the most intriguing features of the transition metal ions is their vast array of colors. The blues, greens, and reds that we associate with chemicals are oftentimes due to the presence of transition metal ions. We observed these colors in *Experiments 6, 27, 28, 34* and *35*, where it was noted that some colors are characteristic of certain hydrated transition metal ions; for example, hydrated Cu^{2+} salts are blue, Ni^{2+} salts are green, and Fe^{3+} salts are rust-colored.

A second interesting feature of the transition metal ions is that subtle, and on occasion very significant, color changes occur when molecules or ions other than water bond to the metal ion to form a **complex.** These molecules or ions including water, called **ligands,** are Lewis bases (electron pair donors) that bond directly to the metal ion, producing a change in the electronic energy levels of the metal ion. As a result, the energy (and also the wavelengths) of light absorbed by the electrons in the transition metal ion and, consequently, the energy (and wavelengths) of light transmitted change.[1] The solution has a new color.

Complex: an ion or molecule formed between a metal ion (a Lewis acid) and a number of anions or molecules (Lewis bases)

Ligand: a Lewis base (an electron-pair donor) that combines with a metal ion to form a complex

The complex has a number of ligands bonded to the transition metal ion that form a **coordination sphere.** The complex along with its neutralizing ion is called a **coordination compound.** For example, $K_4[Fe(CN)_6]$ is a coordination compound: the six CN^- ions are the ligands, $Fe(CN)_6$ is the coordination sphere, and $[Fe(CN)_6]^{4-}$ is the complex.

Coordination sphere: the metal ion and all ligands of the complex

Coordination compound: a neutral compound which has a cationic and/or an anionic complex ion

[1] See *Dry Lab 3* for a discussion of the theory of the origin of color in substances.

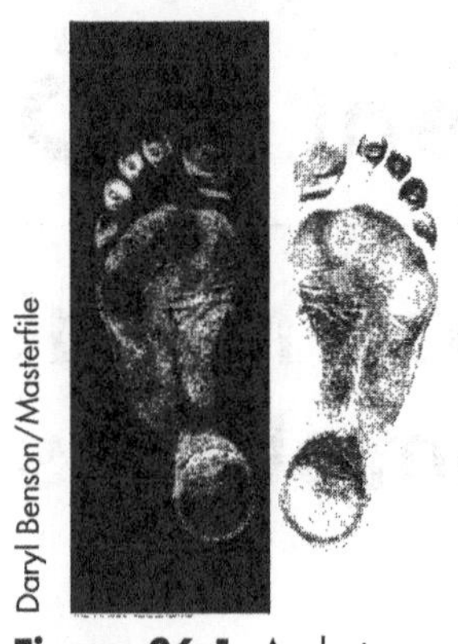

Daryl Benson/Masterfile

Figure 36.1 A photographic negative and a positive print made from it

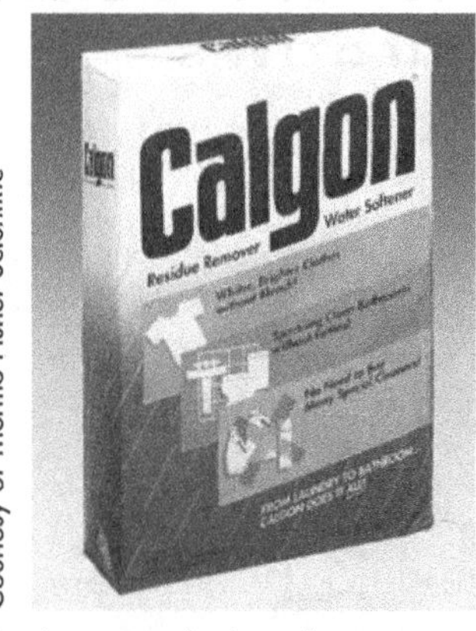

Courtesy of Thermo Fisher Scientific

Sodium tripolyphosphate, a component of Calgon, complexes and solubilizes $Ca^{2+}(aq)$—thus the undesirable "calcium is gone" from the wash water!

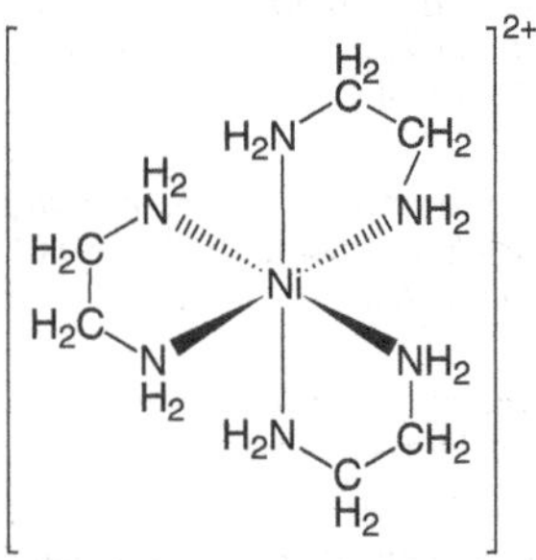

Figure 36.2 The complex shows three ethylenediamine ligands, each as a bidentate ligand. Ethylenediamine is a chelating agent.

More than the intrigue of the color and color changes are the varied uses that these complexes have in our society. A few examples of the applicability of complex formation follow:

- For photographic film development (Figure 36.1), sodium thiosulfate, $Na_2S_2O_3$, called **hypo,** removes the unsensitized silver ion from the film at right in the form of the soluble silver complex, $[Ag(S_2O_3)_2]^{3-}$:

$$AgBr(s) + 2\ S_2O_3^{2-}(aq) \longrightarrow [Ag(S_2O_3)_2]^{3-}(aq) + Br^-(aq)$$

- For the removal of calcium ion hardness from water, soluble polyphosphates, such as sodium tripolyphosphate, $Na_5P_3O_{10}$, may be added to detergents to form a soluble calcium complex:

$$Ca^{2+}(aq) + P_3O_{10}^{5-}(aq) \longrightarrow [CaP_3O_{10}]^{3-}(aq)$$

- For mercury and lead poisoning by ingestion, mercaptol (British anti-Lewisite), $C_3H_8OS_2$, is swallowed for purposes of forming the complex with the metal ion and rendering the free ion ineffective:

$$Hg^{2+}(aq)\ [\text{or } Pb^{2+}\ (aq)] + 2C_3H_8OS_2\ (aq) \longrightarrow [Hg(C_3H_8OS_2)_2]^{2+}(aq)$$

- In the qualitative identification of transition metal ions (*Experiments 38* and *39*), many of the transition metal ions are confirmed present as a result of complex formation: copper ion as $[Cu(NH_3)_4]^{2+}$, nickel ion as $Ni(HDMG)_2$, iron(III) ion as $[FeNCS]^{2+}$, and zinc ion as $[Zn_3[Fe(CN)_6]_2]^{2-}$.
- Trace amounts of metal ions such as zinc, aluminum, and iron tend to catalyze the air oxidation (the spoilage) of various foods. To retard spoilage and extend the shelf life, some food companies add a small amount of calcium disodium ethylenediaminetetraacetate, abbreviated $CaNa_2Y$, to their product. The Y^{4-} ion (Table 36.1) complexes (or sequesters) the metal ions and nullifies their catalytic activity. The H_2Y^{2-} ion is also used to analyze for water hardness, complexing the Ca^{2+} and Mg^{2+} as water-soluble CaH_2Y and MgH_2Y (*Experiment 21*) in a titration procedure.

The bond strength between the transition metal ion and its ligands varies, depending on the electron pair donor (Lewis base) strength of the ligand and the electron pair acceptor (Lewis acid) strength of the transition metal ion. Ligands may be neutral (e.g., H_2O, NH_3, $H_2NCH_2CH_2NH_2$) or anionic (e.g., CN^-, SCN^-, Cl^-).

A single ligand may form one bond to the metal ion (a **monodentate** ligand), two bonds to the metal ion (a **bidentate** ligand), three bonds to the metal ion (a **tridentate** ligand), and so on. Ligands that form two or more bonds to a transition metal ion are also called **chelating agents** and **sequestering agents** (Figure 36.2). In Table 36.1, note that a nonbonding electron pair (a Lewis base) is positioned on each atom of the ligand that serves as a bonding site to the transition metal ion.

The complex formed between a chelating agent (a *poly*dentate ligand) and a metal ion is generally *more* stable than that formed between a monodentate ligand and a metal ion. The explanation is that the several ligand–metal bonds between a polydentate ligand and a metal ion are more difficult to break than a single bond between a monodentate ligand and a metal ion. The stability of complexes having polydentate ligands will be compared with the stability of those having only monodentate ligands in this experiment.

The *number of bonds* between a metal ion and its ligands is called the **coordination number** of the complex. If four monodentate ligands or two bidentate ligands bond to a metal ion, the coordination number for the complex is 4. Six water molecules, or six cyanide ions, or three ethylenediamine (a bidentate ligand) molecules (see Figure 36.2), or two diethylenetriamine (a tridentate ligand) molecules

Table 36.1 Common Ligands

Monodentate Ligands

H_2O:, :NH_3, :CN^-, :SCN^-, :$S_2O_3^{2-}$, :F^-, :Cl^-, :Br^-, :I^- :OH^-

Polydentate Ligands (Chelating Agents)

Ethylenediamine (en)

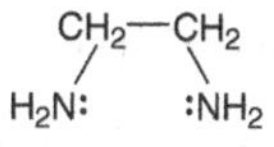

Oxalate ion

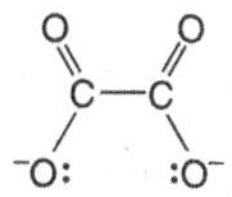

Mercaptol

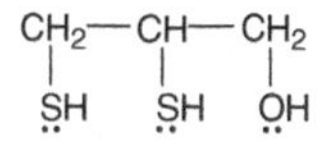

Tartrate ion

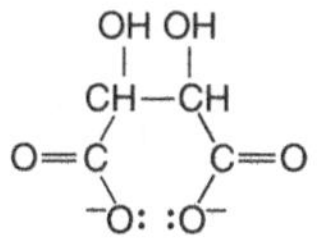

Diethylenetriamine

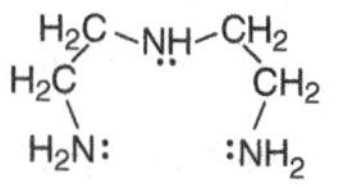

Tripolyphosphate ion, $P_3O_{10}^{5-}$

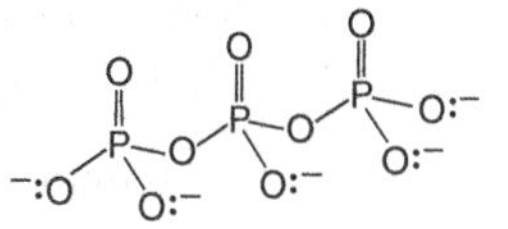

Ethylenediaminetetraacetate ion, Y^{-4}

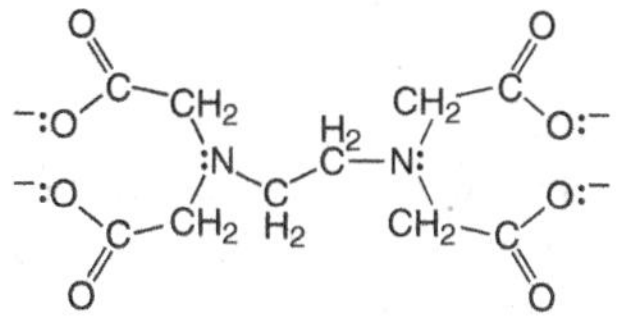

Dimethylglyoxime

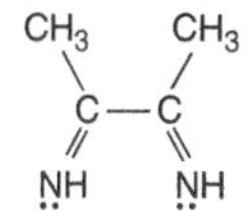

Table 36.2 Common Coordination Numbers of Some Transition Metal Ions

Coordination Number	Transition Metal Ions
2	Ag^+, Au^+
4	Hg^{2+}, Cu^{2+}, Ni^{2+}, Co^{2+}, Zn^{2+}, Pd^{2+}, Pt^{2+}, Au^{3+}
6	Co^{2+}, Co^{3+}, Fe^{2+}, Fe^{3+}, Cr^{3+}, Ni^{2+}, Cu^{2+}

bonded to a given metal ion all form a complex with a coordination number of 6 (Figure 36.3). Coordination numbers of 2, 4, and 6 are most common among the transition metal ions.

Table 36.2 lists the common coordination numbers for some transition metal ions.

In Parts A, B, C, and D of this experiment, we will observe the formation of complexes between Cu^{2+}, Ni^{2+}, and Co^{2+} ions and the ligands Cl^-, H_2O, NH_3, ethylenediamine (en), and the thiocyanate ion, SCN^-. In specified examples, we will determine the stability of the complex.

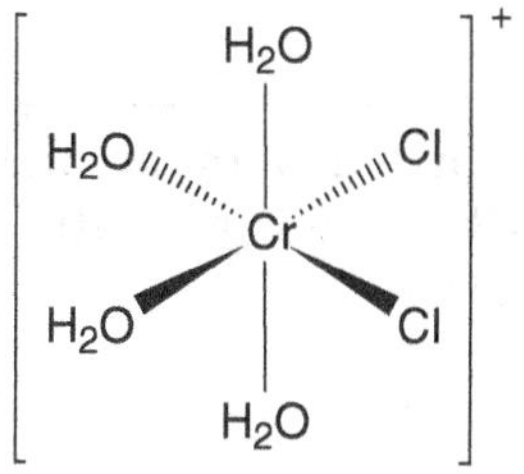

Figure 36.3 The complex has a coordination number of 6; each ligand is monodentate.

Stablity of a Complex

The stability of a complex can be determined by mixing it with an anion known to form a precipitate with the cation of the complex. The anion most commonly used to measure the stability of a complex is the hydroxide ion. For example, consider the copper(II) ion and the generic mondentate ligand, X^-, forming the complex $[CuX_4]^{2-}$:

$$Cu^{2+}(aq) + 4\,X^-(aq) \rightleftharpoons [CuX_4]^{2-}(aq)$$

When hydroxide ion is added to this system (in a state of dynamic equilibrium), the free copper(II) ion has a choice of now combining with the anion that forms the stronger bond—in other words, there is competition for the copper(II) ion between the two anions, X^- and OH^-, in solution. If the ligand forms the stronger bond to the copper(II) ion, the complex remains in solution and no change is observed; if, on the other hand, the hydroxide forms a stronger bond to the copper(II) ion, $Cu(OH)_2$ precipitates from solution:

$$Cu^{2+}(aq) + 2\ OH^-(aq) \rightleftharpoons Cu(OH)_2(s)$$

Therefore, a measure of the stability of the complex is determined.

To write the formulas of the complexes in this experiment, we will assume that the coordination number of Cu^{2+} is always 4 and that of Ni^{2+} and Co^{2+} is always 6.

Parts E, F, and G outline the syntheses of several coordination compounds:

- tetraamminecopper(II) sulfate monohydrate, $[Cu(NH_3)_4]SO_4{\cdot}H_2O$
- hexaamminenickel(II) chloride, $[Ni(NH_3)_6]Cl_2$
- *tris*(ethylenediamine)nickel(II) chloride dihydrate, $[Ni(en)_3]Cl_2{\cdot}2H_2O$

Tetraamminecopper(II) Sulfate Monohydrate Synthesis

Ammonia is added to an aqueous solution of copper(II) sulfate pentahydrate, $[Cu(H_2O)_4]SO_4{\cdot}H_2O$ (molar mass = 249.68 g/mol). Ammonia displaces the four water ligands from the coordination sphere:

$$[Cu(H_2O)_4]SO_4{\cdot}H_2O + 4\ NH_3 \xrightarrow{\text{aqueous}} [Cu(NH_3)_4]SO_4{\cdot}H_2O + 4\ H_2O \qquad (36.1)$$

The solution is cooled, and 95 percent ethanol is added to reduce the solubility of the *deep-blue* tetraamminecopper(II) sulfate (molar mass = 245.61 g/mol) salt, which then crystallizes.

Hexaamminenickel(II) Chloride Synthesis

For the preparation of hexaamminenickel(II) chloride, six ammonia molecules displace the six water ligands in $[Ni(H_2O)_6]Cl_2$ (molar mass = 237.71 g/mol):

$$[Ni(H_2O)_6]Cl_2 + 6\ NH_3 \xrightarrow{\text{aqueous}} [Ni(NH_3)_6]Cl_2 + 6\ H_2O \qquad (36.2)$$

The $[Ni(NH_3)_6]Cl_2$ coordination compound (molar mass = 231.78 g/mol) is cooled and precipitated with 95 percent ethanol; the lower polarity of the 95 percent ethanol causes the *lavender* salt to become less soluble and precipitate.

Tris(ethylenediamine)nickel (II) Chloride Dihydrate Synthesis

Three ethylenediamine (en) molecules displace the six water ligands of $[Ni(H_2O)_6]Cl_2$ (molar mass = 237.71 g/mol) for the preparation of the *violet tris*(ethylenediamine) nickel(II) chloride dihydrate (molar mass = 345.92 g/mol):

$$[Ni(H_2O)_6]Cl_2 + 3\ en \xrightarrow{\text{aqueous}} [Ni(en)_3]Cl_2{\cdot}2H_2O + 4\ H_2O \qquad (36.3)$$

Experimental Procedure

Procedure Overview: Several complexes of Cu^{2+}, Ni^{2+}, and Co^{2+} are formed and studied. The observations of color change that result from the addition of a ligand are used to understand the relative stability of the various complexes that form. One or more coordination compounds are synthesized and isolated.

Notes on observation. Subtle color changes occur for solutions mixed in Parts A–D, so it is important to make careful and close observations. *Always* compare the test solution with the original aqueous solution. After each addition of the ligand-containing solution, tap the test tube to agitate the mixture (Figure 36.4) and view the solution at various angles to note the color (change) (Figure 36.5). If a color change occurs (*not* a change in color intensity), then a new complex has formed. On occasion you may need to discard some of the test solution if too much of the original solution was used.

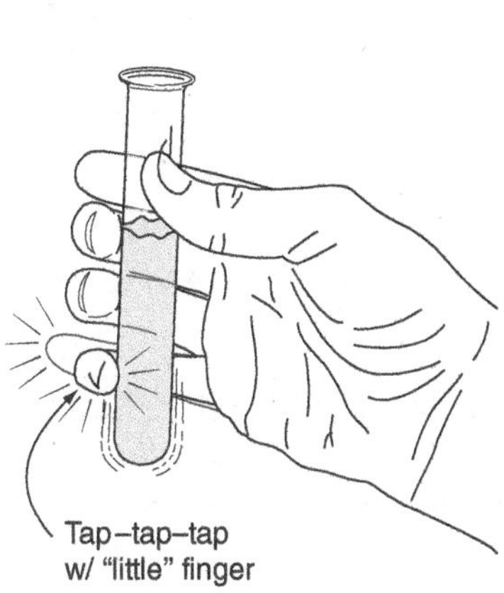

Figure 36.4 Shake the contents of the test tube with the little finger.

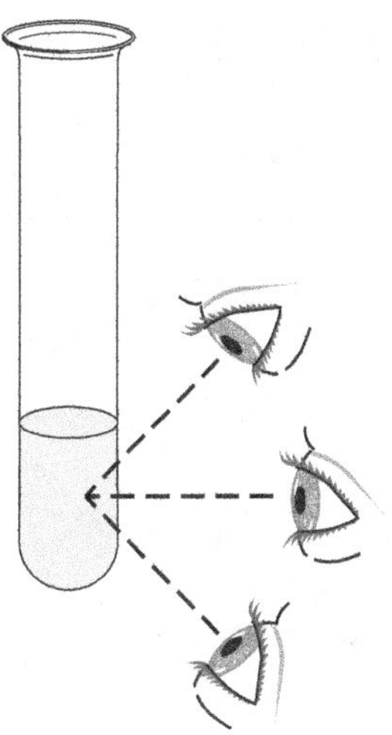

Figure 36.5 View solution from all angles.

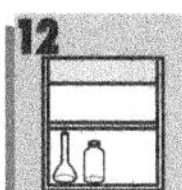

Caution: *Several of the ligand-containing solutions should be handled with care. The conc HCl, conc NH_3, and ethylenediamine reagents produce characteristic odors that are skin and respiratory irritants. Use drops as suggested and avoid inhalation and skin contact. Ask your instructor about the use of a fume hood for Parts A–D.*

From three to six 75-mm test tubes are used for Parts A, B, C, and D of the experiment. Plan to keep them clean, rinsing thoroughly after each use. However, do *not* discard any test solutions until the entire Part of the Experimental Procedure has been completed.

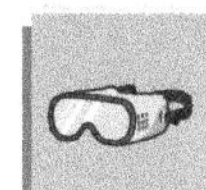

For Parts A–D, perform the experiment with a partner. At each circled superscript(1–9) in the procedure, *stop* and record your observation on the ***Report Sheet***. Discuss your observations with your lab partner and your instructor. Consult with your laboratory instructor to determine which of the coordination compounds outlined in Parts E, F, and G you are to synthesize.

A. Chloro Complexes of the Copper(II), Nickel(II), and Cobalt(II) Ions

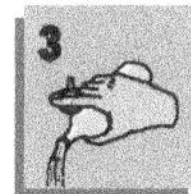
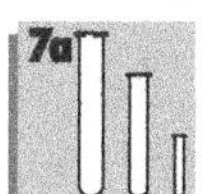

1. **Form the complexes.** Place ~0.5 mL of 0.1 *M* $CuSO_4$, 0.1 *M* $Ni(NO_3)_2$, and 0.1 *M* $CoCl_2$ into each of three separate 75-mm test tubes.(1) Add ~1 mL (20 drops) of *conc* HCl to each. (**Caution:** *Do not allow conc HCl to contact skin or clothing. Flush immediately the affected area with water.*) Tap the test tube to agitate. Record your observations on the ***Report Sheet***.(2)
2. **Dilute the complexes.** Slowly add ~1 mL (20 drops) of water to each test tube. Compare the colors of the solutions to ~2.5 mL of the original solutions. Does the original color return? Record.(3)

B. Complexes of the Copper(II) Ion

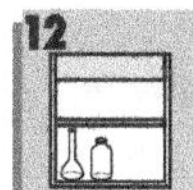

1. **Form the complexes.** Place ~0.5 mL of 0.1 *M* $CuSO_4$ in each of five 75-mm test tubes (Figure 36.6, page 402) and transfer them to the fume hood. Add 5 drops of *conc* NH_3 (**Caution:** *Avoid breathing vapors*) to the first test tube, 5 drops of ethylenediamine (**Caution:** *Avoid breathing its vapors, too*) to the second, 5 drops of 0.1 *M* KSCN to the third test tube, and nothing more to a fourth test tube.

   The fifth test tube can be used to form a complex with a ligand selected by your instructor—the thiosulfate anion, $S_2O_3^{2-}$, the oxalate anion, $C_2O_4^{2-}$, the tartrate anion, $(CHOH)_2(CO_2)_2^{2-}$, and the ethylenediaminetetraacetate anion, Y^{4-}, readily form complexes and are suggested.

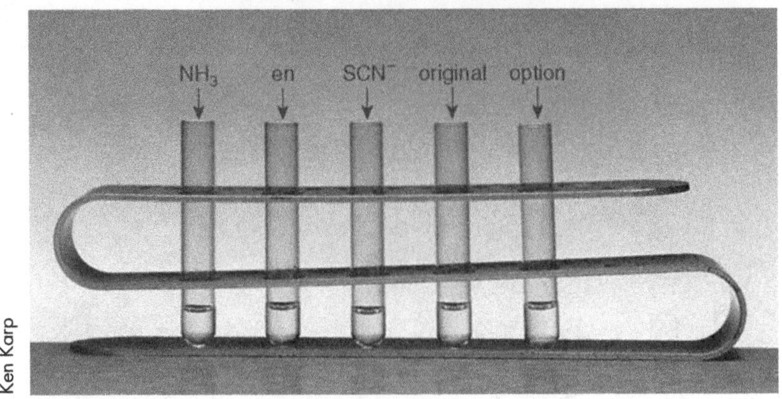

Figure 36.6 Set up of five test tubes for ligand addition to a metal ion.

If a precipitate forms in any of the solutions, *add an excess* of the ligand-containing solution. Compare the appearance of the test solutions with the 1 mL of original $CuSO_4$ solution in the fourth test tube.④

2. **Test for stability.** Add 3–5 drops of 1 *M* NaOH to each of the three (or four) solutions. Account for your observations.⑤

C. Complexes of the Nickel(II) Ion

1. **Form the complexes.** Repeat Part B.1, substituting 0.1 *M* $NiCl_2$ for 0.1 *M* $CuSO_4$. Record your observations.⑥
2. **Test for stability.** Add 3–5 drops of 1 *M* NaOH to each test solution. Account for your observations.⑦

D. Complexes of the Cobalt(II) Ion

1. **Form the complexes.** Repeat Part B.1, substituting 0.1 *M* $Co(NO_3)_2$ for 0.1 *M* $CuSO_4$. Record your observations.⑧
2. **Test for stability.** Add 3–5 drops of 1 *M* NaOH to each test solution. Account for your observations.⑨

Disposal: Dispose of the waste solutions from Parts A, B, C, and D in the Waste Metal Ion Solutions container.

CLEANUP: Rinse the test tubes twice with tap water and twice with deionized water and discard in the Waste Metal Ion Solutions container. Additional rinses can be discarded in the sink, followed by a generous amount of tap water.

E. Synthesis of Tetraamminecopper(II) Sulfate Monohydrate

Data Analysis, A

1. **Dissolve the starting material.** Measure 6 g (±0.01 g) of copper(II) sulfate pentahydrate, $[Cu(H_2O)_4]SO_4{\cdot}H_2O$, in a clean, dry previously mass-measured 125-mL Erlenmeyer flask. Dissolve the sample in 15 mL of deionized water. Heating may be necessary. Transfer the beaker to the fume hood.
2. **Precipitate the complex ion.** Add *conc* NH_3 (**Caution:** *Do not inhale*) until the precipitate that initially forms has dissolved. Cool the deep-blue solution in an ice bath. Cool ~20 mL of 95 percent ethanol (**Caution:** *Flammable, extinguish all flames*) to ice bath temperature and then slowly add it to the solution. The blue, solid complex should form.
3. **Isolate the product.** Premeasure the mass (±0.01 g) of a piece of filter paper and fit it in a Büchner funnel. Vacuum filter the solution (Figure 36.7); wash the solid with two 5-mL portions of cold 95 percent ethanol (*not* water!). Place the filter and

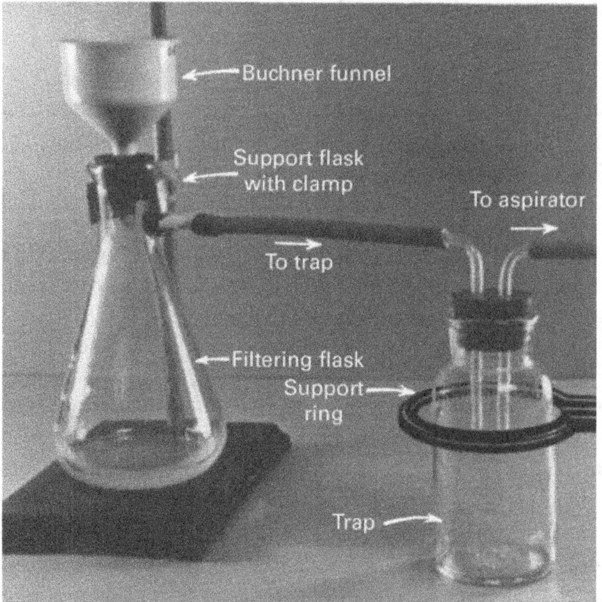

Figure 36.7 A vacuum filtration setup for filtering the coordination compound.

sample on a watchglass and allow the sample to air-dry. Determine the mass of the filter paper and product. Calculate the percent yield.

4. **Obtain the instructor's approval.** Transfer your product to a *clean, dry* test tube, stopper and (properly) label the test tube, and submit it to your instructor for approval.

F. Synthesis of Hexaamminenickel (II) Chloride

1. **Form the complex ion.** In a previously mass-measured 125-mL Erlenmeyer flask, measure and dissolve 6 g (±0.01 g) of nickel(II) chloride hexahydrate, $[Ni(H_2O)_6]Cl_2$, in (no more than) 10 mL of warm (~50°C) deionized water. In a fume hood, slowly add 20 mL of *conc* NH_3 **(Caution!).**

2. **Precipitate the complex ion.** Cool the mixture in an ice bath. Cool ~15 mL of 95 percent ethanol (**Caution:** *Flammable, extinguish all flames*) to ice bath temperature and then slowly add it to the solution. Allow the mixture to settle for complete precipitation of the lavender product. The supernatant should be nearly colorless.

3. **Isolate the product.** Premeasure the mass (±0.01 g) of a piece of filter paper, fitted for a Büchner funnel. Vacuum filter the product; wash with two 5-mL volumes of cold 95 percent ethanol. Air-dry the product and filter paper on a watchglass. Determine the mass of the filter paper and product. Calculate the percent yield.
4. **Obtain the instructor's approval.** Transfer your product to a *clean, dry* test tube, stopper and (properly) label the test tube, and submit it to your instructor for approval.

G. Synthesis of *Tris*(ethylenediamine)nickel (II) Chloride Dihydrate

1. **Form the complex ion.** In a previously mass-measured 125-mL Erlenmeyer flask, measure and dissolve 6 g (±0.01 g) of nickel(II) chloride hexahydrate, $[Ni(H_2O)_6]Cl_2$, in 10 mL of warm (~50°C) deionized water. Cool the mixture in an ice bath. In a fume hood, slowly add 10 mL ethylenediamine. (**Caution:** *Avoid skin contact and inhalation.*)
2. **Precipitate and isolate the product.** Complete as in Parts F.2 and F.3.

3. **Obtain the instructor's approval.** Transfer your product to a *clean, dry* test tube, stopper and (properly) label the test tube, and submit it to your instructor for approval.

> *Disposal:* Dispose of the waste solutions from Parts E, F, and G in the Waste Metal Ion Solutions container.

CLEANUP: Rinse all glassware twice with tap water and discard in the Waste Metal Ion Solutions container. Rinse the glassware twice with deionized water and discard in the sink; follow with a generous supply of tap water.

The Next Step

The formation of coordination compounds is common in nature and the laboratory. The complexing of trace metal ions in soils maintains a stable plant nutrient base. Complexing metal ions in electroplating baths results in the uniform deposition of metal ions at cathodes. The formation of the iron-hemoglobin complex is vital to life. Complexing "hot" metal ions from nuclear reactors assists in cleaning reactor cores. Research the presence of a transition a metal ion complex in nature, and design a plan for its analysis. Research the synthesis and analysis of a transition metal ion complex. Most are quite colorful!

Notes

Experiment 36 *Prelaboratory Assignment*

Transition Metal Complexes

Date ________ Lab Sec. ______ Name ______________________________ Desk No. ________

1. Consider the coordination compound, $[CoCl(NH_3)_4(H_2O)]SO_4$. Use the definitions in the Introduction to identify the following with the formula and charge (if applicable).
   a. the ligand(s)

   b. the complex

   c. the coordination sphere

   d. the coordination number of cobalt

2. Write the formula of the complex ion that forms between
   a. the ligand Cl^- and the platinum(II) ion with a coordination number of four.

   b. the ligand ethylenediamine (abbreviated "en"), and the chromium(III) ion with a coordination number of six.

   c. the ligand dihydrogen ethylenediaminetetraacetate, (abbreviated H_2Y^{2-}), and the zinc(II) ion with a coordination number of four. See Table 36.1.

3. Experimental Procedure, Parts A–D. Identify the chemicals that are cited as **cautions**.

4. Experimental Procedure, Parts A–D. Of the *four* ligands in the study, which is or are polydentate(s)?

5. Experimental Procedure, Parts A–D. The stability for a number of transition metal complexes is determined in this experiment. What is the chemical test that is used? Explain.

6. Ammonia, NH_3, is a stronger ligand than Cl^- but weaker than CN^-. Complete the balanced equations for the reactions that are predicted to occur.

$CoCl_6^{3-}$ (*aq*) + CN^-(*aq*) →

$Co(NH_3)_6^{3+}$(*aq*) + Cl^-(*aq*) →

$Co(CN)_6^{3-}$(*aq*) + NH_3(*aq*) →

7. Experimental Procedure, Part E. A 6.0-g sample of $[Cu(H_2O)_4]SO_4{\cdot}H_2O$ (molar mass = 249.68 g/mol) is dissolved in deionized water. If an excess of ammonia is added to the solution, solid $[Cu(NH_3)_4]SO_4{\cdot}H_2O$ (molar mass = 245.61 g/mol) forms. What is the theoretical yield of product from the reaction?

8. When 6 *M* NaOH is slowly added to a solution containing chromium(III) ion, a precipitate forms. However when an excess of 6 *M* NaOH is added, the precipitate dissolves, forming a complex ion with a coordination number of four.

a. Write the formula of the precipitate.

b. Write the formula of the complex ion (for example, see *Experiment 15*).

9. Compare the stability of an ammonia complex and ethylenediaminetetraacetate, (H_2Y^{3-}) complex with the addition of the hydroxide ion, OH^-(*ag*).

Experiment 36 *Report Sheet*

Transition Metal Complexes

Date ________ Lab Sec. ______ Name ______________________________ Desk No. ________

A. Chloro Complexes of the Copper(II), Nickel(II), and Cobalt(II) Ions

Solution	①Color/H_2O	②Color/HCl	Formula of Complex	③Effect of H_2O
0.1 *M* $CuSO_4$				
0.1 *M* $Ni(NO_3)_2$				
0.1 *M* $CoCl_2$				

For each metal ion, state whether the aqua complex or the chloro complex is more stable:

Cu^{2+} ____________; Ni^{2+} ____________; Co^{2+} ____________

B. Complexes of the Copper(II) Ion

Ligand	④Color	Formula of Complex	⑤Effect of OH^-
NH_3			
Ethylenediamine			
SCN^-			
H_2O			
________			

C. Complexes of the Nickel(II) Ion

Ligand	⑥Color	Formula of Complex	⑦Effect of OH^-
NH_3			
Ethylenediamine			
SCN^-			
H_2O			
________			

D. Complexes of the Cobalt(II) Ion

Ligand	⑧Color	Formula of Complex	⑨Effect of OH^-
NH_3			
Ethylenediamine			
SCN^-			
H_2O			
________			

Review of Data

Of the complexes formed with copper(II), nickel(II), and colbalt(II), which metal ion appears to form the most stable complexes? Explain. Also see Laboratory Question 5.

Synthesis of a Coordination Compound

Name and formula of coordination compound ______________________________

1. Mass of Erlenmeyer flask (*g*) ____________________
2. Mass of Erlenmeyer flask + starting material (*g*) ____________________
3. Mass of starting material (*g*) ____________________
4. Mass of filter paper (*g*) ____________________
5. Mass of filter paper + product (*g*) ____________________ **Data Analysis, A**
6. Mass of product (*g*) ____________________
7. Instructor's approval ______________________________
8. Theoretical yield of product* (*g*) ____________________
9. Percent yield* (%) ____________________ **Data Analysis, E**

*Show calculation.

Laboratory Questions

Circle the questions that have been assigned

1. Part A.2. Is the chloride ion or water a stronger ligand? Explain.
2. Part B.1. Is water or ammonia a stronger ligand. Explain.
3. Part B.2. Is ammonia or ethylenediamine a stronger ligand? Explain.
4. Parts A–D. Of the five ligands—Cl^-, NH_3, $H_2NCH_2CH_2NH_2$, SCN^-, and H_2O—studied in this experiment, which ligand appeared to be the strongest ligand? Why? Which ligand appeared to be the weakest? Why?
5. Parts A–D. Along period 4 of the periodic table, cobalt, nickel, and copper appear in succession. From your data, does a trend in the stability of complexes that they form seem to exist? Explain.
6. Part E.2.
   a. A solution of potassium cyanide, KCN, instead of *conc* NH_3 is added. Write the formula of the expected complex ion.
   b. A solution of potassium chloride, KCl, instead of *conc* NH_3 is added. Write the formula of the expected complex ion.
7. Part E.2. Identify the precipitate that forms *before* the addition of excess *conc* NH_3. *Hint:* Ammonia is a base.
8. Part E.3. Why is 95 percent ethanol used to wash the solid [the tetraamminecopper(II) sulfate monohydrate product] on the filter paper instead of deionized water?

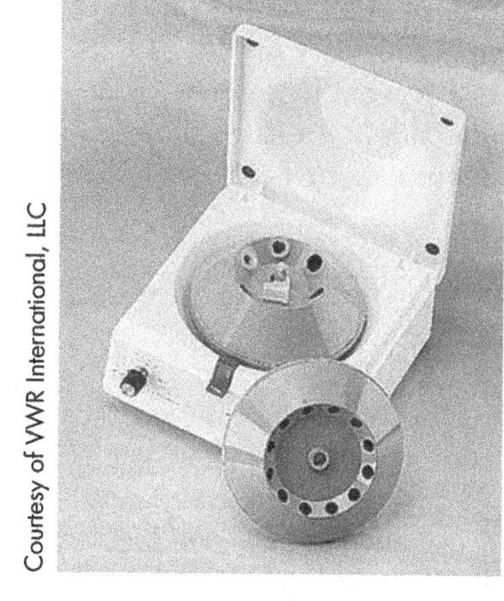
Courtesy of VWR International, LLC

Dry Lab 4

Preface to Qualitative Analysis

A centrifuge compacts a precipitate by centrifugal force.

Some rocks have a reddish tint; others are nearly black. Table salt is white, but not all salts are white. A quick, yet simple, identification of the ions of a salt or in a salt mixture is often convenient. Gold prospectors were quick to identify the presence of gold or silver. It is the characteristic physical and chemical properties of an ion that will allow us in the next series of experiments to identify its presence in a sample. For example, the Ag^+ ion is identified as being present in a solution by its precipitation as the chloride $AgCl(s)$. Although other cations precipitate as the chloride, silver chloride is the only one that is soluble in an ammoniacal solution.[1]

Many ions have similar chemical properties, but each ion also has unique chemical properties. To characteristically identify a particular ion in a mixture, the interferences of ions with similar properties must be eliminated. The chemist must take advantage of the unique chemical properties of the ion in question to determine its presence in a mixture. A procedure that follows this pattern of analysis is called **qualitative analysis**.

Qualitative analysis: a systematic procedure by which the presence (or absence) of a substance (usually a cation or anion) can be determined

The separation and identification of the ions in a mixture require the application of many chemical principles, many of which we will cite as we proceed. An *understanding* of the chemistry of precipitate formation, ionic equilibrium, acids and bases, pH, oxidation and reduction reactions, and complex formation is necessary for their successful separation and identification. To help you understand these principles and test procedures, each experiment presents some pertinent chemical equations, but you are also asked to write equations for other reactions that occur in the separation and identification of the ions.

To complete the procedures for the separation and identification of ions, you will need to practice good laboratory techniques and also develop several new techniques. The most critical techniques in qualitative analysis are the maintenance of clean glassware and the prevention of contamination of the testing reagents.

A. Measuring Test Solutions

Most of the testing for ions are performed in small (~3 mL) test tubes or centrifuge tubes that fit the centrifuges used in your laboratory. Reagents will be added with dropper bottles or dropping pipets (~15–20 drops/mL; you should do a preliminary check with your dropping pipet to determine the drops/mL). If the procedure

[1]This was one test procedure that prospectors for silver used in the early prospecting days.

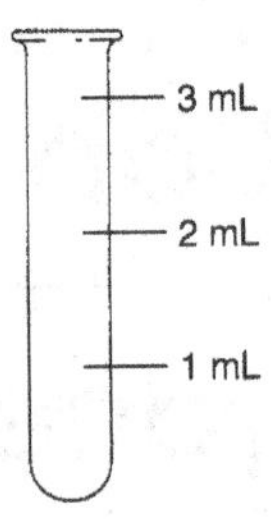

Figure D4.1 Use the 10-mL graduated cylinder or pipet to transfer 1 mL, 2 mL, and 3 mL of water to a small test tube. Mark the test tube at each mark.

dictates the addition of 1 mL, do *not* use a graduated cylinder to transfer the 1 mL; instead, use the dropping pipet or estimate the addition of 1 mL in the (~3-mL) test tube (Figure D4.1). Do *not* mix the different dropping pipets with the various test reagents you will be using and do *not* contaminate a reagent by inserting your pipet or dropping pipet into it. Instead, if the procedure calls for a larger volume, first dispense a small amount of reagent into one of your *small* beakers or test tubes.

B. Testing for Complete Precipitation

Precipitating reagent: a solution containing an ion(s) that, when added to a second solution, causes a precipitate to form

Oftentimes it is advisable to test a supernatant to determine if complete precipitation of an ion has occurred. After the mixture has been centrifuged, add a drop of the **precipitating reagent** to the supernatant (Figure D4.2). If a precipitate forms, add several more drops, disperse the mixture with a stirring rod or by gentle agitation, and centrifuge. Repeat the test for complete precipitation.

C. Washing a Precipitate

A precipitate must often be washed to remove occluded impurities. Add deionized water or wash liquid to the precipitate, disperse the solid thoroughly with a stirring rod or by gentle agitation, centrifuge, and decant. Usually, the wash liquid can be discarded. Two washings are usually satisfactory. Failure to properly wash precipitates often leads to errors in the analysis (and arguments with your laboratory instructor!) because of the presence of occluded contaminating or interfering ions.

As you will be using the centrifuge frequently in the next several experiments, *be sure to read carefully Technique 11F* in the **Laboratory Techniques** section of this manual.

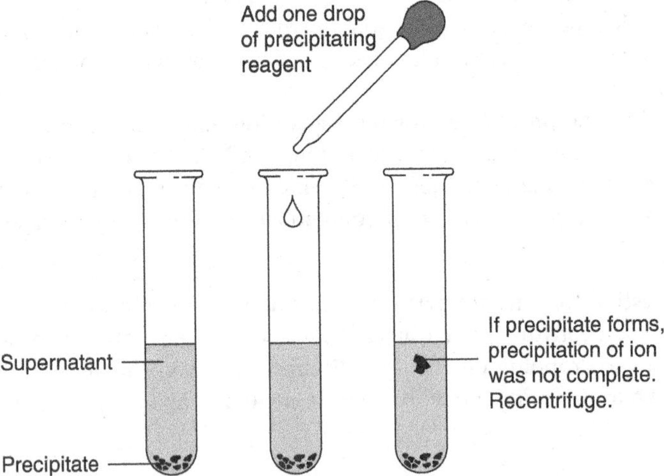

Figure D4.2 A test for the complete precipitation of an ion

D. Constructing Flow Diagrams

A flow diagram is often used to organize the sequence of test procedures for the separation and identification of the large number of ions in a mixture. A flow diagram uses several standard notations:

- Brackets, [ ], indicate the use of a test reagent written in molecular form.
- A longer single horizontal line, ______, indicates a separation of a precipitate from a solution, most often with a centrifuge.
- Two short vertical lines, ||, indicate the presence of a precipitate; these lines are drawn to the *left* of the single horizontal line.
- One short vertical line, |, indicates a supernatant and is drawn to the *right* of the single horizontal line.
- A double horizontal line, ═══, indicates the presence of soluble ions in the solution.
- Two branching diagonal lines, ^, indicate a separation of the existing solution into two portions.
- A rectangular box, □, placed around a compound or the result of a test confirms the presence of the ion.

The flow diagram for the anions is presented in *Experiment 37* page 414. Study it closely and become familiar with the symbols and notations as you read the Introduction and Experimental Procedure. Partially completed flow diagrams are presented in the ***Prelaboratory Assignments*** of *Experiments 38* and *39*.

E. How to Effectively Do "Qual"

The following suggestions are offered before and during the following "qual" experiments:

- Use good laboratory techniques during the analyses. Review the suggested techniques that appear as icons in the Experimental Procedure prior to beginning the analysis.
- *Always* read the Experimental Procedure in detail. Is extra equipment necessary? Is a hot water bath needed? Maintain a water bath during the laboratory period if one is needed. What cautions are to be taken?
- Understand the principles of the separation and identification of the ions. Is this an acid–base separation, redox reaction, or complex formation? Why is this reagent added at this time?
- Closely follow, simultaneously, the principles used in each test, the flow diagram, the Experimental Procedure, and the ***Report Sheet*** during the analysis.
- Mark with a magic marker 1-, 2-, and 3-mL intervals on the small test tube used for testing your sample to quickly estimate volumes (see Figure D4.1).
- Keep a number of *clean* dropping pipets, stirring rods, and small test tubes available; always rinse each test tube several times with deionized water immediately after use.[2]

- Estimate the drops/mL of one or more of your dropping pipets.
- Keep a wash bottle filled with deionized water available at all times.
- Maintain a file of confirmatory tests of the ions in the test tubes that result from the analysis on your *reference* solution; in that way, observations and comparisons of the *test* solution can be quick.

Caution: *In the next several experiments you will be handling a large number of chemicals (acids, bases, oxidizing and reducing agents, and, perhaps, even some toxic chemicals), some of which are more concentrated than others and must be handled with care and respect!*

[2]Failure to maintain clean glassware during the analysis causes more spurious data and reported errors in interpretation than any other single factor in qualitative analysis.

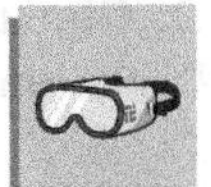

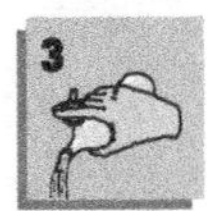

Re-read the **Laboratory Safety** *section, pages 1–4, of this manual.*

Carefully *handle all chemicals.* ***Read the label! Do not*** *intentionally inhale the vapors of any chemical.* ***Avoid*** *skin contact with any chemicals—wash the skin immediately in the laboratory sink, eye wash fountain, or safety shower.* ***Clean up*** *any spilled chemical—if you are uncertain of the proper cleanup procedure, flood the area with water, and consult your laboratory instructor.* ***Be aware*** *of the techniques and procedures of neighboring chemists—discuss potential hazards with them.*

Finally, ***dispose of the waste chemicals*** *in the appropriately labeled waste containers. Consult your laboratory instructor to ensure proper disposal.*

Andrew Lambert Photography/Science Source

Experiment 37

Qual: Common Anions

Calcium ion and carbonate ion combine to form a calcium carbonate precipitate, a preliminary test for the presence of carbonate ion in a solution.

OBJECTIVES

- To observe and utilize some of the chemical and physical properties of anions
- To separate and identify the presence of a single anion in a solution containing a mixture of anions

TECHNIQUES

The following techniques are used in the Experimental Procedure:

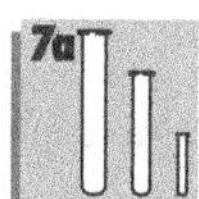

Also review *Dry Lab 4. A, B, and C* for additional techniques.

INTRODUCTION

Common anions in aqueous solution are either single atom anions (Cl^-, Br^-, I^-) or polyatomic anions usually containing oxygen (OH^-, SO_4^{2-}, CO_3^{2-}, PO_4^{3-}). In nature, the most common anions are chloride, silicate, carbonate, phosphate, sulfate, sulfide, nitrate, aluminate, and combinations thereof.

Specific anion tests are subject to interference from other anions and cations. Therefore, to characteristically identify an anion in a mixture, preliminary elimination of the interferences is necessary.[1]

Only six of the many known inorganic anions will be identified in this experiment: phosphate, PO_4^{3-}; carbonate, CO_3^{2-}; chloride, Cl^-; iodide, I^-; sulfide, S^{2-}; and nitrate, NO_3^-. The chemical properties of several of these anions have been seen in previous experiments in this manual (for example, see *Experiments 3, 11,* and *24*). Many anions can be detected directly in the sample solution by the addition of a single test reagent. However, some anion-detection procedures require a systematic removal of the interferences before the use of the test reagent. For example, a test for the presence of PO_4^{3-} requires the prior removal of AsO_4^{3-}; a test for CO_3^{2-} requires the prior removal of SO_3^{2-}.

The separation and identification of the anions are outlined in the **flow diagram** on page 414 (see *Dry Lab 4.D*). Follow the diagram as you read through the Introduction and follow the Experimental Procedure.

3A	4A	5A	6A	7A	Noble Gases
	CO_3^{2-}	NO_3^-			
		PO_4^{3-}	S^{2-}	Cl^-	
				I^-	

Common anions detected in this experiment

Flow diagram: a diagram that summarizes a procedure for following a rigid sequence of steps

[1] For more information on anion qualitative analysis, go to www.chemlin.net/chemistry.

Flow Diagram for Anion "Qual" Scheme

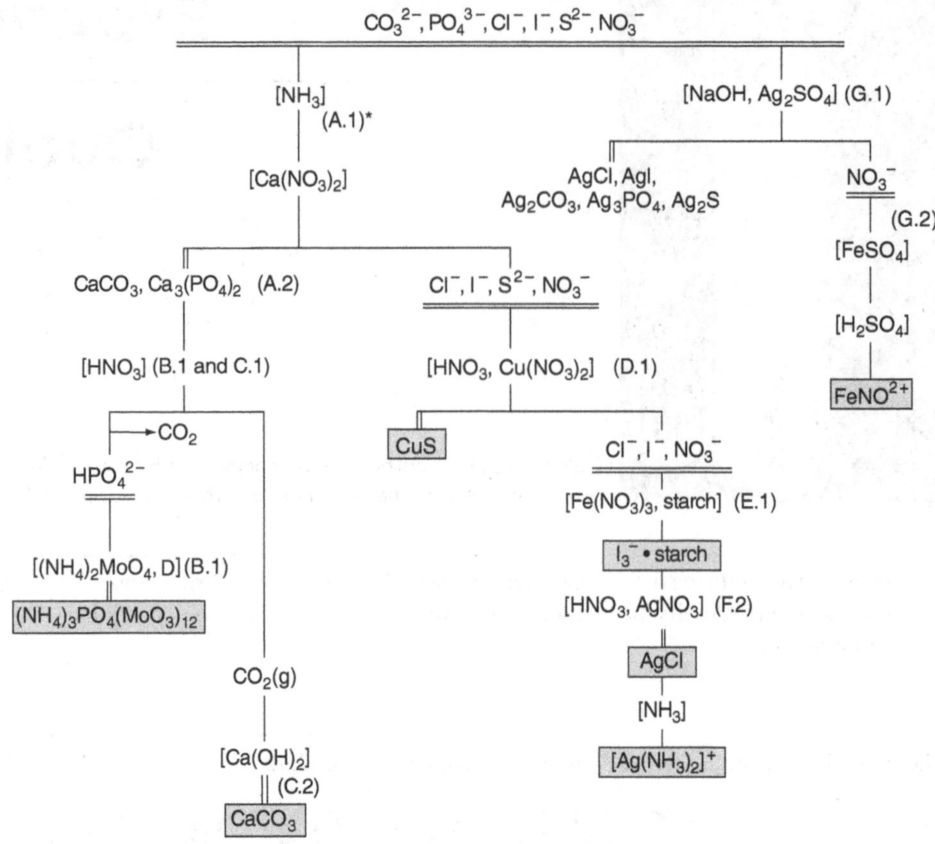

*Numbers in parentheses refer to parts of the Experimental Procedure

Phosphate Ion

The phosphate ion, PO_4^{3-}, is a strong Brønsted base (proton acceptor)

All phosphate salts are *insoluble* except those of the Group 1A cations and ammonium ion (Appendix E). The phosphate salt of calcium forms a *white precipitate* in a basic solution but subsequently dissolves in an acidic solution:

$$3\,Ca^{2+}(aq) + 2\,PO_4^{3-}(aq) \longrightarrow Ca_3(PO_4)_2(s) \quad \downarrow \mathbf{2\,H^+(aq)} \quad 3\,Ca^{2+}(aq) + 2\,HPO_4^{2-}(aq) \tag{37.1}$$

Ammonium molybdate added to an acidified solution of the hydrogen phosphate ion precipitates *yellow* ammonium phosphomolybdate, confirming the presence of phosphate ion in the test solution.

The 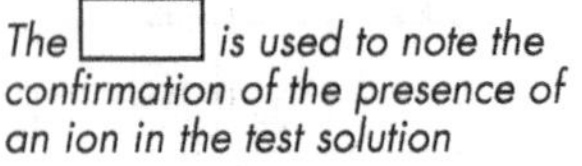 is used to note the confirmation of the presence of an ion in the test solution

$$HPO_4^{2-}(aq) + 12\,(NH_4)_2MoO_4(aq) + 23\,H^+(aq) \longrightarrow \boxed{(NH_4)_3PO_4(MoO_3)_{12}(s)} + 21\,NH_4^+(aq) + 12\,H_2O(l) \tag{37.2}$$

The rate of precipitate formation depends on the concentration of the phosphate ion in solution.

The reactions of the arsenate ion (AsO_4^{3-}) are identical to those of the phosphate ion and therefore would, if present, interfere with the test.

Carbonate Ion

All carbonate salts are *insoluble* except those of the Group 1A cations and ammonium ion (Appendix E). Acidification of a solution containing carbonate ion produces carbon dioxide gas (Figure 37.1).

$$CO_3^{2-}(aq) + 2\,H^+(aq) \longrightarrow H_2O(l) + CO_2(g) \tag{37.3}$$

When the evolved CO_2 (an acidic anhydride) comes into contact with a basic solution containing calcium ion, the carbonate ion re-forms and reacts with the calcium ion, forming a *white precipitate* of calcium carbonate:

$$CO_2(g) + 2\,OH^-(aq) \longrightarrow CO_3^{2-}(aq) + H_2O(l) \qquad (37.4)$$
$$\downarrow \boldsymbol{Ca^{2+}(aq)}$$
$$\boxed{CaCO_3(s)} \qquad (37.5)$$

The precipitate confirms the presence of carbonate ion in the test solution. The sulfite ion, SO_3^{2-}, if present, would interfere with the test; under similar conditions, it produces sulfur dioxide gas and insoluble calcium sulfite.

Jo A. Beran/Trey Hernandez

Figure 37.1 Acidifying a solution containing carbonate ion produces carbon dioxide gas.

Sulfide Ion

Most sulfide salts are insoluble (Appendix E), including CuS. When Cu^{2+} is added to a solution containing sulfide ion, a *black precipitate* of copper(II) sulfide, CuS, forms, confirming the presence of sulfide ion in the test solution:

$$Cu^{2+}(aq) + S^{2-}(aq) \longrightarrow \boxed{CuS(s)} \qquad (37.6)$$

Chloride and Iodide Ions

The salts of the chloride and iodide ions are soluble with the exception of the Ag^+, Pb^{2+}, and $Hg_2{}^{2+}$ halides (Appendix E). A simple reaction with silver ion would cause a mixture of the silver halides to precipitate, and therefore no separation or identification could be made. Instead, differences in the ease of oxidation of the chloride and iodide ions are used for their identification (see *Experiment 11*, Part D). The iodide ion is most easily oxidized. A weak oxidizing agent oxidizes only the iodide ion. In this experiment, iron(III) ion oxidizes iodide ion to the yellow-brown triiodide complex, I_3^-:

$$2\,Fe^{3+}(aq) + 3\,I^-(aq) \longrightarrow 2\,Fe^{2+}(aq) + I_3^-(aq) \qquad (37.7)$$

The I_3^- then reacts with starch to form a *deep-blue complex*, I_3^-•starch, confirming the presence of iodide ion in the sample:

$$I_3^-\,(aq) + \text{starch}(aq) \longrightarrow I_3^-\text{•starch}\ (aq,\ \textit{deep blue}) \qquad (37.8)$$

The chloride ion is then precipitated as a *white precipitate* of silver chloride.[2]

$$Cl^-(aq) + Ag^+(aq) \longrightarrow \boxed{AgCl(s)} \qquad (37.9)$$

To further confirm the presence of chloride ion in the test solution, aqueous ammonia is added to dissolve the silver chloride which again precipitates with the addition of nitric acid:

$$AgCl(s) + 2\,NH_3(aq) \rightleftharpoons [Ag(NH_3)_2]^+(aq) + Cl^-(aq) \qquad (37.10)$$

$$[Ag(NH_3)_2]^+(aq) + Cl^-(aq) + 2\,H^+(aq) \longrightarrow AgCl(s) + 2\,NH_4^+(aq) \qquad (37.11)$$

Nitrate Ion

As all nitrate salts are soluble (Appendix E), no precipitate can be used for identification of the nitrate ion. The nitrate ion is identified by the brown ring test. The nitrate ion is reduced to nitric oxide by iron(II) ions in the presence of concentrated sulfuric acid:

$$NO_3^-(aq) + 3\,Fe^{2+}(aq) + 4\,H^+(aq) \xrightarrow{\textit{conc}\ H_2SO_4} 3\,Fe^{3+}(aq) + NO(aq) + 2\,H_2O(l) \qquad (37.12)$$

[2]A faint cloudiness with the addition of Ag^+ is occasionally inconclusive as the chloride ion is one of those *universal impurities* in aqueous solutions.

The nitric oxide, NO, combines with excess iron(II) ions, forming the *brown* $FeNO^{2+}$ ion at the interface of the aqueous layer and the concentrated sulfuric acid layer (where acidity is high) that underlies the aqueous layer:

$$Fe^{2+}(aq) + NO(aq) \longrightarrow \boxed{FeNO^{2+}(aq)} \qquad (37.13)$$

$FeNO^{2+}$ is more stable at low temperatures. This test has many sources of interference: (1) Sulfuric acid oxidizes bromide and iodide ions to bromine and iodine, and (2) sulfites, sulfides, and other reducing agents interfere with the reduction of NO_3^- to NO. A preparatory step of adding sodium hydroxide and silver sulfate removes these interfering anions, leaving only the nitrate ion in solution.

EXPERIMENTAL PROCEDURE

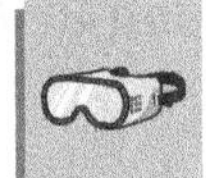

Procedure Overview: Two solutions are tested with various reagents in this analysis: (1) a reference solution containing all six of the anions for this analysis and (2) a test solution containing any number of the anions. Separations and observations are made and recorded. Equations that describe the observations are also recorded. Comparative observations of the two solutions result in the identification of the anions in the test solution. All tests are qualitative; only identification of the anion(s) is required.

To simplify the analysis, take the following steps:

1. **Reference solution:** At each circled superscript (e.g.,①), *stop* and record on the ***Report Sheet***. After each anion is confirmed, *save* it in the test tube so that its appearance can be compared to that of your test solution.
2. **Test solution:** Simultaneously perform the same procedure on the test solution and make a comparative observation. Check (√) the findings on the ***Report Sheet***. Do not discard any solutions (but keep all solutions labeled) until the experiment is complete. Record the test solution number on the ***Report Sheet***.

The test solution may be a water sample from some location in the environment—for example, a lake, a stream, or a drinking water supply. Ask your instructor about this option.

Before proceeding, review the techniques outlined in *Dry Lab 4*, Parts A–C. The review of these procedures may expedite your analysis with less frustration.

Read *Dry Lab 4.E*, Contamination by trace amounts of anions in test tubes and other glassware leads to unexplainable results in qualitative analysis. Thoroughly clean all glassware with soap and tap water; rinse twice with tap water and twice with deionized water before use.

Disposal: Dispose of all test solutions and precipitates in the appropriate waste container.

Caution: *A number of acids and bases are used in the analysis of these anions. Handle each of these solutions with care. Read the* **Laboratory Safety** *section for instructions in handling acids and bases.*

The expression "small test tube" that is mentioned throughout the Experimental Procedure refers to a 75-mm test tube (~3 mL volume) *or* a centrifuge tube of the size that fits into your laboratory centrifuge. Consult with your laboratory instructor.

A. Separation of Carbonate and Phosphate Anions

The Experimental Procedure is written for a single solution. If you are simultaneously identifying anions in *both* a reference solution *and* a test solution, adjust the procedure accordingly. If the test solution is a sample with an environmental origin, gravity filter 10–15 mL before beginning the Experimental Procedure.

Prepare the warm water bath for use in Part B.

1. **Precipitate the CO_3^{2-} and PO_4^{3-}.** Place ~1.5 mL of the reference solution in a small test tube (see *Dry Lab 4.A*). Test the solution with pH paper. If acidic, add drops of 3 *M* NH_3 until the solution is basic; then add 3–4 more drops; mix or stir the solution after each addition. Add 10–12 drops of 0.1 *M* $Ca(NO_3)_2$ until the precipitation of the anions is complete (see *Dry Lab 4.B*).①

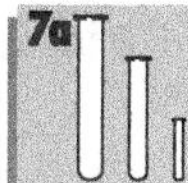

2. **Separate the solution from precipitate.** Centrifuge the solution. Decant the supernatant② into a small test tube and save for Part D. Wash the precipitate *twice* with ~1 mL of deionized water (see *Dry Lab 4.C*). Discard the washings as directed by your instructor. Save the precipitate for Part B.

B. Test for Phosphate Ion

1. **Confirmatory test.** Dissolve the precipitate from Part A.2 with drops of 6 *M* HNO_3 (**Caution!**). Add ~1 mL of 0.5 *M* $(NH_4)_2MoO_4$. Shake and warm slightly in a warm water (~60°C) bath and let stand for 10–15 minutes. A *slow* formation of a *yellow precipitate* confirms the presence of the phosphate ion③ in the solution.[3]

C. Test for Carbonate Ion

1. **Precipitate the CO_3^{2-}.** Repeat Part A. Centrifuge the mixture; save the precipitate but discard the supernatant or save for Part D. Dip a glass rod into a saturated $Ca(OH)_2$ solution.
2. **Confirmatory test.** Add 3–5 drops of 6 *M* HNO_3 to the precipitate and immediately insert the glass rod into the test tube (Figure 37.2). *Do not* let the glass rod touch the test tube wall or the solution. The evolution of the CO_2 gas causes the formation of a *milky solution* on the glass rod, confirming the presence of carbonate ion④ in the solution.

D. Test for Sulfide Ion

1. **Confirmatory test.** To the supernatant from Part A.2 and/or C.1, add 2–4 drops of 6 *M* HNO_3 until the solution is acid to pH paper and then drops of 1 *M* $Cu(NO_3)_2$ until precipitation is complete. Be patient, allow ~2 minutes to form.⑤ Centrifuge; save the supernatant for Part E. The *black precipitate* confirms the presence of sulfide ion in the solution.

E. Test for Iodide Ion

1. **Confirmatory test.** To ~1 mL of the supernatant from Part D.1 add ~5 drops of 0.2 *M* $Fe(NO_3)_3$. Agitate the solution. The formation of I_3^- is slow—allow 2–3 minutes. Add ~2 drops of 1 percent starch solution. The *deep-blue* I_3^-•starch complex confirms the presence of iodide ion in the sample.⑥

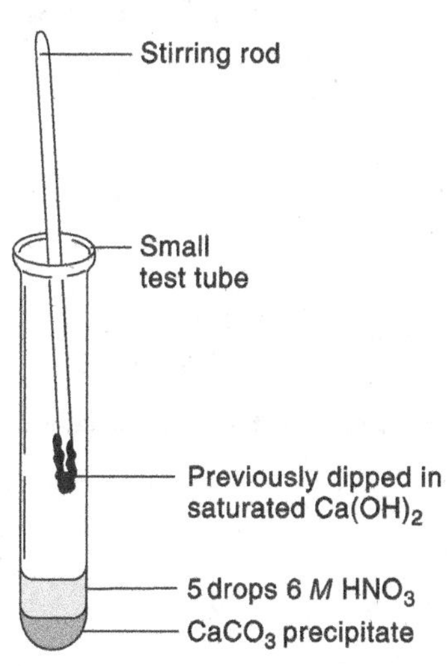

Figure 37.2 Position a stirring rod dipped into a saturated $Ca(OH)_2$ solution just above the solid/HNO_3 mixture.

[3]A *white precipitate* may form if the solution is heated too long or if the solution is not acidic enough. The precipitate is MoO_3, *not* a pale form of the phosphomolybdate precipitate.

F. Test for Chloride Ion

1. Add 2–3 drops of 6 M HNO_3 to the solution from Part E.1.
2. **Confirmatory test.** Add drops of 0.01 M $AgNO_3$ to the aqueous solution (sample) and centrifuge. A *white precipitate* indicates the likely presence of Cl^-.⑦ Discard the supernatant. The addition of several drops of 6 M NH_3 quickly dissolves the precipitate if Cl^- is present.⑧ Reacidification of the solution with drops of 6 M HNO_3 re-forms the silver chloride precipitate.

G. Test for Nitrate Ion

1. **Precipitate the "other" anions.** Place ~1½ mL of the reference solution into a small test tube. Add drops of 3 M NaOH until the solution is basic to pH paper. Add drops of a saturated (0.04 M) Ag_2SO_4 solution until precipitation appears complete. Centrifuge and save the supernatant for Part G.2⑨ Test for complete precipitation in the supernatant (see *Dry Lab 4.B*) and, if necessary, centrifuge again.
2. **Confirmatory test.** Decant 0.5 mL (~10 drops) of the supernatant into a small test tube and acidify (to pH paper) with 3 M H_2SO_4. Add ~0.5 mL (see *Dry Lab 4.A*) of a saturated iron(II) sulfate, $FeSO_4$, solution and agitate. Cool the solution in an ice bath.

This procedure should be performed by your lab instructor. Holding the test tube at a 45° angle (Figure 37.3) with test tube tongs, add, with a dropping pipet, *slowly and cautiously,* down its side, about 0.5 mL of *conc* H_2SO_4. (**Caution:** *Concentrated H_2SO_4 causes severe skin burns.*)[4] Do *not* draw *conc* H_2SO_4 into the bulb of the dropping pipet. Do *not* agitate the solution. The more dense *conc* H_2SO_4 underlies the aqueous layer. Use extreme care to avoid mixing the *conc* H_2SO_4 with the solution. Allow the mixture to stand for several minutes. A *brown ring* at the interface between the solution and the *conc* H_2SO_4 confirms the presence of the nitrate ion⑩ in the test solution.

> *Disposal:* Dispose of the concentrated acid solution in the Waste Acids container.

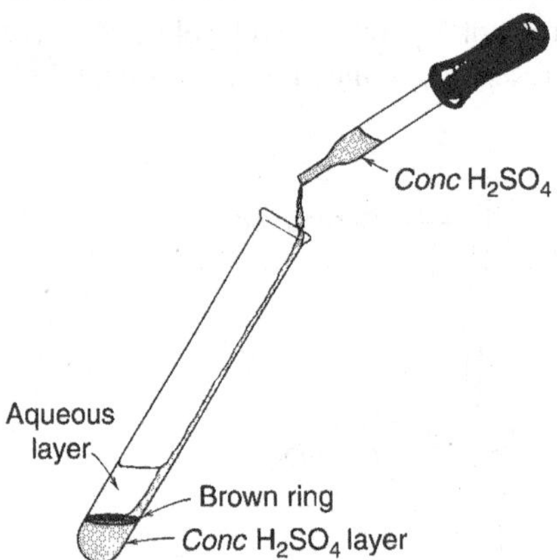

Figure 37.3 Test for the nitrate ion

[4]The *conc* H_2SO_4 has a greater density than water and therefore underlies the aqueous layer.

Experiment 37 *Prelaboratory Assignment*

Qual: Common Anions

Date __________ Lab Sec. ______ Name ______________________________ Desk No. _________

1. A review of the *Dry Lab 4* will make this experiment proceed more smoothly. Complete the following:

a. The approximate volume of a standard 75-mm ("small") test tube is _____ mL.

b. The clear solution above a precipitate is called the ______________________.

c. A ______________________ is an instrument used to separate and compact a precipitate in a test tube.

d. The number of drops of water equivalent to 1 mL is about _______.

2. a. Experimental Procedure, Part A.1. Describe the technique for mixing solutions in a "small" test tube.

7a

b. Experimental Procedure, Part A.2. Describe the technique for washing a precipitate.

3. Refer to *Dry Lab 4.D*. On a flow diagram, what is the meaning of

a. a single horizontal line, —?

b. a pair of short vertical lines, ||?

c. a pair of horizontal lines, =?

d. the brackets, [ ], around a reagent?

4. Three anions in this experiment are identified by the complexes they form. Which anions are so identified?

5. Four anions are confirmed present by the formation of a precipitate. Which anions are so confirmed? Write the formula and indicate the color of the precipitates.

6. Identify the reagent (and its concentration) that is used to confirm the presence of each of the following:

a. CO_3^{2-}: ____________

b. S^{2-}: ____________

c. I^-: ____________

7. Identify a single reagent used in this experiment that distinguishes between the carbonate and chloride ions in a solution, assuming no other anions are present. Write the balanced equation(s) that makes the distinction.

Experiment 37 *Report Sheet*

Qual: Common Anions

Date ________ Lab Sec. ______ Name ____________________________ Desk No. ________

Procedure Number and Ion	Test Reagent or Technique	Evidence of Chemical Change	Chemical(s) Responsible for Observation	Equation(s) for Observed Reaction	Check (√) if Observed in Test Sol'n
①					
②					
③ PO_4^{3-}					☐
④ CO_3^{2-}					☐
⑤ S^{2-}					☐
⑥ I^-					☐
⑦ Cl^-					☐
⑧					
⑨					
⑩ NO_3^-					☐

Anions present in unknown test solution no. _____: ______________________

Instructor's approval: ______________________________

Laboratory Questions

Circle the questions that have been assigned.

1. Part A.1. The *test* solution is made basic and drops of 0.1 *M* $Ca(NO_3)_2$ are added but no precipitate forms. To what part of the Experimental Procedure do you proceed? Explain.
2. Part A.1. The *reference* solution is made acidic instead of basic. How would this change the composition of the precipitate and the test in Part C.1? Explain.
3. Part B. Write the formula of the precipitate that dissolves when the HNO_3 is added.
4. Part C.2. The 6 *M* HNO_3 could not be found on the reagent shelf, so the 6 *M* HCl was used instead. Explain how (or if) the observation may be different.
5. Part D.1. 6 *M* HNO_3 could not be found on the reagent shelf. Instead 6 *M* HCl is added to the *test* solution.
   a. What effect does this have on the test for sulfide ion? Explain.
   b. What effect does this have on subsequent tests of the supernatant from Part D.1? Explain.
6. Part E.1. The starch solution was inadvertently omitted from the analysis. Assuming the iodide ion to be present, what would be observed after the addition of the ferric nitrate solution?
7. Part F.2. 6 *M* NH_3, a basic solution, cannot be found on the reagent shelf, but 6 *M* NaOH, also a base, is available. What would be observed if the 6 *M* NaOH is substituted for the 6 *M* NH_3 in testing the *reference* solution? Explain.
8. Part F.2. The *test* solution is known to contain only the iodide and chloride ions. Describe the appearance of the solution if drops of 0.01 *M* $AgNO_3$ had been added directly to the test solution and then centrifuged.
9. Part G.2. There is no other brown ring test commonly known in chemistry. What substance is producing the brown ring?

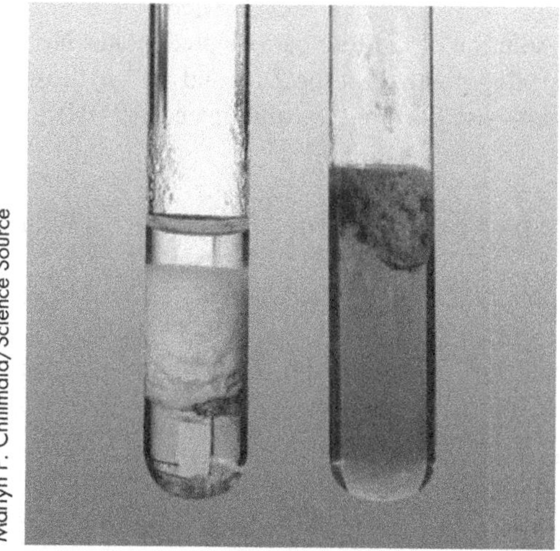

Nickel(II) ions (left) and iron(III) ions (right) readily form hydroxide precipitates.

Experiment 39

Qual II. Ni^{2+}, Fe^{3+}, Al^{3+}, Zn^{2+}

OBJECTIVES

- To observe and utilize the chemical and physical properties of Ni^{2+}, Fe^{3+}, Al^{3+}, Zn^{2+}
- To separate and identify the presence of one or more of the cations, Ni^{2+}, Fe^{3+}, Al^{3+}, and Zn^{2+} in an aqueous solution

TECHNIQUES

The following techniques are used in the Experimental Procedure:

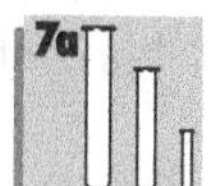

Also review *Dry Lab 4. A, B, C* for additional techniques.

INTRODUCTION

The Qual II cations are perhaps more relevant to our industrial society than the Qual I cations. The use of iron as the major component of steel, of aluminum for lightweight construction materials, and of zinc for coinage alloys and galvanizing steel are all familiar in our everyday lives. Aqueous solutions containing these cations tend to be quite colorful as well—the rust color of Fe^{3+} and the green color of Ni^{2+}—as well as the compounds that confirm the presence of Fe^{3+} and Ni^{2+}. However, solutions containing Al^{3+} and Zn^{2+} tend to be colorless, but the compounds that confirm their presence do have color. Only Cu^{2+} of the Qual I cations has color (sky-blue) as does its confirmation (deep dark blue).

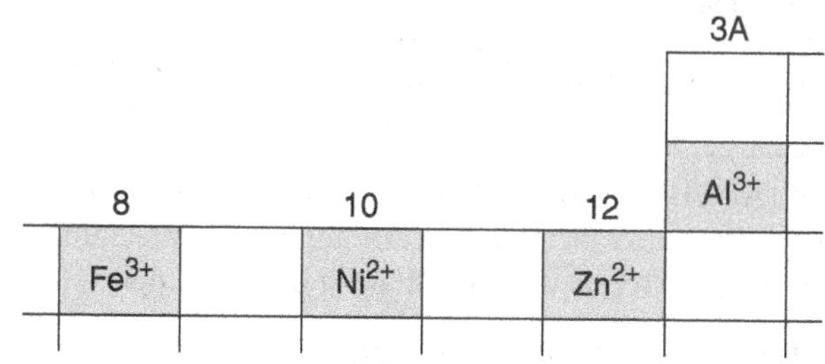

Cations of the Qual II Group

As a way to understand the separation and identification of these four cations, read through the following chemistry of the Qual II cations, the Experimental Procedure, and complete the flow diagram in ***Prelaboratory Assignment*** question 6 *before* beginning the experiment.

The separation of Al^{3+} and Zn^{2+} from the Ni^{2+} and Fe^{3+} cations is accomplished by the addition of a highly concentrated NaOH solution (Figure 39.1). Thereafter, the Al^{3+} and the Zn^{2+} are further separated and characteristically identified through pH control. Once separated from the Al^{3+} and Zn^{2+}, the Fe^{3+} and Ni^{2+} are independently identified with specific test reagents.

Figure 39.1 Formation of the aluminum hydroxide precipitate.

Separation of Ni^{2+}, and Fe^{3+} from Zn^{2+} and Al^{3+}

Gelatinous: jellylike due to adsorbed and occluded water molecules

Amphoteric (also amphiprotic): the chemical property of a substance as having both acidlike and baselike properties

Structures of $[Al(OH)_4]^-$ and $[Zn(OH)_4]^{2-}$

A strong base, OH^-, added to an aqueous solution of the four cations precipitates Ni^{2+} and Fe^{3+} as **gelatinous** hydroxides (see opening photo), but the Zn^{2+} and Al^{3+} hydroxides, being **amphoteric**, redissolve in excess base, forming the aluminate, $[Al(OH)_4]^-$, and zincate, $[Zn(OH)_4]^{2-}$, ions:

$$Al^{3+}(aq) + 4\ OH^-(aq) \rightleftharpoons [Al(OH)_4]^-(aq) \quad (39.1)$$

$$Zn^{2+}(aq) + 4\ OH^-(aq) \rightleftharpoons [Zn(OH)_4]^{2-}(aq) \quad (39.2)$$

The gelatinous hydroxides of Ni^{2+} and Fe^{3+} dissolve with the addition of nitric acid after the soluble aluminate and zincate ions are separated.

Iron(III) Ion

When a reference solution containing the Ni^{2+} and Fe^{3+} ions is treated with an excess of ammonia, NH_3, *brown* $Fe(OH)_3$ precipitates, and the soluble *blue* hexaammine complex, $[Ni(NH_3)_6]^{2+}$, forms in solution:

$$Fe^{3+}(aq) + 3\ NH_3(aq) + 3\ H_2O(l) \longrightarrow Fe(OH)_3(s) + 3\ NH_4^+(aq) \quad (39.3)$$

$$Ni^{2+}(aq) + 6\ NH_3(aq) \rightleftharpoons [Ni(NH_3)_6]^{2+}(aq) \quad (39.4)$$

Structure of $[Ni(NH_3)_6]^{2+}$

Acid dissolves the $Fe(OH)_3$ precipitate; addition of thiocyanate ion, SCN^-, forms the *blood-red* thiocyanatoiron(III) complex, $[FeNCS]^{2+}$, a confirmation of the presence of Fe^{3+} in the test solution (see *Experiment 34*):

$$Fe^{3+}(aq) + SCN^-(aq) \longrightarrow \boxed{[FeNCS]^{2+}(aq)} \quad (39.5)$$

Other forms of the Fe^{3+}–SCN^- complex are $[Fe(NCS)_2]^+$, $[Fe(NCS)_4]^-$, and $[Fe(NCS)_6]^{3-}$, depending on the SCN^- concentration.

Nickel Ion

A supernatant from the test for iron(III) ion is used to test for the presence of nickel ion. The confirmation of Ni^{2+} ion in the reference solution is the appearance of a bright *pink* (or brick-red) *precipitate* formed with the addition of dimethylglyoxime, H_2DMG,[1] to a solution of the hexaamminenickel(II) complex ion:

$$[Ni(NH_3)_6]^{2+}(aq) + 2\ H_2DMG(aq) \longrightarrow \boxed{Ni(HDMG)_2(s)} + 2\ NH_4^+(aq) + 4\ NH_3(aq) \quad (39.6)$$

Structure of $Ni(HDMG)_2(s)$

Aluminum Ion

A solution containing $[Al(OH)_4]^-$ and $[Zn(OH)_4]^{2-}$ ions, acidified with HNO_3, re-forms the Al^{3+} and Zn^{2+} ions. The subsequent addition of ammonia reprecipitates Al^{3+} as the gelatinous hydroxide, but Zn^{2+} forms the soluble tetraammine complex, $[Zn(NH_3)_4]^{2+}$:

$$[Al(OH)_4]^-(aq) + 4\ H^+(aq) \longrightarrow Al^{3+}(aq) + 4\ H_2O(l) \quad (39.7)$$

$$\downarrow \textit{3 NH}_3\textit{(aq)}$$

$$Al(OH)_3(s) + 3\ NH_4^+(aq) + H_2O(l) \quad (39.8)$$

$$[Zn(OH)_4]^{2-}(aq) + 4\ H^+(aq) \longrightarrow Zn^{2+}(aq) + 4\ H_2O(l) \quad (39.9)$$

$$\downarrow \textit{4 NH}_3\textit{(aq)}$$

$$[Zn(NH_3)_4]^{2+}(aq) \quad (39.10)$$

[1]Dimethylglyoxime, abbreviated as H_2DMG for convenience in this experiment, is an organic chelating agent (see *Experiment 36*), specific for the precipitation of the nickel ion.

$Al(OH)_3$, an opaque, blue-white, gelatinous precipitate (Figure 39.1), is not easy to detect. To confirm the presence of Al^{3+} ion, the $Al(OH)_3$ precipitate is subsequently dissolved with HNO_3, aluminon reagent[2] is added, and the $Al(OH)_3$ is reprecipitated with the addition of NH_3. In the process of reprecipitating, the aluminon reagent, a red dye, adsorbs onto the surface of the gelatinous $Al(OH)_3$ precipitate, giving it a *pink* or *red* appearance, confirming the presence of Al^{3+} in the test solution:

$$Al^{3+}(aq) + 3\ NH_3(aq) + 3\ H_2O(l) + \text{aluminon}(aq) \longrightarrow \boxed{Al(OH)_3 \cdot \text{aluminon}(s)} + 3\ NH_4^+(aq) \quad (39.11)$$

Zinc Ion

When potassium hexacyanoferrate(II), $K_4[Fe(CN)_6]$, is added to an acidified solution of the $[Zn(NH_3)_4]^{2+}$ ion, a *light-green precipitate* of $K_2Zn_3[Fe(CN)_6]_2$ forms, confirming the presence of Zn^{2+} in the test solution:

$$3\ [Zn(NH_3)_4]^{2+}(aq) + 4\ H^+(aq) \longrightarrow 3\ Zn^{2+}(aq) + 4\ NH_4^+(aq) \quad (39.12)$$

$$\downarrow 2\ K_4[Fe(CN)_6](aq)$$

$$\boxed{K_2Zn_3[Fe(CN)_6]_2(s)} + 6\ K^+(aq) \quad (39.13)$$

Experimental Procedure

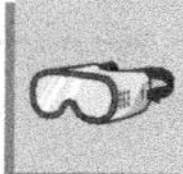

Procedure Overview: Two solutions are tested with various reagents in this analysis: (1) a reference solution containing the Ni^{2+}, Fe^{3+}, Al^{3+}, and Zn^{2+} ions of Qual II and (2) a test solution containing any number of Qual II cations. Separations and observations are made and recorded. Equations that describe the observations are also recorded. Comparative observations of the two solutions result in the identification of the cations in the test solution. All tests are qualitative; only identification of the cation(s) is required.

To simplify the analysis, take the following steps:

1. **Reference solution:** At each circled superscript (e.g.,①), *stop* and record on the ***Report Sheet***. After each cation is confirmed, *save* it in the test tube so that its appearance can be compared with that of your test solution.
2. **Test solution:** Simultaneously perform the same procedure on the test solution and make a comparative observation. Check (√) the findings on the ***Report Sheet***. Do not discard any solutions (but keep all solutions labeled) until the experiment is complete. Record the test solution number on the ***Report Sheet***.

The test solution may be a water sample from some location in the environment—for example, a lake, a stream, or a drinking water supply. Ask your instructor about this option.

Before proceeding, review the techniques outlined in *Dry Lab 4*, Parts A–C. The review of these procedures may expedite your analysis with less frustration.

Read *Dry Lab 4.E.* Contamination by trace amounts of metal ions in test tubes and other glassware leads to unexplainable results in qualitative analysis. Thoroughly clean all glassware with soap and tap water; rinse twice with tap water and twice with deionized water before use.

Caution: *A number of acids and bases are used in the analysis of these cations. Handle each of these solutions with care. Read the* **Laboratory Safety** *section for instructions in handling acids and bases.*

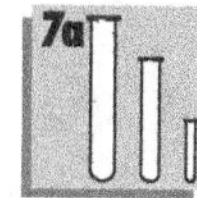

The expression "small test tube" that is mentioned throughout the Experimental Procedure refers to a 75-mm test tube (~3 mL volume) *or* a centrifuge tube of the size that fits into your laboratory centrifuge. Consult with your laboratory instructor.

[2]The aluminon reagent is the ammonium salt of aurin tricarboxylic acid, a red dye.

A. Separation of Ni^{2+} and Fe^{3+} from Zn^{2+} and Al^{3+}

The Experimental Procedure is written for a single reference solution. If you are simultaneously identifying cations in *both* a reference solution *and* a test solution, adjust the procedure accordingly. If the test solution is a sample with an environmental origin, then gravity filter 10–15 mL before beginning the Experimental Procedure.

Prepare the hot water bath for use in Parts A and D.

1. **Separate the hydroxide precipitates from the amphoteric hydroxides.** To 2 mL of the reference solution (in a small test tube) add 10 drops of 6 *M* NaOH **(Caution!)** (see *Dry Lab 4.A*). Centrifuge and save the precipitate.① Test for complete precipitation (see *Dry Lab 4.B*) by adding several drops of 6 *M* NaOH to the supernatant. Decant the supernatant② into a small test tube and save for Part D.

2. **Dissolve the hydroxide precipitates.** Dissolve the precipitate③ with a minimum number of drops of *conc* HNO_3. (**Caution:** *Be careful!*) If necessary, heat the solution in the hot water bath for several minutes.

B. Test for Iron(III) Ion

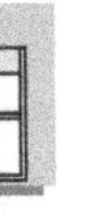

1. **Separate Fe^{3+} from Ni^{2+} ions.** To the solution from Part A.2, add ~5 drops of 4 *M* NH_4Cl and then drops of *conc* NH_3 (**Caution:** *Do not inhale—use a fume hood if available*) until the solution is basic to pH paper; add an additional 2 drops of *conc* NH_3 to ensure the complexing of the Ni^{2+}. Centrifuge, save the precipitate,④ and transfer the supernatant⑤ to a small test tube for testing in Part C.

2. **Confirmatory test.** Dissolve the precipitate with 6 *M* HCl and add ~5 drops of 0.1 *M* NH_4SCN.⑥ The *blood-red* solution due to the thiocyanatoiron(III) complex confirms the presence of iron(III) ion in the test solution.

C. Test for Nickel Ion

1. **Confirmatory test.** To the supernatant solution from Part B.1, add ~3 drops of dimethylglyoxime solution.⑦ Appearance of a *pink* (brick-red) *precipitate* confirms the presence of nickel ion in the test solution.

D. Test for Aluminum Ion

To digest the precipitate: to make the precipitate more compact

1. **Separate Al^{3+} from Zn^{2+}.** Acidify the supernatant from Part A.1 to pH paper with drops of 6 *M* HNO_3. Add drops of 6 *M* NH_3 until the solution is now basic to pH paper; then add ~5 more drops. Heat the solution in the hot water bath for several minutes to **digest the** gelatinous **precipitate.**⑧ Centrifuge and decant the supernatant⑨ into a small test tube and save for the Zn^{2+} analysis in Part E.

2. **Confirmatory test.** Wash the precipitate (see *Dry Lab 4.C*) *twice* with ~1 mL of hot, deionized water and discard each washing. Centrifugation is necessary after each washing. Add drops of 6 *M* HNO_3 until the precipitate *just* dissolves. Add ~2 drops of the aluminon reagent, stir, and add drops of 6 *M* NH_3 until the solution is again basic and a precipitate re-forms. Centrifuge the solution; if the $Al(OH)_3$ *precipitate* is now *pink or red* and the solution is colorless, then Al^{3+} is present in the sample.⑩

E. Test for Zinc Ion

1. **Confirmatory test.** To the supernatant from Part D.1, add drops of 6 *M* HCl until the solution is acid to pH paper; then add ~3 drops of 0.2 *M* $K_4[Fe(CN)_6]$ and stir. A very-light-green precipitate⑪ confirms the presence of Zn^{2+} in the sample. The precipitate is slow to form and difficult to see. Centrifugation may be necessary.

Disposal: Dispose of all test solutions and precipitates in the Waste Metal Salts container.

CLEANUP: Rinse each test tube twice with tap water. Discard each rinse in the Waste Metal Salts container. Thoroughly clean each test tube with soap and tap water; rinse twice with tap water and twice with deionized water.

The Next Step

The qualitative analysis of inorganic cations and anions is a study in itself. If further interest in the separation and identification of ions seems intriguing, research various qualitative analysis schemes online. Complete textbooks are also written on the subject.

Experiment 39 *Prelaboratory Assignment*

Qual II. Ni^{2+}, Fe^{3+}, Al^{3+}, Zn^{2+}

Date __________ Lab Sec. ______ Name ______________________________ Desk No. __________

1. Identify the reagent (and its concentration) that is used to confirm the presence of each of the following:

a. Ni^{2+} ______________

b. Fe^{3+} ______________

c. Zn^{2+} ______________

2. Confirmatory tests for the various ions are often colorful. Identify the confirmatory compound/ion and the color for each of the following ions:

Ion	Confirmatory Compound/Ion	Color
Fe^{3+}		
Ni^{2+}		
Al^{3+}		
Zn^{2+}		

3. Identify the reagent that separates

a. Fe^{3+} from Zn^{2+}. Explain the chemistry of the separation.

b. Fe^{3+} from Ni^{2+}. Explain the chemistry of the separation.

c. Al^{3+} from Zn^{2+}. Explain the chemistry of the separation.

4. Aluminum hydroxide is amphoteric, but ferric hydroxide is not. Write equations to show the difference in this chemical property of the two ions.

5. Refer to *Dry Lab 4.B*. Describe the technique used to test for the completeness of the precipitation of an ion.

6. Complete the Qual II flow diagram (see *Dry Lab 4.D, page 411*).

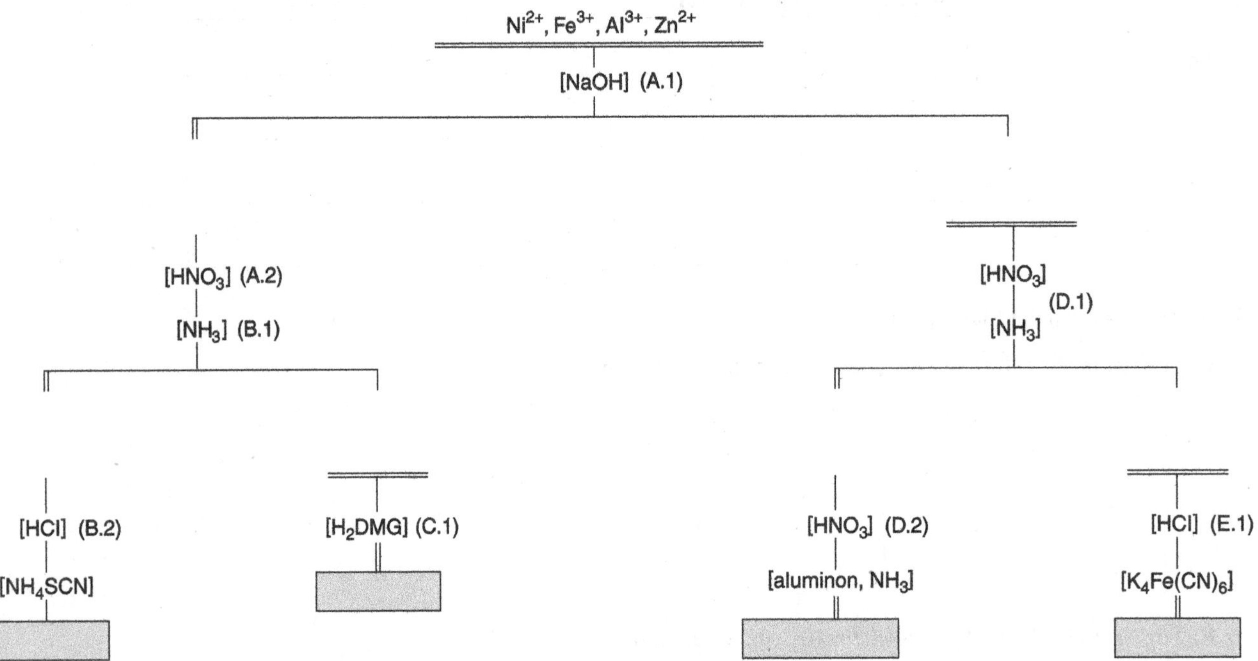

*Numbers in parentheses refer to parts of the Experimental Procedure.

Experiment 39 *Report Sheet*

Qual II. Ni^{2+}, Fe^{3+}, Al^{3+}, Zn^{2+}

Date ________ Lab Sec. ______ Name ______________________________ Desk No. ________

Procedure Number and Ion	Test Reagent or Technique	Evidence of Chemical Change	Chemical(s) Responsible for Observation	Equation(s) for Observed Reaction	Check (√) if Observed in Test Sol'n
①					
②					
③					
④ Fe^{3+}					
⑤					
⑥					☐
⑦ Ni^{2+}					☐
⑧ Al^{3+}					
⑨					
⑩					☐
⑪ Zn^{2+}					☐

Cations present in unknown test solution no. _____: ______________________________

Instructor's approval: ______________________________

Laboratory Questions

Circle the questions that have been assigned.

1. Part A.1. Instead of 6 *M* NaOH being added to the test solution, 6 *M* NH_3 is added (both are bases). How will this affect the separation of the ions in the test solution? Explain.
2. Part B.1. A red-brown precipitate does not form even after the addition of the "additional 2 drops of *conc* NH_3." What can you conclude, and what is the next step in the analysis?
3. Part B.1. The supernatant is colorless after the addition of the "additional 2 drops of *conc* NH_3." What can you conclude, and what is the next step in the analysis?
4. Part B.1. Instead of *conc* NH_3 being added to the test solution, 6 *M* NaOH is added (both are bases). How will this affect the separation of the Fe^{3+} from the Ni^{2+} ions in the test solution? Explain.
5. Part D.1. After adding the NH_3, no precipitate ever formed. What can you conclude from this observation? What is the next step in the analysis?
6. Part D.2. Aluminon is a dye. Explain how aluminon is used in the detection of the aluminum ion in the test solution.
7. Part E.1. Why is the test solution acidified with 6 *M* HCl before the addition of $K_4[Fe(CN)_6]$? Explain.

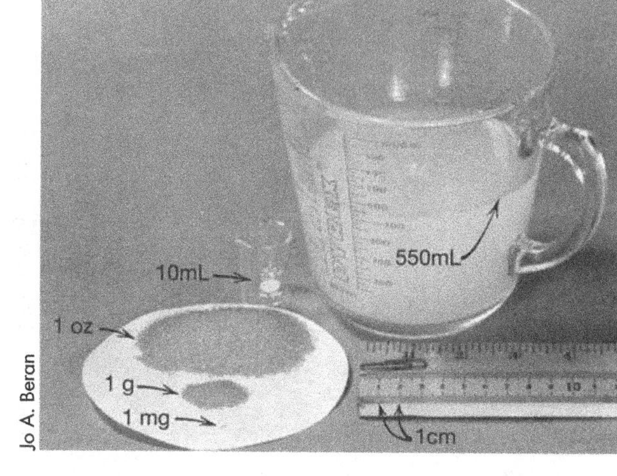

Jo A. Beran

Appendix A

Conversion Factors[1]

The magnitude of a measurement must be familiar to a chemist.

Length
1 meter (*m*) = 39.37 in. = 3.281 ft = distance light travels in 1/299,792,548th of a second
1 inch (*in.*) = 2.54 cm (exactly) = 0.0254 m
1 kilometer (*km*) = 0.6214 (statute) mile
1 angstrom (*Å*) = 1×10^{-10} m = 0.1 nm
1 micron or micrometer (*μm*) 1×10^{-6} m

Mass
1 gram (*g*) = 0.03527 oz = 15.43 grains
1 kilogram (*kg*) = 2.205 lb = 35.27 oz
1 metric ton = 1×10^{6} g = 1.102 short ton
1 pound (*lb*) = 453.6 g = 7,000 grains
1 ounce (*oz*) = 28.35 g = 437.5 grains

Temperature
°F = 1.8°C + 32
K = °C + 273.15

Volume
1 liter (*L*) = 1 dm^3 = 1.057 fl qt = 1×10^{3} mL = 1×10^{3} cm^3 = 61.02 $in.^3$ = 0.2642 gal
1 fluid quart (*fl qt*) = 946.4 mL = 0.250 gal = 0.00595 bbl (oil)
1 fluid ounce (*fl oz*) = 29.57 mL
1 cubic foot (*ft^3*) = 28.32 L = 0.02832 m^3

Pressure
1 atmosphere (*atm*) = 760 torr (exactly) = 760 mm Hg = 29.92 in. Hg = 14.696 lb/$in.^2$ = 1.013 bar = 101.325 kPa
1 pascal (*Pa*) = 1 kg/(m • s^2) = 1 N/m^2
1 torr = 1 mm Hg = 133.3 N/m^2

Energy
1 joule (*J*) = 1 kg • m^2/s^2 = 0.2390 cal = 9.48×10^{-4} Btu 1 = 1×10^{7} ergs
1 calorie (*cal*) = 4.184 J = 3.087 ft•lb
1 British thermal unit (*Btu*) = 252.0 cal = 1054 J = 3.93×10^{-4} hp • hr = 2.93×10^{-4} kW • hr
1 liter atmosphere (*L • atm*) = 24.2 cal = 101.3 J
1 electron volt (*eV*) = 1.602×10^{-19} J
1 kW • hr (*kWh*) = 3,412 Btu = 8.604×10^{5} cal = 3.600×10^{6} J = 1.341 hp•hr

Constants and Other Conversion Data
velocity of light (*c*) = 2.9979×10^{8} m/s = 186,272 mi/s
gas constant (*R*) = 0.08206 L • atm/(*mol • K*) = 8.314 J/(*mol • K*) = 1.986 cal/(*mol • K*) = 62.37 L • torr/(*mol • K*)
Avogadro's number (N_o) = 6.0221×10^{23}/mol
Planck's constant (*h*) = 6.6261×10^{-34} J • s/photon
Faraday's constant ($\mathfrak{F}$) = 96,485 C/mol e^-

[1]For additional conversions, go to http://www.onlineconversion.com.

Appendix B

Familiar Names of Common Chemicals

Vincent LaRussa/John Wiley and Sons

Sodium bicarbonate is commonly called baking soda or bicarbonate of soda.

Familiar Name	Chemical Name	Formula
alcohol	ethanol (ethyl alcohol)	C_2H_5OH
aqua regia	mixture of *conc* nitric and hydrochloric acids	$HNO_3 + 3\ HCl$ by volume
aspirin	acetylsalicylic acid	$CH_3COOC_6H_4COOH$
baking soda	sodium bicarbonate	$NaHCO_3$
banana oil	amyl acetate	$CH_3COOC_5H_{11}$
bauxite	hydrated aluminum oxide	$Al_2O_3 \cdot xH_2O$
bleaching powder	calcium chloride hypochlorite	$Ca(ClO)_2$, $Ca(ClO)Cl$
blue vitriol	copper(II) sulfate pentahydrate	$CuSO_4 \cdot 5H_2O$
borax (tincal)	sodium tetraborate decahydrate	$Na_2B_4O_7 \cdot 10H_2O$
brimstone	sulfur	S_8
calamine	zinc oxide	ZnO
calcite	calcium carbonate	$CaCO_3$
Calgon	polymer of sodium metaphosphate	$(NaPO_3)x$
calomel	mercury(I) chloride	Hg_2Cl_2
carborundum	silicon carbide	SiC
caustic soda	sodium hydroxide	$NaOH$
chalk	calcium carbonate	$CaCO_3$
Chile saltpeter	sodium nitrate	$NaNO_3$
copperas	iron(II) sulfate heptahydrate	$FeSO_4 \cdot 7H_2O$
cream of tartar	potassium hydrogen tartrate	$KHC_4H_4O_6$
DDT	dichlorodiphenyltrichloroethane	$(C_6H_4Cl)_2CHCCl_3$
dextrose	glucose	$C_6H_{12}O_6$
Epsom salt	magnesium sulfate heptahydrate	$MgSO_4 \cdot 7H_2O$
fool's gold	iron pyrite	FeS_2
Freon	dichlorodifluoromethane	CCl_2F_2
Glauber's salt	sodium sulfate decahydrate	$Na_2SO_4 \cdot 10H_2O$
glycerin	glycerol	$C_3H_5(OH)_3$
green vitriol	iron(II) sulfate heptahydrate	$FeSO_4 \cdot 7H_2O$
gypsum	calcium sulfate dihydrate	$CaSO_4 \cdot 2H_2O$
hypo	sodium thiosulfate pentahydrate	$Na_2S_2O_3 \cdot 5H_2O$
invert sugar	mixture of glucose and fructose	$C_6H_{12}O_6 + C_6H_{12}O_6$
laughing gas	nitrous oxide	N_2O
levulose	fructose	$C_6H_{12}O_6$
lye	sodium hydroxide	$NaOH$
magnesia	magnesium oxide	MgO
marble	calcium carbonate	$CaCO_3$
marsh gas	methane	CH_4
milk of lime (limewater)	calcium hydroxide	$Ca(OH)_2$
milk of magnesia	magnesium hydroxide	$Mg(OH)_2$
milk sugar	lactose	$C_{12}H_{22}O_{11}$
Mohr's salt	iron(II) ammonium sulfate hexahydrate	$Fe(NH_4)_2(SO_4)_2 \cdot 6H_2O$
moth balls	naphthalene	$C_{10}H_8$
muriatic acid	hydrochloric acid	$HCl(aq)$
oil of vitriol	sulfuric acid	$H_2SO_4(aq)$

Familiar Name	Chemical Name	Formula
oil of wintergreen	methyl salicylate	$C_6H_4(OH)COOCH_3$
oleum	fuming sulfuric acid	$H_2S_2O_7$
Paris green	double salt of copper(II) acetate and copper(II) arsenite	$Cu(CH_3CO_2)_2 \cdot Cu_3(AsO_3)_2$
plaster of Paris	calcium sulfate hemihydrate	$CaSO_4 \cdot \frac{1}{2}H_2O$
potash	potassium carbonate	K_2CO_3
quartz	silicon dioxide	SiO_2
quicklime	calcium oxide	CaO
Rochelle salt	potassium sodium tartrate	$KNaC_4H_4O_6$
rouge	iron(III) oxide	Fe_2O_3
sal ammoniac	ammonium chloride	NH_4Cl
salt (table salt)	sodium chloride	NaCl
saltpeter	potassium nitrate	KNO_3
silica	silicon dioxide	SiO_2
sugar (table sugar)	sucrose	$C_{12}H_{22}O_{11}$
Teflon	polymer of tetrafluoroethylene	$(C_2F_4)_x$
washing soda	sodium carbonate decahydrate	$Na_2CO_3 \cdot 10H_2O$
white lead	basic lead carbonate	$PbCO_3 \cdot Pb(OH)_2$
wood alcohol	methanol (methyl alcohol)	CH_3OH

For a listing of more common chemical names, go to www.chemistry.about.com and www.sciencecompany.com (patinas for metal artists).

Appendix C

Vapor Pressure of Water

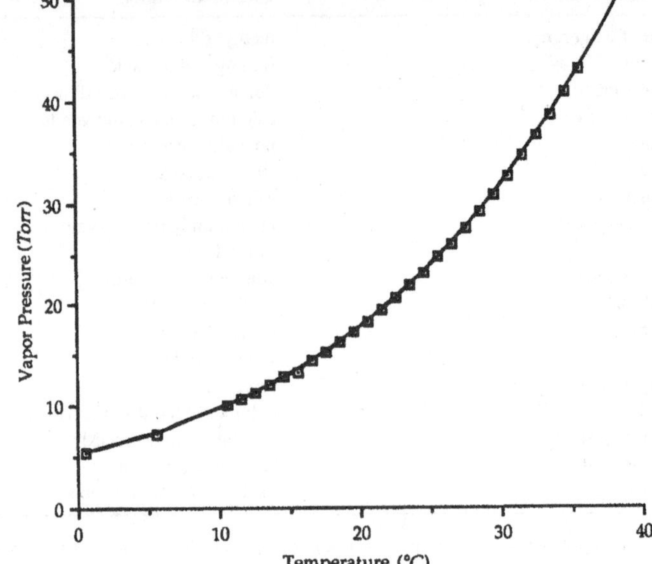

Vapor pressure of water as a function of temperature

Temperature (°C)	Pressure (Torr)
0	4.6
5	6.5
10	9.2
11	9.8
12	10.5
13	11.2
14	12.0
15	12.5
16	13.6
17	14.5
18	15.5
19	16.5
20	17.5
21	18.6
22	19.8
23	21.0
24	22.3
25	23.8
26	25.2
27	26.7
28	28.3
29	30.0
30	31.8
31	33.7
32	35.7
33	37.7
34	39.9
35	42.2
37*	47.1
—	—
100	760

*Body temperature

Appendix 

Concentrations of Acids and Bases

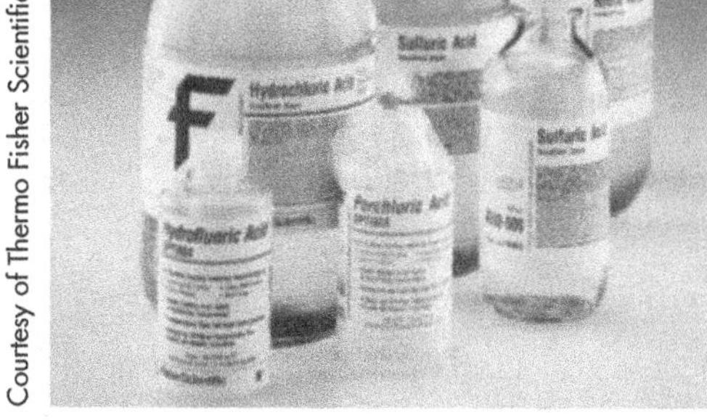

Concentrated laboratory acids and bases

Reagent	Approximate Molar Concentration	Approximate Mass Percent	Specific Gravity	mL to Dilute to 1 L for a 1.0 *M* Solution
Acetic acid	17.4 (*conc*)	99.5	1.05	57.5
Hydrochloric acid	11.6 (*conc*)	36	1.18	86.2
Nitric acid	16.0 (*conc*)	71	1.42	62.5
Phosphoric acid	18.1 (*conc*)	85	1.70	68.0
Sulfuric acid	18.0 (*conc*)	96	1.84	55.6
Ammonia (*aq*) (ammonium hydroxide)	14.8 (*conc*)	28%(NH_3)	0.90	67.6
Potassium hydroxide	13.5	50	1.52	74.1
Sodium hydroxide	19.1	50	1.53	52.4

Caution: *When diluting reagents, add the more concentrated reagent to the more dilute reagent (or solvent).* ***Never*** *add water to a concentrated acid!*

Appendix E

Water Solubility of Inorganic Salts

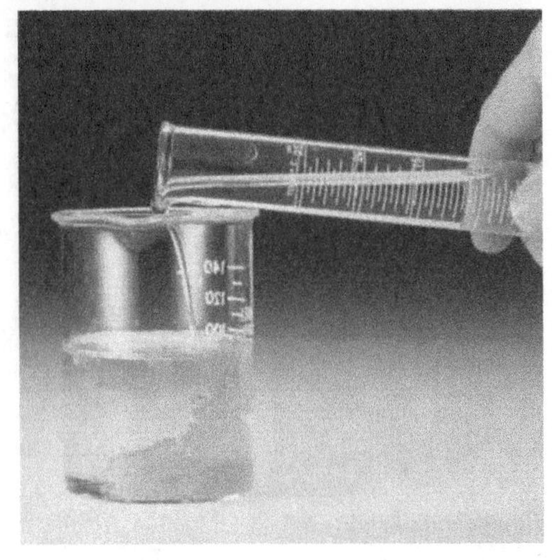
Michael Watson

Many salts, such as cadmium sulfide, have very low solubilities.

Water-Soluble Salts

1. All salts of the chloride ion (Cl^-), bromide ion (Br^-), and iodide ion (I^-) are soluble *except* those of Ag^+, Hg_2^{2+}, Pb^{2+}, Cu^+, and Tl^+, BiI_3, and SnI_4 are insoluble. $PbCl_2$ is three to five times more soluble in hot water than in cold water.
2. All salts of the acetate ion ($CH_3CO_2^-$), nitrate ion (NO_3^-), chlorate ion (ClO_3^-), perchlorate ion (ClO_4^-), and permanganate ion (MnO_4^-) are soluble.
3. All common salts of the Group 1A cations and ammonium ion (NH_4^+) are soluble.
4. All common salts of the sulfate ion (SO_4^{2-}) are soluble *except* those of Ba^{2+}, Sr^{2+}, Pb^{2+}, Hg^{2+} and Ag^+ (at higher concentrations).
5. All Group 1A and 2A salts of the bicarbonate ion (HCO_3^-) are soluble.
6. *Most* salts of the fluorosilicate ion (SiF_6^{2-}), thiocyanate ion (SCN^-), and thiosulfate ion ($S_2O_3^{2-}$) are soluble. *Exceptions* are the Ba^{2+} and Group 1A fluorosilicates, the Ag^+, Hg_2^{2+}, and Pb^{2+} thiocyanates, and the Ag^+ and Pb^{2+} thiosulfates.

Water-Insoluble Salts

1. All common salts of the fluoride ion (F^-) are insoluble *except* those of Ag^+, NH_4^+, and Group 1A cations.
2. In general, all common salts of the carbonate ion (CO_3^{2-}), phosphate ion (PO_4^{3-}), borate ion (BO_3^{3-}), arsenate ion (AsO_4^{3-}), arsenite ion (AsO_3^{3-}), cyanide ion (CN^-), ferricyanide ion ($[Fe(CN)_6]^{3-}$), ferrocyanide ion ($[Fe(CN)_6]^{4-}$), oxalate ion ($C_2O_4^{2-}$), and the sulfite ion (SO_3^{2-}) are insoluble, *except* those of NH_4^+ and the Group 1A cations.
3. All common salts of the oxide ion (O^{2-}), and the hydroxide ion (OH^-) are insoluble *except* those of the Group 1A cations, Ba^{2+}, Sr^{2+}, and NH_4^+. $Ca(OH)_2$ is slightly soluble. Soluble oxides produce the corresponding hydroxides in water.
4. All common salts of the sulfide ion (S^{2-}) are insoluble *except* those of NH_4^+ and the cations that are isoelectronic with a noble gas (e.g., the Group 1A cations, the Group 2A cations, Al^{3+}, etc.).
5. Most common salts of the chromate ion (CrO_4^{2-}) are insoluble *except* those of NH_4^+, Ca^{2+}, Cu^{2+}, Mg^{2+}, and the Group 1A cations.
6. All common salts of the silicate ion (SiO_3^{2-}) are insoluble *except* those of the Group 1A cations.

Table E.1 Summary of the Solubility of Salts

Anion	Soluble Salts with These Cations	"Insoluble Salts" with These Cations
Acetate, $CH_3CO_2^-$	Most cations	None
Arsenate, AsO_4^{3-}	NH_4^+, Group 1A (except Li^+)	Most cations
Arsenite, AsO_3^{3-}	NH_4^+, Group 1A (except Li^+)	Most cations
Borate, BO_3^{3-}	NH_4^+, Group 1A (except Li^+)	Most cations
Bromide, Br^-	Most cations	Ag^+, Hg_2^{2+}, Pb^{2+}, Cu^+, Tl^+
Carbonate, CO_3^{2-}	NH_4^+, Group 1A (except Li^+)	Most cations
Chlorate, ClO_3^-	Most cations	None
Chloride, Cl^-	Most cations	Ag^+, Hg_2^{2+}, Pb^{2+}, Cu^+, Tl^+
Chromate, CrO_4^{2-}	NH_4^+, Ca^{2+}, Cu^{2+}, Mg^{2+}, Group 1A	Most cations
Cyanide, CN^-	NH_4^+, Group 1A (except Li^+)	Most cations
Ferricyanide, $[Fe(CN)_6]^{3-}$	NH_4^+, Group 1A (except Li^+)	Most cations
Ferrocyanide, $[Fe(CN)_6]^{4-}$	NH_4^+, Group 1A (except Li^+)	Most cations
Fluoride, F^-	Ag^+, NH_4^+, Group 1A	Most cations
Fluorosilicate, SiF_6^{2-}	Most cations	Ba^{2+}, Group 1A
Hydroxide, OH^-	NH_4^+, Sr^{2+}, Ba^{2+}, Group 1A	Most cations
Iodide, I^-	Most cations	Ag^+, Hg_2^{2+}, Pb^{2+}, Cu^+, Tl^+, Br^{3+}, Sn^{4+}
Nitrate, NO_3^-	Most cations	None
Nitrite, NO_2^-	Most cations	None
Oxalate, $C_2O_4^{2-}$	NH_4^+, Group 1A (except Li^+)	Most cations
Oxide, O^{2-}	NH_4^+, Sr^{2+}, Ba^{2+}, Group 1A	Most cations
Perchlorate, ClO_4^-	Most cations	None
Permanganate, MnO_4^-	Most cations	None
Phosphate, PO_4^{3-}	NH_4^+, Group 1A (except Li^+)	Most cations
Silicate, SiO_3^{2-}	Group 1A	Most cations
Sulfate, SO_4^{2-}	Most cations	Sr^{2+}, Ba^{2+}, Pb^{2+}, Hg^{2+}
Sulfide, S^{2-}	NH_4^+, Groups 1A and 2A	Most cations
Sulfite, SO_3^{2-}	NH_4^+, Group 1A (except Li^+)	Most cations
Thiocyanate, SCN^-	Most cations	Ag^+, Hg_2^{2+}, Pb^{2+}
Thiosulfate, $S_2O_3^{2-}$	Most cations	Ag^+, Pb^{2+}

Cations	Soluble Salts with These Anions	"Insoluble Salts" with These Anions
Ammonium, NH_4^+	Most anions	No common anions
Group 1A	Most anions	No common anions

448

Periodic Table of the Elements

Atomic number: 6
Symbol : C
Name (IUPAC) : Carbon
Atomic mass : 12.011

IUPAC recommendations:
Chemical Abstracts Service group notation :

1 IA	2 IIA	3 IIIB	4 IVB	5 VB	6 VIB	7 VIIB	8 VIIIB	9 VIIIB	10 VIIIB	11 IB	12 IIB	13 IIIA	14 IVA	15 VA	16 VIA	17 VIIA	18 VIIIA
1 H Hydrogen 1.0079																	2 He Helium 4.0026
3 Li Lithium 6.941	4 Be Berylium 9.0122											5 B Boron 10.811	6 C Carbon 12.011	7 N Nitrogen 14.007	8 O Oxygen 15.999	9 F Fluorine 18.998	10 Ne Neon 20.180
11 Na Sodium 22.990	12 Mg Magnesium 24.305											13 Al Aluminum 26.982	14 Si Silicon 28.086	15 P Phosphorus 30.974	16 S Sulfur 32.065	17 Cl Chlorine 35.453	18 Ar Argon 39.948
19 K Potassium 39.098	20 Ca Calcium 40.078	21 Sc Scandium 44.956	22 Ti Titanium 47.867	23 V Vanadium 50.942	24 Cr Chromium 51.996	25 Mn Manganese 54.938	26 Fe Iron 55.845	27 Co Cobalt 58.933	28 Ni Nickel 58.693	29 Cu Copper 63.546	30 Zn Zinc 65.409	31 Ga Gallium 69.723	32 Ge Germanium 72.64	33 As Arsenic 74.922	34 Se Selenium 78.96	35 Br Bromine 79.904	36 Kr Krypton 83.798
37 Rb Rubidium 85.468	38 Sr Strontium 87.62	39 Y Yttrium 88.906	40 Zr Zirconium 91.224	41 Nb Niobium 92.906	42 Mo Molybdenum 95.94	43 Tc Technetium (98)	44 Ru Ruthenium 101.07	45 Rh Rhodium 102.91	46 Pd Palladium 106.42	47 Ag Silver 107.87	48 Cd Cadmium 112.41	49 In Indium 114.82	50 Sn Tin 118.71	51 Sb Antimony 121.76	52 Te Tellurium 127.60	53 I Iodine 126.90	54 Xe Xenon 131.29
55 Cs Cesium 132.91	56 Ba Barium 137.33	57 *La Lanthanum 138.91	72 Hf Hafnium 178.49	73 Ta Tantalum 180.95	74 W Tungsten 183.84	75 Re Rhenium 186.21	76 Os Osmium 190.23	77 Ir Iridium 192.22	78 Pt Platinum 195.08	79 Au Gold 196.97	80 Hg Mercury 200.59	81 Tl Thallium 204.38	82 Pb Lead 207.2	83 Bi Bismuth 208.98	84 Po Polonium (209)	85 At Astatine (210)	86 Rn Radon (222)
87 Fr Francium (223)	88 Ra Radium (226)	89 #Ac Actinium (227)	104 Rf Rutherfordium (261)	105 Db Dubnium (262)	106 Sg Seaborgium (266)	107 Bh Bohrium (264)	108 Hs Hassium (277)	109 Mt Meitnerium (268)	110 Ds Darmstadtium (281)	111 Rg Roentgenium (272)	112 Cn Copernicium (285)	113 Uut (284)	114 Fl Flerovium (289)	115 Uup (288)	116 Lv Livermorium (293)	117 Uus (294)	118 Uuo (294)

*Lanthanide Series	58 Ce Cerium 140.12	59 Pr Praseodymium 140.91	60 Nd Neodymium 144.24	61 Pm Promethium (145)	62 Sm Samarium 150.36	63 Eu Europium 151.96	64 Gd Gadolinium 157.25	65 Tb Terbium 158.93	66 Dy Dysprosium 162.50	67 Ho Holmium 164.93	68 Er Erbium 167.26	69 Tm Thulium 168.93	70 Yb Ytterbium 173.04	71 Lu Lutetium 174.97
# Actinide Series	90 Th Thorium 232.04	91 Pa Protactinium 231.04	92 U Uranium 238.03	93 Np Neptunium (237)	94 Pu Plutonium (244)	95 Am Americium (243)	96 Cm Curium (247)	97 Bk Berkelium (247)	98 Cf Californium (251)	99 Es Einsteinium (252)	100 Fm Fermium (257)	101 Md Mendelevium (258)	102 No Nobelium (259)	103 Lr Lawrencium (262)

Experiment 10: Biological Chemistry

INTRODUCTION

This is a three-part experiment performed in a single lab period. Make sure that you complete a pre-lab for all three sections.

This experiment integrates principles of biology and chemistry. The chemical behavior of biological building blocks, specifically proteins and nucleic acids, will be examined. In Part A, you will learn about chromatography and how it can be used to separate a mixture of amino acids. In Part B, you will isolate casein proteins from milk and analyze your sample using four qualitative tests. In Part C, you will isolate DNA from an onion.

Experiment 10A: Identifying a Mixture of Amino Acids using Paper Chromatography

INTRODUCTION

Cellulose in paper makes an excellent stationary phase for chromatography, creatively called paper chromatography. In this experiment, you will use paper chromatography to separate and identify a mixture of amino acids.

THEORETICAL BACKGROUND

Amino acids are organic molecules that consist of a basic amino group ($-NH_2$), an acidic carboxyl group (-COOH), and an organic side chain (R) that is different for each amino acid. Structurally:

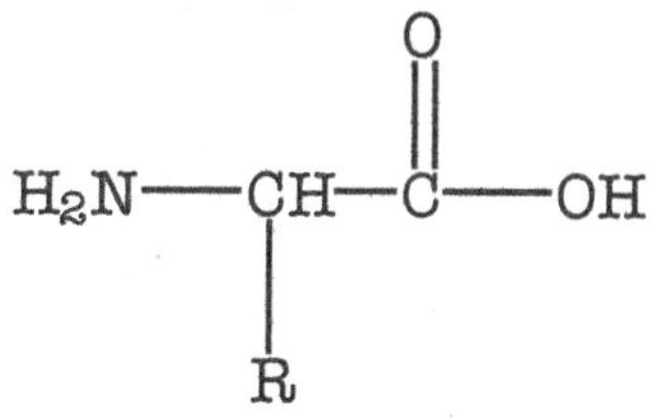

```
               O
               ‖
H2N—CH—C—OH
      |
      R
```

Figure 10.1

Although more than a hundred amino acids occur naturally, only twenty are commonly used in protein synthesis in living organisms. The human body cannot synthesize nine of these amino acids (essential amino acids), making them necessary in the diet. The remaining 11 (nonessential amino acids) are synthesized by an oxidation-reduction reaction called transamination. Additionally, plants contain other non-protein amino acids, which they use, for example, to synthesize alkaloids.

The properties common to all amino acids are due to the relative arrangement of the carboxyl (-COOH) and amino ($-NH_2$) groups. The physical and chemical properties unique to each amino acid are a consequence of the structural and chemical properties of the unique -R group. Amino acids are grouped according to the polarity (tendency to interact with water at neutral pH) and charge of the R group. The R groups for the amino acids used in this experiment are listed in Table 10.2.

Alanine (Ala)	Aspartic acid (Asp)	Leucine (Leu)	Lysine (Lys)
$-CH_3$	$-CH_2-COOH$	$-CH_2-CH-(CH_3)_2$	$-CH_2-(CH_2)_3-NH_2$

Table 10.1

Paper chromatography can be used to separate and identify amino acids in synthetic or natural preparations. Water absorbed on the highly polar paper fibers is the stationary phase and the free solvent is the mobile phase. The polar components are attracted to the polar stationary phase and, therefore, will move along the paper more slowly, thus effecting a separation of the components in the mixture.

The ratio of the distance traveled by the component to that traveled by the solvent is the R_f (ratio to the front) value.

$$R_f = \frac{\text{Distance traveled by the component}}{\text{Distance traveled by the solvent front}}$$ Equation 10.1

The R_f value is a function of the characteristics of both the solvent and the component. The closer the R_f value is to 1.0, the more the component remained in the mobile phase. Comparing the R_f values of unknowns to those of standard known compounds can help identify unknown components in a mixture (these components must be compared with the standards under identical conditions).

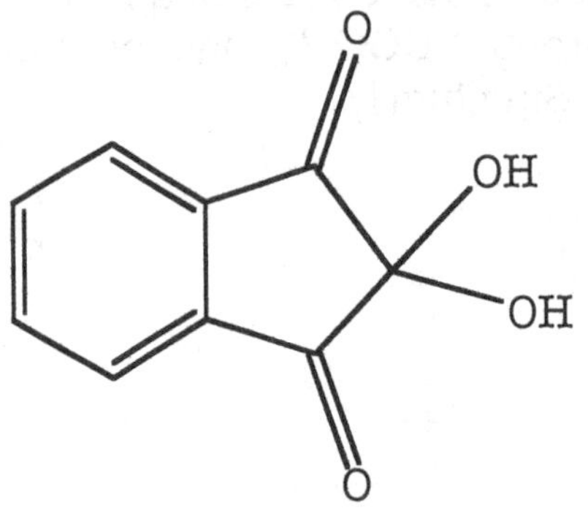

Figure 8.2: Ninhydrin (1,2,3-triketohydrindene hydrate

Amino acids are colorless. Therefore, to identify the positions of the amino acids, the dried paper is sprayed with ninhydrin, which reacts with free amines to yield purple to reddish–brown spots at each amino acid location. The variation in color and intensity is due to the differences in the number of sites on the amino acids that ninhydrin binds to.

INSTRUMENTATION

Hair dryer

WASTE

Used solutions (liquid waste) should be discarded into the designated liquid waste container. Capillary tubes should be placed in the contaminated glass waste receptacle (blue bin).

PROCEDURE

Be sure to wear your gloves throughout this entire procedure! Touching the paper with your fingers may give inaccurate results.

1. Obtain a No. 2 Whatman® filter paper from the front desk. Using a pencil and a metric ruler, trace a 10 cm x 11 cm rectangle on it. Measure 0.5 cm from each of the traced lines and cut the excess edges. Draw a 2 cm line above the base according to the diagram below.

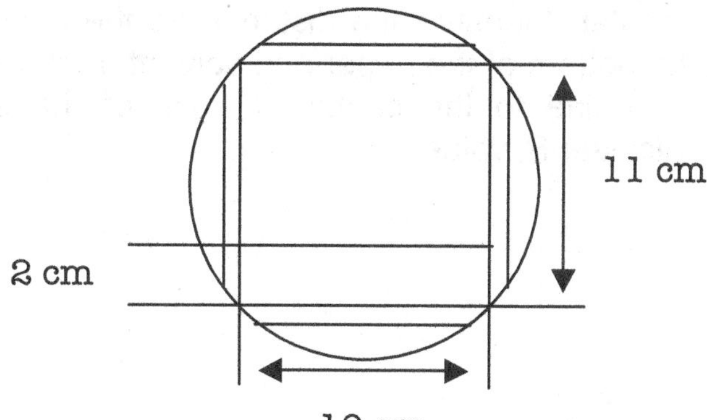

Figure 10.3

Make six evenly-spaced marks (x) on the line. Number them 1 to 6 (1 for asp, 2 for ala, 3 for leu, 4 for lys, 5 for mixture and 6 for the unknown).

2. Place the paper on a sheet of aluminum foil and place a pencil or pen beneath the paper just above the line so that the surface of the paper is above the bench surface, and the paper is not contaminated during the application of samples.

3. Apply the samples and unknown on the marks (1 to 6), using a clean capillary tube for each spot. Be careful to only lightly touch the paper; you do not want to poke any holes. It is important to add the samples in small amounts. Let each sample dry and then re-apply to get more of the sample onto a small spot on the paper. Do not add all of the material at once since doing so creates a large spot. Larger spots on your paper will result in wider bands for each compound in your chromatogram.

4. Fold the paper in half down the center with the spots on the outside. Check that it fits in your 600 mL beaker. Then remove it before adding the solvent.

5. Pour 50 mL of the developing solvent (acetic acid, 1-butanol and water) into the 600mL beaker and put the beaker under the canopy hood.

6. Carefully, insert the paper into the beaker so that the spots are about 1 cm above the surface of the solvent; just the bottom edge of the paper should touch the solvent. Tightly cover the mouth of the beaker with a piece of aluminum foil.

7. The solvent will begin to move up the paper. Allow the solvent front to travel about 8 cm above the base line.

8. Remove the paper from the beaker and immediately mark the solvent front with a light pencil line. Allow the paper to dry thoroughly; use a hair dryer to assist in the drying process.

9. In the hood, spray the paper with a mist of ninhydrin solution. Colored spots should appear within 15 minutes. Slightly heat the paper with a hair dryer in order to make these spots appear more quickly.

10. Now mark each spot at its center. Measure the distance, to the nearest 0.01 cm, between the original line at the bottom of the paper and solvent front. Also, measure the distances from the bottom line to the center of each of the spots. These measurements are used to calculate R_f values.

DATA TABLES

Data tables must be copied into your laboratory notebook before you arrive in lab.

Sample	Distance (cm)	Color	Solvent front distance (cm)
Alanine	±		±
Aspartic Acid	±		±
Leucine	±		±
Lysine	±		±
Mixture Spots	± ± ± ±		± ± ± ±
Unknown	±		±

WRITE-UP & CALCULATIONS

Include a sample of all calculations performed and ***error analysis****. Don't forget to include a report sheet with the lab report.* ***No discussion is required for this write-up.***

1. Calculate the R_f value for each spot in the chromatogram. **Don't forget to include error analysis.**

2. Identify the unknown using its R_f value and the colors of the spots.

Experiment 10B: Isolation and Identification of Casein

INTRODUCTION

You will isolate casein from milk under isoelectric conditions and perform some chemical tests to identify the protein.

THEORETICAL BACKGROUND

Casein is the most important protein in milk. Nutritionally, milk is an almost complete food, containing proteins, fats, carbohydrates, many minerals, and a number of important vitamins. Milk proteins include casein, lactalbumin and lactoglobin. Casein makes up about 80% of the protein in cow's milk and about 40% of the protein in human milk.

The casein in milk is a phosphoprotein containing about 0.7% phosphorus. Casein is present as calcium caseinate in cow's milk and as potassium caseinate in human milk.

Casein can be isolated from milk by acidification to bring the protein to its isoelectric point. The isoelectric point is the pH at which the protein has an equal number of positive and negative charges, giving it an overall neutral charge. Molecules with both positive and negative charges are referred to as zwitterions.

Proteins are least soluble in water at their isoelectric points because they tend to aggregate due to electrostatic attraction. The positive end of one protein molecule attracts the negative end of another protein molecule, which continues until the aggregate precipitates from the solution.

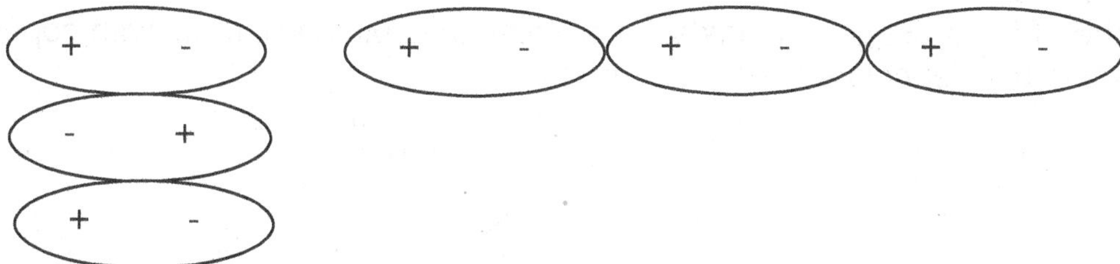

Figure 10.4: Protein aggregation

Each amino acid has an N-terminus, as well as a C-terminus. Because a protein is a chain of amino acids, each protein has an N-terminus, as well as a C-terminus.

$$H_2N-CH(R)-C(=O)-OH$$

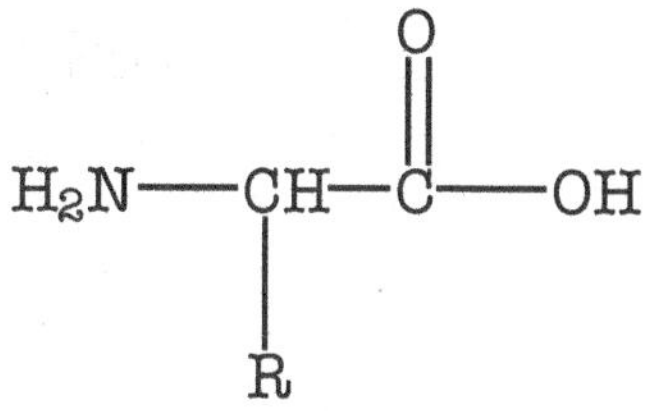

Figure 10.5: The generic structure of an amino acid

If a protein molecule has a net positive (at low pH, acidic conditions) or a net negative charge (at high pH, basic conditions), its solubility in water is increased, see Figure 10.6.

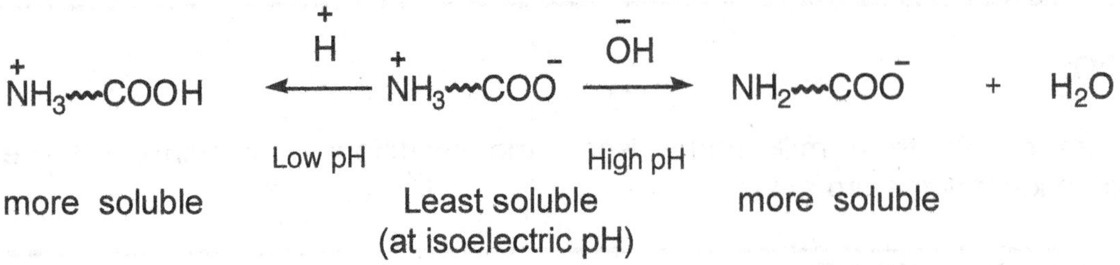

$$\overset{+}{N}H_3\text{\textasciitilde}COOH \xleftarrow[\text{Low pH}]{\overset{+}{H}} \overset{+}{N}H_3\text{\textasciitilde}COO^- \xrightarrow[\text{High pH}]{\overset{-}{OH}} NH_2\text{\textasciitilde}COO^- + H_2O$$

more soluble — Least soluble (at isoelectric pH) — more soluble

Figure 10.6: Proteins are least soluble at their isoelectric pH

In the first part of this experiment, you will isolate casein from milk, which has a pH of about 7. Casein will be separated as an insoluble precipitate by acidification of the milk to its isoelectric point, pH = 4.6. The fat that precipitates along with the casein can be removed by dissolving it in alcohol.

Milk contains a number of different types of casein proteins. These proteins form micelles, spheres with hydrophobic portions together on the inside of the micelle and hydrophilic portions on the outside. The hydrophilic portions on the outside keep the micelle soluble in water. Colloidal calcium phosphate holds the micelle together and is kept soluble by the micelle. By lowering the pH, calcium phosphate becomes soluble and the micelle dissolves. Once the casein proteins are free in solution, they are able to aggregate at their isoelectric point.

You will next prove that the precipitated milk product is a protein. The identification will be achieved using the following chemical tests: the Biuret Test, the Ninhydrin Test, the Heavy Metal Ion Test and the Xanthoprotein Test.

1. The Biuret Test.
   This is one of the most general tests for proteins. A protein will react with copper (II) ions, forming a violet-colored copper complex.

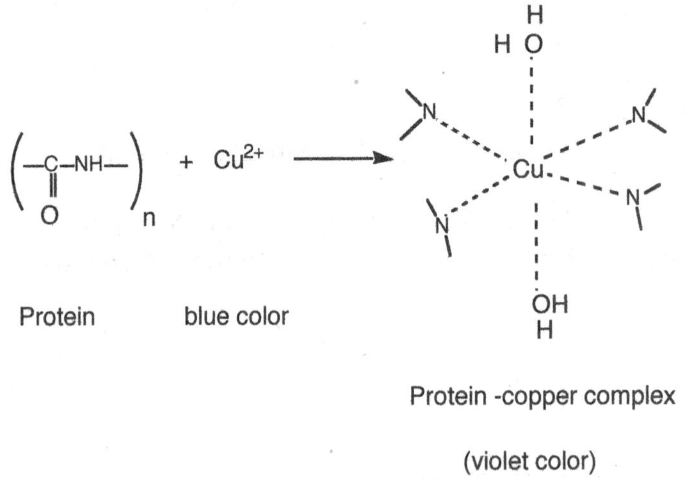

$$\left(-\underset{\underset{O}{\|}}{C}-NH-\right)_n + Cu^{2+} \longrightarrow \text{Protein-copper complex}$$

Protein — blue color — Protein -copper complex (violet color)

Figure 10.7: Biuret Test

8

The Biuret Test will be positive when a peptide bond is present in a molecule, i.e. a protein.

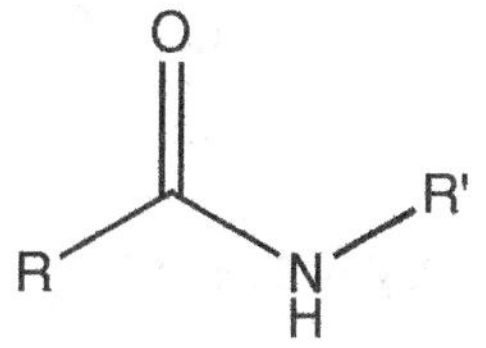

Figure 10.8

2. The Ninhydrin Test.
Amino acids and proteins containing a free amino group ($-NH_2$) will yield a positive result by a reaction with ninhydrin. A purple color is observed with primary amines, while a yellow color is observed with secondary amines.

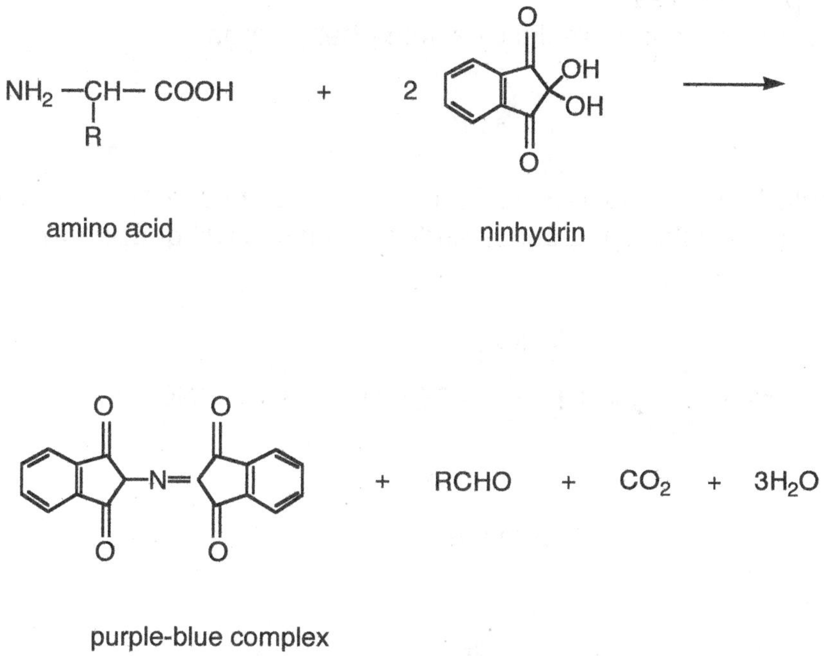

$NH_2-CH(R)-COOH$ + 2 ninhydrin →

amino acid ninhydrin

+ RCHO + CO_2 + $3H_2O$

purple-blue complex

Figure 10.9: Ninhydrin Test

3. Heavy Metal Ion Test.
Heavy metal ions precipitate proteins from solution. The ions that are most commonly used for protein precipitation are Zn^{2+}, Fe^{3+}, Cu^{2+}, Sb^{3+}, Ag^{+}, Cd^{2+} and Pb^{2+}.

Among these metal ions, Hg^{2+}, Cd^{2+} and Pb^{2+} are notoriously toxic. They can cause serious damage to proteins (especially enzymes) by denaturing them, which can result in death. The precipitation occurs because proteins become cross-linked by heavy metals as shown in Figure 10.10.

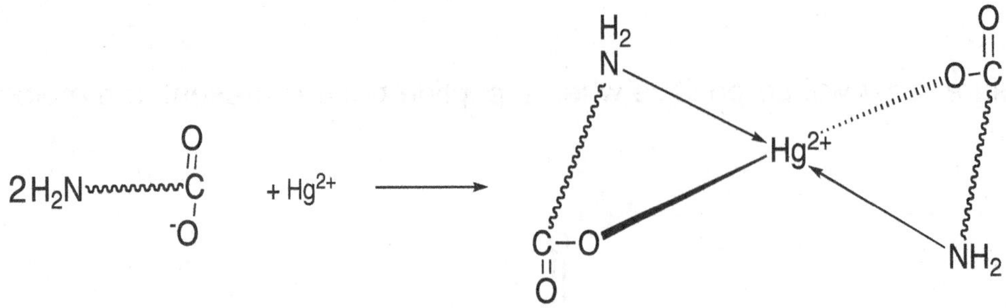

$$2H_2N\text{~~~}C(=O)O^- + Hg^{2+} \longrightarrow$$

Figure 10.10: Heavy Metal Test

People who have swallowed Hg^{2+} or Pb^{2+} ions are often treated with an antidote of a food rich in proteins. Such antidotes can combine with mercury or lead ions in the victim's stomach and sometimes prevent absorption of the ions. Milk and raw egg whites are used most often. The insoluble complexes are then immediately removed from the stomach by an emetic (a substance that causes vomiting). Heavy metals also denature the sulfide bonds in the proteins.

4. The Xanthoprotein Test.
   This is a standard test for molecules with phenyl rings

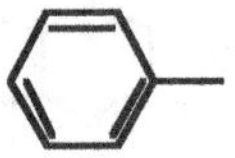

Concentrated nitric acid reacts with the phenyl ring to give a yellow or orange-colored aromatic nitro compound. Addition of alkali will deepen the color. See Figure 10.11.

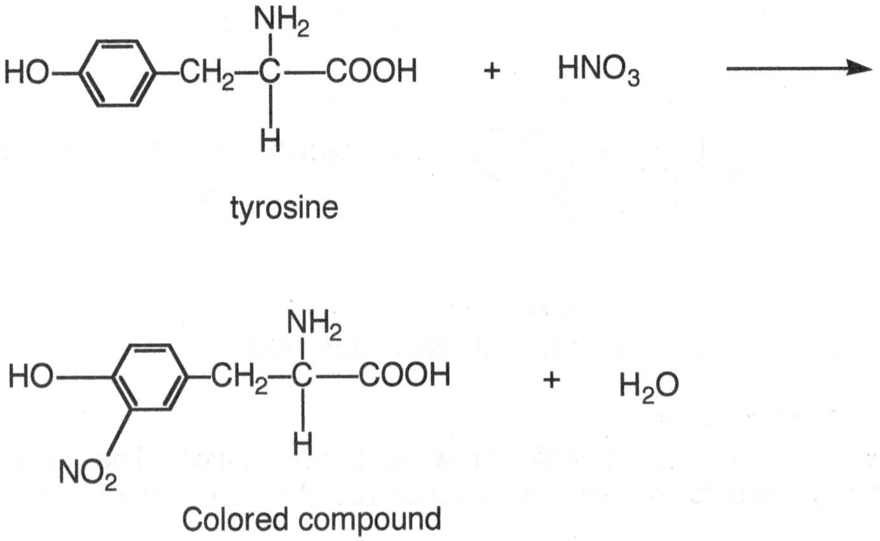

$$HO-C_6H_4-CH_2-CH(NH_2)-COOH + HNO_3 \longrightarrow$$

tyrosine

$$HO-C_6H_3(NO_2)-CH_2-CH(NH_2)-COOH + H_2O$$

Colored compound

Figure 10.11: Xanthoprotein Test

INSTRUMENTATION

Hot Plate

WASTE

All liquid waste must be disposed of in the designated liquid waste container.

PROCEDURE

Part One: Isolation of Casein

1. Set up a water bath using a 600 mL beaker with about 200 mL of tap water and a magnetic stir bar. Put it on a stirring hot plate. Set the heat at medium-low and the stirring rate at 2-3.

2. Weigh about 50 g of milk in a 250 mL Erlenmeyer flask, and clamp the flask in the water bath with the water above the level of the milk. See Figure 10.12. Clamp a thermometer so that the end is located in the water bath next to the flask. Heat the system to about 40°C, stirring constantly with a stirring rod. (Wait until the milk is warm as well).

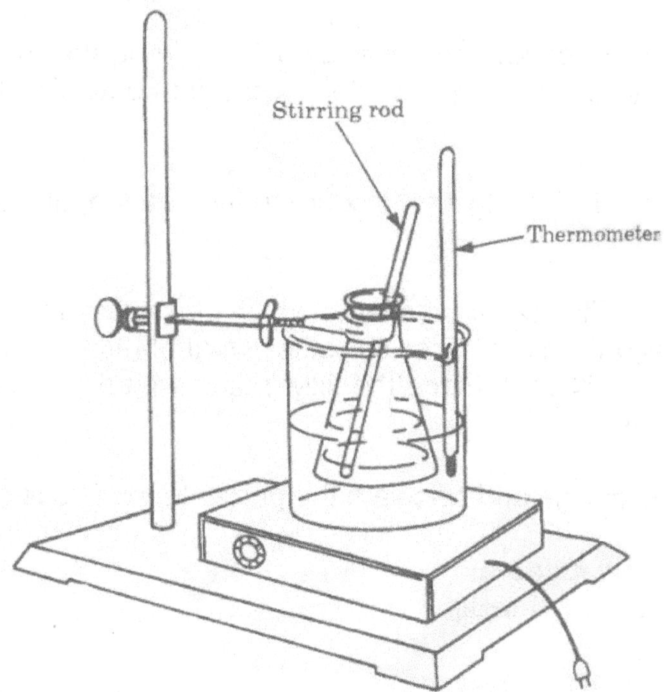

Figure 10.12: Set-up for the precipitation of casein

3. Remove the flask from the water bath and add about 10 drops of glacial acetic acid while stirring. Note the formation of a precipitate.

4. Cover the mouth of a 250 mL beaker with a piece of cheesecloth and secure the cloth with a rubber band. Dip the center of the cloth slightly to accommodate your mixture. Filter the mixture through the cheesecloth and into the beaker. See Figure 10.13. Release the rubber bands and squeeze the cloth gently to remove most of the liquid from the precipitate. Using a spatula, scrape as much of the precipitate as possible from the cheesecloth back into the empty flask.

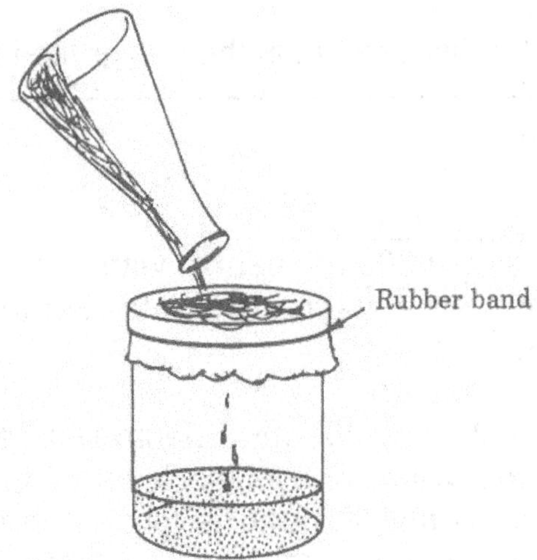

Figure 10.13: Filtration of Casein

5. Add 25 mL of 95% ethanol to the flask. After stirring the mixture for 5 minutes, allow the solid to settle. Carefully, decant the fat-containing liquid into a beaker and discard it.

6. Add 25 mL of a 1:1 ether:ethanol mixture to the residue, and stir the mixture for 5 minutes.

7. Weigh a piece of filter paper on a large watch glass. Use this filter paper to set up a vacuum filtration system. Filter the ether-ethanol mixture, rinsing the flask with small amounts of ethanol. Place the filter paper with the residue on the weighed watch glass to dry.

8. Weigh the dried casein and calculate the percentage of casein in the milk.

Part Two: Chemical Analyses of Proteins

1. **The Biuret Test:** Obtain four clean test tubes. Add 15 drops of each of the following solutions into different clean test tubes and label the test tubes.
   a) 2% glycine
   b) 2% gelatin
   c) The casein prepared in Part One (a spatula tip) and 15 drops of distilled water
   d) 1% tyrosine
   To each of the test tubes, add 5 drops of 10% NaOH solution and 2 drops of dilute $CuSO_4$ solution while swirling. The development of a purplish-violet color is evidence for the presence of proteins. Record any observations

2. **The Ninhydrin Test:** Obtain four more clean test tubes. Add 15 drops of each of the following solutions into different clean test tubes and label the test tubes.
   a) 2% glycine
   b) 2% gelatin
   c) The casein prepared in Part One (a spatula tip) and 15 drops of distilled water
   d) 1% tyrosine
   To each of the test tubes, add 5 drops of ninhydrin reagent. Heat the test tubes in a boiling water bath for approximately 5 minutes. Record any observations.

3. **Heavy Metal Ion Test:** Transfer some milk (it is not necessary to measure) in each of two clean, labeled test tubes. Add a few drops of each of the following metal ions to the corresponding test tubes as indicated below:
   a) Pb^{2+} as $Pb(NO3)_2$ in test tube no. 1
   b) Na^+ as $NaNO_3$ in test tube no. 2

4. **The Xanthoprotein Test: (PERFORM EXPERIMENT UNDER THE HOOD)**
   Obtain four clean test tubes. Add 15 drops of each of the following solutions into different clean test tubes and label the test tubes.
   a) 2% glycine
   b) 2% gelatin
   c) The casein prepared in Part One (a spatula tip) and 15 drops of distilled water
   d) 1% tyrosine
   To each test tube, add 10 drops of concentrated HNO_3 while stirring. Heat the test tubes carefully in a warm water bath. Observe any changes in color and record.

DATA TABLES

Data tables must be copied into your laboratory notebook before you arrive in lab.

Part One: Isolation of casein

1. Weight of milk __________ g
2. Weight of filter paper and watch glass __________ g
3. Weight of filter paper, watch glass and dried casein __________ g
4. Weight of casein __________ g
5. Percentage of casein in milk sample __________ g

Part Two: Chemical Analysis of Proteins

Biuret Test	Observations
2% Glycine	
2% Gelatin	
Casein + water	
1% Tyrosine	

Ninhydrin Test	Observations
2% Glycine	
2% Gelatin	
Casein + water	
1% Tyrosine	

Heavy Metal Test	Observations
$Pb(NO_3)_2$	
$NaNO_3$	

Xanthoprotein Test	Observations
2% Glycine	
2% Gelatin	
Casein + water	
1% Tyrosine	

WRITE-UP & CALCULATIONS

No discussion is required for this write-up. *Include a sample of each type of calculation performed. Include a report sheet with every lab report.*

Note: No error analysis required. Be careful of significant figures though.

Calculate the % of casein in milk.

Experiment 10C: Extraction of DNA from Onion

INTRODUCTION

Deoxyribonucleic acid (DNA) is a macromolecule that is present in the cells of all living organisms. It contains the genetic information found in every living cell and is the hereditary "blueprint" of life. The purpose of this laboratory is to give you firsthand experience with DNA by isolating it from plant tissue. You will start with whole onions and end with a relatively pure preparation of DNA, containing literally millions of genes. Once isolated, the DNA can be stored in alcohol or dried.

THEORETICAL BACKGROUND

DNA (Deoxyribonucleic acid) is the molecule that forms chromosomes. A section of a chromosome that dictates a particular trait is called a gene. Structurally, DNA is a double helix; two strands of genetic material spiraled around each other. Each strand of DNA is composed of a backbone where sugars alternate with phosphates, and a nucleotide base is attached to each sugar. Each base (also called nucleotide) is one of four molecules: adenine, guanine, cytosine and thymine.

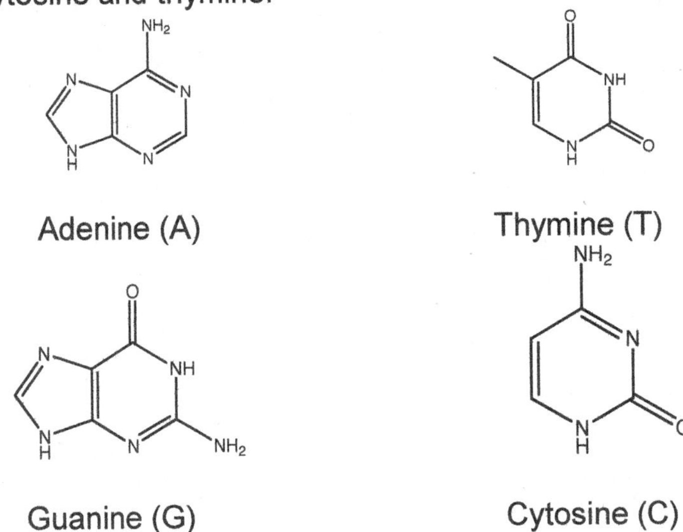

Figure 10.14: Nucleotide Bases

Two strands of DNA are connected pair-wise at each base through hydrogen bonding: adenine (A) will only pair with thymine (T), and guanine (G) will only pair with cytosine (C). In this way, one strand of DNA might look like this:

A-A-C-T-G-A-T-A-G-G-T-C-T-A-G Figure 10.15

The complimentary DNA strand that binds to it will look like this:

T-T-G-A-C-T-A-T-C-C-A-G-A-T-C Figure 10.16

Together, the section of DNA would be represented like this:

T-T-G-A-C-T-A-T-C-C-A-G-A-T-C
A-A-C-T-G-A-T-A-G-G-T-C-T-A-G

Figure 10.17

DNA strands are read in a particular direction, from the top (called the 5' or "five prime" end) to the bottom (called the 3' or "three prime" end). In a double helix, the strands run in opposite directions.

5' T-T-G-A-C-T-A-T-C-C-A-G-A-T-C 3'
3' A-A-C-T-G-A-T-A-G-G-T-C-T-A-G 5'

Figure 10.18

The chemical structure of all DNA is the same. The only difference between two people or any two animals or plants is the order and number of the base pairs. There are many millions of base pairs in each person's DNA, giving every person a different sequence (except for identical twins). Using these sequences, every person could be identified solely by the sequence of their base pairs. However, because there are so many millions of base pairs, the task would be very time-consuming. Instead, scientists use a shorter method based on identifying repeating patterns in DNA.

DESCRIPTION OF THE EXPERIMENT

The isolation of DNA is the first step for many laboratory procedures in biotechnology. In this lab, you will extract DNA from onion tissue. Onion is used in this experiment because it has a low starch content, allowing the DNA to be seen clearly.

DNA is found in the membrane-bound nucleus of eukaryotic cells. Cell and nuclei membranes are composed of lipids and proteins. Mechanical blending breaks open the cells and releases their contents, including the nuclei. The detergent, sodium dodecyl sulfate (SDS), causes the cell and nuclei membranes to break down by disrupting the bonds that hold the lipids and the proteins together. The detergent then forms complexes with the lipids and proteins, causing them to precipitate out of solution.

The sugar and phosphate components of DNA (the backbone) are both readily soluble in water, so this will facilitate the removal of the DNA using the SDS detergent molecules. The phosphate groups on the outside of DNA carry a negative charge. These negative charges are attracted to and are neutralized by cations such as sodium. Sodium added to DNA forms a protective "shell" around it, which keeps it in aqueous solution. Thus, the DNA will remain dissolved in SDS while the proteins and lipids will precipitate, allowing for separation by filtration.

Since DNA is minimally soluble in ethanol (ethyl alcohol), adding ethanol to the filtered solution will precipitate the DNA.

At room temperature, DNA begins to denature by the action of DNAse (an enzyme that denatures DNA and is present in cell extracts). To prevent the breakdown of DNA, extraction procedures must be carried out on ice.

MATERIALS AND INSTRUMENTATION

The following materials will be shared by each group of students:

- Blender
- Fresh white onion
- Cutting board
- Knife
- Ice
- Balance
- 95% ethanol kept on ice

The following materials are needed for each pair of students:

- Plastic gloves
- 50 mL homogenization medium
- 60° C water bath
- Thermometer
- Cheesecloth
- 2-100 mL graduated cylinders (one kept on ice)
- One 250 mL, two 600mL and one 1000 mL beakers
- Glass stirring rod

The following chemicals are required for the preparation of the homogenization medium:

- Sodium dodecyl sulfate (SDS)
- Sodium chloride
- Sodium citrate
- Ethylenediamine tetraacetic acid (EDTA)

WASTE

Used solutions (liquid waste) should be discarded in the designated liquid waste container.

PROCEDURE

Be sure to wear your gloves throughout this entire procedure! Nitrile gloves prevent the DNAse of your hands from cleaving the onion DNA into small fragments. Cleaved DNA is much more difficult to collect.

Before DNA can be released from the nuclei of the onion tissues, the cell walls and membranes must first be broken down. This step can be accomplished by homogenizing the onion tissues in a blender. The detergent solution causes the cell membrane to break down by disrupting the polar interactions that hold it together and emulsifies the lipids and proteins of the cell. The DNA can then be separated from the chromosomal proteins because the homogenizing medium will cause the proteins to precipitate out of solution, but not the DNA.

1. Wearing gloves, dice a medium-sized onion into cubes no larger than 5 mm. Gloves prevent DNAse enzymes on your hands from cleaving the DNA into small fragments.

2. Weigh out 25 g of diced onion. Transfer all of the weighed material to a 600 mL beaker.

3. Add 50 mL of homogenizing medium to the diced onion and incubate the beaker in a 60° C water bath for 15 minutes (no longer!). The heat treatment softens the onion tissue and enables penetration by the homogenization solution. Heating also denatures many enzymes that could interfere with the isolation procedure.

4. Quickly cool your preparation to 15-20° C in an ice bath (a slush of ice and water in a 1000 mL beaker). This step should be accomplished in about 6 minutes and prevents denaturing of the DNA.

5. Pour your cooled preparation into a blender and fasten the lid. Homogenize for 45 seconds at low speed, followed by 30 seconds at high speed. Homogenization breaks open the cells and releases their contents (carbohydrates, proteins, fats, and nucleic acids).

6. Pour the homogenate from the blender into a 600 mL beaker (some foam can be left in the blender if the beaker is full). Allow it to stand in an ice bath for 15-20 minutes.

7. Filter the homogenate through one thickness of cheesecloth into a 250-mL beaker, taking care to leave the foam behind.

Precipitation of DNA:
The homogenate should contain only DNA and the components of the homogenizing medium. Of the components remaining in the homogenate, only DNA is not soluble in ice-cold ethanol. Therefore, all the components of the homogenizing medium stay in solution except for the DNA.

If the instructions have been followed carefully so that the molecular structure of DNA remains intact, the genetic substance should precipitate as a thick, stringy white mass that may be spooled out by winding it on a glass rod or wooden stick. If the DNA has been damaged, it will still precipitate, but as a white, fuzzy mass that cannot be collected as easily.

8. Place your beaker, with its filtered homogenate into an ice bath. Let it cool until it reaches 10-15° C.

9. Measure out 80 ml of ice-cold ethanol into a cold graduated cylinder. Slowly add the ethanol down the side of your beaker until the white, stringy DNA precipitate appears. It may take less than 80 ml of the alcohol to precipitate your DNA.

10. Spool out, or wind up, the stringy DNA onto a glass rod or wooden stick by rotating the rod in one direction only in the beaker of DNA. Continue to rotate the rod as you move it in large circles through the beaker.

11. If you want to keep your DNA, gently ease it off the end of the glass rod into a vial filled with ethanol. Be sure the cap is tight enough to prevent leakage.

Preparation of homogenization medium
(This solution will be provided for you in lab.)

Sodium dodecyl sulfate (SDS)	50.000 g
Sodium chloride	8.770 g
Sodium citrate	4.410 g
Ethylenediamine tetraacetic acid (EDTA)	0.292 g

Add distilled water to the above materials to make 1 liter of solution that can be used by 10 groups. Do not refrigerate or the SDS will turn the solution an opaque white color. If the homogenization medium gets cold at any time, it will turn white, but this will not affect its function.

Important information:

1. Ethanol must be cold for this procedure to work. Place a bottle of ethanol and one graduated cylinder in the cooler at the start of lab. Be sure the cap on the ethanol bottle is slightly loose and the bottle is not completely full.

2. Wear gloves and do not to touch the inside of containers because DNAse enzymes from your hands will cleave the DNA into small fragments so that it will not spool at the end of the lab. Rinse all glassware with distilled water.

3. Follow the directions carefully, since the temperatures and timings are crucial to the procedure.

4. Scoring the end of the glass rod with sandpaper will help the DNA adhere to the rod while spooling. Do not touch the end of the rod with your fingers.

5. Small vials and ethanol will be available so that you may save your DNA.

DATA TABLES

Data tables must be copied into your laboratory notebook before you arrive in lab.

Create your own data tables for this portion of the lab.

WRITE-UP & CALCULATIONS

No Calculations are required for this part of the experiment, but you will receive points for the isolation of the onion DNA. Make sure you show your isolated DNA to your TA before leaving lab. No discussion is required for this write-up.

Name:______________________ TA Name: __________________
Lab Partner_____________________________ Drawer #: ________

Experiment 10: Biological Chemistry

Experiment 10A: Identifying Components in a Mixture of Amino Acids with Paper Chromatography

*Error analysis required for Part A.

Sample	**Distance (cm)**	**Color**	**Solvent front distance (cm)**	**R_f**
Alanine	±		±	
Aspartic Acid	±		±	
Leucine	±		±	
Lysine	±		±	
Mixture Spots	± ± ± ±		± ± ± ±	
Unknown	±		±	

Name of the Unknown:_____________________________________

Experiment 10B: Isolation and Identification of Casein

*No error analysis required for Part B.

Part One: Isolation of Casein

1. Weight of milk _____________ g

2. Weight of filter paper and watch glass _____________ g

3. Weight of filter paper, watch glass and dried casein _____________ g

4. Weight of casein _____________ g

5. Percentage of casein in milk sample _____________ %

Part Two: Chemical Analysis of Proteins

The Biuret Test

Substance	Color Change	Was the Test +/- ?	Conclusion Drawn
2% Glycine			
2% Gelatin			
Casein + water			
1% Tyrosine			

The Ninhydrin Test

Substance	Color Change	Was the Test +/- ?	Conclusion Drawn
2% Glycine			
2% Gelatin			
Casein + water			
1% Tyrosine			

The Heavy Metal Test

Substance	Observations & Precipitates formed	Was the Test +/- ?	Conclusion Drawn
$Pb(NO_3)_2$			
$NaNO_3$			

The Xanthoprotein Test

Substance	Color Change	Was the Test +/- ?	Conclusion Drawn
2% Glycine			
2% Gelatin			
Casein + water			
1% Tyrosine			

No Report Sheet for DNA Isolation (10C)